Burgess

LIFE SCIENCE SERIES

Consulting Editors

ROBERT H. BURRIS, Biochemistry

HERMAN C. LICHSTEIN, Microbiology

PRINCIPLES OF RADIOISOTOPE METHODOLOGY . . Chase

IDENTIFICATION OF
ENTEROBACTERIACEAE . . . . Edwards-Ewing

PROCEDURES FOR ROUTINE
DIAGNOSIS OF VIRUS AND
RICKETTSIAL DISEASES . . . . Kalter

HANDBOOK OF CELL AND
ORGAN CULTURE . . . . Merchant-Kahn-Murphy

ELEMENTARY BIOCHEMISTRY . . . . Mertz

NUCLEIC ACID OUTLINES:
Vol. I—Structure and Metabolism . . . . Potter

BEHAVIOR OF ENZYME SYSTEMS . . . . Reiner

THE ORGANIC CONSTITUENTS OF
HIGHER PLANTS: THEIR CHEMISTRY
AND INTERRELATIONSHIPS . . . . Robinson

METABOLIC MAPS, Volume II . . . . Umbreit

MANOMETRIC TECHNIQUES . . . . Umbreit-Burris-Stauffer

THE ORGANIC CONSTITUENTS OF HIGHER PLANTS

Their Chemistry and Interrelationships

(1963)

by

TREVOR ROBINSON
Chemistry Department
University of Massachusetts
Amherst, Mass.

with contributions by
ERNEST SONDHEIMER
Department of Forest Chemistry
New York State College of Forestry
Syracuse, New York

BURGESS PUBLISHING COMPANY
426 South 6th Street, Minneapolis 15, Minn.

Library of Congress Catalog Card No. 63-8920

Printed in the United States of America

PREFACE

Chemistry is becoming more and more an essential tool for biological investigations. Yet, although the biologist to be effective in many areas of study needs a strong knowledge of chemistry, the kinds of things he needs to know are not necessarily the same things which a chemist needs to know. In many ways the biologist's knowledge of chemistry must be more comprehensive than the chemist's since he is usually unable to choose the compounds which he must work with. They are presented to him in a bewildering variety. On the other hand, the lifeblood of chemical investigations into natural products is made up of degradations, proof of structure, and synthesis; none of these are usually of much concern to the biologist. What the biologist wants to know is, "What sort of compound is this which I have found to be involved in such and such a process; from what precursors is it made, and what happens to it later?" The exact structure of a compound down to the location of every double bond and the precise spatial configuration and conformation of the atoms are problems which ultimately must be faced, but by a chemist rather than a biologist. Because of this difference between chemical and biological outlook, the wealth of literature and courses on the chemistry of natural products seldom gives the biologist satisfying answers to his questions, or else delivers these answers with effort and in the midst of much extraneous information. There are multivolume and multiauthor works which direct their discussions of the chemistry of natural products toward biologists, but despite their enormous coverage and depth, even if the individual could afford to have them all at his fingertips, he would find large gaps and unevenness in the information which they provide. Certain classes of compounds are not adequately described, others are well-treated *per se* but not contrasted with other types of compounds which they resemble or which are found in nature along with them. Sometimes detailed and elaborate methods of characterization are given which are essential for laboratories engaged in an intensive investigation of a certain type of compound but which merely frustrate an individual who just wants to know if he has a compound of that type. It is for these various reasons, and others, that this book was conceived.

It may appear that we have given undue prominence to some relatively unimportant classes of compounds. This has been intentional, and it is an important justification for the book. A reader who desires general information about carbohydrates or amino acids can turn to many excellent sources; but should he want to know something about naturally-occurring lignans or acetylenes, he can at present find no discussion at a level of complexity suitable for the interested non-specialist.

It should be evident that we have intended to present a book of chemistry rather than biochemistry. Although the metabolic interrelationships of compounds are summarized, we have avoided the temptation to discuss the enzymology of these processes or their place in the total picture of plant physiology. Nevertheless, a brief summary of metabolic pathways should be helpful in orientation, and, if one compound has been found, may point the way to finding others that may be associated with it. We have assumed that the reader is familiar with elementary organic and biological chemistry. Many simple concepts which are well covered in general textbooks of these subjects are therefore omitted, assumed, or briefly referred to.

While this book has been directed primarily toward botanists and pharmaceutical chemists, perhaps by glancing through it organic chemists with an intensive knowledge of one area or another will be brought to see an immense number of untouched problems which await their notice. Certain classes of natural products have received much attention from many chemists; others may be the private province of a single laboratory or even completely ignored.

Dr. Ernest Sondheimer has prepared Chapter 10 and given valuable advice throughout the rest of the book. Preparation of the manuscript commenced while I was a member of the Department of Bacteriology and Botany, Syracuse University, and I am grateful for the time away from my regular duties which was granted me to work on it there. Thanks are also due to all my present colleagues and former teachers whose knowledge and encouragement really made this book possible; to Mrs. Cecile Gitlin and Mrs. Viva Rice whose expert typing and good humor expedited preparation of the manuscript; and finally to my wife and children who were of no help to the book but lots of fun to live with.

Trevor Robinson

Amherst, Mass.
August 1, 1962

CONTENTS

Chapter 1
INTRODUCTION

This chapter is intended to provide an orientation in the field of plant chemistry, the general nature of compounds encountered, methods of dealing with them, and the ways that they are biochemically interrelated. With one or two exceptions the other chapters are all organized into the following sections:

1. A general view of the compounds included, their chemical and physical properties, occurrence and function in plants.
2. Methods used for isolating the compounds from plant material.
3. Qualitative analytical methods useful for characterizing the compounds.
4. A brief synopsis of present knowledge regarding the biochemical pathways by which the compounds are synthesized and broken down.
5. Pertinent literature. Rather than an exhaustive review a few key articles have usually been selected. These will lead to others.

In the present, introductory chapter, the topics listed above will be discussed in more general terms with indications as to what may be expected in the specific chapters.

LITERATURE

The literature on plant chemistry extends across several special fields, each with a slightly different point of view. Four chief points of view may be summarized as follows:

BOTANICAL - the functions of the compounds in plants
BIOCHEMICAL - the chemical reactions (usually enzymatic) which the compounds undergo in plants
CHEMICAL - the chemical properties and non-enzymatic reactions of the compounds
PHARMACEUTICAL - plant constituents useful in medicine, their isolation and identification

In each of these areas a variety of general textbooks are available. These will be familiar to the reader or easily discovered. A few works stand out as indispensable references regardless of the special field of interest. The general textbook Organic Chemistry by Paul Karrer is outstanding for its emphasis on the chemistry of plant products. The multi-volume encyclopedias edited by Paech and Tracey and Ruhland (listed below under "Botany") provide exhaustive and basic information. In each of the following chapters appropriate references to them are indicated simply as "Paech and Tracey" or "Ruhland." After these books, any literature review in this area should probably proceed to Chemical Abstracts - in particular the sections on "Organic Chemistry," "Botany," and "Pharmaceutical Chemistry."

It is sometimes desirable to know what plants contain a certain compound or what compounds are present in a certain plant. To some extent, Paech and Tracey offers this kind of information, especially for some classes of compounds; but three other references are specifically intended for this purpose, viz.,:

Wehmer, C. Die Pflanzenstoffe Fischer Verlag, Jena 1931, 1935.
Outdated, but complete for older literature, arranged taxonomically.

Schermerborn, J. W. and Quimby, M. W., The Lynn Index, Massachusetts College of Pharmacy, Boston, Mass. 1957-1960.
A series of monographs arranged taxonomically with a chemical cross-reference to be prepared. At this writing four monographs of the series have been published.

Karrer, W., Konstitution und Vorkommen der Organischen Pflanzenstoffe, Birkhauser Verlag, Basel, 1958.
Includes every compound reported to occur in plants, arranged according to chemical nature with a botanical index.

The following list is an attempt to summarize some of the more advanced literature which is pertinent to investigations in the chemistry of plant constituents. Journals have been selected to be illustrative rather than exhaustive and also to include journals which are not well known, though frequently valuable in this area.

Journals of general science which often contain pertinent papers:

- Science
- Nature
- Die Naturwissenschaften
- Experientia
- Compts rendues d'Academie des Sciences
- Zeitschrift fur Naturforschung, b series

Botany, advanced texts, reviews:

- Ruhland, W., Handbuch der Pflanzenphysiologie 18 vols., Springer Verlag, Berlin, 1958.
- Paech, K. and Tracey, M. V., Moderne Methoden der Pflanzenanalyse, 4 vols. Springer Verlag, Berlin, 1956.
- Annual Review of Plant Physiology, Annual Reviews, Inc., Palo Alto, California, Vol. 1 1950-present.
- Steward, F. C., Plant Physiology, A Treatise 6 vols. Academic Press, N. Y., 1959.
- The Botanical Review

Botany, primary journals:

- Economic Botany
- Plant Physiology
- Planta

Biochemistry, advanced texts, reviews:

- Bonner, J., Plant Biochemistry, Academic Press, N. Y., 1950.
- Annual Review of Biochemistry, Annual Reviews, Inc., Palo Alto, California, yearly 1 1932-present.

Biochemistry, primary journals:

- Phytochemistry
- The Biochemical Journal
- Archives of Biochemistry and Biophysics
- The Journal of Biochemistry (Japan)
- Federation Proceedings

Chemistry, advanced texts, reviews:

- Gilman, H., Organic Chemistry, 4 vols., John Wiley, N. Y., 1 and 2 1943, 3 and 4 1953.
- Zechmeister, L. editor, Fortschritte der Chemie Organischer Naturstoffe, Springer Verlag, Vienna, Vol. 1 1938-present.
- Chemical Reviews, American Chemical Society.
- Cook, J. W., ed., Progress in Organic Chemistry, Academic Press, Vol. 1 1952-present.
- Quarterly Reviews
- Record of Chemical Progress
- Annual Reports on the Progress of Chemistry
- Crane, E. J., Paterson, A. M., Marr, E. B., A Guide to the Literature of Chemistry, 2nd ed. John Wiley, N. Y., 1957.
- Dyson, G. M., A Short Guide to Chemical Literature, Longmans, Green, N. Y., 1959.
- Searching the Chemical Literature, American Chemical Society, Washington, D. C., 1961.
- A Key to Pharmaceutical and Medicinal Chemistry Literature, American Chemical Society, Washington, D. C., 1956.
- Bibliography of Chemical Reviews, 3 vols., American Chemical Society, Washington, D. C., 1960-1961.

Chemistry, primary journals:

- Chemistry and Industry
- Tetrahedron
- Journal of the American Chemical Society
- Chemische Berichte
- Helvetica Chimica Acta
- Journal of Organic Chemistry
- Acta Chemica Scandinavica
- Analytical Chemistry

Pharmacy, advanced texts, reviews:

- Allport, N. L., The Chemistry and Pharmacy of Vegetable Drugs, Chemical Publ. Co., Brooklyn 1944.
- Jenkins, G. L., Hartung, W. H., Hamlin, K. E., and Data, J. B., The Chemistry of Organic Medicinal Products, John Wiley, N. Y., 1957.

Pharmacy, primary journals:

- Die Pharmazie
- Planta Medica
- Archiv der Pharmazie
- Journal of the American Pharmaceutical Association

PROPERTIES, OCCURRENCE, AND FUNCTION

For the compounds discussed usually only a few salient properties are described under this heading in order to give a general picture. More specific properties are more conveniently described in the section "Characterization". Within any group of compounds several specific compounds are selected for structural representation. The most familiar or important compounds of a group are almost always included; beyond this there is no attempt at an exhaustive survey of plant products. Rather, structures have been chosen to illustrate the range of possibilities within a group. In order to make this gamut clear, rare compounds at the extreme ends of it have sometimes been depicted to the exclusion of more common derivatives which lie well within the range of variation. Knowing what the extreme cases are, the reader can presumably interpolate other structures which probably occur in nature. For example, if two natural benzene derivatives are indicated differing in that one has only a single phenolic hydroxyl group while the other has three methoxyl groups, it may be assumed that other compounds probably exist with intermediate structures. Reference to the organic chemical literature or such books as that of W. Karrer will then confirm or deny the validity of such interpolation.

As with structures chosen, examples of the natural occurrence of plant products are illustrative rather than exhaustive. In general, coverage has been restricted to the higher plants (botanically the *Embryophyta*), but occasional references to algae and fungi have been made when it seemed pertinent to do so. Where a plant is named as the source of a compound, it is almost never true that it is the only plant which has this constituent --- though it will usually be the one richest in it. Almost every natural product is found in more than one species although there is often a taxonomic pattern restricting a compound or a class of compounds to a certain genus, family, or order. In other cases such restriction is statistical rather than absolute or quantitative rather than qualitative. Usually no indication is given as to the part of a plant richest in a constituent or the stage of maturity at which the highest concentration may be found, although these variables are of crucial importance to anyone wishing to isolate a compound. Reference to the books of Paech and Tracey or W. Karrer will usually lead rapidly to such information if it is required.

Only very brief indications are given as to the functions of compounds in plants or their pharmacological properties. These two extremely interesting areas fall just beyond the scope of the present book, but they are worthy of mention since it is because of such properties that workers in botany or pharmacy are led to seek information on the chemistry of plant constituents.

ISOLATION METHODS

Procedures for isolating substances from plants are nearly as varied as the substances themselves, but we have tried to indicate methods which are generally useful for a group of compounds rather than methods which have been used for specific members of the group. Often particular compounds continue to be isolated by tried and true methods rather than by adopting recent methods of more general utility. Thus, while the recommended way to purify an unknown alkaloid might well be chromatography on a cation exchange resin, it would be unusual to purify strychnine in this way.

In preparing plant materials for isolation of individual compounds the most important precaution is the avoidance of artifacts. If living tissue is processed too slowly, enzymatic action may cause profound changes in certain constituents. Oxidation and hydrolysis are the most common degradative processes; and if constituents are sought which are subject to them, care must be taken to avoid such effects. On the other hand, if tissues are heated to prevent enzymatic action, certain heat-labile substances may undergo change. Probably the safest general method for all eventualities is immersion in liquid nitrogen followed by freeze-drying, and extraction of dried material with solvents which do not permit degradative changes to occur. Such drastic measures are seldom necessary, however, and a consideration of the properties of the substances to be isolated will usually point the way to simpler yet adequate procedures for preparing the plant material. General methods for preparing extracts are reviewed by Pirie (1). Newer methods of isolating natural products have recently been reviewed (2).

Chromatographic methods have become more and more prominent in the isolation and purification of unknown compounds. A full discussion of such methods is beyond the scope of the present book. Several helpful reviews are available on methods of preparative chromatography, (3, 4, 5). Countercurrent distribution methods are also widely used although they require more complex apparatus than most chromatographic procedures. Reviews of this technique may be found in articles by Hecker (6) and Thompson *et al.*, (7).

Cheronis (8) has proposed a general fractionation procedure applicable to any aqueous plant tissue extract. The broad outlines of this procedure are indicated by the following diagram. Further separation of the different fractions can be achieved by appropriate methods of column chromatography.

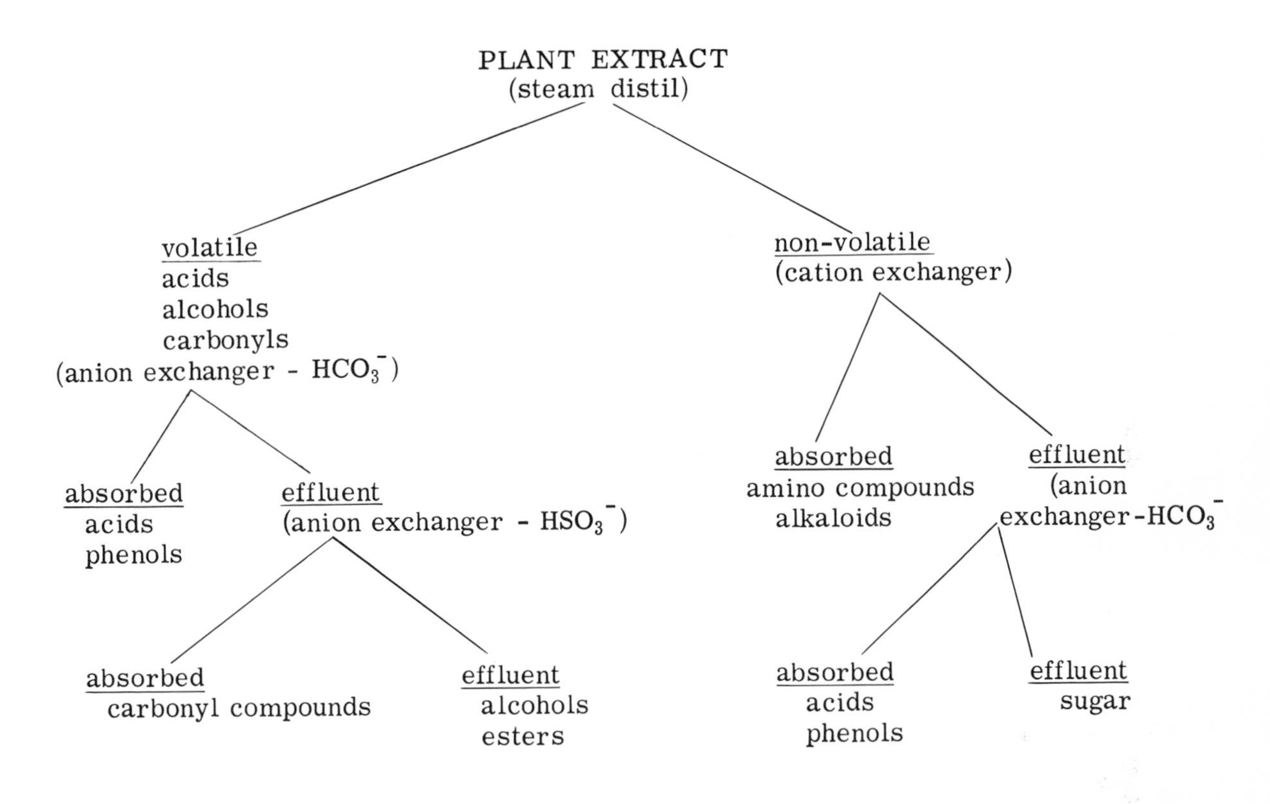

Obviously many types of compounds present in plants are not shown in this scheme, but everything must fall (even though incompletely) into one fraction or another, so that as a preliminary separation the method has much to offer. Further fractionation must take into account the properties of the desired compounds. As with any fractionation scheme, it can be applied most intelligently if some qualitative information is available regarding the constituents of the original mixture. The following discussion of "Characterization" is intended to suggest means for obtaining such information.

CHARACTERIZATION

Under characterization are included methods for identifying a pure compound and also methods for determining what types of compounds are present in a crude mixture. Many times characterization procedures necessarily include the separation of somewhat purified compounds from mixtures, so that characterization cannot be strictly distinguished from the isolation methods described in the previous section. Complete characterization of a mixture requires quantitative analysis of the constituents in addition to knowledge of what they are. However, becaue of the space that would be required, all quantitative determinations have been excluded from this book. In most cases qualitative determinations performed with care permit some rough quantitative conclusions to be drawn, so that major and minor components of a mixture can be distinguised from one another. The work of Paech and Tracey describes quantitative procedures for a large number of plant constituents. Hamilton (9) has reviewed recent developments in biochemical analysis.

Over the years many simple color tests and spot reactions have been developed to indicate the presence of particular compounds or classes of compounds. Some of these tests have proven themselves to be consistently specific and sensitive. Others, unfortunately, have resulted in false conclusions which still persist in the literature. The most useful spot tests and color reactions have been described, with their limitations in the appropriate chapters. A complete coverage of such methods may be found in the works of Feigl (10).

Chromatographic methods are now the preferred way of characterizing compounds or mixtures. By column chromatography, as mentioned under "Isolation", mixtures are separated into fractions which may then be characterized by their physical and chemical properties. The quantities involved may be large enough to permit several tests to be performed on each fraction, and it is these tests rather than the chromatographic separation itself which are most important for characterization. In chromatography on paper sheets the quantities of material involved are usually much smaller (e.g. 1-100 micrograms), only a few tests may be applied to the separated compounds, and the way that they migrate in various solvent systems offers important information for characterizing them. In thin layer chromatography, adsorbants with plaster of Paris or another binder are spread on glass strips then used much in the same way as paper sheets. Separations are much faster than on paper, however, and often better resolution is attained (11). Gas chromatography permits fine separation of minute amounts of material and rapid determination of the number of components in a mixture. Tentative identification of compounds can be made by comparison of their retention times on the column with the times of known materials. Final identification must, however, depend on isolation of a fraction and its characterization by other techniques. Even compounds not ordinarily considered to be volatile may be separated by high temperature gas chromatography (12).

There are several excellent books on chromatography. The newcomer to this field is particularly referred to those by Williams (13) and Smith (14) and an article by Johnson (14a). Other works (5, 15, 16, 17) offer extensive and detailed reviews of methods which have been used for different classes of compounds. The special application of chromatography to analysis of plants is described by Linskens (18) and by Thompson *et al.*, (19). Heftmann (20) has reviewed recent developments in chromatography. In the chapters which follow we have selected solvent mixtures and detection reagents which seem generally applicable to a class of compounds. Reference to the above books will usually reveal several other procedures that may be used once some indication is available regarding the nature of the compounds to be characterized. The R_f value is a physical constant for each compound and is defined as the distance from the starting point to which the compound has migrated divided by the distance the solvent has migrated. R_f values vary with temperature, direction of paper grain, amount of material applied to the paper, etc. They therefore can not be relied upon without question for identification. Known compounds should be run for comparison alongside of unknowns. In addition to specific detection reagents useful to indicate various types of compounds on paper chromatograms, there are a few general reagents which detect almost any organic compound. Alkaline silver nitrate is a common one of these, and its use is described in detail by Smith (14). Other such general reagents are iodine vapor (21) and alkaline potassium permanganate solution.

One of the most important and widely used techniques for characterization of organic compounds is the measurement of absorption spectra by the use of photoelectric spectrophotometers. The light absorption spectrum of a molecule is one of its most distinctive properties, and excellent instruments are available which permit determination of this spectrum with very small quantities of material. In addition the material is not destroyed by making such measurements, and may be used later for other tests. Often in recent years the combination of chromatography with spectrophotometry has made possible the complete fractionation of a very small quantity of some natural mixtures and the unequivocal identification of each component.

Three types of absorption spectra are commonly distinguished, infrared, visible, and ultraviolet. Absorption of radiation in the infrared region depends on the vibration and rotation of atoms in the molecule. Rotational spectra have been little studied, and for practical purposes the infrared spectra which are normally measured are entirely due to vibration. Different atomic groups can vibrate only at specific frequencies and absorb radiation of just these frequencies. These absorption bonds appear in the region of wavelengths from 2 - 100 microns, but most instruments cover this range only up to about 25μ. From about 2-8μ the absorption bonds observed are highly characteristic certain atomic groups and therefore give good indications as to what functional groups are present. For example, hydroxyl groups absorb at about 2. 8μ, carbonyl groups at 5. 8μ, nitrile groups at 4. 4μ, etc. The region above 8μ is referred to as the "fingerprint region" since it is unique for the molecule as a whole rather than for specific groups. Frequently the positions of infrared absorption bands are expressed as wavenumbers rather than wavelengths. The wavenumber is the reciprocal of the wavelength expressed in centimeters (1 cm. = 10, 000μ). The identity of the infrared spectrum of a pure, unknown compound with that of a known sample may be taken (with rare exceptions) as proof that the two compounds are identical.

Ultraviolet and visible absorption spectra depend not on the vibration of atoms in a molecule but on the fact that certain loosely-held electrons may be raised to higher energy levels by absorbing radiation of specific wavelengths. For this reason ultraviolet and visible spectra may be lumped together as electronic spectra. There is no theoretical difference between them. Since loosely-held electrons are required for absorption to occur, molecules with unsaturated bonds are the ones which absorb in this region. However, specific absorption bands do not indicate specific functional groups as in infrared spectra, rather they are more characteristic of the molecule as a whole. They may often permit decisions to be made as to the class of compounds involved (e. g. an anthocyanin vs. a naphthoquinone) but give little indication as to details of structure. The common commercial instruments permit spectral measurements to be made over the ranges 200 - 400 mμ (ultraviolet) and 400 - 750 mμ (visible). Observations in the near infrared (750 - 2000 mμ) can be made but are seldom useful. While electronic spectra are not as important as infrared for identification or structural determination of a molecule, they have other important advantages----usually smaller amounts of material are required; it is easier to determine the quantity of a substance which is present; and many solvents are available which do not absorb in the ultraviolet - visible regions.

There is no space here for a more thorough description of spectrophotometric theory and procedures. General discussions of both types of spectra may be found in the articles of Miller (22) and Glover (23) or the book of Oster and Pollister (24). Infrared spectroscopy is the subject of several excellent books (25, 26); and the infrared spectra of natural products are discussed by Cole (27). Comprehensive catalogs of spectral data are also available (28-34).

With the advent of commercial instruments the application of nuclear magnetic resonance spectra to the characterization of natural products will undoubtedly increase. As yet, however, only a few plant constituents have had their structures elucidated by this technique; and since a brief explanation is impossible, we wish merely to call attention to the method. Nuclear magnetic resonance (NMR) spectra are dependent on the absorption of radio frequency signals on exposure of certain atomic nuclei to a radio frequency field and a strong magnetic field. Of the so-called magnetic nuclei which respond in this way almost the only one of interest in natural products is hydrogen. Therefore

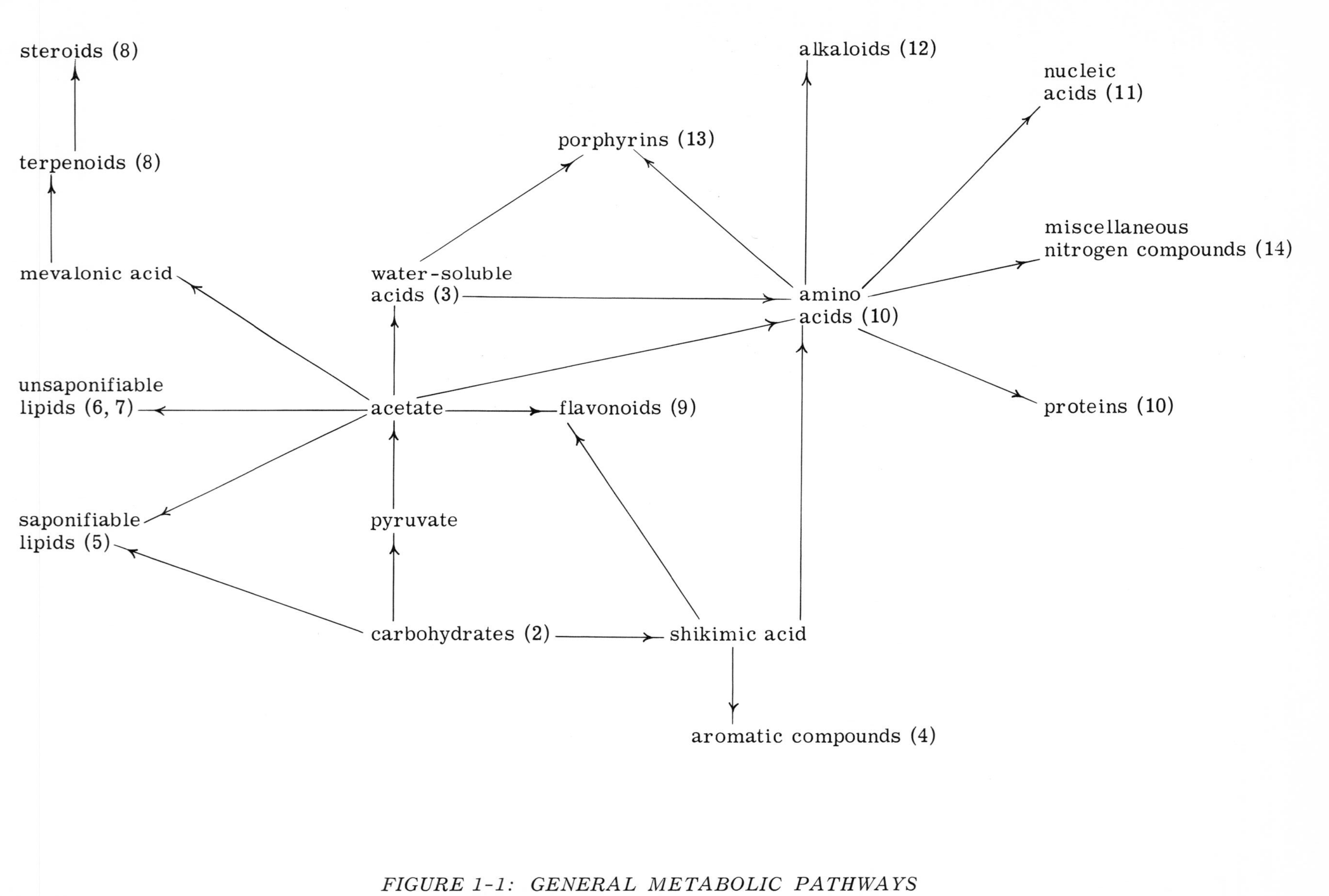

FIGURE 1-1: GENERAL METABOLIC PATHWAYS

it is possible to limit consideration to this nucleus and speak of proton resonance spectroscopy. Spectra are plotted as signal strength vs. magnetic field strength. Although only the hydrogen nuclei of a molecule are responsible for the spectrum, a variety of peaks is obtained depending on the environments of the different hydrogen nuclei. Thus, indirectly, functional groups may be detected since, for example, the hydrogen of a hydroxyl group will show a peak different from the hydrogen of an aldehyde group. The technique is especially valuable for indicating molecular configuration and is often the best, if not the only, method available for this purpose. Additional information may be found in a short article (35) and two books (36, 37).

Other very specialized techniques which at present are likely to be of only rare interest to the reader of this book are mass spectrometry and optical rotatory dispersion. These methods have been the subject of recent reviews (38, 39).

METABOLIC PATHWAYS

Although metabolism as such is outside the central scope of the book, division into chapters has been made on the basis of metabolic pathways. The brief sections on metabolism are therefore intended to demonstrate the unity which a knowledge of biosynthesis can bring to the diversity of natural products. Organization on this basis is novel and has placed together compounds which are traditionally discussed separately. For example, terpenoids (which are usually included with "essential oils") and steroids are covered in the same chapter since their biosynthesis proceeds along almost identical pathways. For some natural products the pathways of biosynthesis remain unknown, but by analogy it is often possible to arrive at reasonable hypotheses. For instance, the stimulating ideas of Birch have introduced a unity into Chapter 6 which is very attractive although extensive metabolic studies have not been carried out to establish the complete reliability of this apparent unity.

Presentation of many metabolic pathways may be found in the valuable books of Umbreit (40) and Greenberg (41). However, both of these books ignore many natural products which are prominent in higher plants but not found elsewhere. An abbreviated, overall scheme of the metabolic pathways which we have assumed is shown in Figure 1-1. The numbers in parentheses indicate the chapters in which the various classes of compounds are discussed. More detailed schemes are presented in each chapter.

BIBLIOGRAPHY

1. Pirie, N. W. in Paech and Tracey, 1 26.
2. Tiselius, A., Experientia 17 433 (1961).
3. Braunitzer, G. in Paech and Tracey 1 95.
4. Ritter, F. J. and Meyer, G. M., Nature 193 941 (1962).
5. Lederer, E. and Lederer, M., Chromatography, 2nd ed., Elsevier, Amsterdam, 1957.
6. Hecker, E., in Paech and Tracey 1 66.
7. Thompson, C. R., Curl, A. L. and Bickoff, E. M., Anal. Chem. 31 838 (1959).
8. Cheronis, N. D., Trans., N. Y. Acad. Sci. 18 516 (1956).
9. Hamilton, P. B., Anal. Chem. 34 3R (1962).
10. Feigl, F., Spot Tests in Organic Analysis, 6th ed., Elsevier, Amsterdam, 1960.
11. Stahl, E., Angew. Chem. 73 646 (1961).
12. Burchfield, H. P. and Storrs, E. E., Biochemical Applications of Gas Chromatography, Academic Press, New York, 1962.
13. Williams, T. I., The Elements of Chromatography, Blackie and Son, Glasgow, 1954.
14. Smith, I., Chromatographic Techniques, 2nd ed., William Heinemann, London, 1960.
14a. Johnson, M. J., Manometric Techniques, W. W. Umbreit, R. H. Burris, and J. F. Stauffer, eds., Burgess, Minneapolis, 1957.
15. Block, R. J., Durrum, E. L. and Zweig, G., A Manual of Paper Chromatography and Paper Electrophoresis, 2nd ed., Academic Press, N. Y., 1958.

16. Heftmann, E., ed., Chromatography, Reinhold, N. Y., 1958.
17. Hais, I. M. and Macek, K., Handbuch der Papierchromatographie, 2 vols., Gustav Fischer, Jena, 1960.
18. Linksens, H. F., Papier Chromatographie in der Botanik, Springer Verlag, Berlin, 1955.
19. Thompson, J. F., Honda, S. I., Hunt, G. E., Krupka, R. M., Morris, C. J., Powell, L. E., Silberstein, O. O., Towers, G. H. N. and Zacharius, R. M., Bot. Rev. 25 1 (1959).
20. Heftmann, E., Anal. Chem. 34 13R (1962).
21. Barrett, G. C., Nature 194 1171 (1962).
22. Miller, F. A. in H. Gilman, Organic Chemistry 3 122 John Wiley, N. Y., 1953.
23. Glover, J. in Paech and Tracey 1 149.
24. Oster, G. and Pollister, A. W., Physical Techniques in Biological Research, 1, Optical Techniques, Academic press, N. Y., 1955.
25. Bellamy, L. J., The Infra-Red Spectra of Complex Molecules, John Wiley, N. Y., 1959.
26. Cross, A. D., Introduction to Practical Infra-Red Spectroscopy, Butterworth's, London, 1960.
27. Cole, A. R. H., Fortscher. Chem. Org. Naturstoffe 13 1 (1956).
28. Friedel, R. A. and Orchin, M., Ultraviolet Spectra of Aromatic Compounds, John Wiley, N. Y., 1951.
29. Hershenson, H M., Ultraviolet and Visible Absorption Spectra, Academic Press, N. Y., 1956.
30. Hershenson, H. M., Infrared Absorption Spectra, Academic Press, N. Y., 1959.
31. Kamlet, M. J., ed., Organic Electronic Spectral Data, 1, Interscience Publishers, N. Y., 1960.
32. Ungnade, H. E., ed., Organic Electronic Spectral Data, 2, Interscience Publishers, N. Y., 1960.
33. Sadtler, P., Infrared Spectra, S. P. Sadtler and Son, Philadelphia, 1960.
34. Sadtler, P., Ultra-Violet Spectra, S. P. Sadtler and Son, Philadelphia, 1960.
35. Martin, J. C., J. Chem. Educ. 38 286 (1961).
36. Jackman, L. M., Applications of Nuclear Magnetic Resonance Spectroscopy in Organic Chemistry, Pergamon Press, N. Y., 1959.
37. Roberts, J. D., Nuclear Magnetic Resonance, Applications to Organic Chemistry, McGraw-Hill, N. Y., 1959.
38. Biemann, K., Angew. Chem. 74 102 (1962).
39. Djerassi, C., Science 134 649 (1961).
40. Umbreit, W. W., Metabolic Maps, Burgess, Minneapolis, 1960.
41. Greenberg, D. M., Metabolic Pathways. Academic Press, N. Y., 1960, 1961.

Chapter 2
CARBOHYDRATES

The universal distribution and physiological importance of carbohydrates have entitled them to rather full treatment in general texts of organic and biochemistry. Therefore, many elementary aspects of their chemistry can be passed over lightly in a work such as the present one. As early products of photosynthesis carbohydrates are key compounds in the biochemistry of green plants. Ultimately, all other constituents can be derived from them. Aside from this role as precursors, the different varieties of carbohydrates themselves serve several quite different functions. Starch and the simple sugars are generally involved with the storage and utilization of the energy required for the processes of growth, ion transport, water uptake, etc. As cellulose and the hemicelluloses, carbohydrates contribute to structural strength and binding cells together. Other less common derivatives -- glycosides, esters, esters, gums -- have less clear roles and are frequently assigned a protective function in wound healing or as being toxic to parasites. Linkage with a carbohydrate moiety may improve solubility characteristics.

As the different classes of carbohydrates are discussed, it must be noted that nomenclature described with reference to one class is frequently directly transferable to another class (e.g. prefixes such as *arabo, threo* defined for the monosaccharides may be applied just as well to the sugar acids or alcohols.) Comprehensive rules of carbohydrate nomenclature are given in reference (1).

MONOSACCHARIDES

The monosaccharides or simple sugars are fundamentally polyhydroxy aldehydes or ketones, although glycolaldehyde with only one hydroxyl group can be included. They are colorless, optically active, water-soluble compounds. The vast majority have straight carbon chains.

When the structures are written vertically with the carbonyl group nearest the top of the chain, the configuration around the lowest asymmetric carbon atom determines whether the sugar belongs to the D or L series. Sugars of both series occur naturally although L-arabinose is the only common L-sugar (as a component of many polysaccharides and free in the heartwood of conifers). Structures of the D-family of sugars are given in Figure 2-2. The open-chain aldehyde formulas are shown for convenience although it is well-known that sugars normally exist as cyclic hemiacetals where such a structure is possible. The hexoses are more frequently found with a six-membered pyranose ring, but may in some cases have the five-membered furanose ring. Pentoses are also found with either a furanose or pyranose ring. This type of structural representation is given for some common sugars in Figure 2-3. It will be noted that free hydroxyl groups written to the right in the straight chain formula are written below the plane of the ring. The designations α and β describe the position of the new free hydroxyl group generated by ring closure, the α form having this hydroxyl group below the plane of the ring for D-sugars. The pair of isomers differing only in the configuration around this carbon are called "anomers." If asymmetric carbons are present in the "tail" portion extending from the ring their configurations are represented by the straight chain convention(cf. glucofuranose).

- Sugars
  - Monosaccharides (aldoses and ketoses)
    - Trioses
    - Tetroses
    - Pentoses
    - Hexoses etc.
  - Oligosaccharides
    - Disaccharides
    - Trisaccharides etc.
- Sugar derivatives
  - Alcohols
  - Acids
  - Esters
  - Glycosides
- Polysaccharides (glycans)
  - Hexosans
    - Glucans
    - Fructans
    - Galactans
    - Mannans
    - Glucomannans
    - Galactomannans
  - Pentosans
    - Xylans
    - Arabans
  - Glycouronans (polyuronides)
    - Glucouronans
    - Galactouronans

FIGURE 2-1: OUTLINE OF THE CARBOHYDRATES

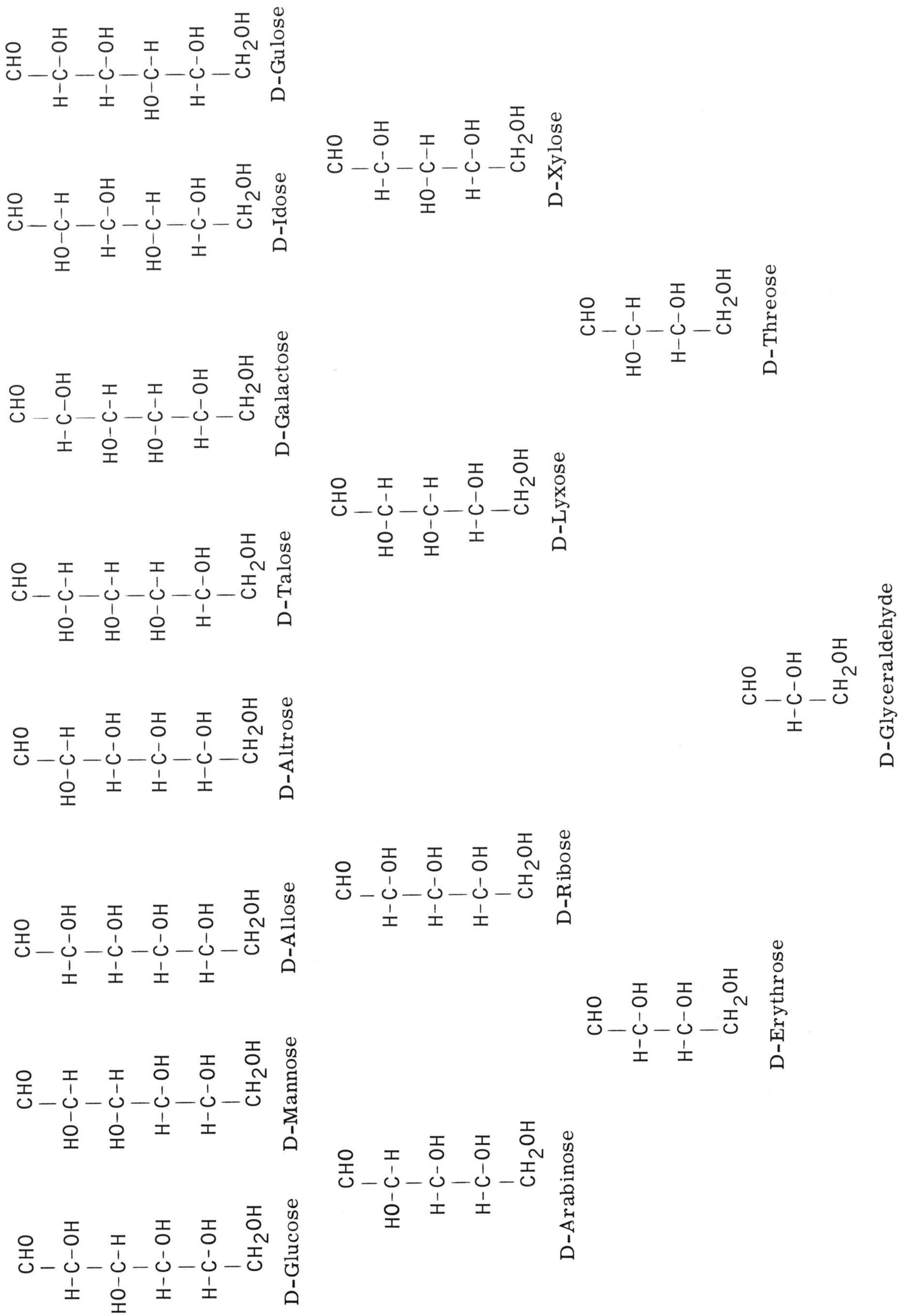

```
CHO
|
H-C-OH
|
HO-C-H
|
H-C-OH
|
H-C-OH
|
CH2OH
```
D-Glucose

```
CHO
|
HO-C-H
|
HO-C-H
|
H-C-OH
|
H-C-OH
|
CH2OH
```
D-Mannose

```
CHO
|
H-C-OH
|
H-C-OH
|
H-C-OH
|
H-C-OH
|
CH2OH
```
D-Allose

```
CHO
|
HO-C-H
|
H-C-OH
|
H-C-OH
|
H-C-OH
|
CH2OH
```
D-Altrose

```
CHO
|
HO-C-H
|
HO-C-H
|
HO-C-H
|
H-C-OH
|
CH2OH
```
D-Talose

```
CHO
|
H-C-OH
|
HO-C-H
|
HO-C-H
|
H-C-OH
|
CH2OH
```
D-Galactose

```
CHO
|
HO-C-H
|
H-C-OH
|
HO-C-H
|
H-C-OH
|
CH2OH
```
D-Idose

```
CHO
|
H-C-OH
|
H-C-OH
|
HO-C-H
|
H-C-OH
|
CH2OH
```
D-Gulose

```
CHO
|
HO-C-H
|
H-C-OH
|
H-C-OH
|
CH2OH
```
D-Arabinose

```
CHO
|
H-C-OH
|
H-C-OH
|
H-C-OH
|
CH2OH
```
D-Ribose

```
CHO
|
HO-C-H
|
HO-C-H
|
H-C-OH
|
CH2OH
```
D-Lyxose

```
CHO
|
H-C-OH
|
HO-C-H
|
H-C-OH
|
CH2OH
```
D-Xylose

```
CHO
|
H-C-OH
|
H-C-OH
|
CH2OH
```
D-Erythrose

```
CHO
|
HO-C-H
|
H-C-OH
|
CH2OH
```
D-Threose

```
CHO
|
H-C-OH
|
CH2OH
```
D-Glyceraldehyde

FIGURE 2-2: STRUCTURES OF THE D-ALDOSES

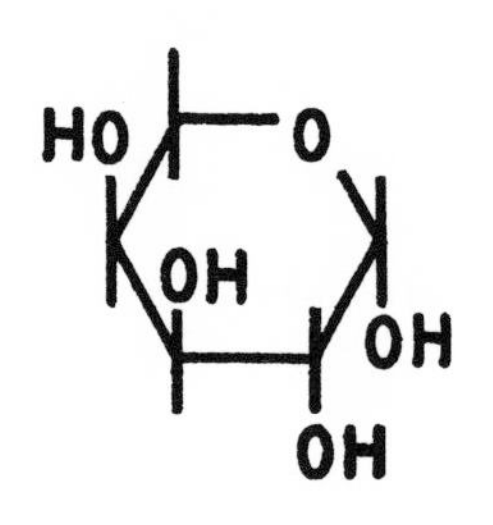

β-L-arabinopyranose

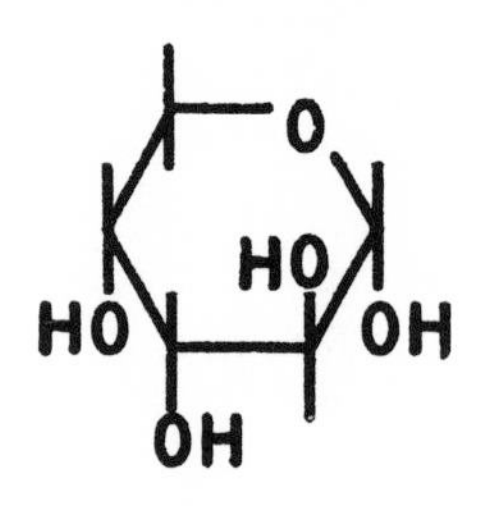

α-D-arabinopyranose

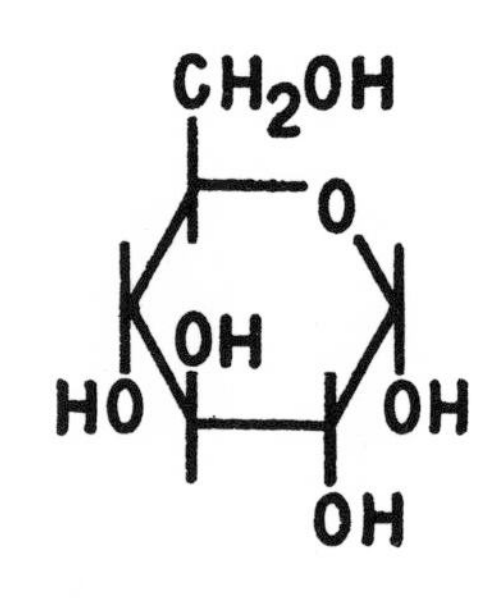

α-D-glucopyranose

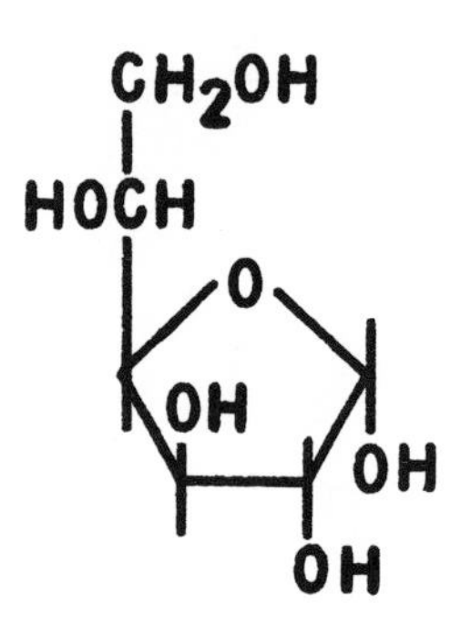

α-D-glucofuranose

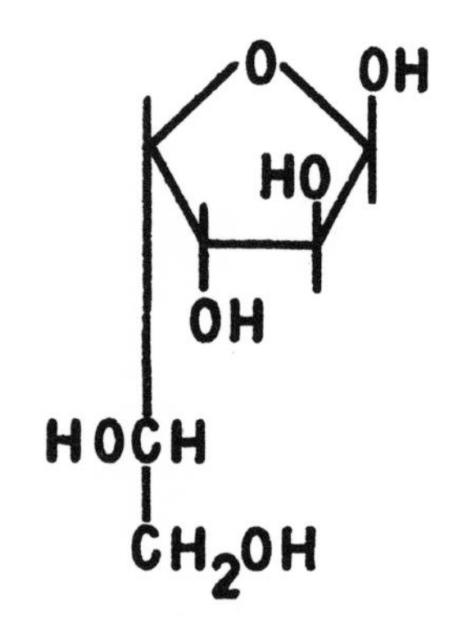

α-L-glucofuranose

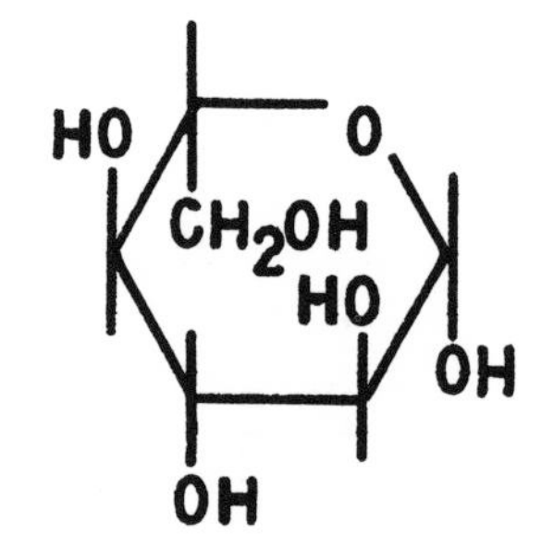

β-L-glucopyranose

(to illustrate the conventions)

FIGURE 2-3: CYCLIC FORMS OF SOME SUGARS

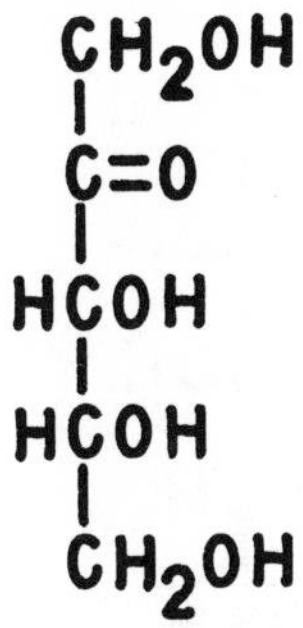

CH_2OH
C=O
HCOH
HCOH
CH_2OH

D-ribulose
(D-*erythro*-pentulose)

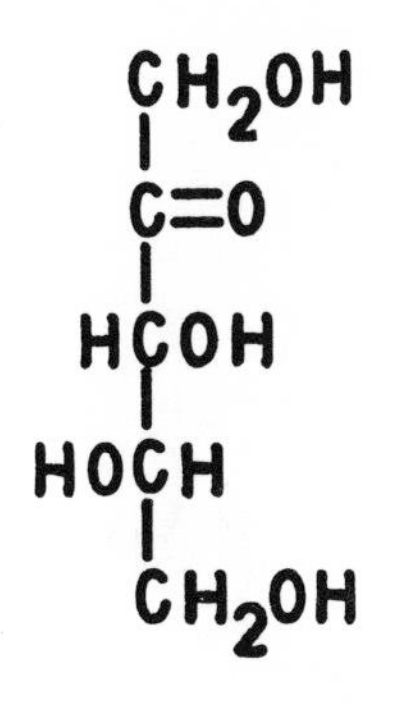

L-xylulose
(L-*threo*-pentulose)

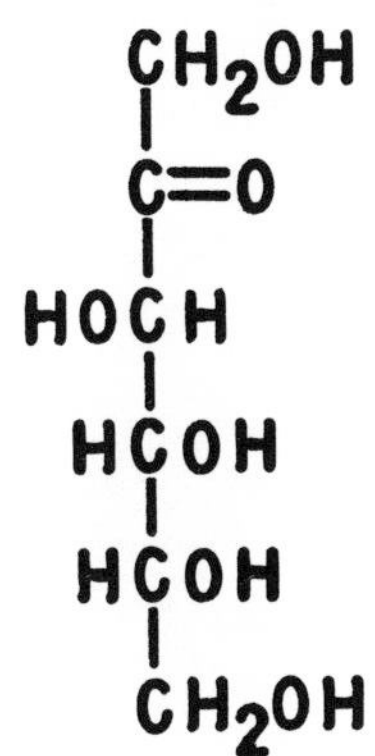

keto-D-fructose

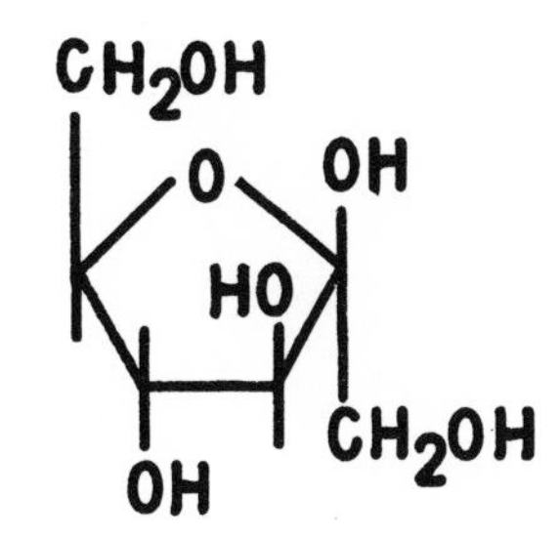

β-D-fructofuranose

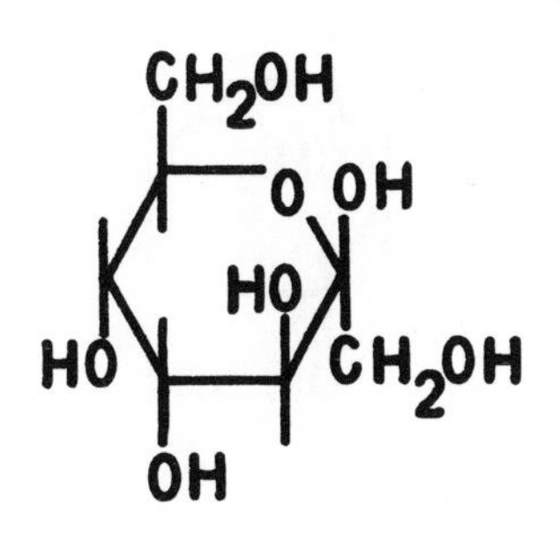

sedoheptulose
(β-D-*altro*-heptulofuranose)

FIGURE 2-4: SOME KETOSES

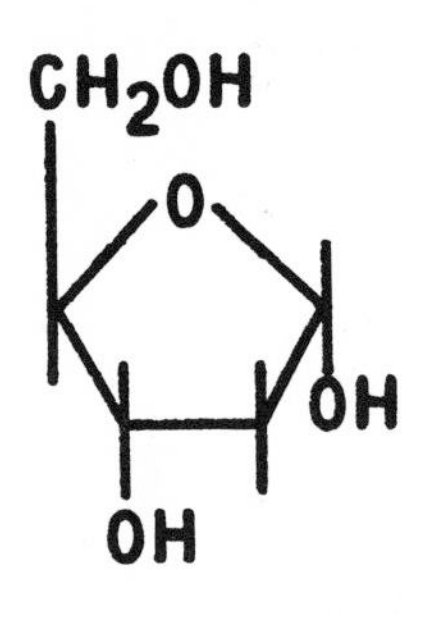

2-deoxy-D-*erythro*-pentofuranose

(2-deoxy-D-ribose)

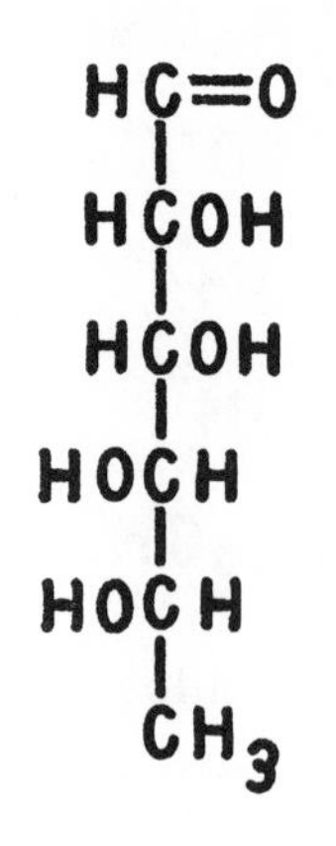

aldehydo-L-rhamnose

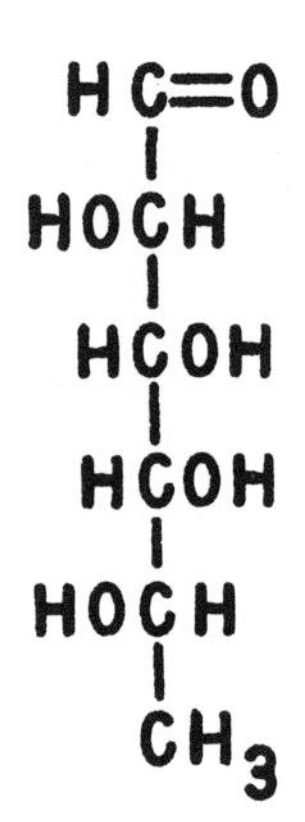

aldehydo-L-fucose

(6-deoxy-L-galactose)

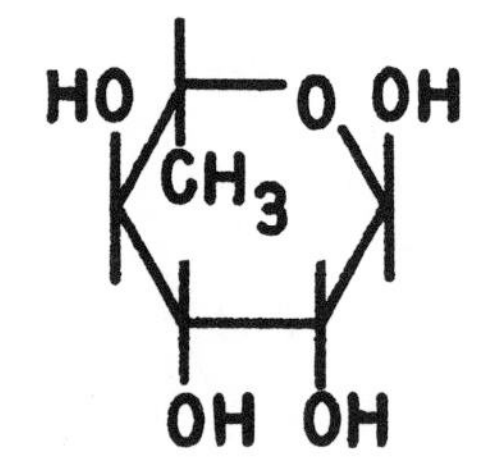

α-L-rhamnopyranose

FIGURE 2-5: SOME DEOXY SUGARS

The names of the common aldehyde sugars have been used to derive prefixes descriptive of hydroxylation patterns in less common carbohydrates. For example, sedoheptulose may be named as D-*altro*-heptulose to indicate:

a. It belongs to the D-series (i. e. the highest numbered asymmetric carbon is written to the right in the open chain structure).
b. It has four asymmetric hydroxylated carbons with the same configuration as the four in altrose.
c. It has seven carbons.
d. It is a keto sugar.

This prefix system is not likely to supplant the common names of already known sugars, but it is useful in naming new or little known sugars or their derivatives. The ending "-ulose" is used to designate keto sugars. (Although not all keto sugars are named in accordance with this rule.) Structures of some of the keto sugars are given in Figure 2-4.

Some of the most widespread sugars contain non-hydroxylated carbons and are named as deoxy sugars. Some illustrations are given in Figure 2-5.

A few of the monosaccharides are found free in plant saps. Glucose is almost universally found in this way. Others which occur free are fructose in many fruits, D-*manno*-heptulose and D-*glycero*-D-*manno*-octulose in avocados *(Persea americana)* (2), sedoheptulose in succulent plants, and rhamnose in poison ivy *(Rhus radicans)*. Many more of the monosaccharides do not occur as free sugars but are very common as esters, polymers, glycosides and other derivatives to be discussed below.

Some rare monosaccharides have branched carbon chains. For instance, apiose occurs as the glycoside apiin of parsley *(Petroselinum hortense)*, and hamamelose is found as an ester in the tannin of witch hazel *(Hamamelis virginiana)*.

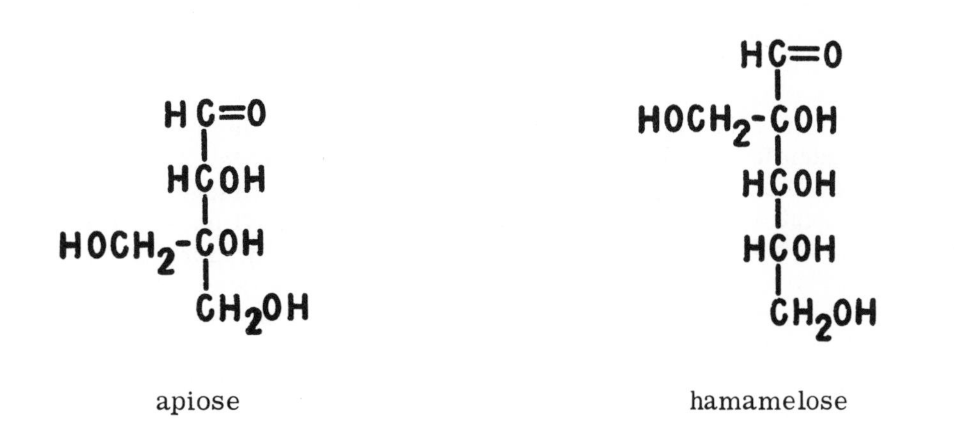

apiose hamamelose

GLYCOSIDES AND OTHER ETHERS

As hydroxyl compounds the carbohydrates are capable of forming ethers with other alcohols. Most important of these are the glycosides, which have the ether group linked to the anomeric carbon atom. Ethers involving the other carbon atoms are important as synthetic compounds and for studies of carbohydrate structure, but they are rare in nature. 3-O-methyl-D-galactose is found in the hydrolysis products of slippery elm *(Ulmus fulva)* mucilage. Other methyl ethers are found in more complex carbohydrates.

The glycosides are distinguished from other ethers by their ease of hydrolysis. Short boiling in dilute acid is usually sufficient to hydrolyze the sugar moiety from the aglycone. Glycosides may be named by designating the attached alkyl group first and replacing the "-ose" ending of the sugar with "-oside" as in α-methyl-D-glucoside. Many common glycosides are best known by trivial names which do not indicate their structures (e. g. "arbutin" is hydroquinone β-D-glucoside). Nearly all natural glycosides have the β configuration. Both chemically and physiologically the natural glycosides are distinguished more by their aglycone portions than by their glycosyl portions; and they are accordingly treated in this book --- for instance, under terpenoids, flavonoids, etc. Glycosidic bonds are also found, of course, in the oligosaccharides and polysaccharides.

Glucose is the sugar most frequently found in glycosides. However, other common sugars are not found as often as one would expect. Some rare sugars are peculiar to specific glycosides. In particular the cardiac glycosides regularly contain deoxy sugars that are not encountered in any other place. Rhamnose is deoxy sugar that occurs widely in glycosides but not in other forms.

Nucleosides may be thought of as glycosides where the aglycone is an amine rather than an alcohol. They share some of the properties of the other glycosides and are sometimes referred to as N-glycosides in contrast to the O-glycosides. Peculiar azoxy-glycosides are found in cycad roots (2).

Thioglycosides have a thiol rather than an alcohol as the aglycone. These are discussed under their aglycones in Chapter 14.

ESTERS

As alcohols the carbohydrates are capable of forming esters with acids. Many have been synthesized and are important derivatives in characterizing sugars. A few esters of aromatic acids also occur naturally and are evidently widespread (3, 4). They may be important intermediates in the transformations of aromatic compounds (cf. Chapter 4). More important are the hydrolyzable tannins which are complex esters of phenolic acids and sugars. They are discussed under their acid components (e. g. gallic acid). Most important physiologically are the phosphate esters, which are the prime intermediates in transformations of the sugars. Phosphorylated sugar moieties also go to make up several coenzymes and nucleic acid derivatives (q. v.). The phosphates are strong acids which are conveniently isolated as their slightly soluble barium salts. Their stability in water varies with the location of the phosphate group. The glycosyl phosphates (phosphorylated at the anomeric carbon, as glucose-1-phosphate) are notably more easily hydrolyzed than compounds phosphorylated in other positions. Phosphate adjacent to the carbonyl function is also more readily hydrolyzed than phosphate farther removed. Thus in fructose-1, 6-diphosphate the 1-phosphate is hydrolyzed more than ten times faster than the 6-phosphate. Triose phosphates are peculiarly unstable in alkali, and their determination may be based on this characteristic.

There has been some indication of the natural occurrence of sugar sulfates. Indeed Benson and Shibuya (5) have found as many as 60 organic compounds containing labelled sulfur after feeding radioactive inorganic sulfate to *Chlorella*. Some of these compounds are evidently sulfur analogues of the better known phosphorylated sugars, but their function is at present quite obscure. Sulfates of certain polysaccharides are widespread in nature but apparently not found in higher plants. A sulfonic acid derived from glucose is present in chloroplast lipids (Chapter 5).

ALCOHOLS *(Glycitols)*

Reduction of the carbonyl group of a sugar yields a polyhydroxy alcohol. A few of these are well-known natural products. Except for lack of the reducing function, they generally resemble the sugars in their properties. It must be noted that reduction of the anomeric carbon changes the possibilities for isomerism, so that the same sugar-alcohol may be derived from several different sugars, as sorbitol from glucose, gulose, or fructose.

Glycerol is undoubtedly the best-known sugar-alcohol, but it is important as a building block of the lipids rather than in its free form. The higher sugar-alcohols are given the ending -itol. The four carbon erythritol occurs in algae, lichens, and grasses. Ribitol is found free in *Adonis vernalis* but more importantly as a part of the ubiquitous riboflavin molecule. The six and seven carbon sugar-alcohols are the most common representatives of this class. Mannitol and sorbitol are found in many plants, the former in exudates, the latter especially in fruits but also in leaves. Only two natural heptitols are known. An octitol has been reported in avocado (6).

The carbocyclic inositols, although not derived from sugars by simple reduction, are conveniently treated here since they are quite similar in chemical properties. The particular isomer *myo*-inositol (formerly called meso-inositol) occurs widely in plants both free and as phytic acid, an anhydride of its hexaphosphate. Phytin is a calcium-magnesium salt of phytic acid. Certain lipids are also derived from inositol, and the sugar beet contains galactinol, 1-O-α-D-galactosyl *myo*-inositol. In addition to *myo*-inositol, pinitol (a methyl ether of D-inositol), and quebrachitol, (a methyl ether of L-inositol) are very widespread. Plouvier (7) has found inositol methyl ethers in a wide variety of plant species. Structures and occurrence of these and other inositol compounds are given in Figure 2-6. A review of the chemistry and natural occurrence of inositols and related compounds has been presented by Angyal and Anderson (8). *Myo*-inositol acts as an essential growth factor for certain plant tissue cultures (9).

SUGAR ACIDS

Oxidation of one or both of the terminal carbon atoms of a sugar molecule to a carboxyl group yields a sugar acid. Oxidation of the aldehyde group forms an aldonic acid. If the other terminal carbon is oxidized, the product is a uronic acid. The simplest of these would be glyoxylic and glycolic acids; but since they are important in organic acid metabolism rather than carbohydrate metabolism, they are treated in Chapter 3. D-glyceric acid is chiefly important as its phosphate esters, which are intermediates in carbohydrate breakdown and in photosynthesis. The tartaric acids may be thought of as erythrose derivatives with both terminal carbons oxidized to carboxyl groups. The six-carbon sugar acids occur in small amounts, chiefly as intermediates in the degradation of hexoses to form pentoses and as building blocks and degradation products of pectin, gums, and mucilages. All are water soluble and frequently exist as lactones so that their acidic properties are not apparent on titration in the cold. The uronic acids are easily decarboxylated by boiling with acid. This leads to errors when polysaccharides containing them are broken down by acidic hydrolysis. Structures of the important sugar acids appear in Figure 2-9 (p. 33).

The most important free sugar acid, L-ascorbic acid, is not only a vitamin for man but may play a role in the metabolism of plants. One established function is as a coenzyme for a mustard oil glycosidase (10). It is a strong reducing agent and may be readily distinguished by this property, although the four-carbon enediol, dihydroxy-fumaric acid occurs in nature to a limited extent and has similar properties. Ascorbic acid owes its

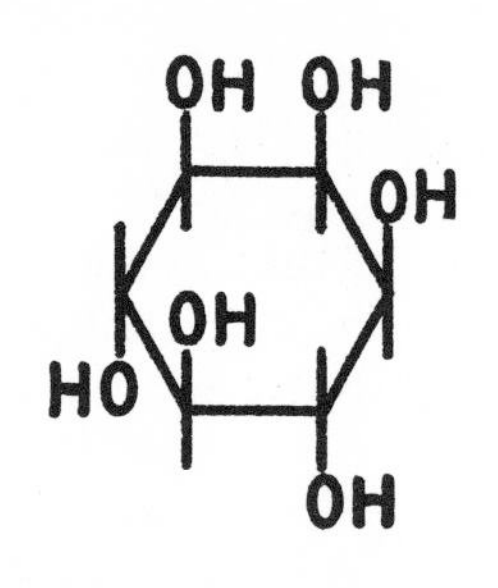

myo-inositol

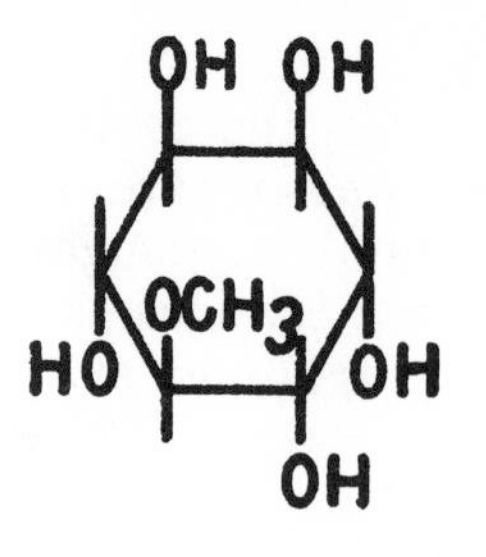

pinitol

(5-O-methyl-D-inositol)

(in many conifers and some other plants)

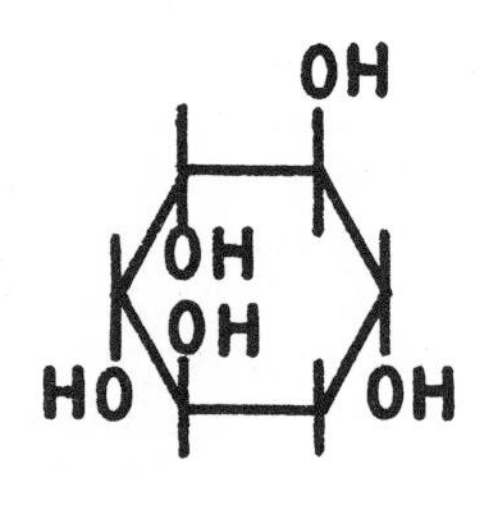

(+)-quercitol

(D-1-deoxy-*muco*-inositol)

(in acorn and other places)

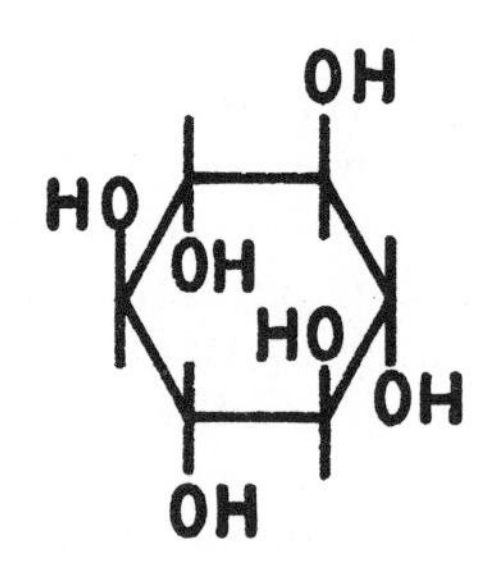

scyllo-inositol

(in dogwood, palms, acorns)

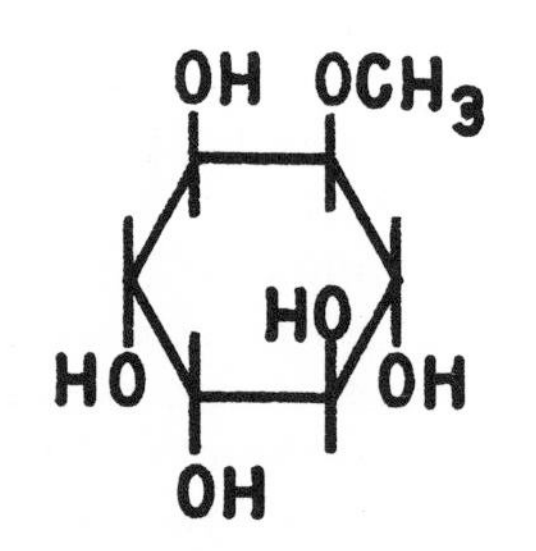

quebrachitol

(1-O-methyl-L-inositol)

(in many plants)

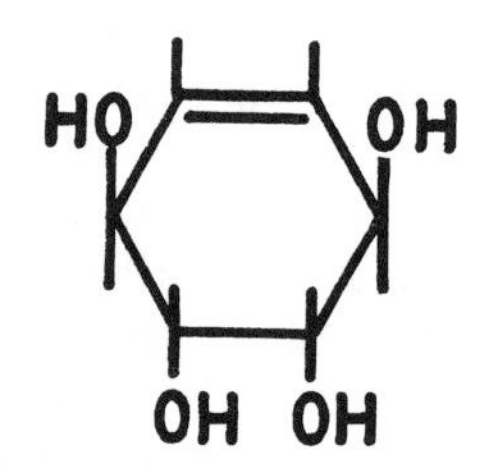

conduritol

(bark of condurango tree)

FIGURE 2-6: SOME INOSITOL DERIVATIVES

acidic nature to the two enolic hydrogens since it has a lactone ring rather than a free carboxyl group. Ascorbic acid occurs in certain plants as an indole derivative ascorbigen, (cf. Chapter 14). Many aspects of ascorbic acid are reviewed in a symposium publication (11).

OLIGOSACCHARIDES

The oligosaccharides are polymers formed by the linking together of several monosaccharide units through glycosidic bonds. Although oligosaccharides are arbitrarily limited to molecules containing less than ten monosaccharide units, the commonest have only 2, 3, or 4 units; and hexose units are by far the most frequent. One awkward case is the water-soluble glucan (polyglucoside) of barley roots which contains 7-11 units and may therefore be classed as either an oligosaccharide or a polysaccharide (12).

Aldobiouronic acids are oligosaccharides containing uronic acid units. They are found as hydrolysis products of certain gums, mucilages, and polysaccharides (q. v.) but apparently do not occur as natural plant constituents.

The oligosaccharides are water-soluble, optically active compounds, distinguished most readily from the monosaccharides by their hydrolysis to the monomers. They may be reducing or non-reducing, depending on whether or not all the potential carbonyl groups are tied up in glycosidic linkages. Oligosaccharides also occur as components of glycosides. For example, rutinose is a part of the flavonoid compounds rutin and hesperidin but apparently does not occur in the free state. Other rare oligosaccharides are components of steroid and triterpene glycosides. Some fructosyl sucroses (trisaccharides) which occur in monocots may be intermediates in fructan biosynthesis. These and oligofructosides generally have been discussed by Bacon (13, 14).

Structures and occurrence of some of the natural oligosaccharides are given in Table 1.

POLYSACCHARIDES GENERALLY

Polysaccharides or glycans are arbitrarily defined as polymers of monosaccharides (and their derivatives) containing 10 or more units. However, most natural polysaccharides contain many more than 10 units and may have several thousand. Despite the vast number of polysaccharides that would be possible, the known representatives account for only a few of the structural possibilities. Where a polysaccharide is composed of more than one monosaccharide, the units fall into an orderly sequence; and only certain ones of the available hydroxyl groups are utilized in forming the glycosidic bonds. Generally, the structural polysaccharides are straight-chain compounds, while reserve food polysaccharides tend to be branched. Branched molecules are more easily dispersed in water to form hydrophilic colloid systems that may be very viscous. The straight-chain polysaccharides, on the other hand, are slightly soluble or insoluble. Polysaccharides are usually obtained as amorphous rather than crystalline solids, although a degree of crystal order may be detected by x-ray diffraction methods. Some of the different classes of polysaccharides will be discussed separately. Ideally a classification should be based on structure, but this is possible to only a limited extent with present knowledge.

STRUCTURAL POLYSACCHARIDES

Cellulose is one of the main constituents of plant cell walls, in particular the secondary cell walls which are most important for structural strength. Cellulose is a linear

TABLE 1. STRUCTURES AND OCCURRENCE OF SOME OLIGOSACCHARIDES

Gentiobiose: 6-O-β-D-glucopyranosyl-D-glucose (various glycosides)

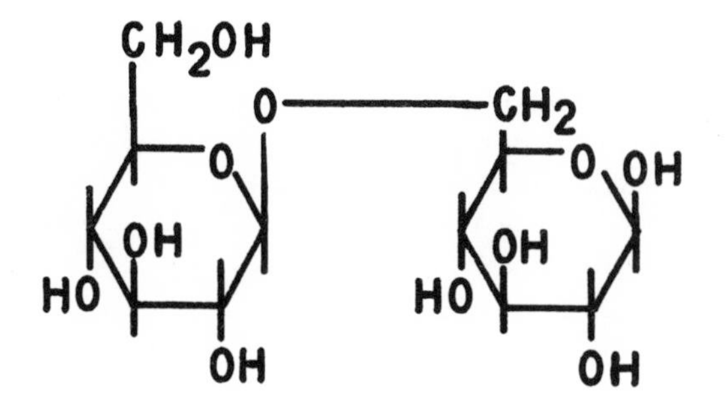

Melibiose: 6-O-α-D-galactopyranosyl-D-glucose (*Fraxinus* spp.)

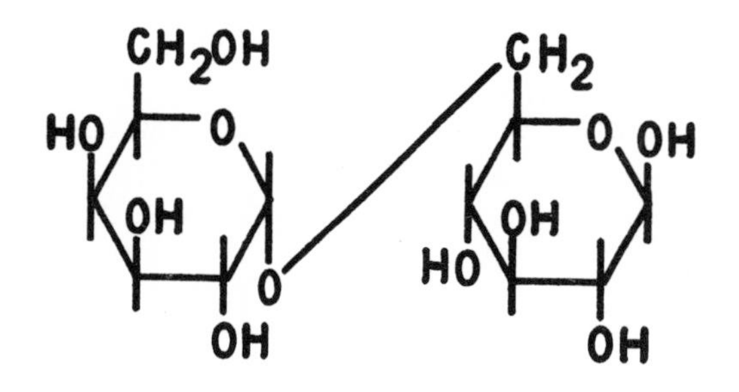

Sucrose: α-D-glucopyranosyl-β-D-fructofuranoside (throughout the plant kingdom)

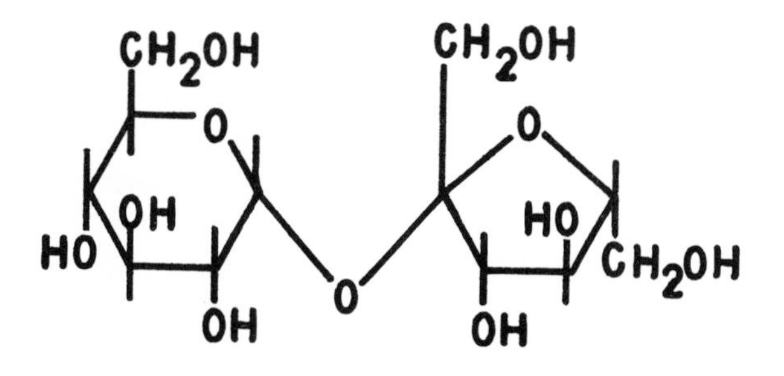

Trehalose: α-D-glucopyranosyl-α-D-glucopyranoside *(Selaginella lepidophylla)*

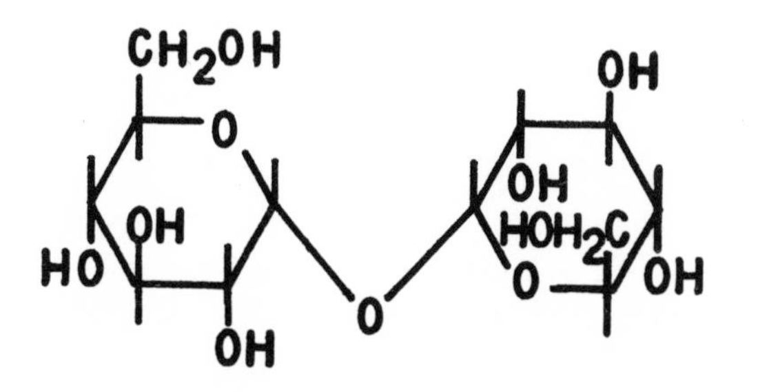

Table 1. Continued

Primoverose: 6-O-β-D-xylosyl-D-glucose (various glycosides)

Rutinose: 6-O-β-L-rhammosyl-D-glucose (glycosides)

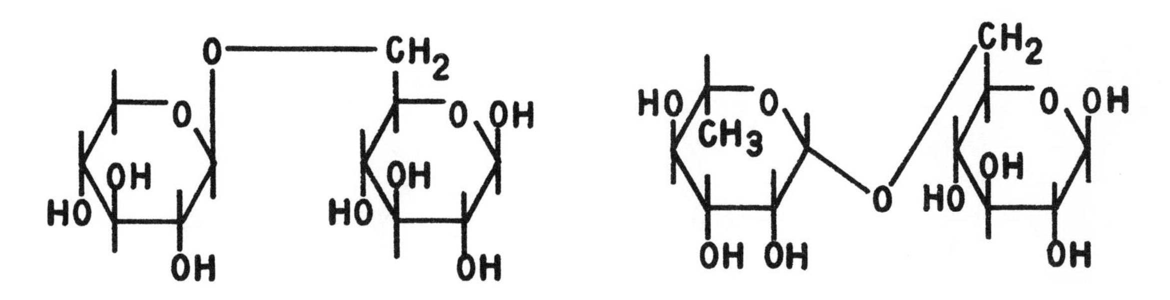

Gentianose: O-β-D-glucopyranosyl (1→6)-O-α-D-glucopyranosyl-(1→2)-β-D-fructofuranoside. (rhizomes of *Gentiana* spp.).

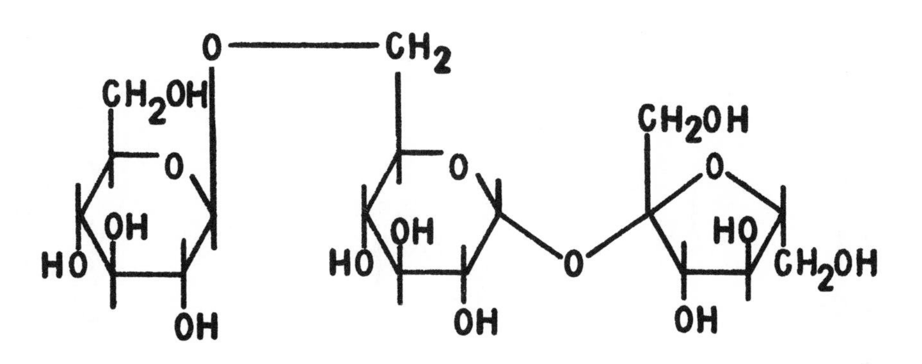

Melezitose: O-α-D-glucopyranosyl-(1→3)-O-β-D-fructofuranosyl-(2→1)-α-D-glucopyranoside. (exudates of many trees)

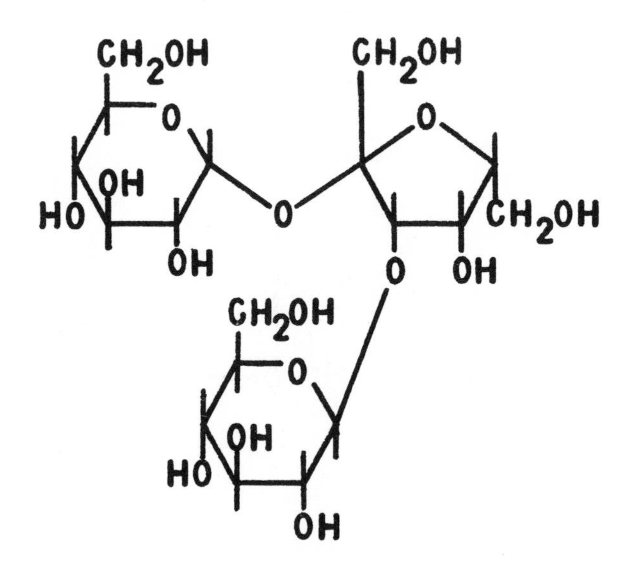

Table 1. Continued

Raffinose: O-α-D-galactopyranosyl-(1→6)-O-α-D-glucopyranosyl-(1→2)-β-D-fructofuranoside (throughout the plant kingdom)

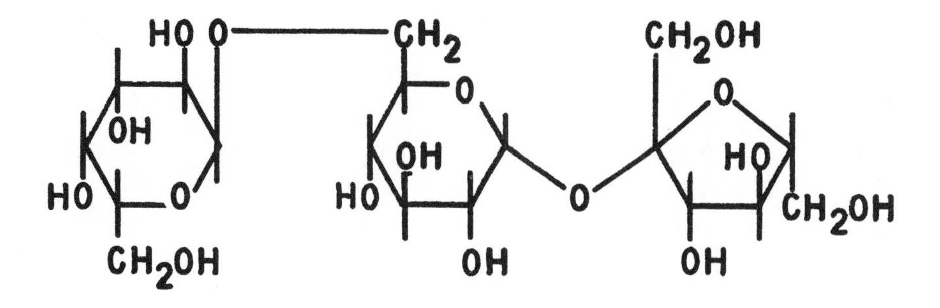

Stachyose: O-α-D-galactopyranosyl-(1→6)-O-α-D-galactopyranosyl-(1→6)-O-α-D-glucopyranosyl-(1→2)-β-D-fructofuranoside. (widely distributed)

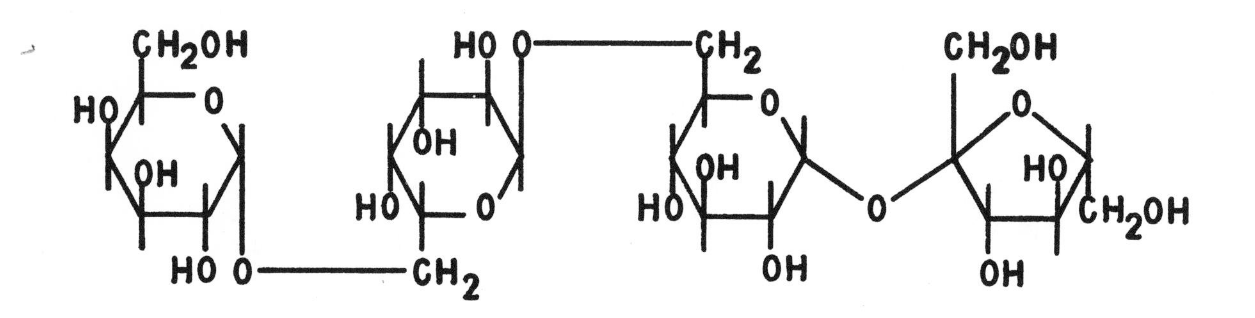

Verbascose: O-α-D-galactopyranosyl-(1→6)-O-α-D-galactopyranosyl-(1→6)-O-α-D-galactopyranosyl-(1→6)-O-α-D-glucopyranosyl-(1→2)-β-D-fructofuranoside. (roots of *Verbascum thapsus*)

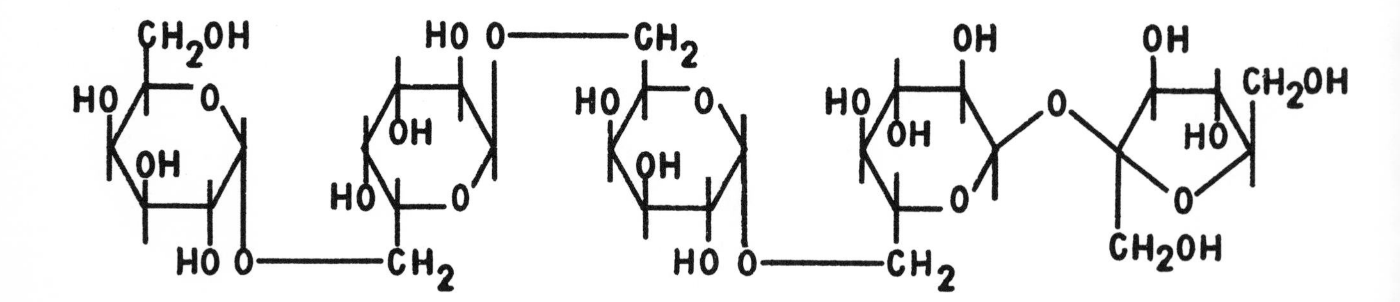

polymer of D-glucose units with β-(1→4) linkages. In cotton cellulose there are about three thousand glucose units comprising a molecule that is about 16, 000A long and 4x8A in cross-section. In the cell wall cellulose molecules are grouped together parallel to each other to form micelles with a diameter of about 60A. In the micelles certain regions show a crystalline structure where the cellulose molecules are arranged in an orderly way; other areas show a random arrangement. The micelles are in turn arranged into microfibrils (diameter 200-250A) and these into fibrils, visible in the ordinary microscope. Hydrolysis of cellulose by acid or enzymes yields first cellodextrins containing 30 or fewer glucose units, then cellobiose and finally glucose. The intermediates between glucose and cellulose do not occur naturally.

The hemicelluloses were originally named because they were found associated with cellulose in cell walls and thought to be intermediates in its formation. They comprise the polysaccharide material extractable from cell walls by 17. 5% sodium hydroxide, but wherever possible it is advisable to avoid the term "hemicellulose" and refer to the components of this group in terms of their specific structures (e. g. "xylans", "mannans" etc.).

The most abundant polysaccharide cell wall materials after cellulose are the xylans. There are several different types, occurring in almost all higher plants. They seem to occur especially in association with lignin. In non-lignified tissues pectic substances become more prominent. The basic unit of xylan structure is D-xylose; but, depending on the plant source, they may be branched or unbranched and may or may not contain additional units such as L-arabinose or D-glucuronic acid. Corn cob xylan contains about 200 sugar units as a straight chain with β-(1→4) links. On the contrary wheat straw xylan has only about 40 D-xylose units but in addition five L-arabinose units and three D-glucuronic acid units. Other hemicelluloses may have L-arabinose rather than D-xylose as their principal monosaccharide component. The "acidic hemicelluloses" are those with a relatively large proportion of glucuronic acid units connected to the xylose or arabinose backbones. They are readily soluble in dilute (4%) sodium hydroxide. However, there is no sharp dividing line between neutral and acidic hemicelluloses, so that extraction with increasing concentrations of alkali may yield a series of fractions with gradually increasing content of uronic acid. Hydrolysis of hemicelluloses which contain glucuronic acid produce along with the monosaccharides some aldobiouronic acid, a disaccharide in which the glycosyl group is a uronic acid. These appear in the hydrolysate because the glycosidic bond is peculiarly resistant to hydrolysis when it is formed from a uronic acid.

The pectic substances of plants are found in primary cell walls and intercellular cement. They are a mixture (and to some extent a chemical combination) of an araban, a galactan, and the methyl ester of a galacturonan. The araban is a low molecular weight branched chain of α(1→5) and α(1→3) L-arabinofuranose units. The galactan is a straight chain of about 120 β-(1→4) D-galactopyranose units. Most of the properties of pectin, however, and the name itself are referrable to the galactouran component which has about 200 (1→4)-α-D-galactopyranosyluronic acid units. Pectin actually occurs in plants as insoluble protopectin which contains bound calcium and phosphate and has a much larger molecular weight (1000 or more units). With senescence or acid treatment of the plant tissue water-soluble pectin is obtained by hydrolysis of some of the glycosidic bonds. Alkaline hydrolysis of pectin removes the methyl ester leaving pectic acid. The so-called pectinic acids are intermediate hydrolysis products with some carboxyl and some ester groups. The calcium and magnesium salts of pectic acid are the important cementing substances of the middle lamella.

Arabans have not been found except associated with pectin. However, a few galactans are known to occur apart from pectin. The best-known source of these is the wood of Western larch (*Larix occidentalis*) which may contain as much as 18% galactan. This molecule is highly branched with 1, 6 and 1, 3 linkages. A small amount of arabinose may also be present in the polymer, most likely as end-groups.

Although chitin, the structural polysaccharide of fungi and invertebrates, has not been reported in higher plants, its monomer, N-acetylglucosamine, has been found as its uridine diphosphate derivative in mung bean seedlings *(Phaseolus mungo)* (15). Free glucosamine has been reported in soy beans *(Glycine max)* (16).

FOOD RESERVE POLYSACCHARIDES

Starch, like cellulose is composed only of D-glucose units, but joined by α rather than β glycosidic linkages. Starch is normally a mixture of two types of polysaccharide, amylose and amylopectin. The former is a straight chain molecule of about 300 units joined 1→4. The latter contains a thousand or more units of which a majority are also 1→4 but with about 4% 1→6 linkages so that there is on an average about one branch for every 25 glucose residues. In most starches there is about 25% amylose to 75% amylopectin; but the ratio may be reversed in some varieties. In some starches (e. g. potato) the amylopectin is partially esterified with phosphates at C-6 positions. Starch is found widely in the plant kingdom where it serves as food storage material. However, some higher plants do not contain starch and use other carbohydrates as food reserves.

Fructans (polymeric fructosides) take the place of starch in a wide variety of plants and supplement starch as food reserves in others. The best known of these is inulin which contains about 25-28 2→1-linked fructofuranoside units per molecule and is soluble in hot but not cold water. It occurs especially in the *Compositae*. Other shorter chain fructans are also known, especially in the grasses (14). In contrast to inulin these contain only about 10 units, are linked 2→6 and are soluble in cold water. Many of the fructans, including inulin, seem to contain glucose, probably as terminal groups. Some fructans are linear, while others are highly branched. Of taxonomic interest is the observation of Quillet (17) that among the liverworts the Jungermanniales have fructans while the Marchantiales have starch.

Mannans are also distributed in groups as widely separated as grasses and conifers. At least in some cases they serve as reserve carbohydrate but may be structural material in other cases. Some plant mucilages also contain mannans. The mannans of palm seeds have been most studied. They contain about seventy-five mannose residues linked with β-(1→4) bonds.

Galactomannans, polysaccharides containing both D-galactose and D-mannose, serve as a food reserve in many legume endoperms and seeds of palm and coffee trees. The carob bean *(Ceratonia siliqua)*, in particular, is a commercial source of these galactomannans which are used as thickeners. They have a linear chain of β (1→4)-mannopyranoside units with galactopyranose units linked α-(1→6) as side chains. Because of their physical properties and occurrence in seeds the galactomannans have sometimes been classed with the mucilages. If a distinction is to be made, it must be in terms of function---i. e., the galactomannans seem to be food reserves, while the mucilages are more concerned with binding water.

An interesting polysaccharide has been reported in the fruit of the chicle plant *(Achras sapota)* by Venkataramen and Reithel (18). It is apparently composed of glucose and galactose since as the fruit ripens, lactose appears as a breakdown product. This accounts for one of the rare appearances of lactose in the plant kingdom.

PLANT GUMS AND MUCILAGES

Both of these constituents are polymers containing more than one type of monosaccharide, but uronic acids are generally present. Traditionally, mucilages have been defined as normal plant constituents; and since they occur in xerophytes, seeds, and young buds, they may be concerned with imbibition and holding of water. Gums, on the other hand, are produced in response to injury and are found as exudates on various trees, sometimes associated with triterpenoid compounds as gum-resins.

Gums and mucilages are all either soluble in water or strongly hydrophilic. Solutions are levorotatory. They frequently occur with some of the glucuronic acid groups as sodium, potassium, or calcium salts, but enough free carboxyl groups usually remain to produce a slightly acidic reaction. The monosaccharide components of some plant gums and mucilages are listed in Table 2. It must be noted that hydrolysis normally results in the appearance of aldobiouronic acids which are cleaved to the monosaccharides only under more drastic treatment. Occasionally hydroxyl groups may be methylated or acetylated.

ISOLATION

Many of the carbohydrates are soluble in water. Prolonged extraction of defatted material with neutral boiling water will leave undissolved the cell-wall polysaccharides, as well as non-carbohydrate materials. Lignin can be removed from the insoluble cell-wall material by treatment with chlorine dioxide (19). Extraction with cold alkali now removes hemicelluloses leaving a residue of cellulose. The strength of alkali can be varied if selective extraction of hemicelluloses is desired. 24% KOH (or 17.5% NaOH) is commonly used and leaves a residue known as "α-cellulose," which may, however, contain as much as 40% other polysaccharides such as xylans, mannans, etc., depending on the source. It is therefore apparent that alkaline extraction does not quantitatively remove all hemicelluloses. Further purification of the cellulose involves solution in 85% phosphoric acid and precipitation of cellulose by adding three volumes of distilled water (20). Cellulose so obtained has suffered considerable degradation (e.g. to a chain length of about 160 glucose units as compared to several thousand in native cellulose). Unfortunately purification is necessarily attended by degradation, and pure, native cellulose can only be obtained from a plant source like cotton which is almost pure cellulose already.

Returning to the alkaline solution of hemicelluloses, this may be fractionated making it acidic (pH ca. 4.5) whereupon the hemicelluloses of high molecular weight precipitate. The hemicelluloses remaining in solution may then be precipitated by adding alcohol, acetone, etc., to the supernatant solution. Further separations take advantage of special properties of the different types of compounds. Xylans and mannans may be separated from other cell wall polysaccharides by virtue of the fact that they form an insoluble copper complex in alkaline solution (21). This can be separated and the polysaccharides regenerated by acidification. It is not normally required to separate xylan from mannan since they do not usually occur together.

The hot water extract contains low molecular weight compounds in free solution as well as colloidal suspensions of the hydrophilic polysaccharides (and non-carbohydrate material such as organic acids and amino acids). If fructans are known to be present, a cold water extract may be preferred since some of them are readily hydrolyzed. Pectic substances are usually extracted using dilute acid (pH 2.5) or ammonium oxalate solution (0.5%). Depending on the source, the polysaccharides in the water extract might be gums, mucilages, starch, fructans, pectic substances, galactomannans, etc. There is no need of general methods to separate any one of these from all the others since in a given material only two or three types at most will be present, and methods chosen will depend on previous characterization. Generally all of them can be precipitated by adding ethanol to reach a concentration of 80%. (0.5% ammonium sulfate may aid the ethanol precipitation.) However, some of the shorter chain fructans are soluble in this concentration of ethanol. Amylose is separated from amylopectin by adding compounds such as butanol, thymol or nitrobenzene to a hot starch suspension. Amylose is precipitated as an insoluble complex which can be decomposed by ethanol to recover the amylose.

TABLE 2. SUGAR COMPONENTS OF SOME PLANT GUMS AND MUCILAGES

Name	Source	Hydrolysis Products
GUMS		
Gum arabic	*Acacia*	D-galactose, L-arabinose, L-rhammose, D-glucuronic acid
Mesquite gum	*Prosopis* spp.	L-arabinose, D-galactose, 4-O-methyl-D-glucuronic acid
Cherry gum	*Prunus* spp.	L-arabinose, D-xylose, D-mannose, D-galactose, D-glucuronic acid
MUCILAGES		
Flaxseed Mucilage	*Linum* spp.	D-xylose, L-galactose, L-rhamnose, D-galacturonic acid
Blond Psyllium Mucilage	*Plantago* spp.	D-xylose, L-arabinose, L-rhamnose, D-galacturonic acid
Slippery elm Mucilage	*Ulmus fulva* spp.	D-galactose, 3-O-methyl-D-galactose, L-rhamnose, D-galacturonic acid

Low molecular weight carbohydrates may be obtained from the 80% ethanol supernatant prepared as described above; or if only these carbohydrates are of interest, they may be extracted immediately from plant material using ethanol sufficient to give a concentration of 80% when diluted by whatever water is present. Some components (e. g. diphosphates) are strongly bound to tissue and must be extracted with 20% ethanol or other solvents. Ionic substances (salts, amino acids, organic acids) are best removed by ion exchange resins although strongly basic or acidic resins may have some effect on the sugars. Sugar acids and phosphates will be removed by anion exchange resins but may be separated from non-carbohydrate components either by appropriate fraction cutting, or, in the case of phosphates, by precipitation with barium hydroxide and conversion to sodium salts.

Special methods may be available for purification of the remaining neutral sugars. If one is in large excess, simple concentration of the solution may allow it to crystallize. If the desired component is not metabolized by yeast, impurities can frequently be removed by yeast fermentation.

The most general method for purification of the neutral sugars and derivatives is column chromatography using such adsorbents as charcoal, cellulose powder, starch and Florex, with rather polar developing solvents such as lower alcohols and mixtures of them with water. (See review by Binkley, 22.) On addition of borate, polyhydroxy compounds form anionic borate complexes which may be separated on a column of anion exchange resin using borate buffers as eluants. After elution, cations are removed from the fraction with a cation exchange resin in the hydrogen form and borate removed as volatile methyl borate by repeated distillation with methanol. The separated compounds may then be crystallized from a concentrated solution. In the presence of borate, sugars may also be separated by electrophoretic methods. Sugar mixtures can be separated according to molecular size using ion exchange resins (23).

A generalized outline of the procedures described above is shown below. Obviously each plant is a special case, and this outline cannot be followed rigidly, but it may be a useful guide. Consultation of the literature will fill in experimental details for known plants and carbohydrates, but no cut-and-dried procedure can substitute for an understanding of the principles involved or for constant checking of each step in the isolation by characterization of the product obtained.

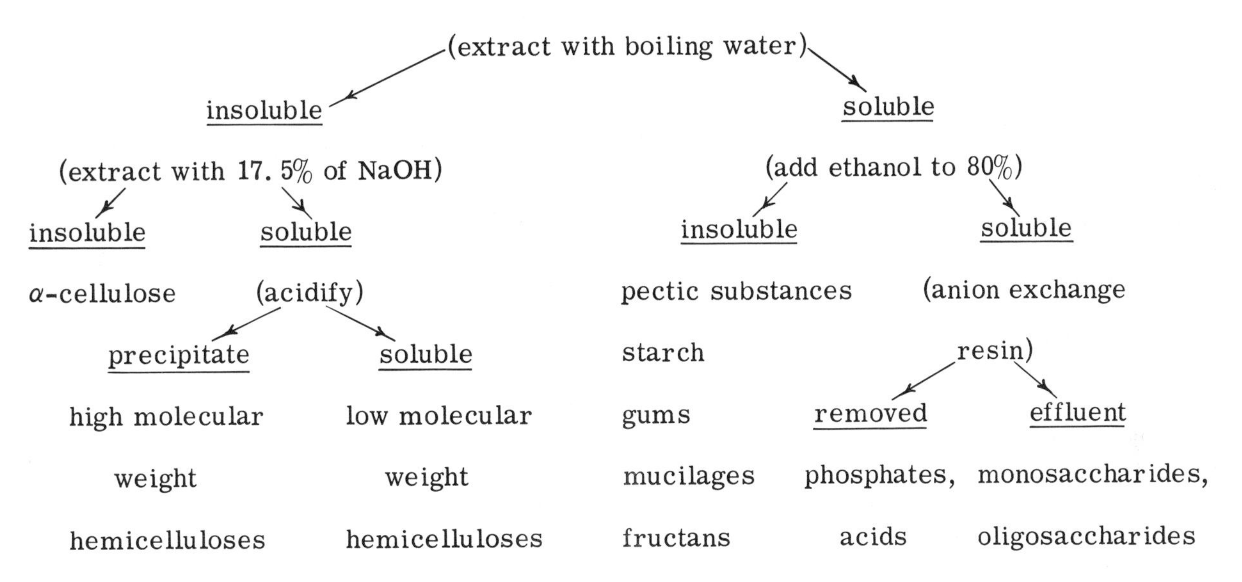

CHARACTERIZATION

Aside from the standard methods of organic chemistry, innumerable color tests have been developed for the different classes of carbohydrates. A general reaction given by all carbohydrates is the formation of a color when heated with sulfuric acid and a phenol such as resorcinol, anthrone, α-naphthol, thymol, etc. Cellulose is distinguished by its lack of solubility in all but the strongest acids and alkalies but ready solubility in cuprammonium hydroxide (Schweizer's reagent). Starch gives the well-known blue color with iodine due to its amylose component. Amylopectin gives a red-purple color with iodine. Pentoses and polysaccharides containing them give a red-violet color with phloroglucinol in hydrochloric acid. Uronic acids also give a positive test; but they may be distinguished by not giving the Bial reaction (a blue color on heating with orcinol and $FeCl_3$ in hydrochlorc acid). Ketoses are detected by heating with hydrochloric acid and resorcinol when they give a red color (Seliwanoff test). A blue-green color with diazouracil (Raybin reaction) is given by sucrose and other oligosaccharides containing a sucrose moiety such as raffinose and stachyose (24). Fructose and fructans give a red color on heating with urea in concentrated hydrochloric acid (25). The presence of uronic acids and their polymers can be detected by the evolution of carbon dioxide on heating with 12% hydrochloric acid. Other tests for certain classes of carbohydrates depend on their non-specific reducing power as in the reaction with Fehling's solution, Benedict's solution, ammoniacal silver nitrate, alkaline dinitrosalicyclic acid, etc. Ascorbic acid is distinguished by its especially strong reducing action as shown by reduction of the dye 2, 6-dichlorophenolindophenol, or of silver nitrate in *acidic* solution.

With pure compounds measurement of optical rotation is useful in identification. This method can be applied even to polysaccharides which give cloudy aqueous solutions by adding calcium chloride to cause clarification.

The characterization of polysaccharides may be divided into two problems-- (a) identification of the monosaccharide components, and (b) the structural arrangement and number of monomers comprising the polymer molecule. Only the first of these two-problems is considered to be within the scope of this book, although some idea of the proportions of different monomers in a polysaccharide may be gained by relatively simple methods. Conditions for acidic hydrolysis of polysaccharides vary widely. Cellulose requires strong acids and/or high temperatures, whereas fructans are readily hydrolyzed by very dilute acid on short boiling. Whatever conditions are used, a mixture of monosaccharides is obtained, and the problem is resolved to one of identifying them. The method of choice is unquestionably paper chromatography.

The literature on paper chromatography of carbohydrates is extensive. In addition to chapters in the general references and works on chromatography, the subject has been reviewed by Kowkabany (26). The commonest solvents have been water-saturated phenol or mixtures of two, three and four-carbon alcohols with water. Addition of acid to the solvent is not usually as necessary with the sugars as with ionizing substances; but it does help prevent background color with some sprays, and is helpful in improving separation of the acidic sugar phosphates and glucuronic acid. A brief listing of some common detection reagents is given below. Many others have been used.

1. Ammoniacal silver nitrate. Allow to dry at room temperature and then heat for a few minutes at 80-100° C. Strong reducing substances give dark spots before heating. Others (including some non-reducing sugars) show up on heating (27).
2. 3% anisidine hydrochloride (recently purified) in butanol followed by heating at 100°. Aldohexoses give green-brown spots; 6-deoxyaldohexoses emerald green, ketohexoses lemon yellow; uronic acids red (28).
3. 1% lead tetraacetate in benzene sprayed on paper moistened with xylene. All 1, 2-dioxy compounds give white spots on a brown background--especially useful for non-reducing carbohydrates (29).
4. Spray dry paper with a fresh mixture of equal volumes N $NH_2OH \cdot HCl$ and 1. 1 N KOH both in methanol. Dry about 10 min. and spray lightly with 1-2% $FeCl_3$ in 1% HCl. Lactones or esters of sugar acids show as blue-mauve spots. Free acids may be detected by first exposing paper to diazomethane so that methyl esters are formed (30).
5. Periodate oxidation procedures are rather involved but very useful for non-reducing carbohydrates and specific detection of deoxy sugars. In some cases important conclusions can be drawn concerning the structure of unknown sugars. See references (29) and (31) for details.
6. Nitrobrucine is a specific reagent for detection of ascorbic acid (32).
7. Phosphorylated sugars may be detected by the molybdate reagent of Hanes and Isherwood (33). When sprayed on dry paper this reagent shows an immediate yellow spot for inorganic phosphate and a yellow-blue spot for glucose-1-phosphate on heating to 85° C. for one minute. Blue spots for other phosphates appear on treatment with ultra-violet radiation for 10 minutes. The Wade-Morgan method is also suitable for phosphorylated sugars although it was originally used for nucleotides (cf. Chap. 11). Fructose phosphates are specifically detected by the procedure of Steinitz (34).
8. Schwimmer and Bevenue (35) have described a method for distinguishing between 1→4 and 1→6 linked oligosaccharides on paper chromatograms.

METABOLIC PATHWAYS

Reviews by Porter (36) and Gibbs (37) summarize well the interrelationships of the carbohydrates in higher plants and are the primary sources of information for the accom-

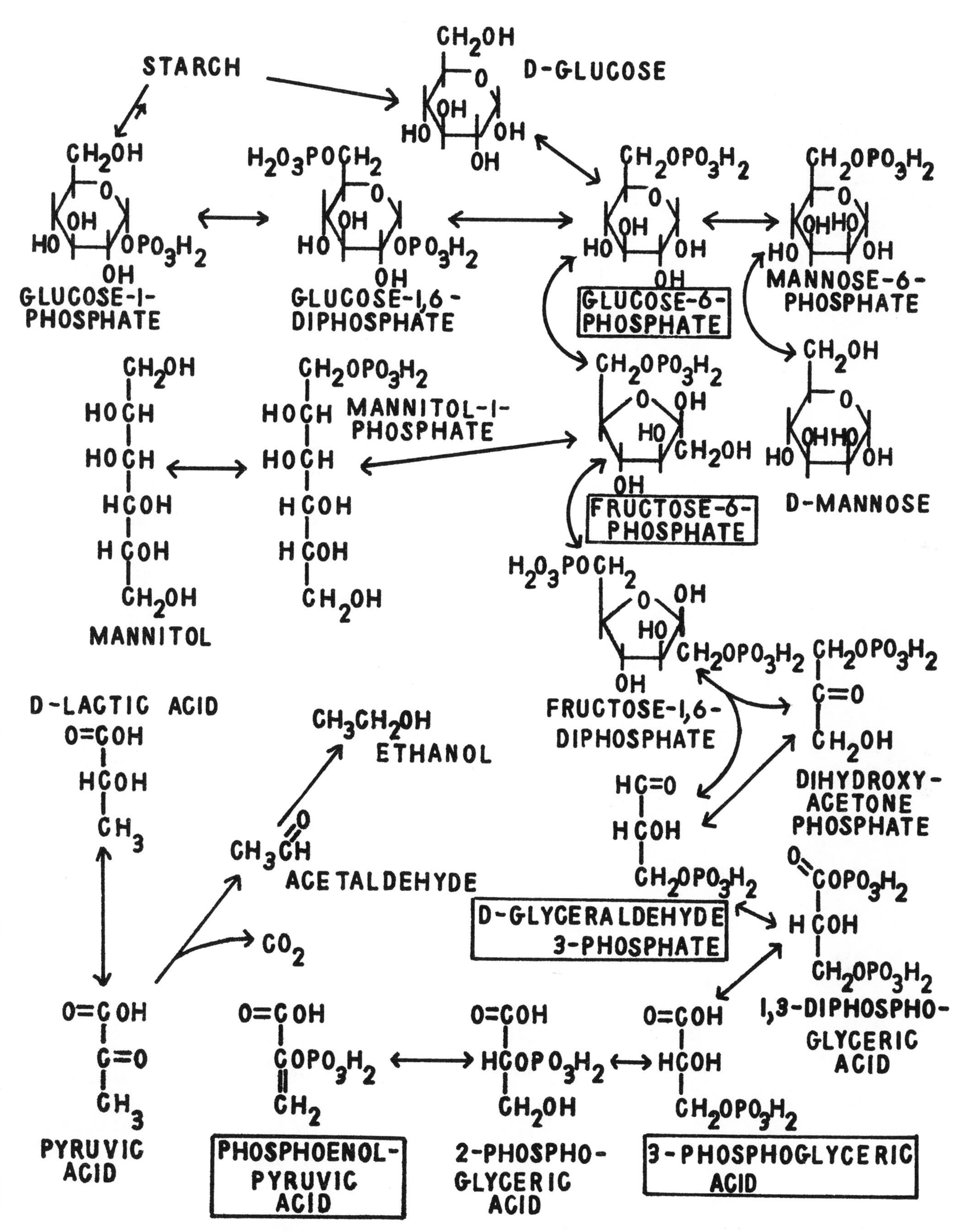

FIGURE 2-7: GLYCOLYTIC AND RELATED PATHWAYS

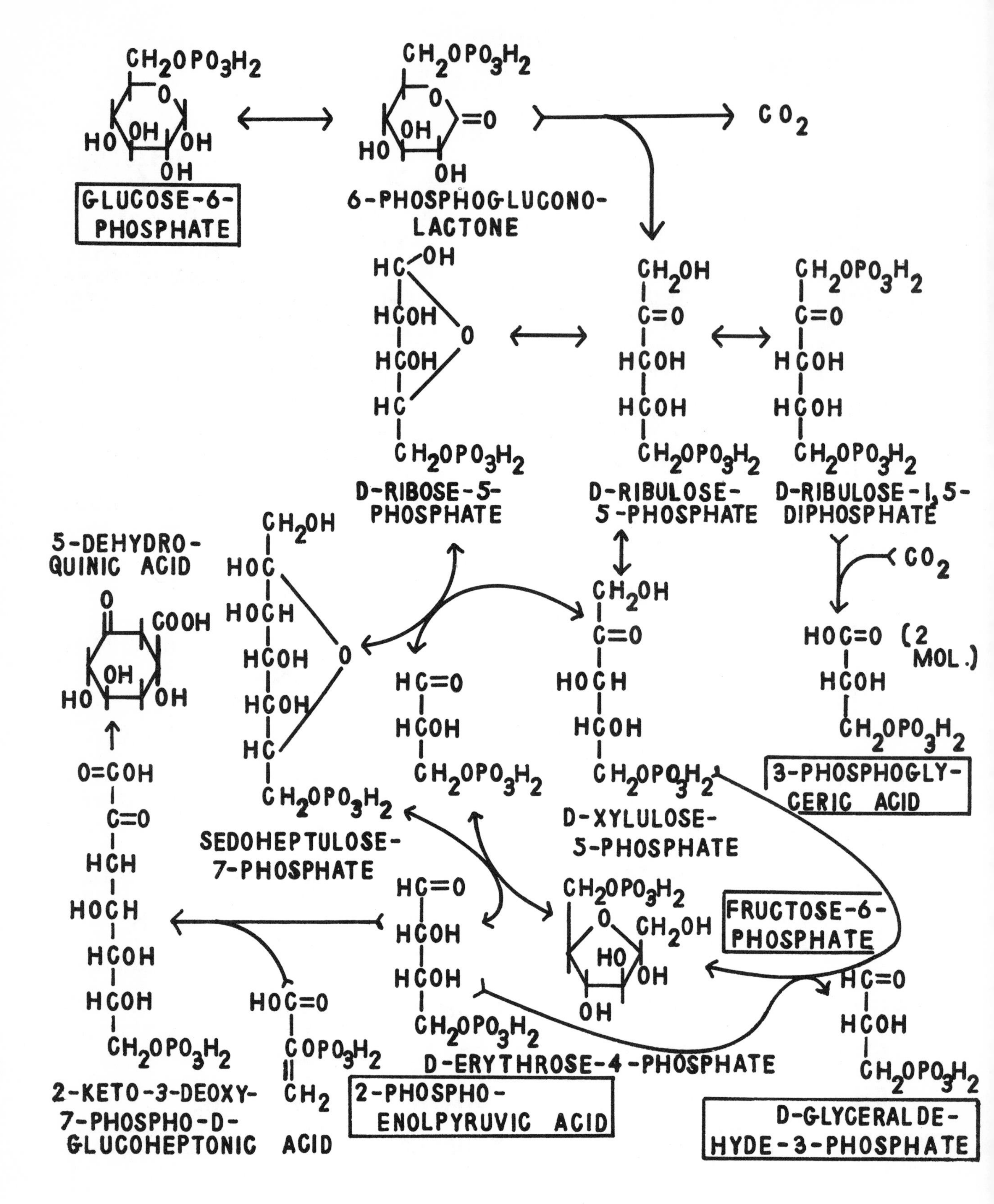

FIGURE 2-8: PENTOSE PHOSPHATE CYCLE AND PHOTOSYNTHETIC CARBON DIOXIDE FIXATION

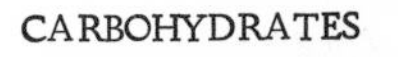

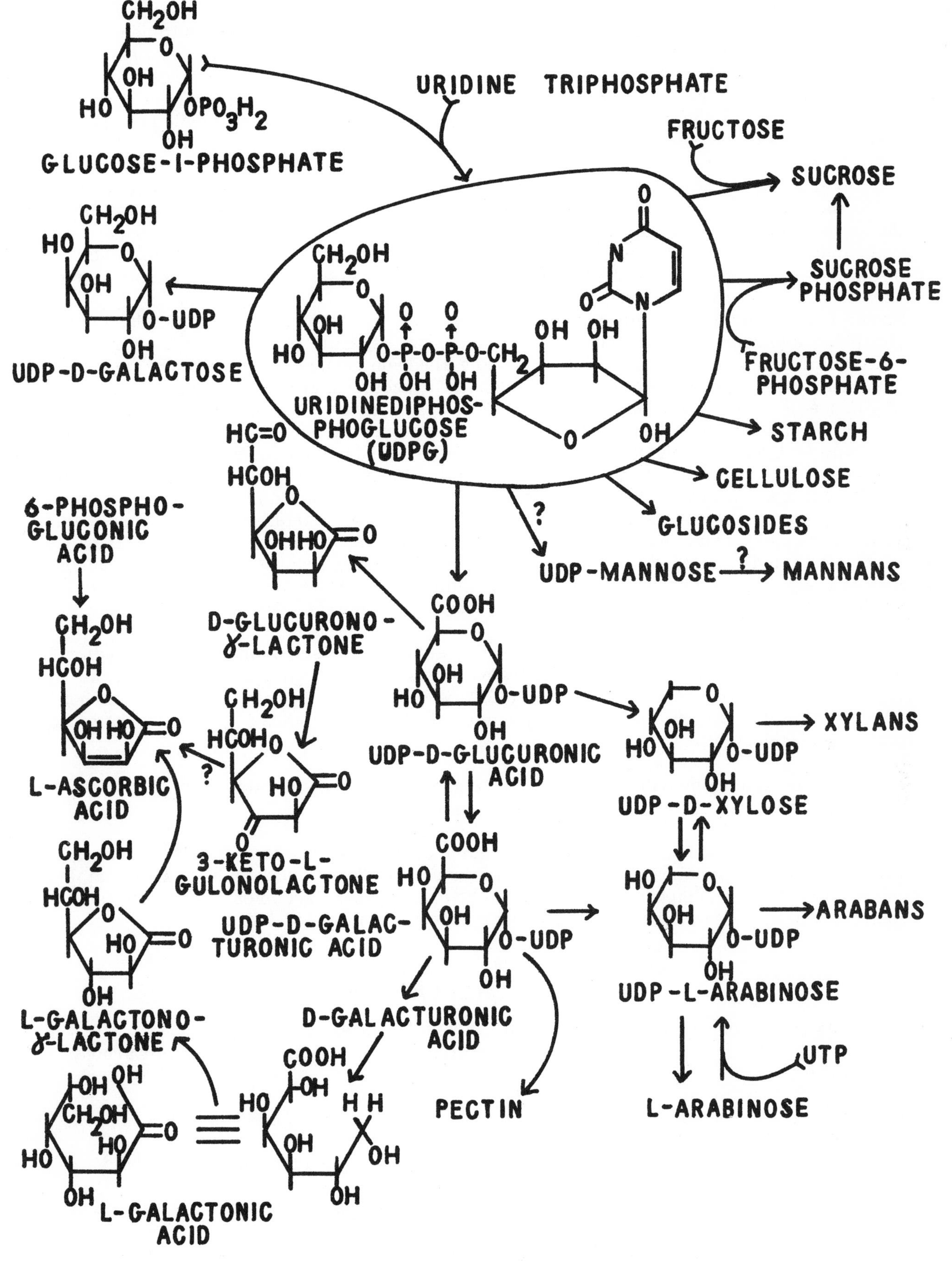

FIGURE 2-9: URIDINE NUCLEOTIDE PATHWAYS

panying diagrams. The glycolytic and pentose cycles are so well-known as to need little clarification here. These two cycles are both widespread in higher plants, and neither can be described as more important than the other. Their relative importance probably varies from plant to plant, organ to organ, and time to time. In the diagrams the two schemes are shown separately but with the compounds common to each circled to indicate their many points of interconnection.

A third group of pathways which has taken on importance in recent years is shown in the third diagram which indicates the key importance of uridinediphosphoglucose as the gateway to many important syntheses. In addition to the formation of UDP-sugars by transformation of UDP-glucose, other sugars may enter the pathway directly by reaction of their 1-phosphates with uridine triphosphate. The UDP-sugar intermediates are then used for such diverse processes as oxidation, epimerization, glycosylation, etc., (38). Starch is probably formed chiefly by the UDP-glucose pathway rather than the classical phosphorylase reaction (39). There appear to be two separate pathways for the formation of ascorbic acid in plants. By one pathway the aldehyde group carbon becomes the carboxyl carbon of L-ascorbic acid; by the other the glucose chain is "inverted" so that C-6 of glucose becomes C-1 of ascorbic acid. The first pathway goes by way of galactose, D-galacturonic acid and L-galactono-γ-lactone. The second goes from 6-phosphogluconate with inversion of configuration at C-5 (11, 40). Belkhode and Nath (41) have implicated glucose cycloacetoacetate as an intermediate in the biosynthesis of ascorbic acid by mung bean seedlings *(Phaseolus mungo)*. The questioned pathway shown from 3-keto-L-gulonolactone occurs in mammals but has not so far been found in plants. As with ascorbic acid, plants have two mechanisms for sucrose synthesis, the most important one using fructose-6-phosphate and forming sucrose phosphate, the other using fructose and forming sucrose immediately. There is a possibility that thymidine diphosphate sugar derivatives may in some cases act the same way as UDP derivatives in sugar transformation (42).

Details of the photosynthesis reaction are still under discussion (43, 44). Kandler and Gibbs (45) have discussed the labelling patterns found in sugars resulting from incorporation of $C^{14}O_2$. Moses and Calvin (36) have ruled out the participation of 2-carboxyl -4-ketopentitol-1, 5-diphosphate as an intermediate between ribulose-1, 5-diphosphate and phosphoglyceric acid.

Tracer studies by Sato *et al.*, (37) have shown that, as with other methyl groups, the methyl ester found in pectin is derived from methionine.

Biosynthesis pathways of the deoxy sugars, tartaric acid, the inositols, fructans, mannans and galactomannans have been little investigated; but what evidence is available indicates that these compounds all fit more closely into these schemes of carbohydrate metabolism than with the pathways of other classes of compounds (48, 49).

GENERAL REFERENCES

Advances in Carbohydrate Chemistry, Vol., 1, 1945 to present.

Arnold, A., editor, Formation, Storage, Mobilization, and Transformation of Carbohydrates, Ruhland 6.

Kertesz, Z. I. The Pectic Substances, Interscience Publishers, N. Y., 1951.

McIlroy, R. J., The Plant Glycosides, Edward Arnold and Co., London, 1951.

Pigman, W., ed., The Carbohydrates, Academic Press, N. Y., 1957.

Smith, F. and Montgomery, R., Chemistry of Plant Gums and Mucilages, Reinhold, N. Y., 1959.

Whistler, R. L. and Smart, C. L., Polysaccharide Chemistry, Academic Press, N. Y., 1953.

Whistler, R. L. and Wolfrom, M. L., Methods in Carbohydrate Chemistry, Academic Press, New York, 1962.

Many articles in Paech and Tracey 2.

BIBLIOGRAPHY

1. Tipson, R. S., J. Chem. Document. 1 3 (1961).
2. Langley, B. W., Lythgoe, B. and Riggs, N. V., J. Chem. Soc. 1951 2309.
3. Avadhani, P. N. and Towers, G. H. N., Can. J. Biochem. Physiol. 39 1605 (1961).
4. Corner, J. J., Harborne, J. B., Humphries, S. G. and Ollis, W. D., Phytochem. 1 73 (1962).
5. Benson, A. A. and Shibuya, I., Fed. Proc. 20 79 (1961).
6. Charlson, A. J. and Richtmyer, N. K., J. Am. Chem. Soc. 82 3428 (1960).
7. Plouvier, V., Compt. rend. 247 2190 (1958).
8. Angyal, S. J. and Anderson, L., Adv. Carbohyd. Chem. 14 135 (1959).
9. Steinhart, C., Anderson, L. and Skoog, F., Plant Physiol. 37 60 (1962).
10. Ettlinger, M. G., Dateo, G. P., Harrison, B. W., Mabry, T. J., and Thompson, C. P., Proc. Nat. Acad. Sci. U. S., 47 1875 (1961).
11. Furness, F. N., ed., Ann. N. Y. Acad. Sci. 92 1 (1961).
12. Hassid, W. Z., J. Am. Chem. Soc. 61 1223 (1939).
13. Bacon, J. S. D., Biochem. J. 73 507 (1959).
14. Bacon, J. S. D., Bull. Soc. Chim. Biol. 42 1441 (1960).
15. Solms, J. and Hassid, W. Z., J. Biol. Chem. 228 357 (1957).
16. Yamada, A. and Matsushita, A., Eiyo to Shokuryo, 7 262 (1954-5). [Chem. Abstr. 53 7327 (1959)]
17. Quillet, M., Compt. rend. 242 2656 (1956).
18. Venkataraman, R. and Reithel, F. J., Arch. Biochem. 75 443 (1958).
19. Wise, L. E., Murphy, M., and D'Addieco, A. A., Paper Trade J., 122 35 (1946).
20. Hirst, E. L., Isherwood, F. A., Jermyn, M. A. and Jones, J. K. N., J. Chem. Soc. 1949 Supp. 182.
21. Jermyn, M. A., in Paech and Tracey 2 221.
22. Binkley, W. W., Adv. Carbohydrate Chem. 10 55 (1955).
23. Jones, J. K. N., Wall, R. A. and Pittet, A. O., Can. J. Chem. 38 2285 (1960).
24. Raybin, H. W., J. Am. Chem. Soc. 59 1402 (1937).
25. Quillet, M., Compt. rend. 242 2475 (1956).
26. Kowkabany, G. N., Adv. Carbohydrate Chem. 9 304 (1954).
27. Partridge, S. M., Biochem. J. 42 238 (1948).
28. Hough, L., Jones, J. K. N. and Wadman, W. H., J. Chem. Soc. 1949 2511.
29. Buchanan, J. G., Dekker, C. A., and Long, A. G., J. Chem. Soc. 1950 3162.
30. Abdel-Akher, M. and Smith, F., J. Am. Chem. Soc. 73 5859 (1951).
31. Barrollier, J. and Watzke, E., Naturwiss. 43 398 (1956).
32. Milletti, M., Ann. Chim. 49 224 (1959).
33. Hanes, C. S., and Isherwood, F. A., Nature 164 1107 (1949).
34. Steinitz, K., Anal. Biochem. 2 497 (1961).
35. Schwimmer, S. and Bevenue, A., Science 123 543 (1956).
36. Porter, H. K., Ann. Rev. Plant Physiol. 13 303 (1962).
37. Gibbs, M., Ann. Rev. Plant Physiol. 10 329 (1959).
38. Hassid, W. Z., Neufeld, E. F. and Feingold, D. S., Proc. Natl. Acad. Sci. U. S. 45 905 (1959).
39. Aspinall, G. O., Ann. Rev. Biochem. 31 79 (1962).
40. Isherwood, F. A. and Mapson, L. W., Ann. Rev. Plant Physiol. 13 329 (1962).
41. Belkhode, M. L. and Nath, M. C., J. Biol. Chem. 237 1742 (1962).
42. Barber, G. A., Biochemistry 1 463 (1962).
43. Calvin, M. and Bassham, J. A., The Photosynthesis of Carbon Compounds, W. A. Benjamin, New York, 1962.
44. Stiller, M., Ann. Rev. Plant Physiol. 13 151 (1962).
45. Kandler, O. and Gibbs, M., Z. Naturforsch 14 b 8 (1959).
46. Moses, V. and Calvin, M., Biochim. et Biophys. Acta 31 550 (1959).
47. Sato, C. S. Byerrum, R. U. and Ball, C. D., J. Biol. Chem. 224 717 (1957).
48. Gyr, J., Compt. rend. 251 263 (1960).
49. Loewus, F. A., Kelly, S. and Neufeld, E. F., Proc. Nat. Acad. Sci. U. S. 48 421 (1962).

Chapter 3
WATER-SOLUBLE ORGANIC ACIDS

The occurrence of a variety of free acids in plants has been well-known for many years. Some plant organs accumulate rather large quantities of specific acids which are primarily concentrated in the vacuolar sap. As a result of such accumulation the pH of this sap may fall to values as low as 2 or 3. Many of the common plant acids are those which participate in the familiar citric acid cycle of metabolism; and since this cycle is believed to be of fundamental importance in the biochemistry of almost all organisms, acids participating in it must occur to some extent in all plants. However, the mere operation of this cycle does not entail any accumulation of acids. Moreover, the reactions of the citric acid cycle take place in the mitochondria, whereas acids which accumulate do so in the vacuole. Therefore while this cycle may provide the reaction pathways for synthesis of several common plant acids, it does not explain how a particular plant organ often accumulates just one acid from the cycle in the vacuoles of its cells. That there is such a selectivity is evident from a consideration of the major acids in some common fruits -- e. g. citric acid in lemons *(Citrus limonica)*, isocitric in blackberries *(Rubus* spp.) and malic in apples *(Malus* spp.).

Besides the plant acids involved in the citric acid cycle several other water-soluble acids are of very common occurrence in plants. Some of these may be grouped as lower members of the fatty acid series (cf. Chapter 5); some are intermediates in the pathway leading from carbohydrates to aromatic compounds (cf. Chapter 4); some are, in fact, carbohydrates (cf. Chapter 2); some are isoprenoid derivatives (Chapter 8); and, finally, some are formed by peculiar or unknown metabolic pathways. Table 1 lists some of the non-citric cycle acids with examples of plants where they are found in relatively high concentrations.

The table on page 37 is by no means complete. The bibliography of Buch listed under general references has about 30 water-soluble, aliphatic plant acids not including sugar acids or lower fatty acids. While most of these acids occur free or as salts, a few (chiefly the lower fatty acids) are often found as esters in essential oils (cf. Chapter 8).

The common plant acids are colorless substances which are usually soluble not only in water but also in organic solvents such as ethanol and ether. They are insoluble in the very non-polar solvents like benzene or petroleum ether. Many of the plant acids are optically active, and normally only one of the enantiomorphs is naturally occurring. Compared with the mineral acids they are only weakly acidic. Their sodium and potassium salts are water soluble, but calcium and barium salts are usually insoluble or only slightly soluble in water. Crystals of calcium oxalate appear as raphides in the cytoplasm of many plant cells.

The function of plant acids in respiratory cycles is well-known; but aside from this role in energy metabolism several other functions have been suggested for them, particularly for those which accumulate or are excreted and apparently are not involved in active metabolism. They are often considered as waste products which are not further utilized. However, they may accumulate at one stage and disappear at a later stage--

TABLE 1. *SOME NATURALLY OCCURRING ORGANIC ACIDS*

Acid	Source
HCOOH formic	stinging nettle hairs *(Urtica urens)*
CH_3COOH acetic	esterified in fruit essential oils
$CH_3CH_2CH_2COOH$ butyric	esterified in fruit essential oils
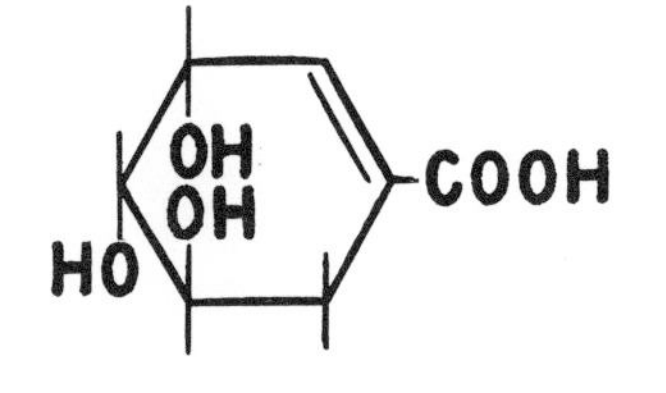 shikimic	*Illicium spp.*
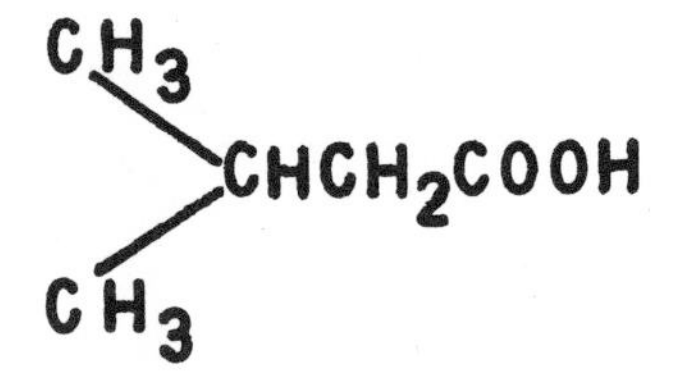 iso-valeric	*Valeriana spp.*
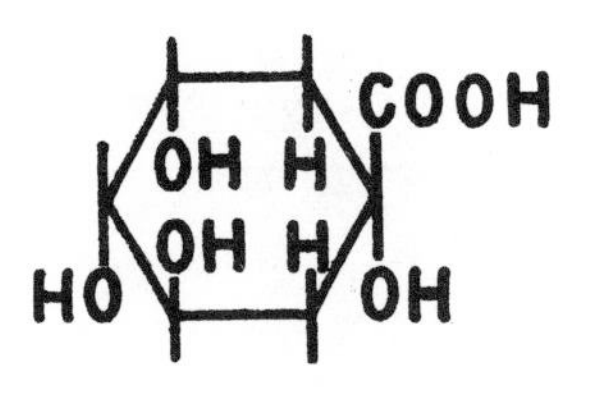 quinic	*Vaccinium spp.*

Table 1. Continued

Acid	Source
COOH–HCOH–HOCH–COOH D-tartaric	*Vitis spp.*
COOH–COOH oxalic	*Oxalis spp.*
HOOC-C(=CH–C(=O)–CH=)C-COOH (ring closed by O) chelidonic	*Chelidonium majus*
CHO–COOH glyoxylic	*Solanum tuberosum*
CH_3—CH(OH)—COOH lactic	*Daucus carota*
CH_2OH–COOH glycolic	*Medicago spp.*
COOH–CH_2–COOH malonic	*many Leguminosae*

as malic acid in green apples. Oxalic acid which seems never to be metabolized further in seed plants is oxidized in mosses by a flavoprotein oxidase (1). Malic acid acts as a specific attracting agent for spermatozoids of some mosses and ferns and is presumably secreted by the archegonia or egg cells (2). Those acids which occur in the vacuole as salts may participate in establishing a proper acid-base balance. Acids which form iron chelates may aid in the vascular transport of this cation (3).

LACTONES

Hydroxy acids may exist as lactones or inner esters if the hydroxyl group is situated so that the lactone has a 5 or 6-membered ring. Of the common plant acids isocitric is often found in the lactone form:

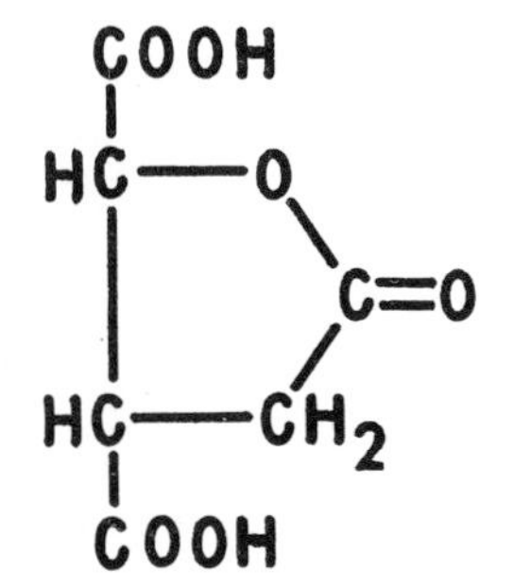

iso-citric lactone

A few unusual hydroxy acids are never found in the free carboxyl form, and only the lactones are known. Among these lactones are several compounds of interest in physiology since they are often very powerful irritants of skin and mucous membranes and some are fungicidal. Structures and occurrence of some simple lactones are shown below. Those with hydroxyl groups may exist naturally as glycosides. Other lactones will be found described in other chapters along with related compounds (e. g., terpenoids, fatty acids, etc.).

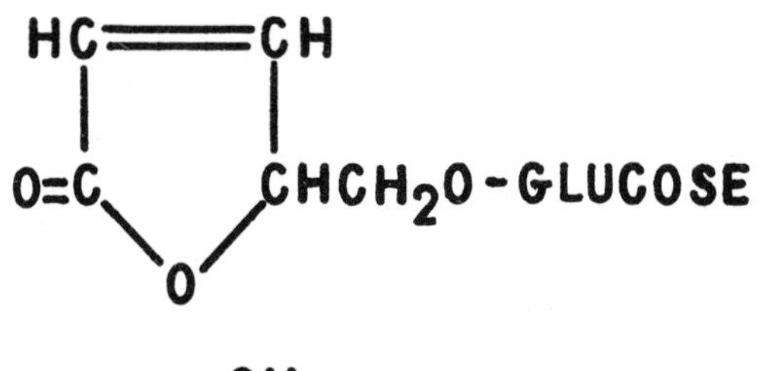

ranunculin *(Ranunculus bulbosus)*

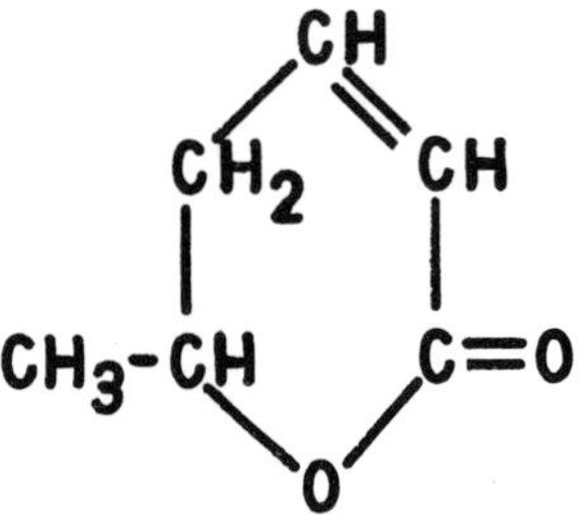

parasorbic acid *(Sorbus aucuparia)*

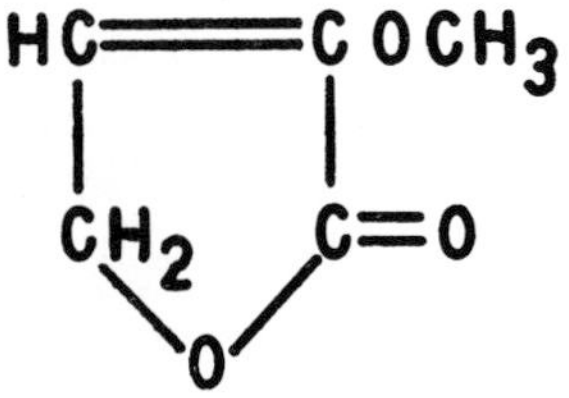

HC=C OCH3
CH2 C=O
O

α-methoxy-2-butenoic lactone *(Narthecium ossifragum)*

Lactones may be recognized by their titration behavior. Unlike the free acids they do not neutralize sodium hydroxide rapidly in the cold but do so on heating or with long standing. On reacidifying, the lactone ring usually reforms. Unsaturated lactones of higher plants are reviewed by Schmid (4).

ISOLATION METHODS

In the standard procedure for isolating low molecular weight acids, the plant material is made strongly acidic (pH 1.0) with sulfuric acid and then extracted thoroughly (sometimes for several days) with peroxide-free ether. The ether extract contains the free acids which may be purified further. This procedure is most conveniently applied to dry material, but the difficulties of drying plant material safely may overcome the simplicity of the extraction procedure. Drying with heat removes volatile acids, destroys keto acids, causes ester formation, etc. Freeze drying is doubtless the best method since it precludes any chemical change, but volatile acids or esters may be lost. If the plant material is neutralized before drying, all acids will be present as non-volatile salts. Interfering lipids and esters may also be removed by a preliminary extraction of the neutralized material with ether.

Rather than ether extraction, the plant acids may be concentrated by the use of anion exchange resins. When an aqueous plant extract is passed through a column of weakly basic anion exchange resin in the hydroxide form, anions are absorbed. After washing the column, free acids may be eluted with 0.1 N HCl. If several fractions of eluate are taken, some separation of the acids can be achieved. If strongly basic anion exchange resin is used in the hydroxide form, there is danger that sugars in the plant extracts will be decomposed to form such acids as lactic and glycolic. Weakly basic resins avoid this difficulty but have a lower exchange capacity.

After preparation of a concentrated extract containing the total organic acids by one of the methods described above, separation of the individual components may be undertaken. If the acid mixture has been obtained by ether extraction, it must be transferred from ether to water by shaking with sodium hydroxide solution. Sodium sulfate may be removed by adjusting the aqueous solution to pH 1 H_2SO_4, adding two volumes of ethanol, and allowing to stand in the cold overnight. The solution of organic acids is then separated by filtration from precipitated sodium sulfate. The lower fatty acids up to caproic (C_6) are volatile with steam and may be prepared by a steam distillation. Caprylic (C_8) and capric (C_{10}) acids are slightly volatile with steam but require long periods of distillation for complete removal. Separation of the different volatile fatty acids can be achieved by gas chromatography of the mixture or partition chromatography on silica gel using as solvents butanol in chloroform for the C_1 - C_4 acids and methanol in isooctane for the C_5 - C_{10} acids. Fractional distillation is inefficient for the separation of acids differing by only two carbon atoms and useful only when dealing with rather large quantities of material.

Separation of the remaining non-volatile acids from each other has often been carried out by converting the free acids to methyl esters and fractionally distilling. It is, however, difficult to achieve complete separations this way unless large amounts are involved. Another method of separation relies on the different solubilities of lead, barium, and calcium salts in water and in alcohol; but, again, this method is suitable only if it is known that a limited number of acids is present so that the strategy can be based on knowledge of the solubilities concerned. Special methods for separating individual acids by such procedures will be found in the general references. In particular, oxalic acid may be separated from all others by the great insolubility of its calcium salt in water. The keto acids may be removed from an aqueous solution by adding 2,4-dinitrophenylhydrazine to precipitate them as hydrazones. The 2,4-dinitrophenylhydrazones may be extracted with ether and further purified by crystallization or subjected to a chromatographic separation.

Column chromatography of dinitrophenylhydrazones may be carried out on diatomaceous earth ("Celite") with ethanol in ethyl ether as the solvent or on cellulose powder with n-amyl alcohol saturated with ammonia as the solvent. The instability of many keto acids makes it desirable to separate them as derivatives rather than as the free acids.

The best, generally applicable procedure for separating and isolating the plant acids from a mixture is column chromatography either using ion exchange methods or partition chromatography. Resins have more capacity per gram than the partition absorbents; but the latter have the advantage that an indicator may be incorporated to follow the passage of acid bands through the column, and they apparently permit somewhat cleaner separations than ion exchange resin columns do. Ion exchange separations may be carried out on strongly basic resins in the hydroxide form if sugars have been removed by a preliminary purification step. No general procedure can be recommended since preparation of the column and the method of elution will vary with the acids to be separated. 0.1 N hydrochloric acid is often used as an eluant, fractions collected arbitrarily, and analyzed for acids by paper chromatography or specific color reactions. Appropriate fractions can then be pooled and concentrated to obtain the pure acids. Several hundred milligrams of mixed acids can be separated using only about 10 g. of resin. Monocarboxylic acids come through first, followed by di - and tricarboxylic compounds. Further discussion of this type of procedure and its application to plant juices may be found in the papers of Owens *et al.* (5) and Goudie and Rieman (6). Separations by partition chromatography have used as support for the aqueous stationary phase such substances as silica gel, celite or cellulose powder. It is desirable either to suppress the ionization of the acids by mixing some dilute mineral acid into the absorbant or to insure complete ionization of the acids by mixing some ammonium hydroxide with the absorbant. In the latter case an indicator such as bromcresol green can also be admixed and changes color where acidic bands are present. As the mobile phase mixtures of 1-butanol and chloroform (saturated with the stationary phase) are most commonly used. The proportion of these two solvents is varied according to the polarities of the acids to be separated, and it is often recommended to increase gradually the ratio of butanol/chloroform as the development proceeds. In some cases the use of ethyl ether as a mobile phase separates pairs of acids that can not be resolved by butanol-chloroform. Some pairs of acids tenaciously resist separation. About 100 mg of mixed acids can be separated on a 25 g. column of silica gel. General books on chromatographic methods offer much useful information regarding these techniques. See also the paper of Wager and Isherwood (7).

Paper sheet chromatography (see below) can also be used to purify rather large amounts (up to 100 mg.) of acids if streaks of the acid mixture are applied to thick sheets of prewashed filter paper.

CHARACTERIZATION

Before attempting to identify the organic acids in a plant tissue or crude extract it is ordinarily desirable to make a preliminary separation of the acids from other plant constituents using one of the methods described in the previous section. Certain color tests and precipitation reactions may be used to indicate the presence of certain acids. Since each one of these represents a special case, the general references should be consulted for their application. The simplest general method for characterization of a mixture of organic acids is paper chromatography, and for best results two dimensional chromatography is recommended. The acids must be converted into a single ionic form to prevent streaking. They can be run as the free acids using highly acidic solvents or as ammonium salts by using solvents which contain ammonium hydroxide. The latter procedure must be used for the volatile acids. If a large amount of oxalic acid is present, it tends to smear and obscure other acids. It may be removed by a preliminary precipitation with calcium or by chromatography on acidic silica gel. Application of an acid mixture to the paper should carry about 10 - 100 μg of each acid unless very thick filter papers are used. One of the best general-purpose acidic solvents is the upper phase of an equilibrated mixture of 1-butanol/90% formic acid/water, 10:3:10, with the lower phase placed in the chamber. A common basic solvent mixture is 1-propanol/conc. ammonium hydroxide, 7:3 or 3:2. Two dimensional chromatograms are generally run using a basic solvent in the first direction and an acidic solvent in the second, but innumerable combinations are possible. One of the most extensive studies is that of Carles *et al.*, (8) who chromatographed about sixty acids two dimensionally using as the first solvent 95% ethanol/conc. ammonium hydroxide, 95:5, and as the second solvent 1-butanol/formic acid/water, 4:1:5, equilibrated. Howe (9) has reported the chromatographic behavior of about 100 acids and has attempted to correlate their migration with structures. Even using two-dimensional chromatography some acids are not completely separated from each other, and specific spray reagents may be used to distinguish among the possibilities. The most generally used detection reagents are acid-base indicators such as bromcresol green or bromthymol blue. Background color may be adjusted by exposing the paper sheet to ammonia vapor to make the best distinction of acidic areas. Spots indicated by this method usually fade rapidly. Another general detection procedure has been developed by Burness and King (10). In this method the chromatograms are developed in a solvent containing ethylamine. When the paper is dried, ethylamine remains as a salt where acids are present, and may be indicated with ninhydrin. Other general reagents will be found in the paper of Carles *et al.*, (8). Special detection reagents are also available for different acids or classes of acids. Keto acids can be first reacted with 2,4-dinitrophenylhydrazine and the dinitrophenylhydrazones.chromatographed (11). This procedure is better than chromatographing the free keto acids which are subject to decomposition, although reagents have been developed to detect free keto acids on chromatograms. The dinitrophenylhydrazones can be eluted from the paper and identified by their absorption spectra in sodium hydroxide solution as well as by their R_F values. Other specific reagents will be found described in the general references and in a paper by Buch *et al.*, (12).

The gas chromatography of organic acids also promises to be of much value in their analysis. Details of this technique can be found in the chromatographic references cited in Chapter 1.

METABOLIC PATHWAYS

A review of organic acid metabolism in plants has been presented by Davies (13).

As stated in the beginning of this chapter most of the plant acids are either in or closely related to the citric acid cycle. Several other major pathways may be discussed in term of their relationship to the citric acid cycle:

1. The so-called glyoxylate cycle was first found by Kornberg and Krebs (14) in several microorganisms. Evidence for its occurrence in higher plants has since been presented (15, 16). It provides a by-pass between isocitrate and malate, a route for the synthesis of glyoxylate (and possibly oxalate), and a point of entry for acetate. The fact that acetate derived from breakdown of lipids can enter the glyoxylate by-pass and lead to a net synthesis of pyruvate provides a pathway for the synthesis of carbohydrate from fat since pyruvate can enter the glycolytic pathways leading back to starch. Pyruvic decarboxylation which forms acetate plus carbon dioxide is an irreversible reaction.
2. The dark fixation of carbon dioxide into organic acids accounts for acid synthesis in some plants. In particular, the succulents *(Crassulaceae)* are noted for their accumulation of malic acid at night via this pathway (17, 18). Such CO_2 fixation is not restricted to the succulents, however, and for example, rhizomes of *Equisetum* also actively fix CO_2 into organic acids (15).

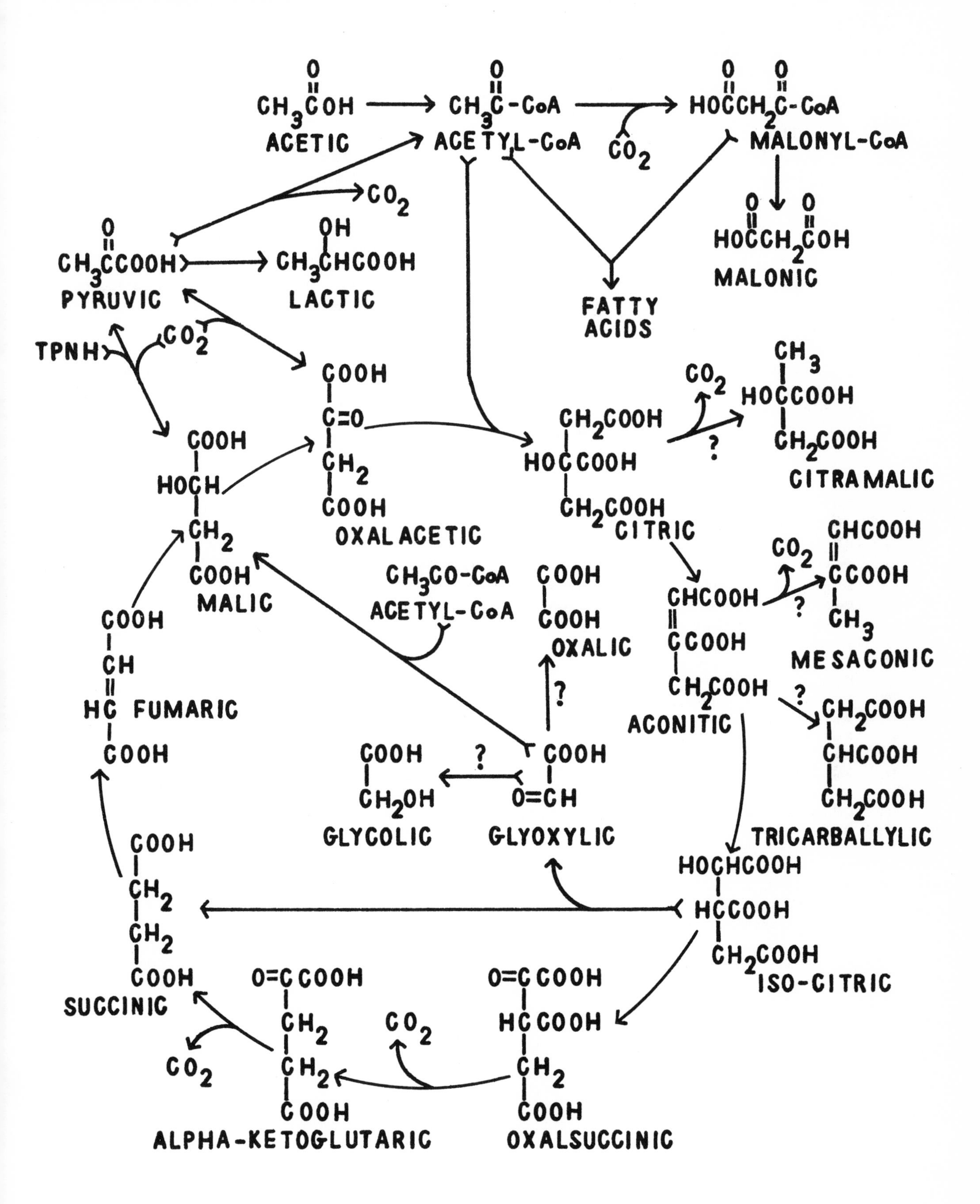

FIGURE 3-1: ACID PATHWAYS

3. Some acids seem structurally related to components of the citric acid cycle but the pathways connecting them have not been demonstrated. They have been so indicated in the accompanying figure by question marks beside the arrows.
4. Recent work on the metabolism of the two-carbon acids and of malonic acid may be found in references (20) and (21).
5. The necic acids, found as esters in the alkaloids of *Senecio* spp., resemble the terpenoids in structure; but recent tracer studies (22) indicate a route of biosynthesis which involves condensation of 4 acetate units and two C_1 units.

GENERAL REFERENCES

Buch, M. L., U. S. Dept. Agric. A.R.S. Serv. 73-18 (1957), published in 1960 as Agricultural Handbook #164 A Bibliography of Organic Acids in Higher Plants.
Burris, R. H., "Organic Acids in Plant Metabolism", Ann. Rev. Plant Physiol. 4 91 (1953).
Ranson, S. L., "Non Volatile Mono- Di- and Tricarboxylic Acids" in Paech and Tracey 2 539.
Scarisbrick, R., "Volatile Acids" in Paech and Tracey 2 444.
Wolf, J., "Nichtfluchtige Mono- Di- and Tricarbonsauren" in Paech and Tracey 2 476.

BIBLIOGRAPHY

1. Datta, P. K. and Meeuse, B. J. D., Biochem. Diophys. Acta 17 602 (1955).
2. Brokaw, C. J., J. Exptl. Biol. 35 192 (1958).
3. Tiffin, L. O. and Brown, J. C., Plant Physiol. 36 Suppl. xiv (1961).
4. Schmid, H., Coll. Intern. Centre Nat. Recherche Sci. 64 303 (1957).
5. Owens, H. S., Goodban, A. E., and Stark, J. B., Anal. Chem. 25 1507 (1953).
6. Goudie, A. J. and Rieman, W., Anal. Chim. Acta 26 419 (1962).
7. Wager, H. G. and Isherwood, F. A., Analyst 86 260 (1961).
8. Carles, J., Schneider, A. and Lacoste, A. M., Bull. Soc. Chim. Biol. 40 221 (1958).
9. Howe, J. R., J. Chromatog. 3 389 (1960).
10. Burness, A. T. H. and King, H. K., Biochem. J. 68 32P (1958).
11. Isherwood, F. A. and Cruikshank, D. M., Nature 173 121 (1954).
12. Buch, M. L., Montgomery, R. and Porter, W. L., Anal. Chem. 24 489 (1952).
13. Davies, D. D., Biol. Revs. 34 407 (1959).
14. Kornberg, H. L. and Krebs, H. A., Nature 179 988 (1957).
15. Marcus, A. and Velasco, J., J. Biol. Chem. 235 563 (1960).
16. Canvin, D. T. and Beevers, H., J. Biol. Chem. 236 988 (1961).
17. Ranson, S. L. and Thomas, M., Ann. Rev. Plant Physiol. 11 81 (1960).
18. Walker, D. A., Biol. Revs. 37 215 (1962).
19. Barber, D. A., Nature 180 1053 (1957).
20. Richardson, K. E. and Tolbert, N. E., J. Biol. Chem. 236 1280 (1961).
21. Hatch, M. D. and Stumpf, P. K., Plant Physiol. 37 121 (1962).
22. Hughes, C. and Warren, F. L., J. Chem. Soc. 1962 34.

Chapter 4
AROMATIC COMPOUNDS

The chemical concept of aromaticity, of course, has nothing to do with aroma. For present purposes it will be sufficient to define aromatic compounds as those whose structural formulas contain at least one benzene ring. A great variety of plant constituents may be classed as aromatic compounds, and several groups of these are included in other chapters. The unity within the present chapter comes from the presumption that all compounds included are biosynthetically derived via 5-dehydroquinic acid. Flavonoids and aromatic amino acids are also derived from 5-dehydroquinic acid but are more conveniently discussed in Chapters 9 and 10 respectively. Aromatic compounds, such as anthraquinones and chromones, which are probably derived from acetate, are covered in Chapter 6; and terpenoid aromatic compounds are in Chapter 8.

SIMPLE PHENOLS AND AROMATIC ACIDS

The simple phenols are colorless solids when pure but usually oxidize and become dark on exposure to air. Water solubility increases with the number of hydroxyl groups present, but solubility in polar organic solvents is generally high. Phenols which are only slightly soluble in water are readily soluble in dilute, aqueous solutions of sodium hydroxide; but under basic conditions their rate of oxidation is increased considerably, so that any prolonged treatment with strong alkali should be avoided.

There are a few naturally occurring aromatic acids which have carboxyl as their only functional group. However, most natural aromatic acids also have phenolic groups and thus share properties with other phenols. Water insoluble phenolic acids can be distinguished from other water insoluble phenols by the fact that they may be dissolved in sodium bicarbonate solution whereas the less acidic phenols require more alkaline solvents. Many natural phenolic compounds have at least one hydroxyl group combined as an ether, ester or glycoside rather than free. Ethers or esters are less soluble in water than the parent phenols while the glycosides are more water-soluble.

The natural aromatic compounds are usually characterized by having at least one aliphatic side chain attached to the aromatic ring. The variety of possible side chains combined with the structural variations already mentioned creates a bewildering array of substances in this class. In certain cases the complexity of the aliphatic side chain makes the aromatic portion of the molecule appear to be an almost incidental structural feature. Table 1 depicts a few simple aromatic compounds found in plants, but it is impossible in so little space to more than hint at the variety found in nature.

Several simple aromatic compounds are of physiological or economic interest. Vanillin, methyl salicylate and piperonal are responsible for the odors of vanilla, wintergreen *(Gaultheria procumbens)* and heliotrope respectively.

TABLE 1. SOME SIMPLE AROMATIC COMPOUNDS, STRUCTURES AND OCCURRENCE

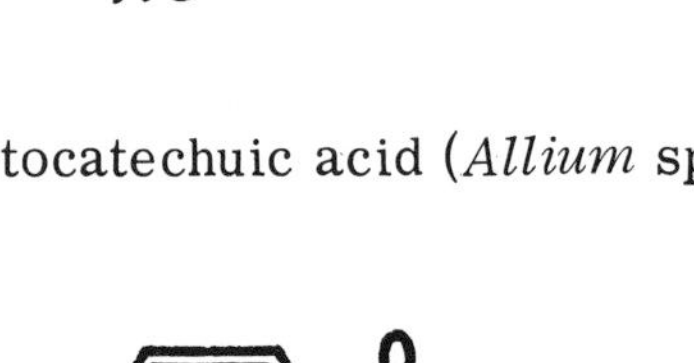

protocatechuic acid (*Allium* spp.)

gentisic acid *(Theobroma cacao)*

salicin (bark of *Salix* spp.)

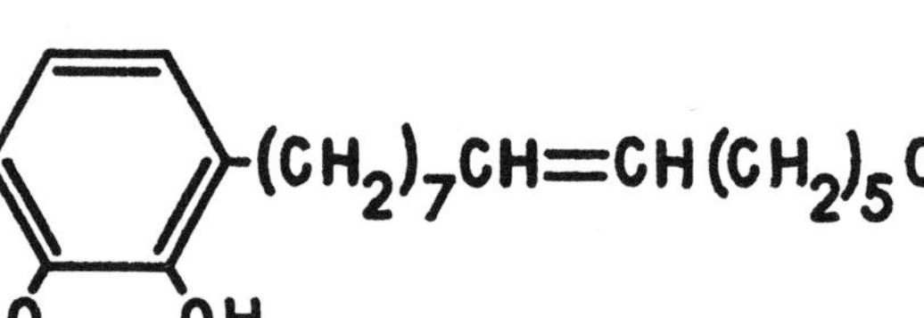
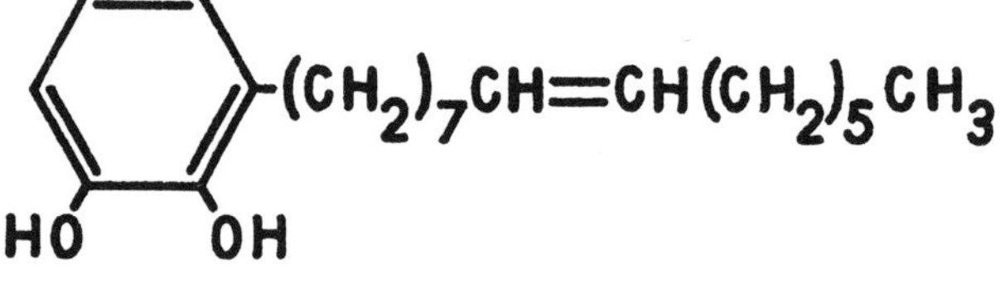

urushiol (*Rhus* spp.)

kavain *(Piper methysticum)*

4-methoxyparacotoin *(Aniba duckei)*

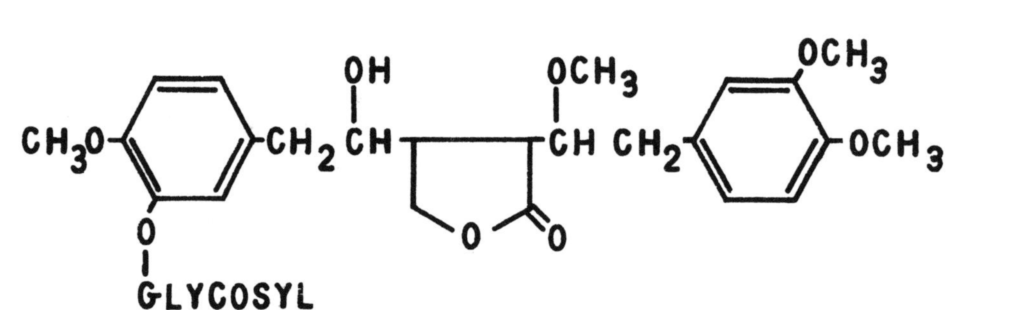

tracheloside *(Trachelospermum asiatica)*

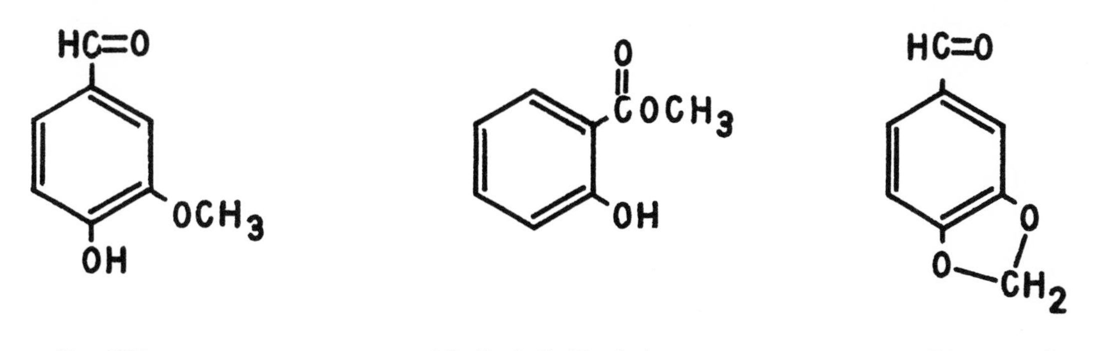

Vanillin Methyl Salicylate Piperonal

Urushiol and similar phenols with long aliphatic side-chains are responsible for the vesicant action of poison ivy, poison sumac and other members of the *Anacardiaceae*. Kavain and similar compounds of kava-kava root *(Piper methysticum)* are responsible for the sedative and intoxicating action of this plant. What, if any, function that the simple aromatic compounds have in plants is unknown although two suggestions seem most worthy of consideration. The fungicidal activity of phenols makes it reasonable that they may act to protect against fungus attack. There is no question but that the presence of protocatechuic acid in certain varieties of onions increases the resistance of these varieties toward attack by certain fungi (1). Another possibility is that by acting as germination inhibitors phenols prevent premature sprouting of certain seeds. Varga and Köves (2) have shown that all the germination inhibitors of dry seeds are phenolic acids and derivatives. The coumarins, to be discussed later in this chapter, are also important plant growth inhibitors.

BENZOQUINONES

Benzoquinones are common fungal pigments but rarely encountered in higher plants. Some of the more important ones (e.g. plastoquinone) seem structurally related to the terpenoids and are therefore included in Chapter 8. Hydroxy- and methoxybenzoquinones are found in a few higher plants and are of some economic importance. 2-methoxybenzoquinone appears as a pink coloration in whole wheat flour after long-standing as the result of hydrolysis and oxidation of a glucoside present in wheat germ. The dried fruit of *Embelia ribes* is used in India for treatment of tapeworm and skin diseases. Its active ingredient, embelin is a dihydroxyquinone. Other alkylhydroxyquinones similar to embelin are found in a few other plants which have been used for many years as vermifuges.

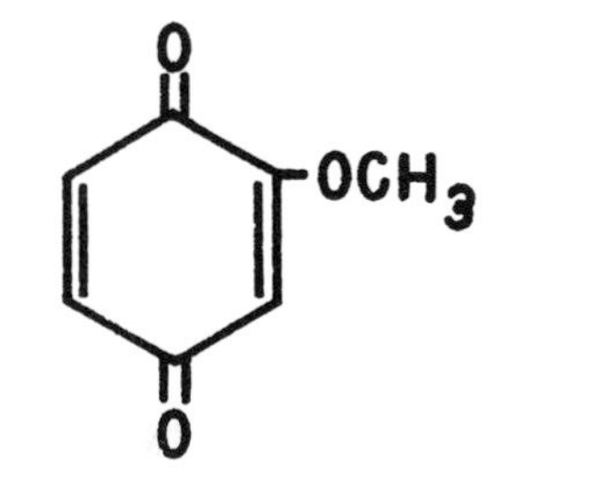

2-Methoxybenzoquinone

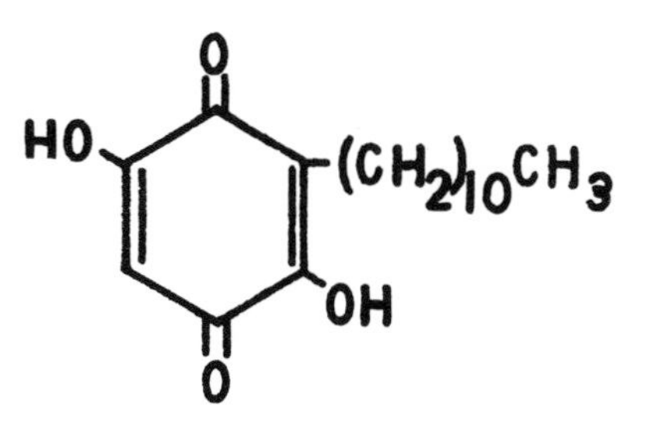

Embelin

These hydroxybenzoquinones are orange, crystalline solids which are readily reduced by sodium dithionite to colorless hydroquinones. Alkaline solutions are blue-purple in color. Naturally occurring quinones are extensively reviewed by Thomson (3).

PHENYLPROPANE COMPOUNDS IN GENERAL

A large number of natural aromatic compounds may be described as phenylpropane derivatives since they have a benzene ring attached to C-1 of a three carbon chain:

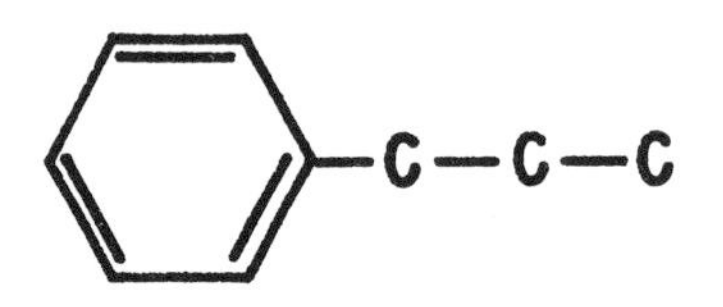

A few other compounds are found which have a phenyl group attached to the middle carbon of the C_3 chain. Some of these may be formed by rearrangement of 1-phenylpropane compounds, whereas others seem to be more closely related to the monoterpenoids. Examples of these two types of 2-phenylpropane derivatives are, respectively, tropic acid (4) and thymoquinone:

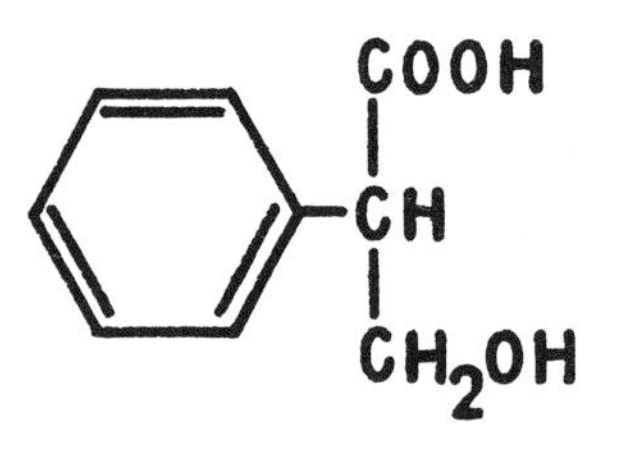

Tropic Acid

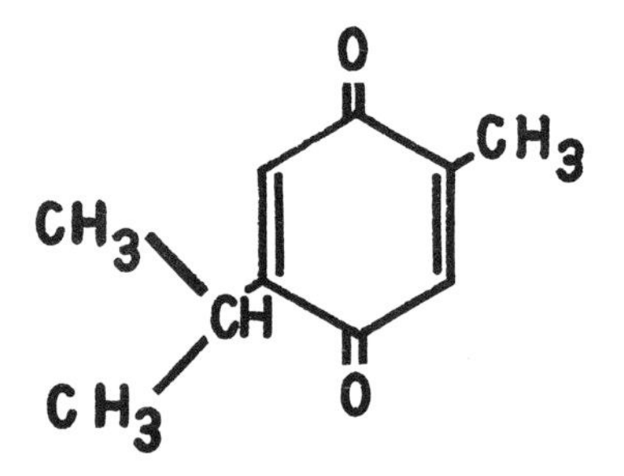

Thymoquinone

Other 1-phenyl propane derivatives will be discussed in more detail in following sections of this chapter. The flavonoids (Chapter 9) also contain a phenylpropane group joined to a phloroglucinol group. Geissman (5) has reviewed the phenylpropane derivatives of plants.

OPEN-CHAIN PHENYLPROPANE DERIVATIVES

Some open-chain phenylpropane derivatives are among the best-known and most widespread natural aromatic compounds. Most of them may be described as hydroxylated cinnamic acid derivatives:

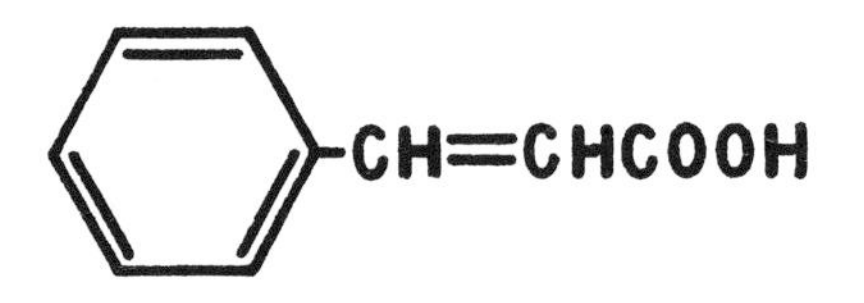

Cinnamic Acid

The variations on this basic structure are distinguished by different patterns of ring hydroxylation or methoxylation and modification of the carboxyl group by esterification or reduction to an aldehyde or alcohol. There are also other open-chain phenylpropanes which cannot conveniently be described at all as derivatives of cinnamic acid. Table 2 illustrates some of the various compounds of this class. The hydroxycinnamic acids have been reviewed by Herrmann (6).

Caffeic acid is one of the most widespread of all plant phenolic compounds (7), followed closely by ferulic and p-coumaric acids. Caffeic acid, however, frequently occurs as esters rather than the free acid. The commonest caffeic acid ester is chlorogenic acid in which the alcohol portion is supplied by quinic acid. Several other complex esters are known in which one or more molecules of one of the hydroxycinnamic acids are esterfied to one molecule of quinic acid. Such esters involving two hydroxy acids are known as "depsides". Chicoric acid of chicory has two molecules of caffeic acid esterified with one molecule of tartaric acid. Phaseolic acid of *Phaseolus vulgaris* is caffeyl malic acid (8). Sugar esters of caffeic acid are widespread in plants (9).

The simple phenylpropanes are colorless, crystalline solids whose chemical reactivity may be understood by reference to the particular functional groups which are present. Those members having several free phenolic hydroxyls are readily oxidized in the air especially under alkaline conditions. The oxidation products are dark-colored polymers. Green substances are formed by oxidation of caffeic acid esters in the presence of ammonia or amino acids. This formation of a green substance accounts for the name of chlorogenic acid. The more volatile members of this group are very important commercially since they contribute the characteristic flavors and odors to many valuable herbs and spices. Cinnamaldehyde of cinnamon, eugenol of cloves, and apiol of parsley and celery are but three of the best-known examples of phenylpropane flavor compounds.

TABLE 2. SOME OPEN CHAIN PHENYLPROPANE DERIVATIVES, STRUCTURES AND OCCURRENCE

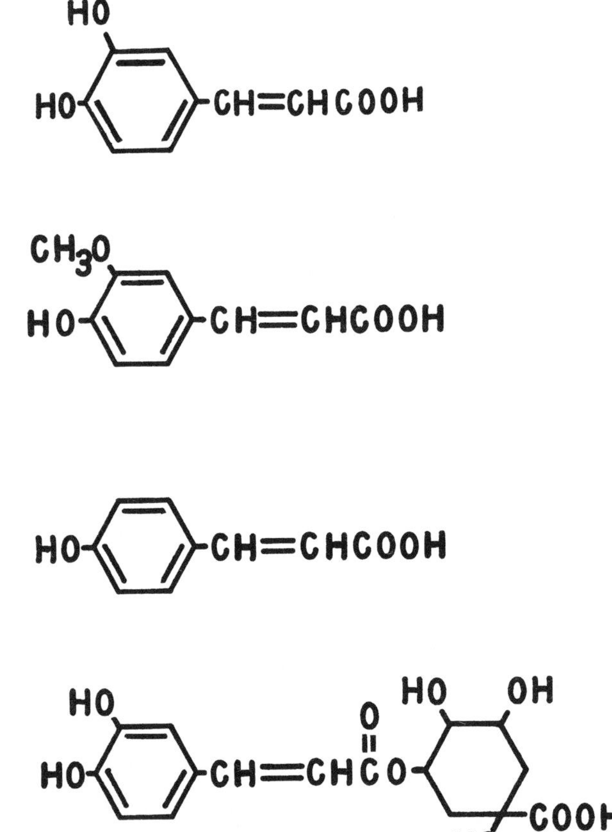

caffeic acid (widespread)

ferulic acid (widespread)

p-coumaric acid (widespread)

chlorogenic acid (widespread)

Table 2. Continued

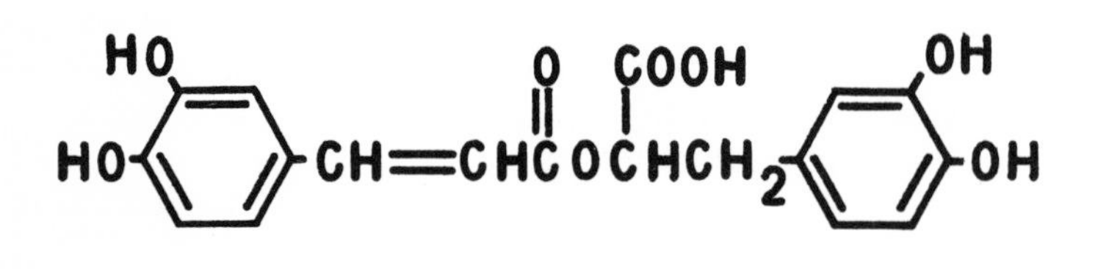

rosmarinic acid
(Rosmarinus officinalis)

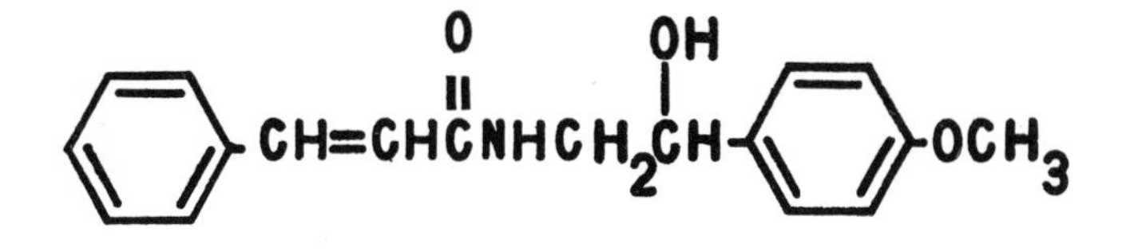

aegelin *(Aegle marmelus)*

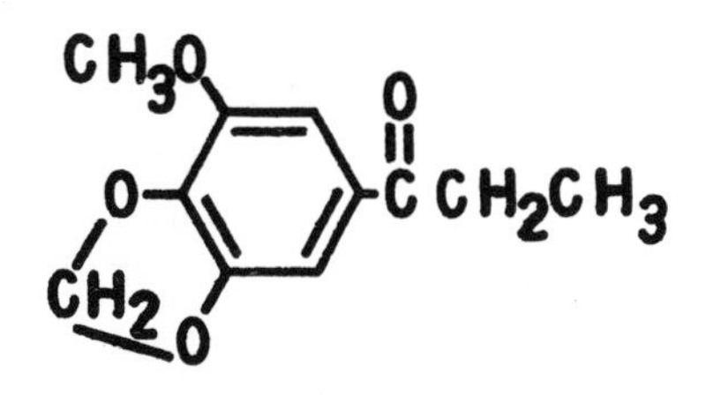

latifoline
(Laserpitium latifolium)

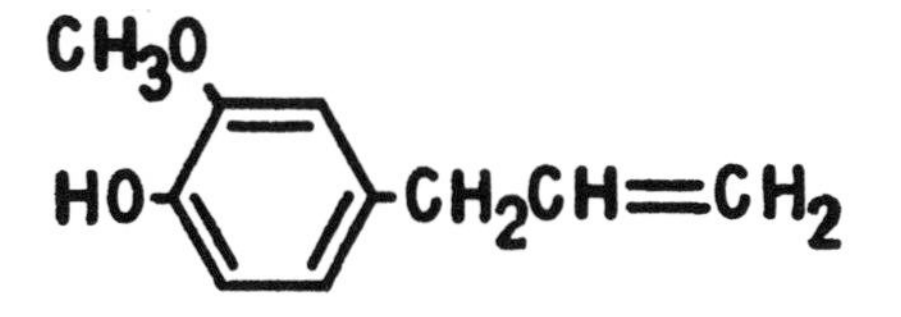

eugenol *(Eugenia aromatica)*

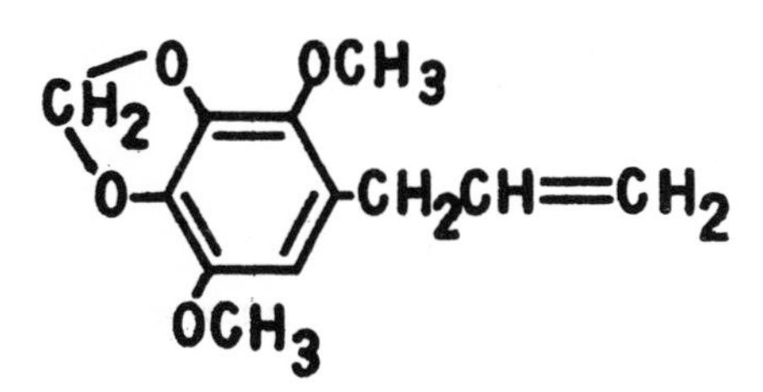

apiol *(Petroselinum crispum)*

The simple aromatic constituents of plants are often dismissed by physiologists as uninteresting "waste products" of metabolism or assigned a vague function in helping to resist parasitic attacks or attracting insects to pollinate flowers. A more specific function may be indicated by the observation of Sondheimer and Griffin (10), that indoleacetic oxidase is activated by p-coumaric acid and inhibited by caffeic and chlorogenic acids. In general monophenols activate and diphenols inhibit. The interplay of these various compounds by controlling enzyme activity could exercise important control over the growth of plant tissues.

COUMARINS AND ISOCOUMARINS

The coumarins are lactones of o-hydroxycinnamic acid. This basic nucleus with its ring-numbering is as follows:

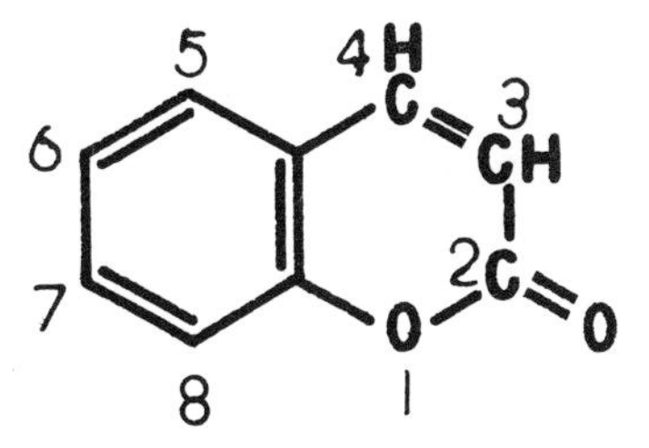

Almost all natural coumarins have oxygen (hydroxyl or alkoxyl) at C-7. Other positions may also be oxygenated, and alkyl side-chains are frequently present. Isoprenoid side-chains are especially common. Some coumarins are found as glycosides. Coumarins may also be artifacts which arise from enzymatic hydrolysis of glycosyl-O-hydroxycinnamic acid and immediate cyclization to the lactone:

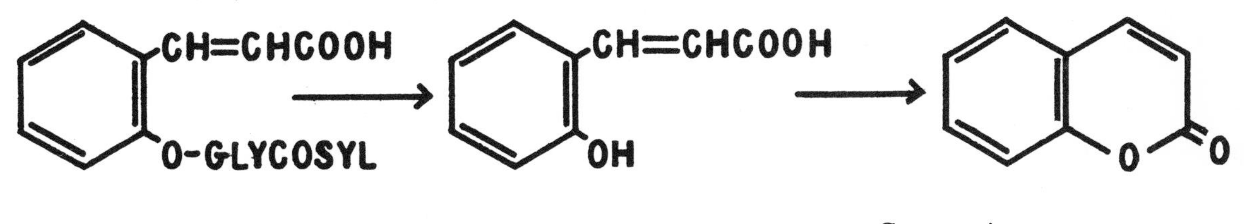

Melilotoside

Coumarin

Ring closure to the lactone occurs only with O-hydroxy-*cis*-cinnamic acids (coumarinic acids). Ortho-hydroxy-*trans*-cinnamic acids (coumaric acids) do not form lactones directly. However, isomerization to the *cis* form can be brought about by treatment with ultraviolet light whereupon immediate ring closure ensues. The lactone ring of coumarins is opened by hydrolysis with warm alkali, but immediately reforms on acidification. Fusion with alkali splits off the alkyl group forming simple phenols (e. g. resorcinol from umbelliferone).

Structures of several natural coumarins are given in Table 3. They occur in all parts of plants and are widely distributed in the plant kingdom but especially common in grasses, orchids, citrus fruits and legumes. Scopoletin is the most common coumarin of higher plants.

Much rarer than the coumarins are isocoumarins or 3, 4-benzopyrones. A dihydroisocoumarin, phyllodulcin, is the sweet principle of *Hydrangea macrophylla* (11) while another is responsible for the bitter taste occasionally found in carrots (12):

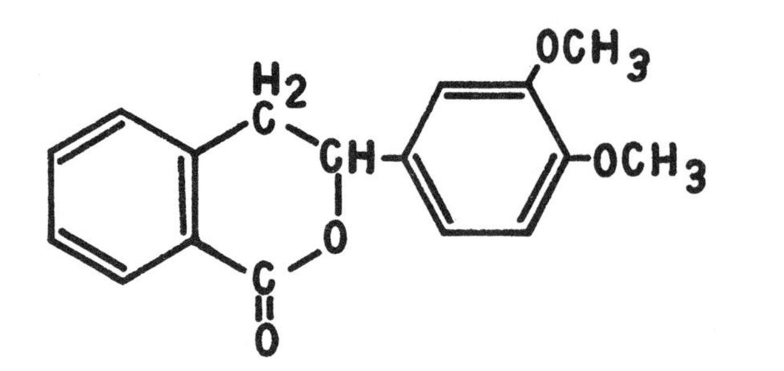

Phyllodulcin

Bergenin from rhizomes of *Bergenia crassifolia* is an unusual isocoumarin which contains a fused ring apparently derived from glucose:

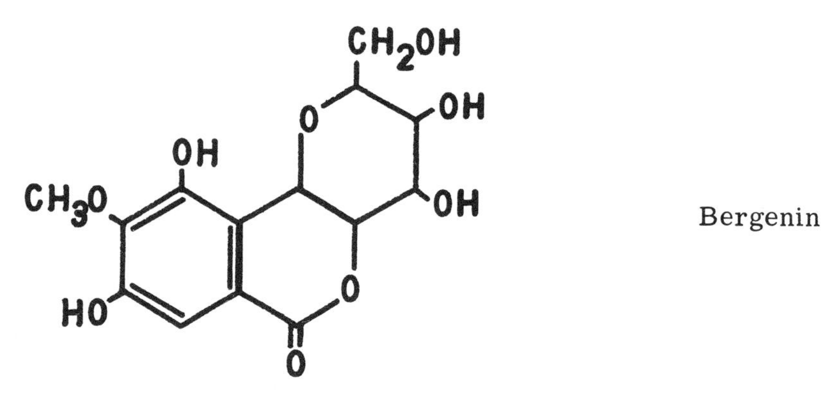

Bergenin

The coumarins have quite varied physiological effects on living organisms. In some cases they act as plant growth inhibitors, but growth stimulation has also been observed. Coumarins also show narcotic and other toxic effects on animals, but they are generally less toxic than the furanocoumarins (see below).

Dean (13) has reviewed the naturally occurring coumarins.

FURANO- AND PYRANOCOUMARINS

Several natural products are known which have a pyran or furan ring fused with the benzene ring of a coumarin:

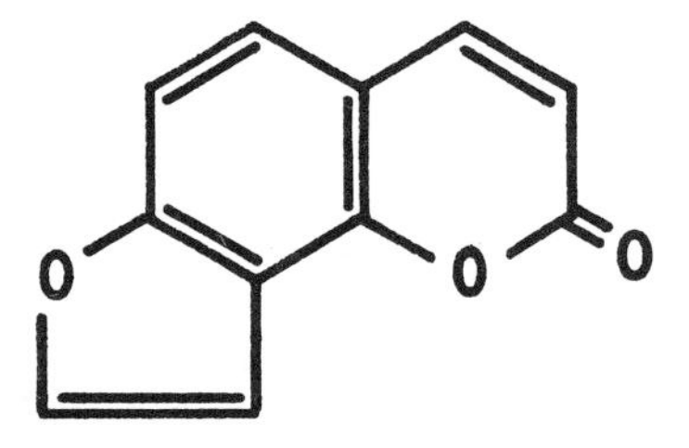

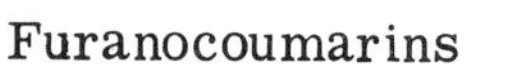

Furanocoumarins

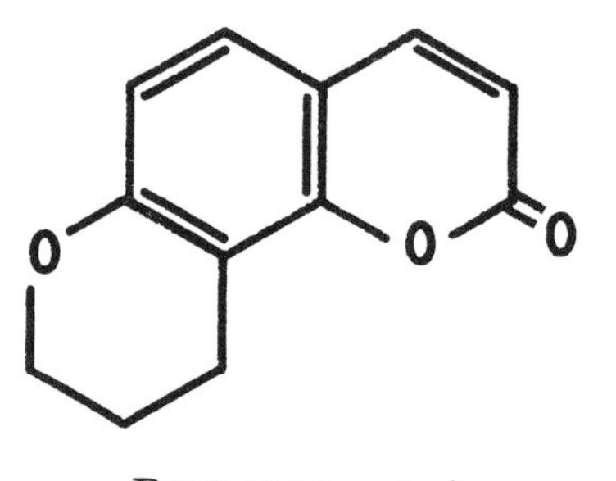

Pyranocoumarins

The ring fusion may also be at positions 6 and 7 of the coumarin nucleus. These compounds resemble the simple coumarins. Alkaline hydrolysis under ordinary conditions affects only the lactone ring, but alkaline fusion or drastic hydrolysis conditions may

TABLE 3. SOME NATURALLY OCCURRING COUMARINS

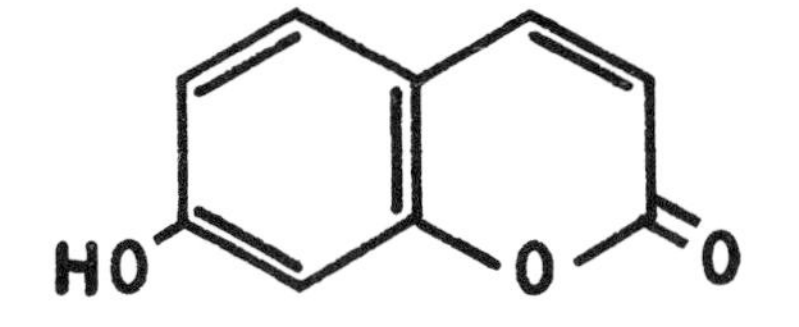

umbelliferone
(resins of *Umbelliferae*)

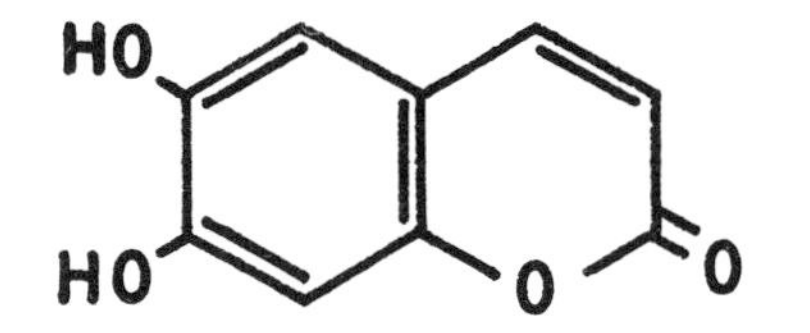

esculetin
(*Aesculus* and *Fraxinus* spp.)

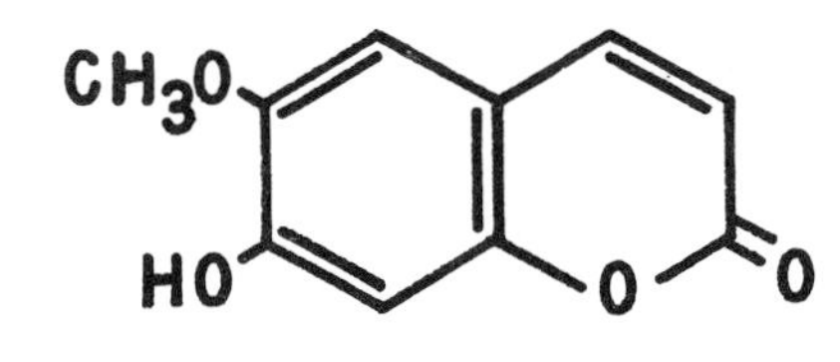

scopoletin
(Murraya exotica)

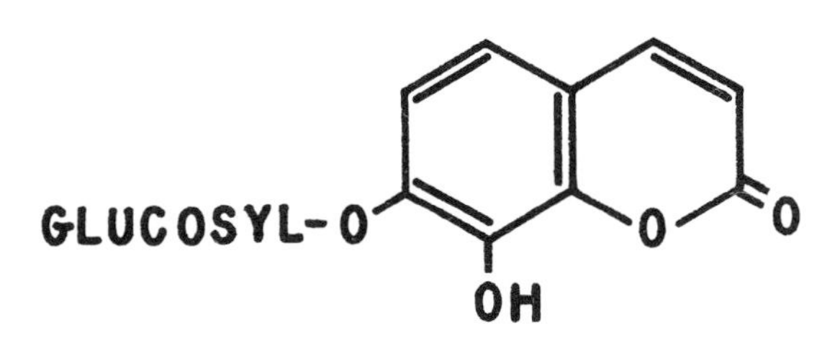

daphnin
(*Fraxinus* spp.)

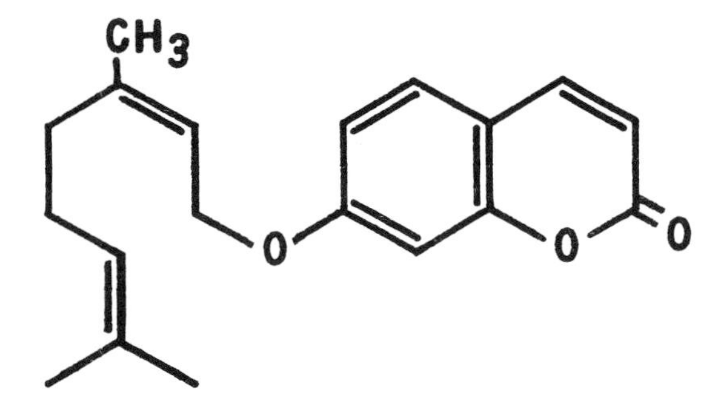

collinin
(Flindersia collina)

Table 3. Continued

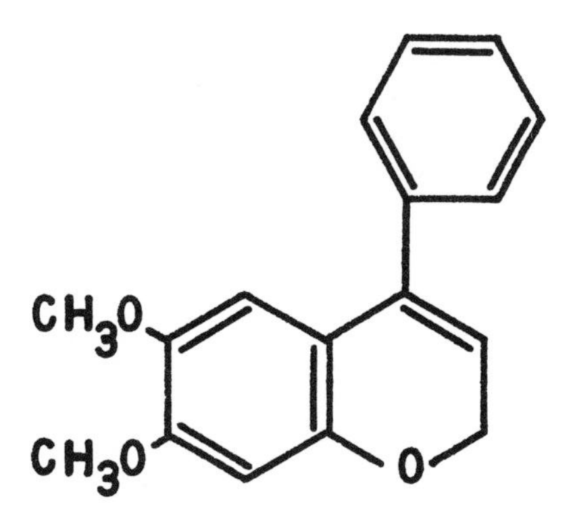

dalbergin methyl ether
(Dalbergia sissoo)

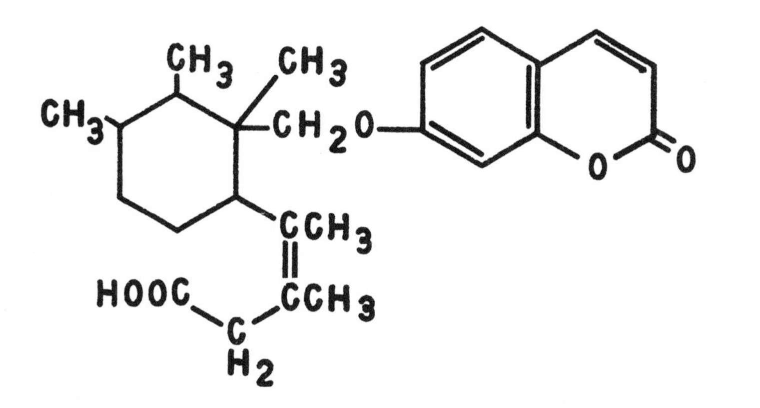

galbanic acid
(*Ferula* spp.)

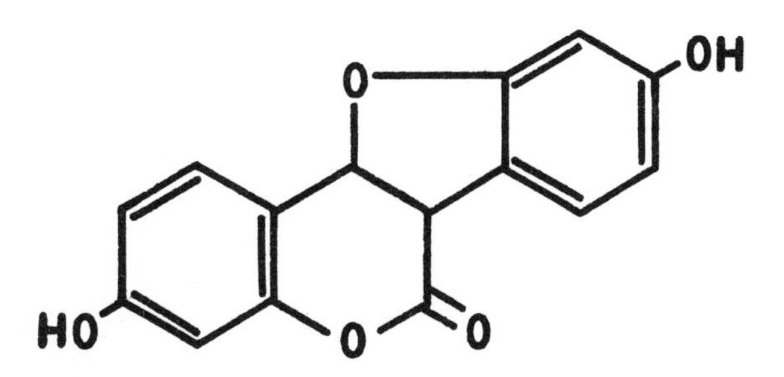

coumestrol
(Trifolium repens)

destroy the two heterocylic rings to form simple phenols. Structures of some representative compounds are given in Table 4. It will be noted that all pyranocoumarins have an isoprenoid carbon skeleton in the pyran ring as do some of the furanocoumarins. It has been suggested (14) that any which do not have an intact isoprene skeleton have been derived by secondary reactions.

The furanocoumarins are of some economic importance as the active ingredients of fish poisons used by some primitive peoples. In higher animals they may show spasmolytic and vasodilating effects. Psoralen derivatives taken orally have been used to promote suntanning of the skin (15).

LIGNANS

The lignans may be regarded as formed by the union of two phenylpropanes through their aliphatic side chains. The usual basic structure is:

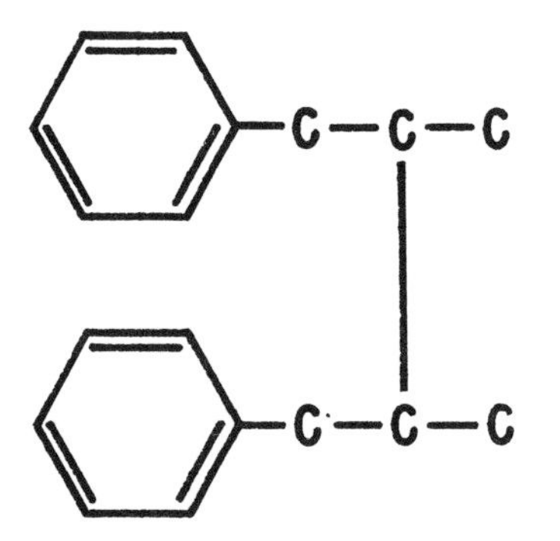

The aromatic rings are always oxygenated. Additional ring closures may also be present. All of the natural lignans contain one or more asymmetric carbon atoms and are optically active. Rarely a lignan with the 2-phenylpropane structure may be encountered as in pinastric acid from *Lepraria flava* (16):

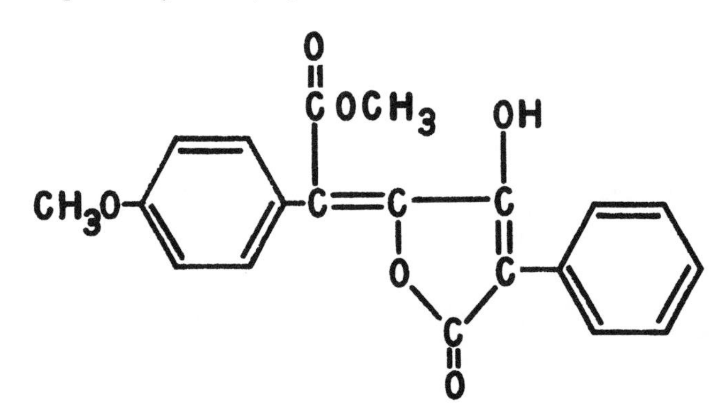

The lignans are colorless, crystalline solids which resemble other simple aromatic compounds in their chemical behavior. They are widespread in the plant kingdom, occurring in heartwood, leaves, resinous exudates, and other plant parts. Occasionally they are found as glycosides.

Examples of some natural lignans are given in Table 5. About three dozen are known at present. Some have shown limited commercial success as antioxidants in food. Sesamin has some importance as synergistic ingredient in pyrethrum insecticides. Lignans are also the active constituents in certain medicinal plants. Podophyllin, a resinous

TABLE 4. SOME FURANO- AND PYRANOCOUMARINS, STRUCTURES AND OCCURRENCE

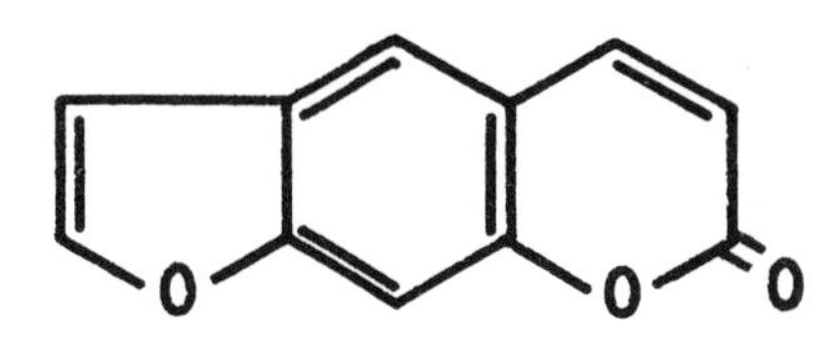

psoralen
(Psoralea corylifolia)

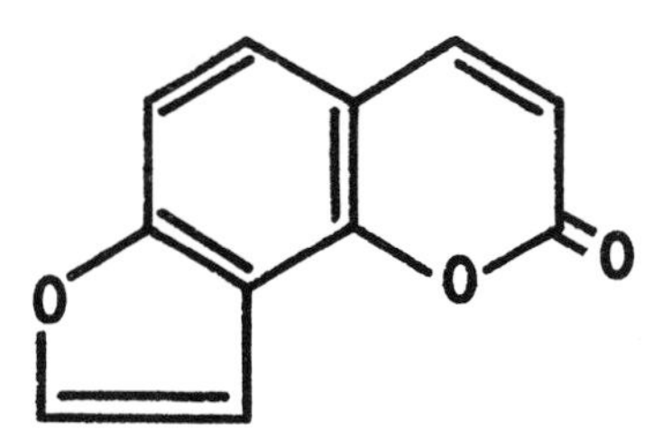

angelicin
(Archangelica officinalis)

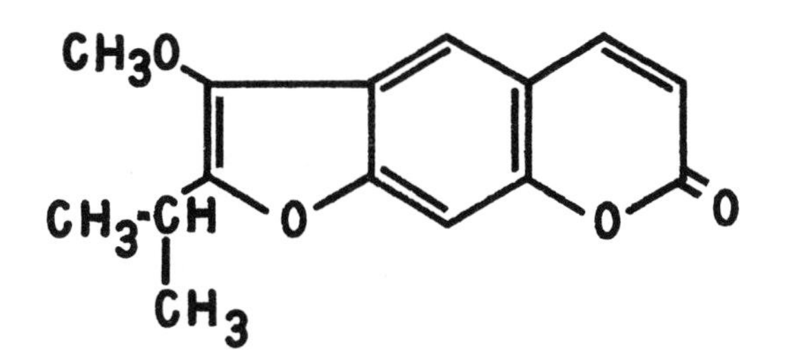

peucedanin
(Peucedanum officinale)

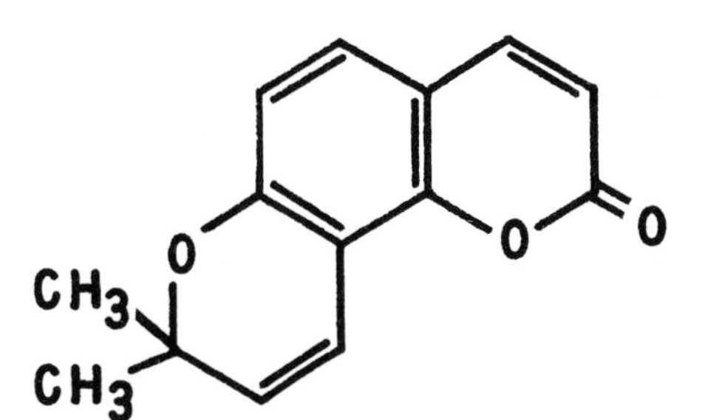

seselin
(Seseli indicum)

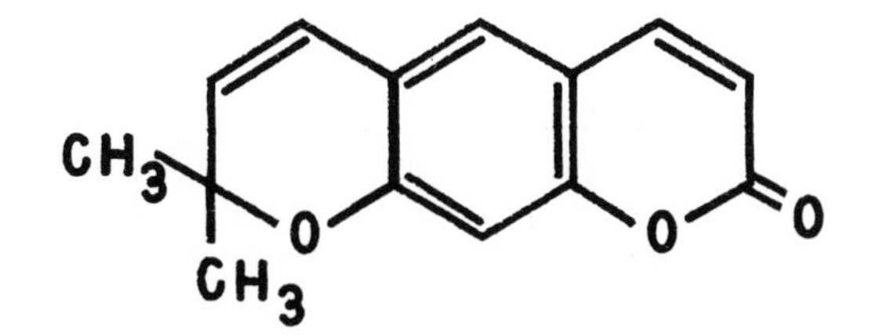

xanthoxyletin
(Xanthoxylum americanum)

TABLE 5. SOME LIGNANS, STRUCTURES AND OCCURRENCE

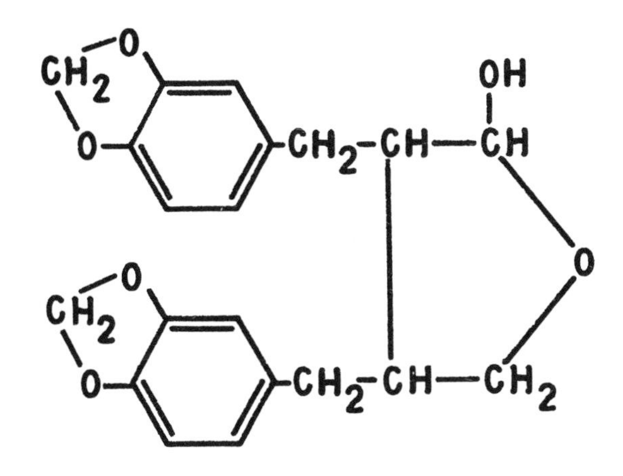

cubebin
(Piper cubeba)

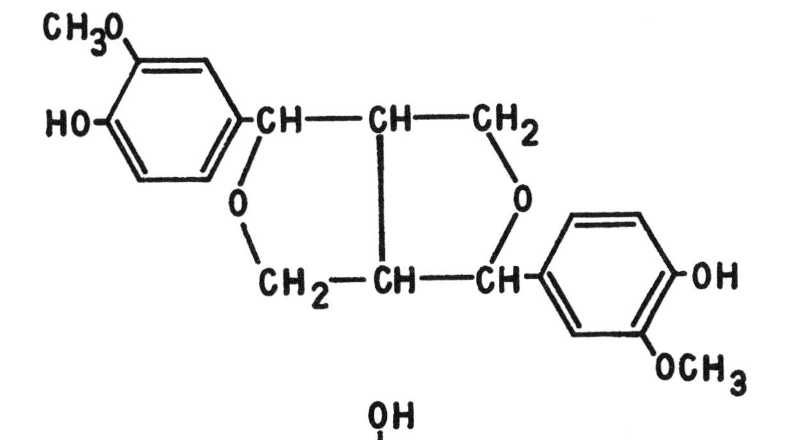

pinoresinol
(*Pinus* and *Picea* spp.)

podophyllotoxin
(*Podophyllum* spp.)

sesamin
(*Sesamum* spp.)

extract of may apple (*Podophyllum peltatum*), has been used as a powerful cathartic. It is a complex mixture (17), but its lignan constituent, podophyllotoxin, is of interest for having a cytotoxic action like that of colchicine. Podophyllotoxin and other lignans having the partially reduced naphthalene nucleus have shown some promise in treatment of certain types of neoplasms. In plants lignans have been regarded as intermediates in the biosynthesis of lignin (see below under "Metabolic Pathways").

There are general reviews of the lignans by Erdtman (18) and Hearon and MacMregor (19). Freudenberg and Weinges (20) have proposed a comprehensive system of nomenclature for the lignans.

LIGNIN

Lignin is the strengthening material which occurs along with cellulose in the cell walls of all woody plants. It is a high polymer made up of several different types of phenylpropane units. All lignins contain units related to coniferyl alcohol. In addition, the lignin of most dicots has sinapyl groups whereas lignin from grasses may contain p-hydroxycinnamyl alcohol units:

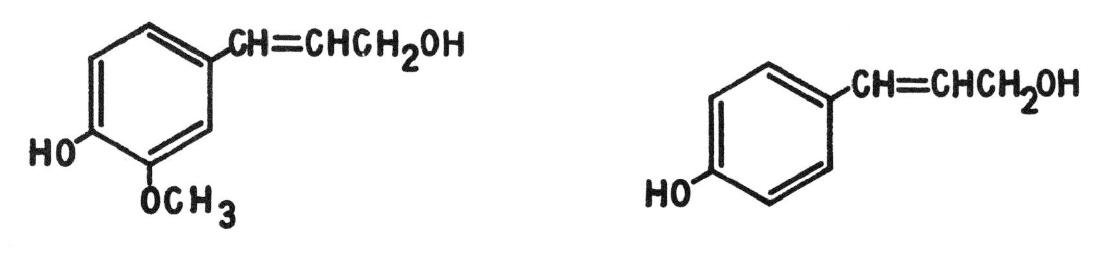

Coniferyl alcohol p-hydroxycinnamyl alcohol

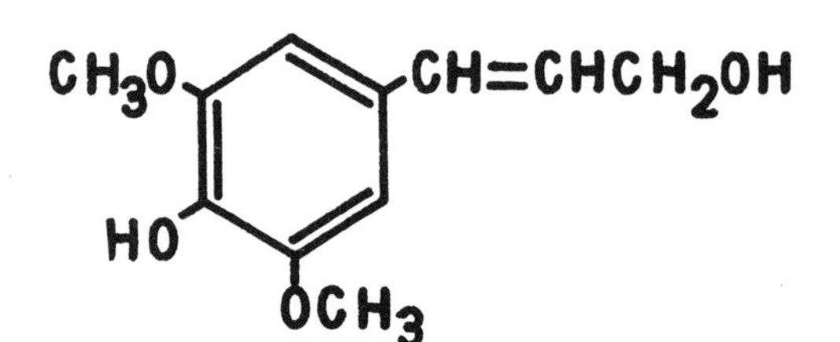

Sinapyl alcohol

These cinnamyl alcohol derivatives also occur in plants as glycosides involving the p-hydroxy groups (e.g. coniferin, syringin).

Lignin itself as obtained by various isolation procedures (see below) is a brown, amorphous solid which is insoluble in water and most organic solvents. Lignin preparations (which may have suffered some degradation during isolation) have shown molecular weights ranging from 2800 to 6700. Lignin in plants is undoubtedly bound in some way to the polysaccharides which occur with it in the cell walls. However, it is still unclear whether this binding involves covalent bonds such as ether or ester links or whether it is merely through hydrogen bonds. It is probable that there is more than one type of linkage between the repeating units of lignin. The dehydrodiisoeugenol structure shown below at least a likely possibility for a part of the molecule:

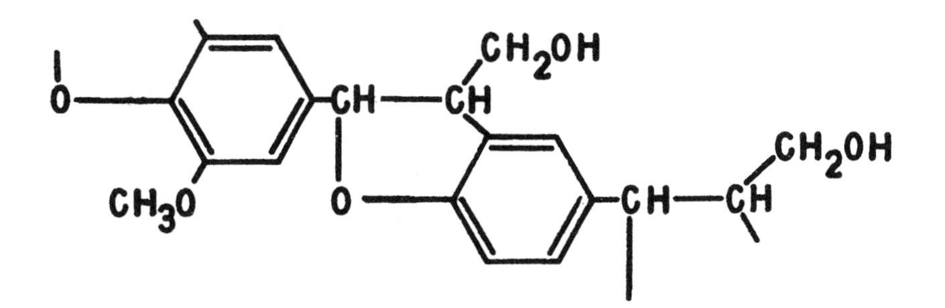

According to this formulation lignin made up solely of sinapyl units cannot occur because the methoxyl group at C-5 blocks condensation with the side chain of another molecule.

Plants contain varying amounts of lignin ranging from a few per cent (herbaceous plants) to about 30% (conifers). Ferns and club mosses apparently contain true lignin, but its occurrence is doubtful in Thallophytes, Bryophytes or *Equisetum* spp. Primitive dicots contain a smaller proportion of sinapyl units than advanced ones (21). The great majority of chemical research on lignin has been carried out using spruce lignin, and most statements regarding lignin may be interpreted as applying strictly only to this particular type of lignin which is composed almost entirely of coniferyl alcohol units.

In addition to the general references there are reviews on lignin by Brauns (22, 23), Kremers (24) and Nord and de Stevens (25).

HYDROLYZABLE TANNINS

A variety of phenolic plant constituents possess an astringent taste and the ability to tan leather, but chemically the plant tannins are divided into two groups. Condensed or catechin tannins are discussed in Chapter 9. The so-called hydrolyzable tannins contain ester linkages which may be hydrolyzed by boiling with dilute hydrochloric acid. The alcoholic component of the ester is usually a sugar, but in Tara tannin it is quinic acid. Structures of some of the phenolic acids found in tannins are shown in Table 6. Gallic acid is probably the one of most common occurrence. Ellagic acid is a secondary product formed on hydrolysis of some tannins which are actually esters of hexaoxydiphenic acid. It appears as a "bloom" on the surface of leather which has been processed with ellagitannins. Similarly, chebulic acid can be a secondary product of tannin hydrolysis, formed by lactonization of a carboxyl group which in the native tannin is esterified with a sugar.

The hydrolyzable tannins are often complex mixtures containing several different phenolic acids esterified to different positions of the sugar molecule. The "tannic acid" of commerce is actually a mixture of free gallic acid and various galloyl esters of glucose. Chinese gallotannin is probably the most thoroughly investigated hydrolyzable tannin. It is found in aphid galls on a sumac plant *(Rhus semialata)* native to southwestern Asia. Chinese gallotannin is a mixture of galloyl esters of glucose. The basic structure is 1, 2, 3, 4, 6-pentagalloyl-β-glucose with 3-5 additional galloyl groups attached by depside linkages to form a chain of 2 or 3 m-galloyl groups (26).

An example of an ellagitannin is chebulagic acid of dividivi, the dried fruit of *Caesalpinia coriaria*. On hydrolysis this tannin yields glucose, gallic acid, ellagic acid, and chebulic acid. Its structure has been formulated as:

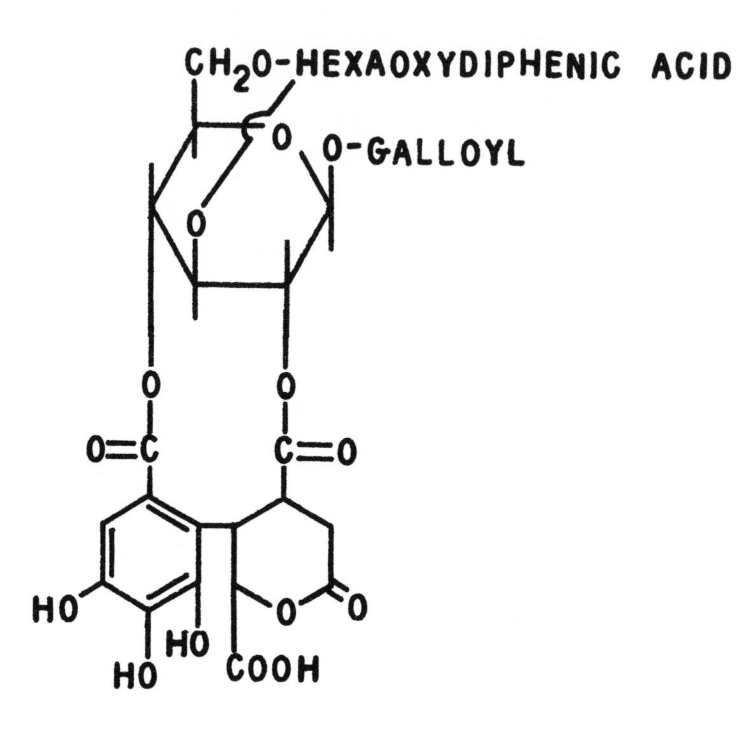

The hydrolyzable tannins are usually amorphous hygroscopic, yellow-brown substances which dissolve in water (especially hot) to form colloidal rather than true solutions. The purer they are, the less soluble they are in water and the more readily they may be obtained in a crystalline form. They are also soluble at least to some extent in polar organic solvents, but not in non-polar organic solvents like benzene or chloroform. From aqueous solution the tannins may be precipitated by mineral acids or salts.

Gallotannins and ellagitannins are reviewed by Mayer (27).

HUMIC ACID

Humic acid is a very poorly defined entity originally prepared by extracting basic substances from humus with dilute acid and then extracting the residue with dilute ammonium hydroxide. Acidification of the ammoniacal extract precipitates a crude mixture known as humic acid. It is generally believed that the humic acid in soil is derived from the lignin or carbohydrates of decaying plants; but it may also contain nitrogen, phosphorus and sulfur (28). The following has been suggested as a possible structural unit (29):

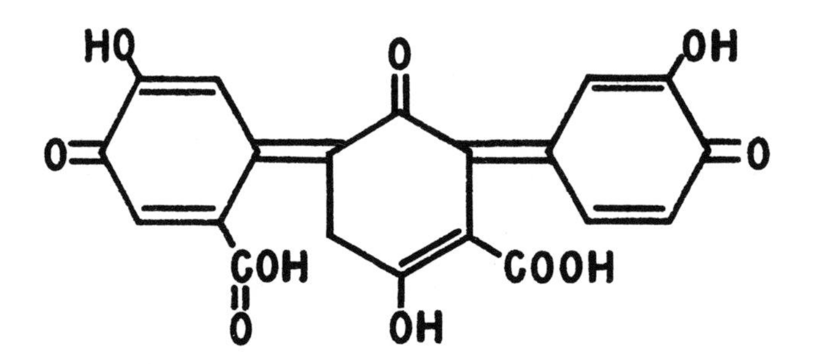

The molecular weight has been estimated as 1200-1500.

TABLE 6. ACID COMPONENTS OF HYDROLYZABLE TANNINS

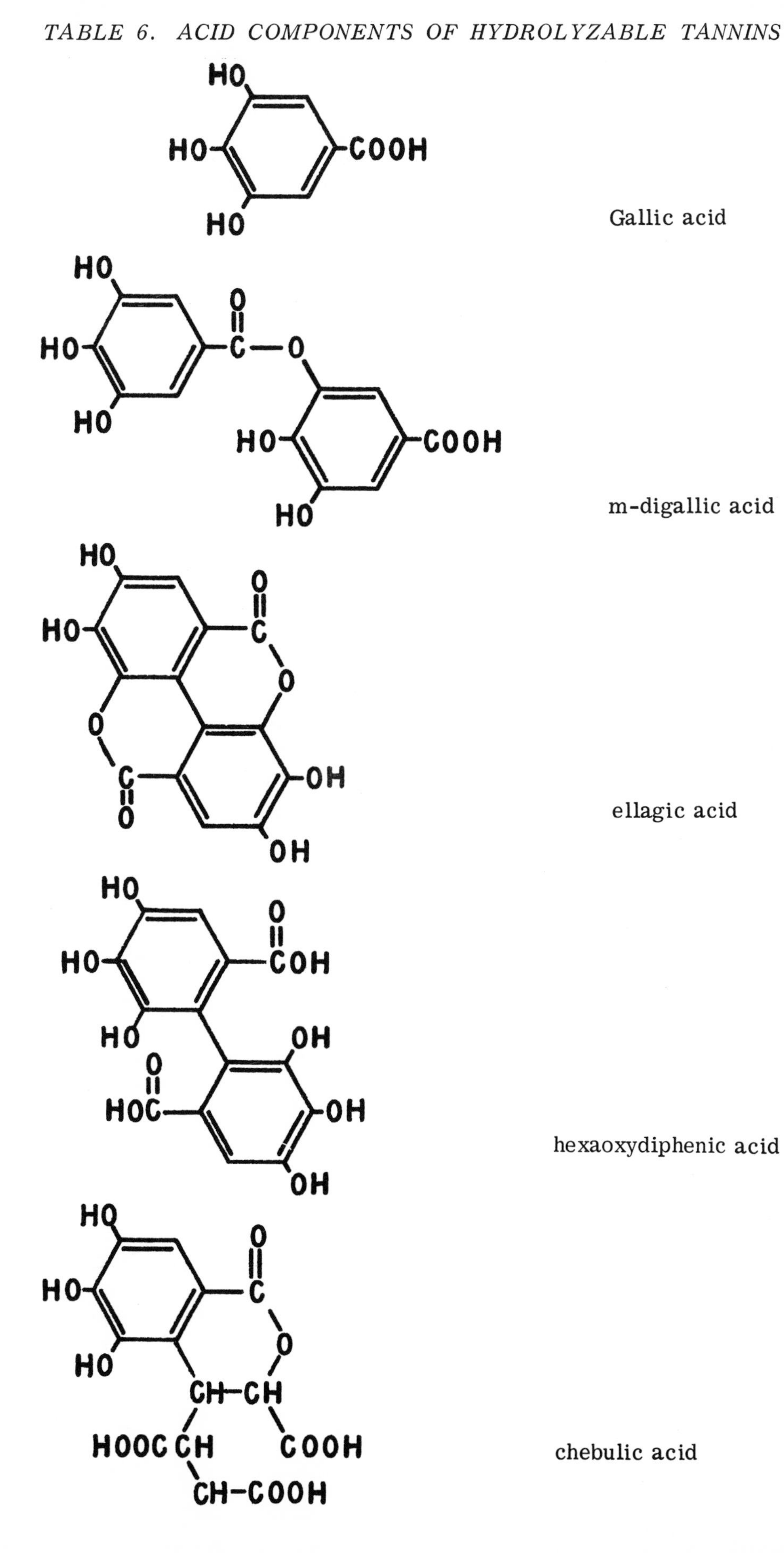

Gallic acid

m-digallic acid

ellagic acid

hexaoxydiphenic acid

chebulic acid

A substance named "humic acid" has been identified as a natural constituent of several plants by Raudnitz (30). The relationship of this to the humic acid of soil is not clear. Humic acid was purified from leaves of *Rhododendron ponticum* and described as a water-soluble, surface-active phosphate ester having a molecular weight of ca. 1200. Plant parts containing this humic acid turn red on heating with acid. In this respect humic acid resembles the leucoanthocyanidins (q. v.). However, the red pigment formed from humic acid may be recognized by its absorption spectrum which shows bands at 459 and 548 mμ.

ISOLATION

Inasmuch as the compounds described in this chapter vary considerably in their properties, no single isolation procedure will suffice to separate all of them as a group from all other plant constituents. In devising isolation schemes the special properties of the particular category under investigation must be considered.

Many of the simple aromatic compounds occurring in plants have free phenolic hydroxyl groups, carboxyl groups, or both. Carboxylic acids may be extracted from plant material or an ether extract of plant material with 2% sodium bicarbonate solution. When this solution is acidified, the acids often precipitate or may be extracted with ether. After removal of carboxylic acids, phenols may be extracted with 5% sodium hydroxide solution. Like the acids, they may be precipitated or extracted into ether after acidification. Because many phenols are highly sensitive to oxidation under alkaline conditions, it may be advisable to exclude air or add a reducing agent like sodium dithionite during the alkali treatment.

Some of the lower molecular weight aromatic compounds may be purified by distillation or sublimation under atmospheric or reduced pressure. Phenols are usually not steam distillable, but phenol ethers or esters, being less polar than the parent hydroxyl compounds, can often be distilled with steam. Coumarin, for example, is customarily isolated by steam distillation.

Solvent extraction procedures find widespread application in purification of natural aromatic compounds. Common organic solvents like acetone, ether and benzene are often employed. Multiple partition between water or buffer solutions and an immiscible organic solvent has been used to purify compounds with suitable solubility properties. The hydrolyzable tannins and glycosides may be extracted with hot water or water-ethanol mixtures.

In purifying coumarins a crude preparation can be treated with warm dilute alkali to open the lactone ring and form a water-soluble sodium coumarinate. Neutral organic impurities may then be extracted with ether. On acidification of the water solution the coumarin reforms so that the coumarin with any acidic compounds can be extracted into ether. Acid impurities can then be removed from the ether by shaking with sodium bicarbonate solution.

Lignans may be extracted with acetone or ethanol and are often precipitated as slightly soluble potassium salts by adding concentrated, aqueous potassium hydroxide to an alcoholic solution. As a variant on this procedure Freudenberg and Knof (31) converted lignans to insoluble, crystalline products using potassium acetate in ethanol. After collecting the crystalline material free lignans could be regenerated by decomposing with water. Acids or alkalies are to be avoided in preparing lignans, as they often produce isomerization.

The problem of isolating native lignin has called forth several special and ingenious approaches. Older procedures relied on either removing cellulose and other polysaccharides with strong sulfuric or hydrochloric acids, or else dissolving the lignin with alkali. Such harsh procedures doubtless cause considerable degradation of the native lignin. A so-called "native lignin" can be extracted from sawdust using acetone or alcohol at room temperature. This extraction procedure, however, removes only 1/2 to 3% of the total lignin. The solubility of lignin can be increased somewhat by grinding the wood flour very fine in a ball mill. Another technique has been to remove cellulose from wood by allowing fungi or purified cellulase to act on sawdust. By such treatments 25-30% of the total lignin can be obtained in a soluble form. It is believed by some workers that any soluble lignin is by definition not native lignin. Nevertheless the study of soluble lignins is necessary for an understanding the chemical nature of lignin.

Traditional methods for preparation of plant tannins have used extraction with hot water, salting out with sodium chloride, reextraction of the precipitate into acetone and removal of lipids from the acetone-extractable material with ether. By adding sodium chloride in successive small portions some fractional precipitation of a tannin mixture can be achieved. Lead or zinc acetates (10%) are often used to precipitate tannins which may be recovered from the precipitate by decomposing it with hydrogen sulfide. Gelatin also forms a precipitate with aqueous solutions of tannins. Ethanol can then be used to redissolve tannin from this precipitate. Precipitation by adding an alcoholic solution solution of potassium acetate to an alcoholic solution of tannin is often of preparative value. in tannin isolation.

Chromatographic procedures have been applied to the purification of practically all the types of compounds discussed in this chapter. Chromatography on silicic acid has been used to separate such compounds as lignan glycosides (32) or caffeic and chlorogenic isomers from various plants (33). Chromatography on alumina using such solvents as ethyl acetate or ethyl acetate-methanol mixtures has been used for lignans (34) and coumarins (35). Tannins have been purified on Solka-Floc, developing with 5% acetic acid (36).

CHARACTERIZATION

Because of the large number of different substances included in this chapter there is a vast number of specific reactions which have been applied to their characterization. Only a few can be mentioned here for each class of compounds.

A large proportion of the natural aromatic compounds have phenolic hydroxyl groups and are therefore distinguished by the weakly acidic nature of this group. Thus, they are often only slightly soluble in water or sodium bicarbonate solution but readily soluble in dilute aqueous sodium hydroxide. The aromatic compounds with free carboxylic groups are (like other organic acids) slightly soluble in water but easily soluble with effervescence in sodium bicarbonate solution. If all phenolic groups are combined as esters or ethers, the oxygenated benzene ring may still be recognized by the formation of colored azo dyes on reaction with diazotized sulfanilic acid or p-nitroaniline (Pauli reaction). Many phenols also reduce Fehling's solution or ammoniacal silver nitrate. Production of color with a 1% ferric chloride solution is also characteristic of many phenols. Other color reactions will be found in the general references. Many paper chromatographic studies of phenolic compounds have been made. Bate-Smith (37) surveyed the leaves of many plants and found that the best solvent system for separating the phenolic compounds was acetic acid/hydrochloric acid/water 30:3:10. Appearance in ultraviolet light and treatment with several different spray reagents could be used to identify different classes of compounds. Other papers on chromatography of plant phenolics are by Inglett and Lodge (38), Ibrahim and Towers (39), and Billek and Kindl (40). The most generally applicable detection methods are observation in ultraviolet light and spraying with diazonium reagent. Pridham (41) has described paper chromatography and electrophoresis of phenols. During paper chromatography caffeic acid can be converted into the coumarin, esculetin, if oxygen, ultraviolet light and traces of metal ions are present (42). All simple phenols show strong absorption of ultraviolet radiation in the range 270-280 mμ.

Most of the common coumarins are strongly fluorescent when exposed to ultraviolet light. Sen and Bagchi (43) determined the absorption spectra of various coumarins and chromones, concluding that these two similar classes may be distinguished from each other on the basis of their spectra. The paper chromatography of coumarins and furocoumarins has been studied by Grujić-Vasić (44). When coumarins are separated by paper chromatography they may be detected by fluorescence or by spraying with Emerson's reagent (0.5% Na_2CO_3, 0.9% of 4-aminoantipyrine, 5.4% $K_3Fe(CN)_6$) (45). The fluorescent spots may also be cut from the paper, eluted, and absorption spectra of the eluates determined for identification. Since coumarins (and other phenols) often occur as glycosides it may be advisable to submit plant materials to acidic hydrolysis before attempting to detect free coumarins.

Furanocoumarins may be identified by the fact that oxidation with hydrogen peroxide in sodium hydroxide produces furan-2, 3-dicarboxylic acid. Since all natural pyranocoumarins have a 2, 2-dimethylpyran structure, they may be identified by the fact that acetone is formed by prolonged alkaline hydrolysis. Alkaline hydrolysis does not affect the furan ring of furanocoumarins.

There is no simple test to distinguish lignans from other natural phenolic compounds Lignans have been separated by paper chromatography using as solvents mixtures of formamide with several other organic liquids (31, 46). Detection of the spots can be done using diazotized sulfanilic acid or antimony pentachloride.

The presence of lignin in plant tissues is easily recognized by such simple reactions as the appearance of a bright red color when moistened with a saturated solution of phloroglucinol in concentrated hydrochloric acid. Other cinnamaldehyde derivatives give the same reaction but they can usually be removed by a preliminary extraction with acetone, which does not dissolve lignin. Lignin containing sinapyl groups may be recognized by the Mäule reaction -- formation of a red color when treated successively with chlorine water and ammonia (47). Gymnosperm lignin, which contains only coniferyl units, gives a brown color in this test. For more complete identification of the units present in lignin oxidation with alkaline nitrobenzene is used to degrade the lignin to benzaldehyde derivatives. Stone and Blundell (48) developed a method using 50 mg. samples of wood placed in stainless steel bombs with nitrobenzene and sodium hydroxide at 160° for 2.5 hours. When reaction was complete, 0.2 ml. of reaction mixture could be spotted directly onto a paper chromatogram and the products detected by spraying with 2, 4-dinitrophenylhydrazine. All lignins form vanillin by this treatment. Dicot lignins show syringylaldehyde as well, and grass lignins usually form p-hydroxybenzaldehyde.

One of the best-known tests for tannins is their precipitation of gelatin. A 0.5% solution of tannin is added to an equal volume of 0.5% gelatin. All tannins show some degree of precipitation, but other phenolic compounds may also give a positive test. The sensitivity of the reaction may be increased by adjusting the pH to about 4 and adding some sodium chloride. Other precipitation reactions with amines or metal ions have often been used to characterize tannins. Like other phenolic compounds the tannins give blue-violet colors with ferric chloride.

Several tests are available to distinguish between the hydrolyzable tannins (gallotannins) and condensed tannins (catechin tannins). Addition of 2 volumes of 10% acetic acid and 1 volume of 10% lead acetate solution to a filtered 0.4% tannin solution forms a precipitate with gallotannins within 5 minutes, but condensed tannins remain in solution. Other special tests can be used to distinguish between different types of hydrolyzable tannins. Several groups of investigators have applied paper chromatography to tannin mixtures.

Solvents containing a good proportion of water seem to be most useful. Spots are revealed by exposure to ammonia and examination in ultraviolet light, or by spraying with ferric chloride solution.

METABOLIC PATHWAYS

Biosynthetic pathways of aromatic compounds in plants have been reviewed by Neish (49). The present discussion is restricted to those aromatic compounds derived from 5-dehydroquinic acid. Other types of aromatic compounds will be found in Chapters 6 and 9. The pathways showin Figures 1 and 2 are at least probable for higher plants, although certain details have been strictly established only for microorganisms. The steps leading from carbohydrates to 5-dehydroquinic acid have been showin Figure 8 of Chapter 2. Only a few points will be made here in clarification of the figures:

1. The conversion of 5-dehydroshikimic acid to protocatechuic acid and gallic acid appears reasonable, and there is some experimental evidence to support it, at least to indicate that gallic acid is formed between glucose and phenylalanine (50).
2. It is now generally believed that the main pathway for forming cinnamic and p-coumaric acids from phenylalanine and tyrosine respectively does not go through the corresponding keto and hydroxy acids but occurs by a one-step elimination of ammonia. Deaminases catalyzing these reactions have been studied and the reactions found to be irreversible (51). Monocots have both enzymes, but dicots have only phenylalanine deaminase and are therefore unable to make p-coumaric acid (or compounds derived from it) from tyrosine.
3. Hydroxylation of the aromatic ring evidently must occur at several points in the scheme, but the exact location of these points is not clear--i. e. o-coumaric acid may first be hydroxylated and then go on to form hydroxycoumarins, or the parent coumarin may be made first and then hydroxylated. Tracer experiments have established that cinnamic acid fed to plants is readily hydroxylated in several positions (52). Model experiments have shown that aromatic hydroxylation may be non-enzymatic or could involve a peroxidase system (53).
4. Several types of evidence (26) indicate that polygalloyl glucose is the parent compound of many, if not all, the hydrolyzable tannins. Thus, it is believed that the ellagitannins are derived by oxidative coupling of two molecules of gallic acid which are already esterified to glucose, rather than by esterification of the sugar with preformed hexaoxydiphenic acid. On the other hand, Wenkert (54) has suggested that diphenyl and diphenyl ether systems may be formed by carbohydrate-type condensation of hydroaromatic precursors rather than by oxidative coupling of aromatic rings.
5. Since the complete structure of lignin remains unknown, the exact mechanism of its formation cannot be shown. Freudenberg (55) has suggested that the first step is enzymatic removal of a phenolic hydrogen atom from coniferyl alcohol to produce a free radical which can undergo non-enzymatic rearrangements and reactions with other molecules leading first to dimers (of which lignans are one type) and finally to lignin. The removal of hydrogen is a reaction which may be catalyzed by phenol oxidase or peroxidase. Stafford (56) incubated leaf sections of timothy grass with hydrogen peroxide.and various cinnamic acid derivatives. Ferulic acid gave rise to a product resembling natural lignin. A recent review on lignin biosynthesis is by Brown (57).
6. Freudenberg and Grion (58) suggest that the well-known binding of lignin to carbohydrate in cell walls may come about by coupling of one of the free radical intermediates mentioned above with the hydroxyl group of a carbohydrate to form an ether bond.

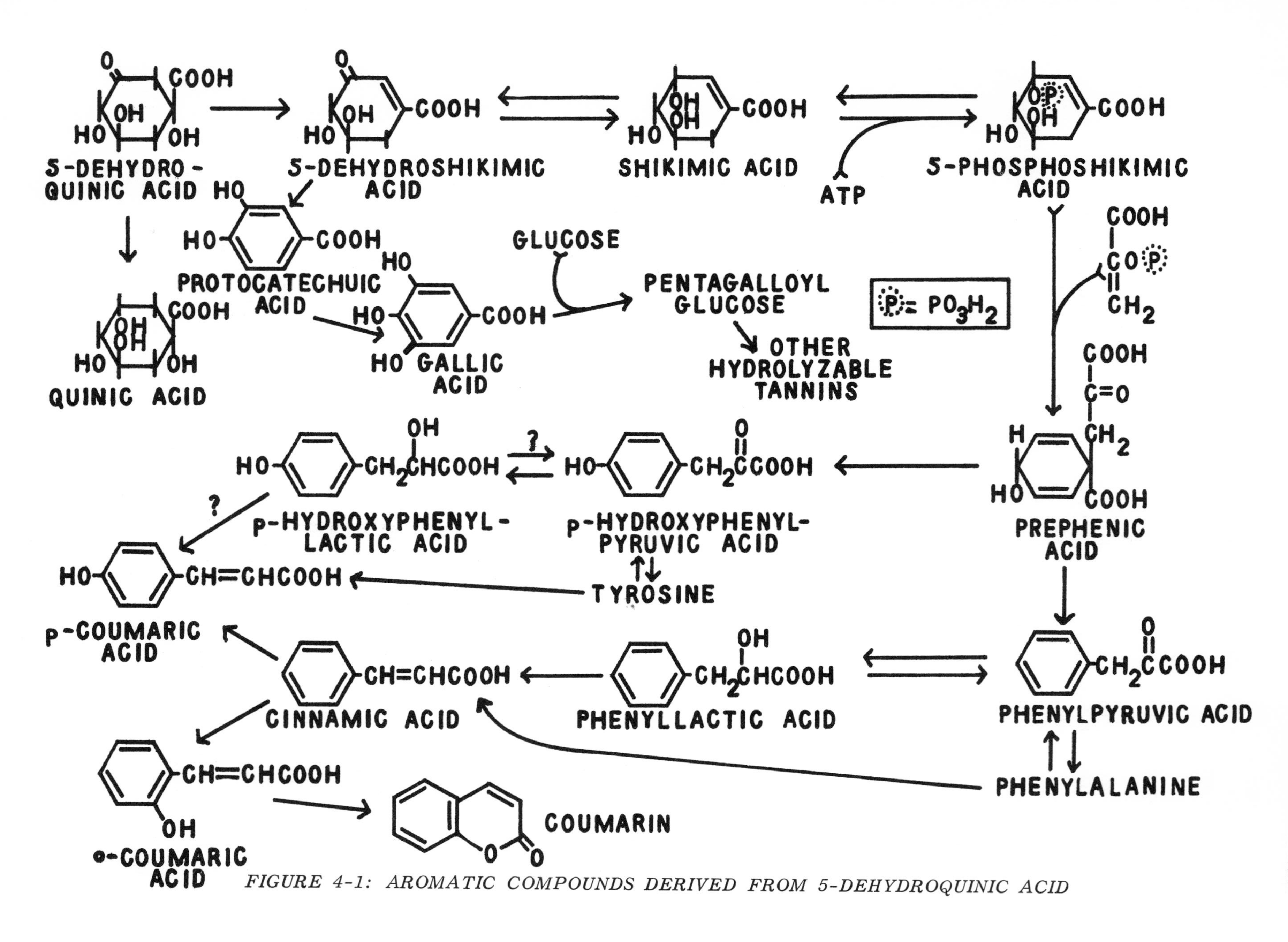

FIGURE 4-1: AROMATIC COMPOUNDS DERIVED FROM 5-DEHYDROQUINIC ACID

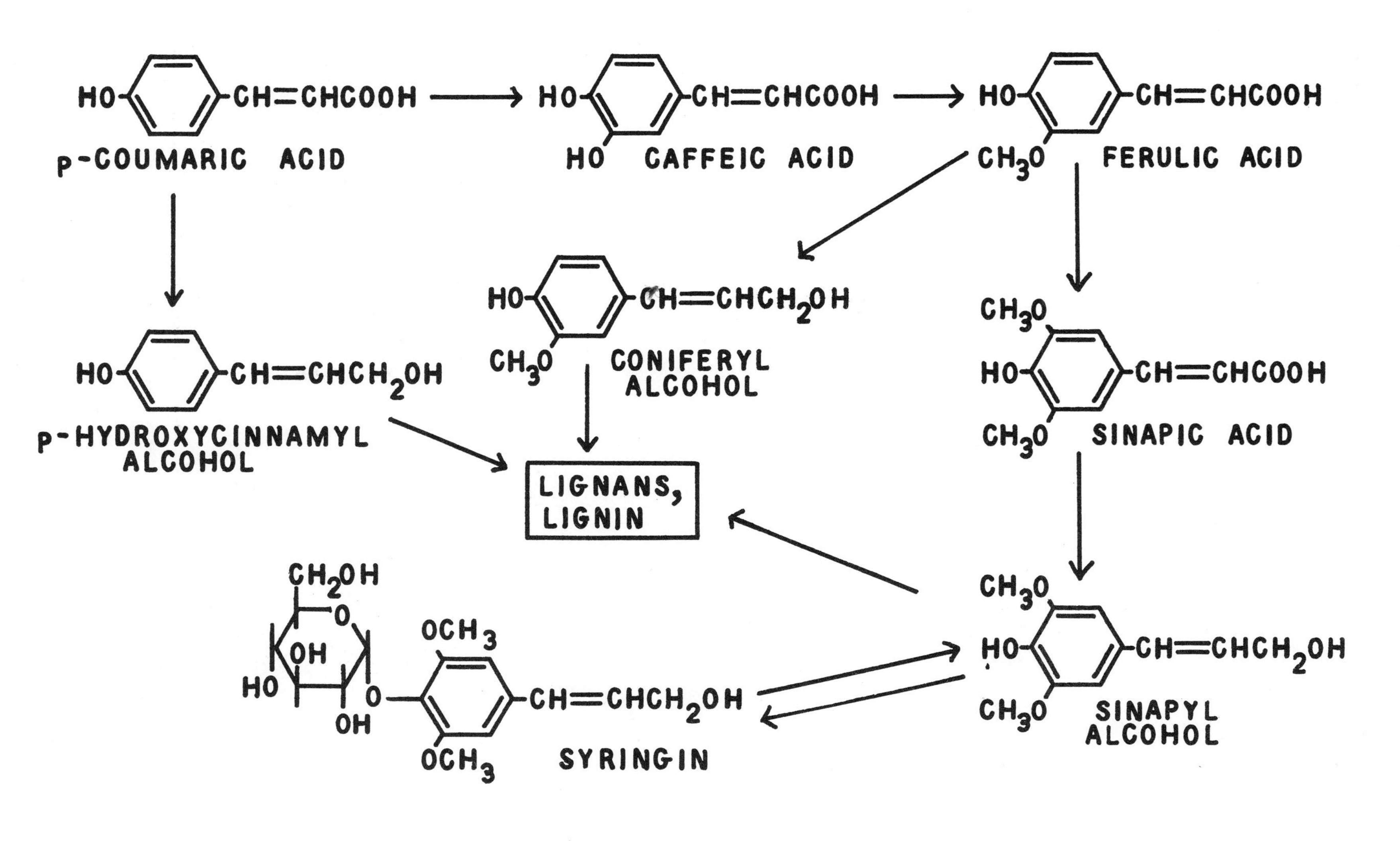

FIGURE 4-2: AROMATIC COMPOUNDS DERIVED FROM p-COUMARIC ACID

7. The methoxyl groups present on many natural aromatic compounds are derived from the usual biological methyl donors such as methionine, formate, and the β-carbon of serine (59).
8. Experiments with partially purified enzyme systems have begun to provide confirmation that the reactions shown do occur in higher plants and have opened the way to a clearer understanding of the details of the various transformations (51, 60, 61, 62).

GENERAL REFERENCES

Fairbairn, J. W., ed. The Pharmacology of Plant Phenolics, Academic Press, New York, 1959.

Ollis, W. D., ed. Recent Developments in the Chemistry of Natural Phenolic Compounds, Pergamon Press, New York, 1961.

Schwarze, P., "Phenole und Chinone und die biogene Bildung von Benzolkernen bei hoheren Pflanzen", in Ruhland 10 507.

Many articles in Paech and Tracey 3.

BIBLIOGRAPHY

1. Walker, J., Link, K. and Angell, H., Proc. Nat. Acad. Sci. U. S. 15 845 (1929).
2. Varga, M. and Köves, E., Nature 183 401 (1959).
3. Thomson, R. H., Naturally Occurring Quinones, Academic Press, N. Y., 1957.
4. Underhill, E. W. and Youngken, H. W., J. Pharm. Sci. 51 121 (1962).
5. Geissman, T. A., In Ruhland 10 543.
6. Herrmann, K., Pharmazie 13 266 (1958).
7. Bate-Smith, E. C., Sci. Proc. Royal Dublin Soc. 27 165 (1956).
8. Scarpati, M L. and Oriente, G., Gazz. chim. ital. 90 212 (1960).
9. Corner, J. J, Harborne, J. B., Humphries, S. G., and Ollis, W. D., Phytochem. 1 73 (1962).
10. Sondheimer, E. and Griffin, D. H., Science 131 672 (1960).
11. Arakwa, H. and Nakazaki, M., Chem. and Ind. 1959 671.
12. Sondheimer, E., J. Am. Chem. Soc. 79 5036 (1957).
13. Dean, F. M., Fortscher. Chem. Org. Naturstoffe 9 225 (1952).
14. Aneja, R., Mukerjee, S. K. and Seshadri, T. R., Tetrahedron 4 256 (1958).
15. Musajo, L. and Rodighiero, G., Experientia 18 153 (1962).
16. Grover, P. K. and Seshadri, T. R., Tetrahedron 6 312 (1958).
17. Hartwell, J. L. and Schrecker, A. W., Fortschr. Chem. Org. Naturstoffe. 15 83 (1958).
18. Erdtman, H., in Paech and Tracey 3 428.
19. Hearon, W. M. and MacGregor, W. S., Chem. Revs. 55 957 (1955).
20. Freudenberg, K. and Weinges, K., Tetrahedron 15 115 (1961).
21. Towers, G. H. N. and Gibbs, R. D., Nature 172 25 (1953).
22. Brauns, F. E., The Chemistry of Lignin, Academic Press, N. Y. 1952.
23. Brauns, F. E. and Brauns, D. A., The Chemistry of Lignin, Supplement I, Academic Press, N. Y., 1960.
24. Kremers, R. E., Ann. Rev. Plant Physiol. 10 185 (1959).
25. Nord, F. F. and de Stevens, G., in Ruhland 10 389.
26. Haworth, R. D., Proc. Chem. Soc. 1961 401.
27. Mayer, W., in Ruhland 10 354.
28. Greene, G. and Steelink, C., J. Org. Chem. 27 170 (1962).
29. Abbott, G. A., Proc. North Dakota Acad. Sci. 13 25 (1959).
30. Raudnitz, H., Science 128 782 (1958).
31. Freudenberg, K. and Knof, L., Chem. Ber. 90 2857 (1957).
32. Wartburg, A. v., Angliker, E. and Renz, J., Helv. Chim. Acta 40 1331 (1957).
33. Sondheimer, E., Arch. Biochem. Biophys. 74 131 (1958).
34. Hartwell, J. L. and Detty, W. E., J. Am. Chem. Soc. 72 246 (1950).
35. Chatterjee, A. and Choudhury, A., Naturwiss. 42 535 (1955).
36. King, H. G. C. and White, T., J. Chem. Soc. 1961 3231.
37. Bate-Smith, E. C., Sci. Proc. Royal Dublin Soc. 27 165 (1956).
38. Inglett, G. E. and Lodge, J. P., Anal. Chem. 31 249 (1959).
39. Ibrahim, R. K. and Towers, G. H. N., Arch. Biochem. Biophys. 87 125 (1960).

40. Billek, G. and Kindl, H., Monatsh. 93 85 (1962).
41. Pridham, J. B., J. Chromatog. 2 605 (1959).
42. Butler, W. L. and Siegelman, H. W., Nature 183 1813 (1959).
43. Sen, K. and Bagchi, P., J. Org. Chem. 24 316 (1959).
44. Grujić-Vasić, J., Monatsh. 92 236 (1961).
45. Fujita, M. and Furuya, T., Chem. Pharm. Bull. 6 511 (1958). (Chem. Abstr. 53 10515).
46. Jørgensen, C. and Kofod, H., Acta Chem. Scand. 8 991 (1954).
47. Towers, G. H. N. and Gibbs, R. D., Nature 172 25 (1953).
48. Stone, J. E. and Blundell, M. J., Anal. Chem. 23 771 (1951).
49. Neish, A. C., Ann. Rev. Plant Physiol. 11 55 (1960).
50. Conn, E. E. and Swain, T., Chem. and Ind. 1961 592.
51. Koukol, J. and Conn. E. E., J. Biol. Chem. 236 2692 (1961).
52. Harborne, J. B. and Corner, J. J., Biochem. J. 80 7P (1961).
53. Buhler, D. R. and Mason, H. S., Arch. Biochem. Biophys. 92 424 (1961).
54. Wenkert, E., Chem. and Ind. 1959 906.
55. Freudenberg, K., Nature 183 1152 (1959).
56. Stafford, H. A., Plant Physiol. 35 612 (1960).
57. Brown, S. A., Science 134 305 (1961).
58. Freudenberg, K. and Grion, G., Chem. Ber. 92 1355 (1959).
59. Hamill, R. L., Byerrum, R. U. and Ball, C. D., J. Biol. Chem. 224 713 (1957).
60. Kaneko, K., Chem. Pharm. Bull. (Tokyo) 8 875 (1960).
61. Nandy, M. and Ganguli, N. C., Biochim. Biophys. Acta 48 608 (1961).
62. Neish, A. C., Phytochem. 1 1 (1962).

Chapter 5
SAPONIFIABLE LIPIDS

The saponifiable lipids are operationally defined as those materials which are insoluble in water but soluble in organic solvents such as ether or chloroform and which on heating with alkali form water-soluble soaps. The soaps are salts of long-chain fatty acids, so that these fatty acids are a necessary component of any saponifiable lipid. In this chapter a few compounds have been included which do not have long enough fatty acid molecules to form real soaps since their salts in water form true solutions rather than colloidal micelles. With this one exception the above definition will be strictly followed. The saponifiable lipids are classified according to their structures into a few major categories:

Fatty acids
Simple lipids (fatty acid esters)
Phospholipids or phosphatides
Glycolipids

These categories are broken down into subgroups which will be described in the following sections.

FATTY ACIDS

All aliphatic carboyxlic acids may be described as "fatty acids," but the term is usually restricted to the longer chain members of the series which are practically insoluble in water but soluble in organic solvents. In this chapter the line will be arbitrarily drawn below the C_8 acids and the lower members included in Chapter 3.

The free acids or their salts are of much less frequent occurrence in the plant kingdom than are their esters which make up the other classes of saponifiable lipids. Nevertheless, occasional examples of unesterified acids are found, particularly in waxes. Fatty acids found in nature almost always have an even number of carbon atoms, but this generality is not followed without exception. All of the straight chain, odd-carbon acids from C_7 - C_{15} have been found free or as esters in higher plants. The vast majority of natural fatty acids have an unbranched carbon chain and differ from one another in chain length and degree of unsaturation. Oleic acid is the most widespread natural fatty acid, occurring in practically every natural lipid mixture. Palmitic acid is nearly as ubiquitous, and these two are then followed by the somewhat less common linoleic, palmitoleic, myristic, and stearic acids. In the structures shown in Table 1 no attempt is made to indicate *cis-trans* isomerism.

Other fatty acids are peculiar to lipids of plants of particular taxonomic groups rather than being widespread in the plant kingdom. They include acids with acetylenic unsaturation, hydroxyl groups, carbocyclic rings, and branched chains. Sometimes the hydroxy acids are found as inner esters or lactones. Examples of some of these more unusual fatty acids are listed in Table 2 with their place of occurrence in the plant kingdom.

Additional fatty acids which are limited in their occurrence will be mentioned where appropriate in the following sections of this chapter.

TABLE 1. SOME COMMON FATTY ACIDS

Name	Structure
Lauric	$CH_3(CH_2)_{10}COOH$
Myristic	$CH_3(CH_2)_{12}COOH$
Palmitic	$CH_3(CH_2)_{14}COOH$
Stearic	$CH_3(CH_2)_{16}COOH$
Arachidic	$CH_3(CH_2)_{18}COOH$
Behenic	$CH_3(CH_2)_{20}COOH$
Lignoceric	$CH_3(CH_2)_{22}COOH$
Palmitoleic	$CH_3(CH_2)_5CH = CH(CH_2)_7COOH$
Oleic	$CH_3(CH_2)_7CH = CH(CH_2)_7COOH$
Linoleic	$CH_3(CH_2)_4CH = CHCH_2CH = CH(CH_2)_7COOH$
Linolenic	$CH_3CH_2CH = CHCH_2CH = CHCH_2CH = CH(CH_2)_7COOH$
Elaeostearic	$CH_3(CH_2)_3CH = CHCH = CHCH = CH(CH_2)_7COOH$
Arachidonic	$CH_3(CH_2)_4CH = CHCH_2CH = CHCH_2CH = CHCH_2CH = CHCH_2(CH_2)_2COOH$
Erucic	$CH_3(CH_2)_7CH = CH(CH_2)_{11}COOH$

TRIGLYCERIDES

Triglycerides are esters of glycerol with three fatty acid molecules:

$$\begin{array}{l} \qquad\quad H_2C-O-\overset{O}{\overset{\|}{C}}-R \\ \qquad\quad\;\, | \\ R'-\overset{O}{\overset{\|}{C}}-O-CH \\ \qquad\quad\;\, | \\ \qquad\quad H_2C-O-\overset{O}{\overset{\|}{C}}-R'' \end{array}$$

The normal situation is for the three fatty acids to be different and the molecule therefore described as a "mixed triglyceride." Those which are solid at room temperature are called fats, whereas liquid triglycerides are called oils. Most natural fats and oils are not single compounds but mixtures of triglycerides, although one may be predominant. Chemically, fats contain a larger proportion of saturated fatty acids, and oils have more of the unsaturated acids. Oils are further subdivided into drying and non-drying oils. The former are oxidized in the air to form tough films which make them valuable in paints and varnishes. The latter, while they may be oxidized and become rancid, remain liquids.

TABLE 2. SOME UNUSUAL FATTY ACIDS, STRUCTURES AND OCCURRENCE

Name of Acid	Structure	Occurrence
tariric	$CH_3(CH_2)_{10}C{\equiv}C(CH_2)_4COOH$	*Picramnia* spp.
ximenynic	$CH_3(CH_2)_5CH{=}CHC{\equiv}C(CH_2)_7COOH$	*Ximenia* spp.
sterculic	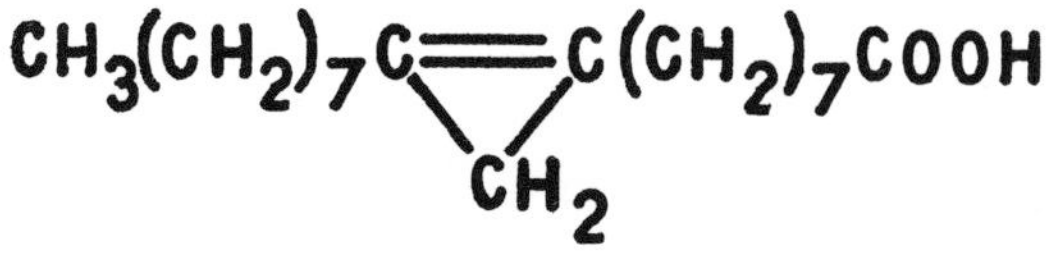 $CH_3(CH_2)_7C{=}C(CH_2)_7COOH$, with the two ring carbons bridged by CH_2 (cyclopropene ring)	*Sterculia* spp.
chaulmoogric	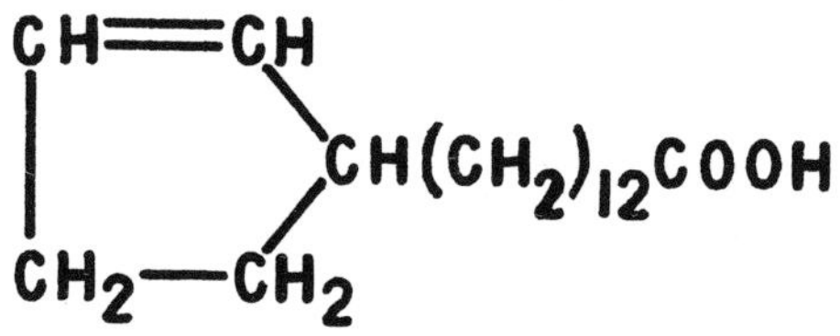 $CH{=}CH$ / $CH_2{-}CH_2$ ring joined to $CH(CH_2)_{12}COOH$ (cyclopentene ring)	*Flacourtiaceae*
ricinoleic	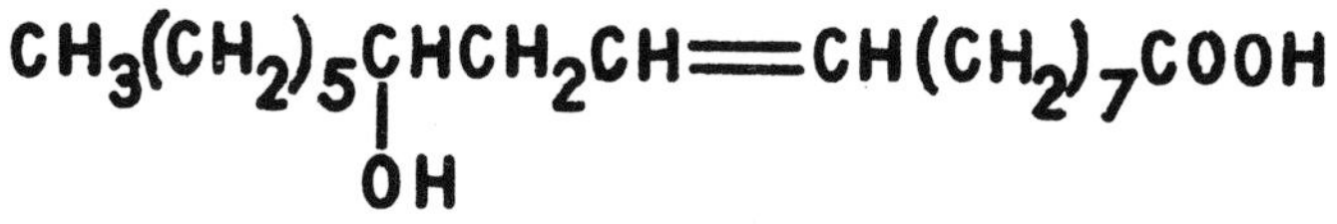 $CH_3(CH_2)_5CH(OH)CH_2CH{=}CH(CH_2)_7COOH$	*Ricinus communis*
vernolic	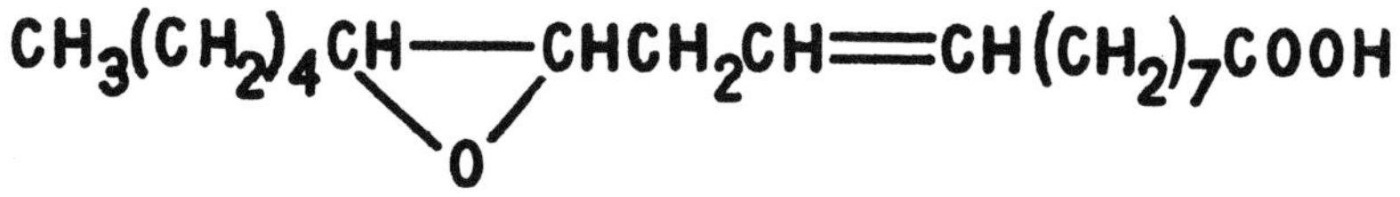 $CH_3(CH_2)_4CH{-}CHCH_2CH{=}CH(CH_2)_7COOH$, with the two CH carbons bridged by O (epoxide ring)	*Vernonia anthelmintica*
japanic	$HOOC(CH_2)_{19}COOH$	*Rhus* spp.
licanic	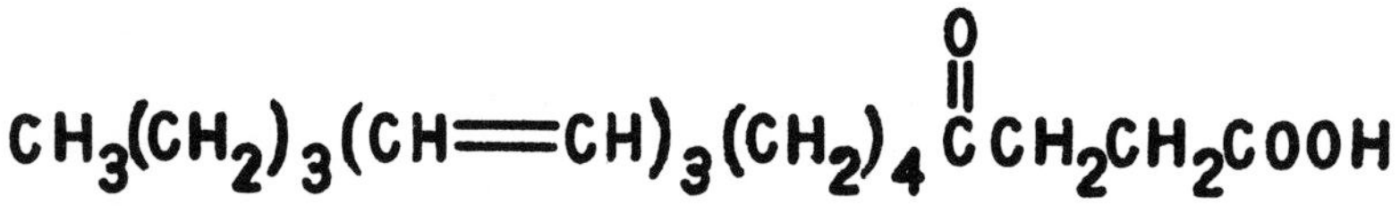 $CH_3(CH_2)_3(CH{=}CH)_3(CH_2)_4C({=}O)CH_2CH_2COOH$	*Licania rigida*

Chemically, the drying oils are characterized by having a high proportion of polyunsaturated acids such as linolenic. The edible oils are characterized rather by having acids such as oleic and palmitoleic. The oxidation of unsaturated fatty acids begins with the attack of oxygen on an allylic carbon atom to form a hydroperoxide:

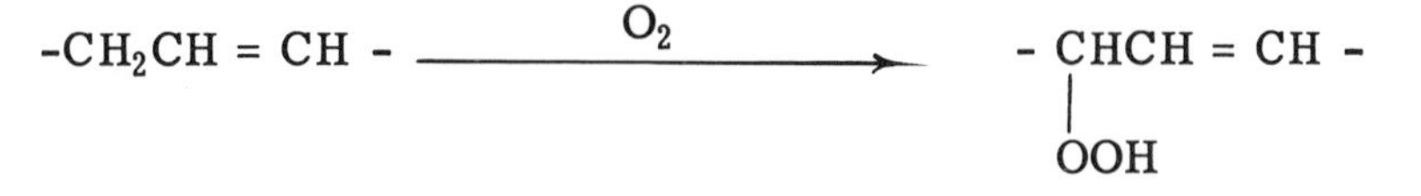

The hydroperoxide then undergoes secondary reactions to produce epoxides, glycols, and split products such as aldehydes and shorter chain carboxylic acids. It is these secondary products which are responsible for the rancid taste of oxidized fats and oils.

In plants fats and oils constitute important food storage materials, but they constitute a negligible fraction of the total lipids in such actively metabolizing organs as leaves (1). Their metabolic breakdown yields more energy per gram than that of any other storage material, and their insolubility in water avoids the osmotic problems associated with maintaining a high concentration of water soluble material in cells. The majority of energy yielded by fat breakdown is probably produced by conversion of the fat to acetyl-CoA and oxidation of this through the glyoxylate and citric acid cycles (Chapter 3).

Table 3 gives the fatty acid composition of some common fats and oils. Extensive surveys by Hilditch (cf. general references) and others have indicated a close relation between plant families and their seed glycerides when fatty acid components are tabulated quantitatively and compared to botanical classification.

OTHER FATTY ACID ESTERS

Besides the triglycerides, other simple esters of long-chain fatty acids are commonly found in plants. Whereas the triglycerides usually function as food storage components, the other fatty acid esters seem to be more concerned in protective coatings on leaves, fruits, stems, etc. They are chemical constituents of the substances known botanically as wax, cutin, cork, etc., although each of these substances, contains other types of compounds as well (cf. Chaps. 6, 8). Rarely, seeds are found which contain high-molecular weight esters used as food reserves, and some triglycerides resemble waxes in being found as coatings on fruit.

The most familiar ester components of plant waxes contain long chain alcohols combined with the fatty acids. The acids found in such waxes are generally longer chain compounds than the acids of triglycerides. The C_{24} - C_{36} acids are most common. The alcohols have the same range of chain-lengths, and both the alcohols and acids are usually saturated. Unsaturated alcohols are more common than unsaturated acids. Secondary alcohols and dihydroxy alcohols are also found occasionally. Small amounts of unesterified fatty acids and alcohols may be found in plant waxes.

As examples of some esters found in common plant waxes carnauba wax contains 75% myricyl cerotate; snow brush wax 80% of a mixture of ceryl palmitate and ceryl stearate.

Other variants on the long chain ester structure are found in certain plant waxes which have hydroxy acids (2). When these are present, esters may form between the carboxyl group and the hydroxyl group of the same acid or with the hydroxyl group of another acid. In the first case lactones are formed. An example is aparajitin from the leaf wax of *Clitoria ternatea*, which is also interesting for its branched chain structure:

TABLE 3. FATTY ACID COMPOSITION OF SOME VEGETABLE FATS AND OILS
Figures are approximate percentage by weight.

olive oil	saturated acids 12, oleic 80, linoleic 8
coconut oil	capric 12, lauric 45, myristic 17, palmitic 8
cacao butter	palmitic 24, stearic 35, oleic 38
peanut oil	palmitic 9, oleic 59, linoleic 21
castor oil	linoleic 5, ricinoleic 92
rape seed oil	oleic 17, linoleic 18, linolenic 1, erucic 49
cottonseed oil	palmitic 20, oleic 30, linoleic 45
soy bean oil	saturated acids 19, oleic 22, linoleic 49, linolenic 10
corn oil	saturated acids 15, oleic 24, linoleic 61
linseed oil	saturated acids 18, oleic 15, linoleic 15, linolenic 52

TABLE 4. SOME LONG CHAIN SATURATED ACIDS AND ALCOHOLS FOUND FREE OR ESTERIFIED IN PLANT WAXES

Number of Carbons	Acid	Alcohol
24	lignoceric	lignoceryl (n-tetrocosanol)
26	cerotic	ceryl (n-hexacosanol)
28	montanic	octacosyl (n-octacosanol)
30	melissic	n-myricyl (n-triacontanol)
32	lacceroic	n-lacceryl (n-dotriacontanol)
34	n-tetratriacontanoic	tetratriacontyl (n-tetratriacontanol)

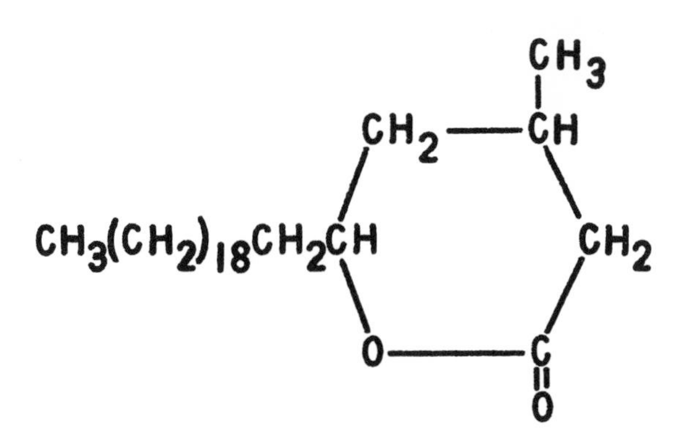

Macrocyclic lactones with a musk-like odor are exaltolide from *Angelica* roots and ambrettolide from seeds of *Hibiscus abelmoschus*.

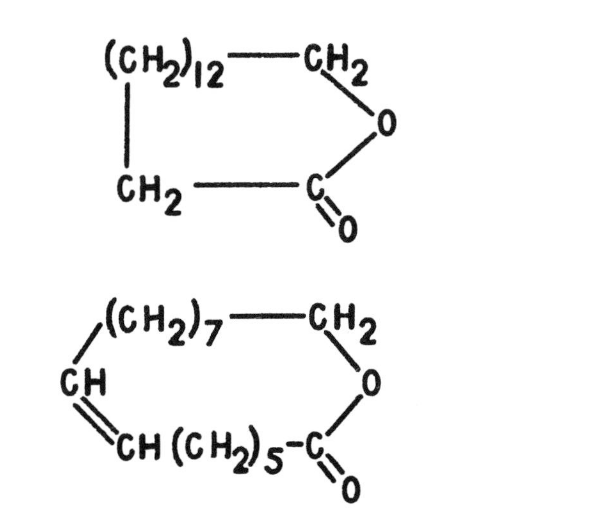

exaltolide

ambrettolide

Waxes containing polymeric esters formed by the linking of several ω-hydroxy acids to each other are especially prominent in the waxy coatings of conifer needles. The two most common acids found in such waxes are sabinic and juniperic:

$HOCH_2(CH_2)_{14}COOH$ juniperic acid

$HOCH_2(CH_2)_{10}COOH$ sabinic acid

The polymers may be linear or cyclic. The general term used for this type of wax constituent is "etholide" or "estolide".

The lipid constituents of cork and cuticle are known respectively as suberin and cutin. Cutin is tightly bound to other constituents within the cuticle layer and is therefore distinguished from easily-removed outer deposits of wax. The exact chemical nature of cutin and suberin remains obscure partly because the drastic chemical measures used in obtaining them may have caused serious degradation to occur. However, what evidence there is indicates that it is reasonable to group these substances with the high molecular weight esters. Hydrolysis of suberin yields a little glycerol but cutin does not. Cutin is also more resistant than suberin to attack by chemical reagents or enzymes. Suberin has been considered to be an impure form of cutin. Saponification of both substances yields several hydroxy fatty acids whose structures are not yet well established although they have been given names. Phloionic, phloionolic, phellonic and phellogenic acids have been isolated from saponified suberin and their structures established. Phloionic acid is also found in cutin.

$$HO(CH_2)_8\overset{OH}{\overset{|}{C}}H\overset{OH}{\overset{|}{C}}H(CH_2)_7COOH \text{ phloionolic acid}$$

$$HOCH_2(CH_2)_{20}COOH \text{ phellonic acid}$$

$$HOOC(CH_2)_7\overset{OH}{\overset{|}{C}}H\overset{OH}{\overset{|}{C}}H(CH_2)_7COOH \text{ phloionic acid}$$

$$HOOC(CH_2)_{20}COOH \text{ phellogenic acid}$$

Cutinic acid and cutic acid of cutin have been assigned the empirical formulas $C_{13}H_{22}O_3$ and $C_{26}H_{50}O_6$ and are evidently also hydroxy acids. It seems likely that cutin and suberin are complex polymeric esters similar to the etholides but possibly having additional ester linkages to other constituents of cuticle or cork such as lignin, cellulose, or tannins. Since the cutin and suberin acids which have more than one hydroxyl group may also form cross-linked polymers.

A group of relatively low molecular weight esters of acetylenic acids is characteristic of the family *Compositae*. Long-chain acetylenic C_{18} acids have already been mentioned as occurring in some triglycerides. The *Compositae* compounds are methyl esters of C_{10} acids. Two of the most widespread compounds in the family are the following:

$$CH_3CH = CH - C{\equiv}C - C{\equiv}C - CH = CH\overset{O}{\overset{\|}{C}}OCH_3$$

matricaria ester

$$CH_3CH_2CH_2C{\equiv}C - C{\equiv}C - CH = CH\overset{O}{\overset{\|}{C}}OCH_3$$

lachnophyllum ester

The composites also contain acetylenic alcohols and hydrocarbons which will be described in Chapter 6. Several reviews on natural acetylenic compounds have appeared recently (3, 4, 5, 6).

PHOSPHOLIPIDS OR PHOSPHATIDES

Several different types of phosphorus-containing lipids are found in plants. All are esters of phosphoric acid and long chain fatty acids. The simplest phospholipids are the phosphatidic acids which have fatty acid groups and phosphoric acid esterified with glycerol:

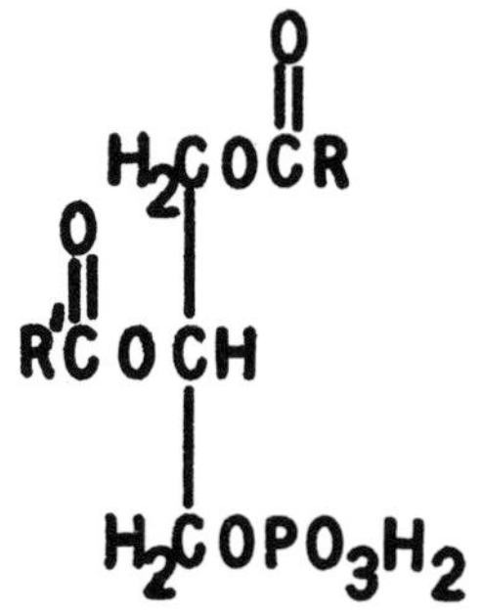

No extensive surveys have been made to indicate how widespread the phosphatidic acids are in plants. They have been isolated from spinach and cabbage leaves but may have been artifacts of the isolation procedure. Reports of the occurrences of phosphatidic acids in plants must be interpreted with caution since active hydrolytic enzymes are often present which would break down other phosphatides to phosphatidic acids when the tissue is disintegrated. The phosphatidic acids are oily liquids soluble in the usual fat solvents. Since they contain a large proportion of unsaturated fatty acids, they are readily oxidized in the air forming hard products which are insoluble in organic solvents. The barium and calcium salts are insoluble in water and alcohol but soluble in ether.

The best-known of all the phospholipids are lecithin and cephalin. These compounds include the phosphatidic acid structure but in addition contain a nitrogenous compound linked as an ester with the phosphate. In lecithin the nitrogen moiety is choline; in cephalin it is either ethanolamine or serine.

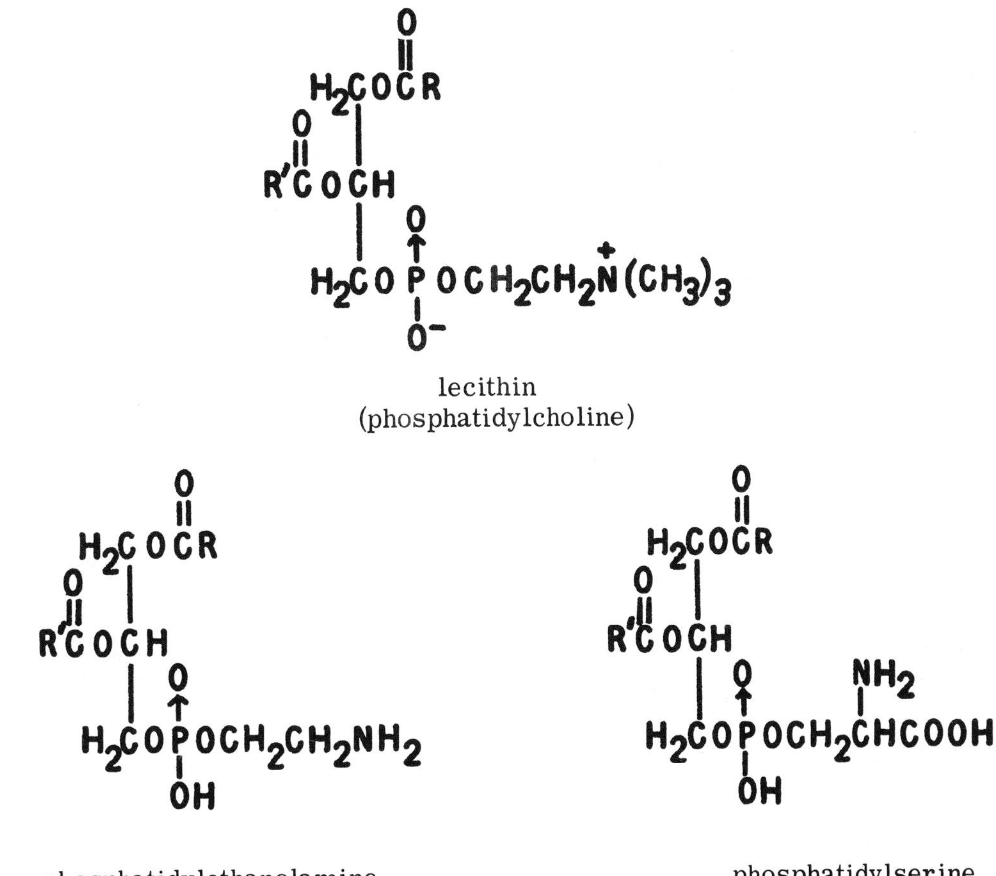

lecithin
(phosphatidylcholine)

phosphatidylethanolamine

phosphatidylserine

cephalins

Apparently at least one of the fatty acids in these compounds is always unsaturated. Lecithin and cephalin are colorless, waxy solids which rapidly oxidize and darken on exposure to light and air. They are soluble in the usual fat solvents with certain exceptions which have been used in separating them from each other. These solubilities may be summarized as follows:

Solvent	Lecithin	Cephalin
Chloroform	+	+
absolute ethyl ether	+	-
moist ethyl ether	+	+
benzene	+	+
alcohol	+	-
acetone	-	-
petroleum ether	+	+

Both substances are hygroscopic but form emulsions rather than true solutions in water. They may be precipitated from these solutions by adding acetone. In recent years, however, solvent fractionation methods of purification have been largely replaced by more effective procedures.

Other types of phospholipid have been found in plants, but much less is known about them. Phosphatidyl glycerol and diphosphatidyl glycerol have been found as major phospholipids in algae and higher plants, especially in chloroplasts (7, 8).

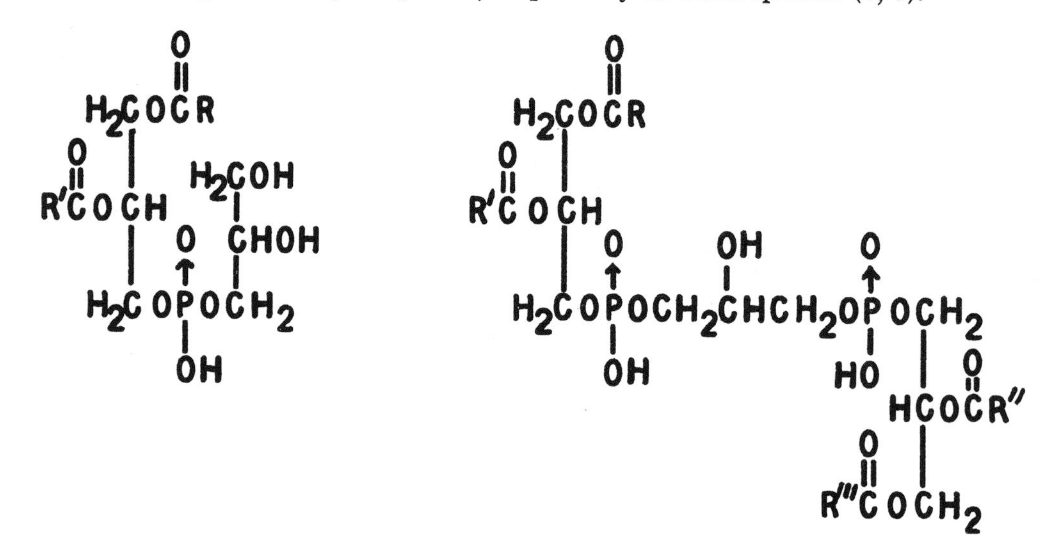

phosphatidyl glycerol diphosphatidyl glycerol

An inositol-containing lipid isolated by Woolley (9) and named lipositol was probably not pure but yielded on hydrolysis inositol, galactose, ethanolamine, oleic acid, phosphoric acid, and tartaric acid. Wagenknecht *et al.*, (10) have isolated from peas the calcium-magnesium salt of a phospholipid which is hydrolyzed to glycerol, inositol, phosphoric acid, C_{16} and C_{18} fatty acids. Phosphatidyl inositol makes up about 20% of the lipid of photosynthetic tissues (10a). Soybean lipids also contain a large percentage of inositol but are apparently more complex as indicated by the work of Carter *et al.*, (11, 12) who found on hydrolysis fatty acids, inositol, phosphoric acid, several sugars including glucosamine and a uronic acid, and a nitrogen base named "phytosphingosine" since it is similar but not identical to the sphingosine of animal tissues. Phytosphingosine appears to have the structure shown below:

$$CH_3(CH_2)_{13}\underset{|}{\overset{OH}{C}}H-\overset{OH}{\underset{|}{C}}H-\overset{NH_2}{\underset{|}{C}}HCH_2OH$$

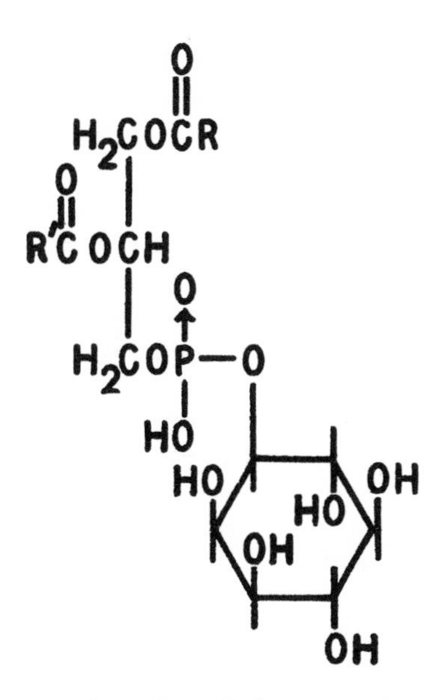

phosphatidyl inositol

The exact way in which these components are joined to form the lipid molecule is unknown. The accepted structure for sphingomyelin from animal tissues is shown below, and plant sphingolipids are presumed to bear some resemblance to it. However, animal sphingomyelin does not contain sugar units. Animal cerebrosides and gangliosides are nitrogenous lipids containing sugar units but no phosphorus.

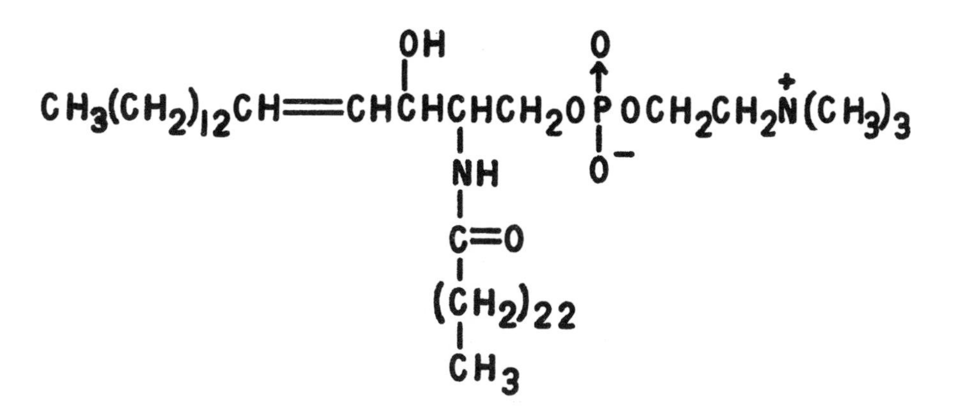

sphingomyelin (animal)

The lipositols and sphingolipids resemble the other phospholipids in many of their properties except for somewhat different solubilities. Since the solubilities are important for purification procedures, they will be described below under "Isolation".

The phospholipids are probably most important in cells because of their involvement in membrane structures and as bridges or binding agents between polar and non-polar cell constituents. This latter function is illustrated by the difficulty found in purifying many plant phospholipids since they are often tightly bound in complexes with carbohydrate and/or protein. The precise structure of such complexes is unknown. Proteolipids are defined as lipid-protein complexes with solubility properties like the lipids, whereas lipoproteins have solubility like the proteins. Bennet-Clark (13) has proposed a mechanism for salt uptake by cells which involves lecithin as a carrier of metal cations. Phospholipids reach their highest concentration in seeds (up to 2% of dry weight).

In addition to the general references, reviews of the phosphatides may be found in the papers of Sperry (14) and of Hörhammer and Wagner (15).

GLYCOLIPIDS

As has been noted in the previous section, some of the complex phospholipids contain sugar moieties. However, the term "glycolipid" is normally reserved for lipids containing sugar units but not phosphorus. Only recently has it become evident that such compounds are widely distributed in plants, especially in green leaves (7, 16). For example, in alfalfa galactosyl compounds are the major component of the lipid fraction. The general structure of a monogalactosyl glyceride is shown below. Higher homologues have as many as 5 galactose residues linked (1→6) to each other.

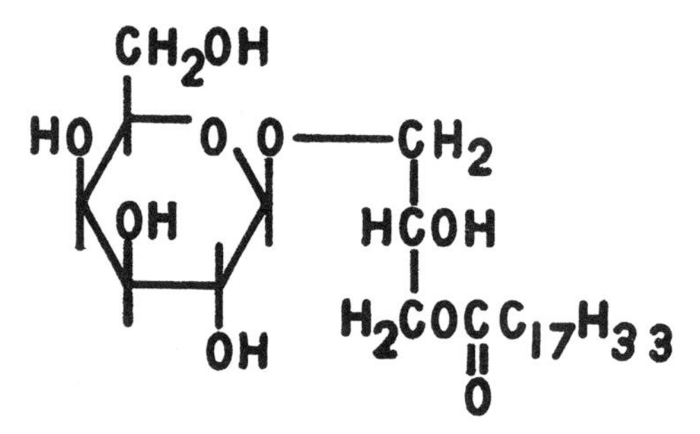

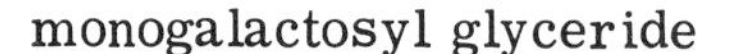
monogalactosyl glyceride

A sulfonic acid related to 6-deoxyglucose is present as the major anionic lipid in chloroplasts of many plants (17). A suggested structure is as follows:

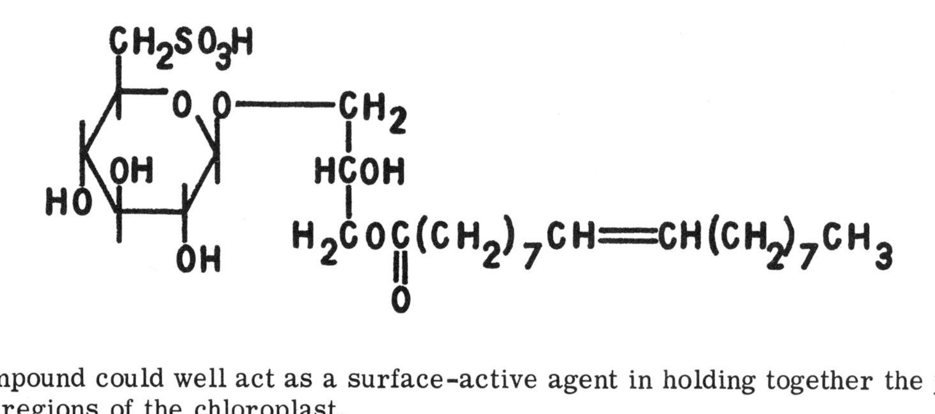

Such a compound could well act as a surface-active agent in holding together the polar and non-polar regions of the chloroplast.

Plant glycolipids differ from the animal cerebrosides in that the latter have sphingosine rather than glycerol. However, both the cerebrosides and plant glycolipids may be described as saponifiable lipids containing one or more sugar units but no phosphorus. True cerebrosides have been reported to occur in plants (18), but they have not been studied extensively.

ISOLATION

Isolation of the different categories of lipids has relied heavily on differences in their solubilities. As with many other plant products the first precaution to be observed is inactivation of degradative enzymes with heat before disintegration of the plant tissue. This precaution is especially necessary for the phospholipids. A second precaution which must be taken when isolating highly unsaturated lipids is to exclude oxygen and strong light.

The total lipid may be extracted from tissue with mixtures of methanol-chloroform, ethanol-chloroform, or ethanol-ether. Boiling solvents have often been used, but homogenization at room temperature offers less chance for degradation to occur. If only non-polar and unbound lipids are desired, the alcohol may be omitted from the extracting medium or solvents like benzene, petroleum ether, etc. employed. Lipid-protein or lipid-carbohydrate complexes may be insoluble in non-polar solvents. In the presence of alcohols these complexes are broken, so that the lipid extracted gives no indication as to how it may have been complexed *in situ*. On the other hand, proteo- or peptido- lipids are known which are soluble in lipid solvents but release amino acids on hydrolysis (19). In the presence of phospholipids many non-lipids are extracted into lipid solvents. They can be effectively removed by mixing a 2:1 chloroform-methanol extract with 0.2 its volume of water. After centrifuging or long standing to separate the layers, non-lipid material is found in the upper, aqueous layer (20). Proteolipids form a fluffy layer at the interface and can be separated from other constituents (21).

By addition of acetone to a lipid extract prepared as described above phospholipids (with small amounts of sterolins and some waxes) are largely precipitated. Triglycerides, other esters, sterols, terpenes, etc. remain in solution. However, if much triglyceride is present, it will carry some phospholipid with it into the acetone-soluble fraction. Fractionation of the phospholipid precipitate will depend to some extent on what types of components are present. If inositol lipids are desired, the other phospholipids can be removed by prolonged extraction with cold, glacial acetic acid and partition between glacial acetic acid and benzene. Inositol lipid goes into the benzene phase. After evaporation of the benzene, sterolins (if present) may be removed by extraction with a 2:1 ethanol-chloroform mixture leaving relatively pure inositol lipid (11). Another method for fractionation of the phospholipids depends on precipitating lecithin as a cadmium salt from alcoholic solution. The cadmium salt is subjected to further purification steps and finally the lecithin recovered by dissolving the salt in chloroform and shaking this solution with an equal volume of 30% methanol. Pure lecithin dissolves in the chloroform layer, and the cadmium chloride goes into the aqueous methanol. After removal of lecithin the remaining phospholipids may be fractionated by dissolving in chloroform and adding ethanol stepwise. Inositol lipids precipitate first followed by phosphatidylserine and finally phosphatidylethanolamine. These processes may be repeated or refined by using countercurrent distribution methods with hexane and methanol as solvents (22).

Going back to the solution of lipids remaining after removal of phospholipids, separation of these constituents in their original form is very difficult. Free fatty acids may be removed by extraction with sodium carbonate solution, long-chain hydrocarbons and alcohols as urea complexes (Chap. 6), and sterols as digitonides or tomatinides (Chap. 8). The lower terpenes and other volatile compounds may be removed by distillation (or steam distillation); higher terpenoid acids will be extracted with free fatty acids into sodium carbonate solution. The long-chain fatty acids may then be separated as urea complexes from the higher terpenoid acids (23). Glycolipids are not precipitated by acetone but can be separated from everything except triglycerides by partitioning the mixture of acetone-soluble components between methanol and heptane. Glycolipids (including sterolins) and triglycerides go into the methanol layer. Further separation depends on chromatography (24).

A mixture containing chiefly triglycerides and/or ester waxes may be separated into its ester components only by tedious and unsatisfactory procedures. Of most general application are fractional distillation at very low pressures or fractional crystallization from acetone at very low temperatures. The more usual procedure is to submit the esters to saponification and then identify the constituent acids and alcohols. This, of course, gives no information as to how they were originally combined. Triglycerides are saponified by refluxing for 1-2 hours with about five times their weight of 6% potassium hydroxide in 95% ethanol. The long chain ester waxes require more drastic conditions for complete hydrolysis---e. g. refluxing for 12 hours a solution of wax in benzene plus an equal volume of 10% KOH in alcohol. This difference in ease of hydrolysis makes it possible to remove some triglycerides from an ester wax by saponification without too much loss of the wax. The chief danger to be noted in saponification is that prolonged heating may cause isomeric charges in the double bond positions of polyunsaturated acids. It is sometimes recommended that lecithin be hydrolyzed by standing with N potassium hydroxide for 16 hours at 37° C.

After hydrolysis long chain alcohols resulting from saponification of ester waxes may be removed (along with any unsaponified material) by extraction with benzene, etc. The remaining mixture is then acidified and fatty acids extracted with ether.

Mixtures of long chain fatty acids either naturally occurring or derived by saponification can be separated by various crystallization and distillation procedures. A common method is to dissolve the fatty acids in acetone and cool to -60° to = -70° C. Polyunsaturated acids remain in solution while others crystallize out. Redissolving the precipitate and recrystallizing at -30° to -40° C. leaves most of the mono-unsaturated acids in solution. A final recrystallization from ether at -30° deposits most of the saturated acids. The separations are not perfect, but by repetition and combination with other methods a satisfactory fractionation can usually be achieved according to degree of unsaturation. Another type of separation depends on the fact that lead salts of the saturated acids are insoluble in ether or alcohol whereas those of the unsaturated acids are soluble. Further fractionation may be achieved by distillation of methyl esters of the acids under reduced pressure (0. 1-5. 0 mm. of mercury).

Chromatographic separation of the saponifiable lipids has not yet been widely applied although it is certain to become more prominent since it offers many advantages over solvent separation methods. Partition chromatography is apparently more useful than adsorption chromatography. Gas chromatography has also been successfully employed (25). Marinetti (26) has reviewed methods of phospholipid chromatography. Cole and Brown (27) have described a procedure for fractionating plant waxes by chromatography on alumina and silica gel. A general review of lipid chromatography on silicic acid has been prepared by Wren (28). Silicic acid chromatography is particularly useful for anionic lipids since less polar lipids move rapidly through the column. Thus phospholipids may be readily separated from other lipids and then further subdivided among themselves. A typical procedure would be to slurry the silica gel with chloroform-methanol 2:1, add the lipid solution in chloroform, and start development with pure chloroform. As non-polar lipids move through the column, the concentration of methanol in the developing solvent is gradually increased. Finally the most polar substances are eluted with pure methanol. Carroll (29) has suggested that Florisil offers many advantages over silicic acid as an adsorbent for lipid chromatography. Separations are similar but more convenient.

The elution peaks can often be recognized by measuring absorption at 300 mμ. This absorption is given by oxidation products of the unsaturated fatty acids when careful exclusion of oxygen is not practiced. Another way of identifying lipid-containing eluate fractions is to spot a small amount on a ferrotype plate. When the volatile solvent evaporates, small amounts of lipid are easily visible (30).

Although the above procedures have been written as though a given lipid mixture might contain every possible constituent, the situation in nature is seldom quite so discouraging. In many cases one lipid, or at least one type of lipid, will be predominant; and the problem is only to remove small amounts of a few other constituents. For instance, cuticle waxes may rise to the surface as a film if fruits, leaves, etc., are merely immersed for a few minutes in boiling water. Such a preparation would contain no phospholipids and probably only traces of triglycerides.

Procedures have not been given for preparation of the rarer types of lipids which have been mentioned. Since at the present state of our knowledge each one is a special case, the original papers on them should be consulted. Although suberin and cutin are hardly rare in the plant kingdom, they are practically defined by the arbitrary and involved methods by which they have been prepared, and small variations in experimental details might yield quite different products. For suberin see the paper of Zetsche and Rosenthal (31); for cutin the paper of Legg and Wheeler (32).

CHARACTERIZATION

Many common methods used for characterization of saponifiable lipids are well described in elementary texts of organic chemistry and biochemistry. They include such determinations as iodine number, saponification value, etc., and depend for their interpretation on a knowledge of what type of lipid is being dealt with. A recent journal tissue is devoted to reviews of methods of lipid analysis (33). Pertinent references are also listed periodically in The Journal of Lipid Research.

Several color tests are available to indicate what types of lipids may be present in a mixture. Phospholipids are indicated by color reactions for phosphorus such as may be given by adding ammonium molybdate solution and concentrated sulfuric acid to an ethereal solution. Glycolipids are indicated by positive tests for carbohydrate such as the Molisch reaction. For identification of other components the simplest procedure is probably saponification of the lipid mixture followed by separation of the non-saponifiable material. The latter may be tested for the presence of sterols, long-chain alcohols, hydrocarbons, etc. by methods described in the appropriate chapters. The presence of soap in the aqueous layer is obvious on shaking and indicates the presence of long chain fatty acids. After acidification of the saponification mixture and removal of the fatty acids, glycerol may be detected by evaporating to a small volume. If triglycerides or other glycerol derivatives were present in the original lipid, the odor of acrolein will be apparent on heating this concentrated solution strongly with sodium bisulfate. Sphingosine is released from sphingolipids only by a combination of basic and acid hydrolysis, but acidic hydrolysis alone produces a free amino group which may be detected by its color reaction with ninhydrin. The other types of nitrogenous compounds released on hydrolysis of phospholipids may be detected by methods described in Chapter 14. Ester waxes may be distinguished from triglycerides by the fact that after saponification long-chain alcohols appear in the benzene-soluble fraction and may be identified by methods described in Chapter 6. If the individual fatty acids are separated and identified, the appearance of acids containing more than 30 carbon atoms is also evidence for the presence of ester waxes.

Characterization by means of paper chromatography has not been of much value when applied to the triglycerides as such. However, Cormier *et al.* (34) have shown that triglycerides as a group can be separated from some other types of lipids on paper impregnated with silicic acid using as a solvent ether-petroleum ether-heptane 4:25:25. Identification was made by dipping in an alcoholic solution of Sudan black, which is tightly bound to lipids, and washing off background dye with alcohol at 50° C. Phospholipids have been separated and characterized also using paper impregnated with silicic acid and a solvent consisting of diisobutyl ketone-acetic acid-water 8:5:1 (26). Phosphatides are detected by spraying with the dye Rhodamine 6G and observing in ultra-violet light while the paper is still wet. Quantitative measurement is possible by eluting the spots and determining phosphorus in them. A more sensitive detection reagent which shows up all types of lipids is a dilute solution of protoporphyrin in hydrochloric acid (35). After washing off excess reagent, lipid spots appear brightly fluorescent in ultraviolet light. Free fatty acids may be separated by reversed phase chromatography using paper impregnated with rubber, silicones, paraffin oil, etc. General guides to paper chromatography give much useful information on these techniques. There are also recent papers by Chayen and Linday (36), and Ballance and Crombie (37). The latter authors were able to get good separation of C_{10}-C_{22} acids using paper impregnated with mineral oil and 70-95% acetic acid as the solvent. Spots were revealed by converting the acids to insoluble copper salts and then detecting copper with dithiooxamide. Sweeley and Moscatelli (38) have developed a method for microanalysis of sphingolipids in which the long-chain bases formed by hydrolysis are isolated and oxidized to aldehydes. The aldehydes can then be characterized by gas chromatography. Gas chromatography has also been successfully employed for the separation of fatty acids (or their methyl esters) (39). Thin layer chromatography of triglycerides and other fatty acid esters may replace paper chromatography since it offers several advantages (40, 41).

Spectral measurements have a special place in the characterization of saponifiable lipids. Compounds with conjugated unsaturations are the only lipids to show absorption peaks in the ultra-violet range from 210-400 mμ. The only common fatty acid with conjugated double bonds is elaeostearic; and fats containing it or other conjugated trienes show absorption at about 270 mμ. Conjugated dienes absorb at about 230 mμ, tetraenes at 310 mμ, and pentaenes at 330 mμ. Conjugated systems containing acetylenic bonds give about the same wavelength maxima as systems of ethylenic bonds, but they may be recognized by other spectral differences such as intensity and side bands. The ultraviolet spectrophotometry of fatty acids has been reviewed by Pitt and Morton (42). Ultraviolet spectrophotometry may also be applied to non-conjugated unsaturated compounds by first heating them 45 minutes at 180° C. in the presence of 7. 5% potassium hydroxide in glycerol or ethylene glycol. This treatment isomerizes 1, 4 unsaturated systems to conjugated 1, 3 systems which then show the absorption spectra described above. By observing the spectrum before and after isomerization both conjugated and non-conjugated constituents may be identified. This procedure can also be used for quantitative estimation by weighing the sample of fat and measuring extinction coefficients at the appropriate wavelengths for the different unsaturated acids.

METABOLIC PATHWAYS

The metabolic pathways for synthesis of the saponifiable lipids may be divided by considering the biosynthesis of the products formed on hydrolysis and then the assembly of these portions to make the complete lipid. Except for the fatty acids, biosynthesis of other lipid components is covered in other chapters. Reviews on fatty acid biosynthesis regularly appear in Annual Reviews of Biochemistry. Stumpf and Bradbeer (43) and Zill and Cheniae (44) have reviewed fat metabolism in higher plants, and most of the pathways summarized in Figures 5-1 and 5-2 will be found discussed in detail in their articles. Biosynthesis of phosphatides and triglycerides is reviewed by Kennedy (45).

In addition to the pathways shown in the diagram only a few points will be stressed here.

1. The conversion of fat to carbohydrate which is common in germinating seeds probably occurs by way of the glyoxylate cycle described in Chapter 3. Fatty acids are broken down to acetyl-CoA which enters the cycle and is converted by way of malate and the malic enzyme to phosphoenolpyruvate. Phosphoenolpyruvate enters the reversible glycolytic sequence shown in Chapter 2.
2. In fatty acid biosynthesis all intermediates are now regarded as bound to a multifunctional enzyme through a thioester bond. Coenzyme A functions only in feeding acetate and malonate to this system and in removing the final product as a CoA derivative which can be utilized in the various ways shown on the diagram (44).

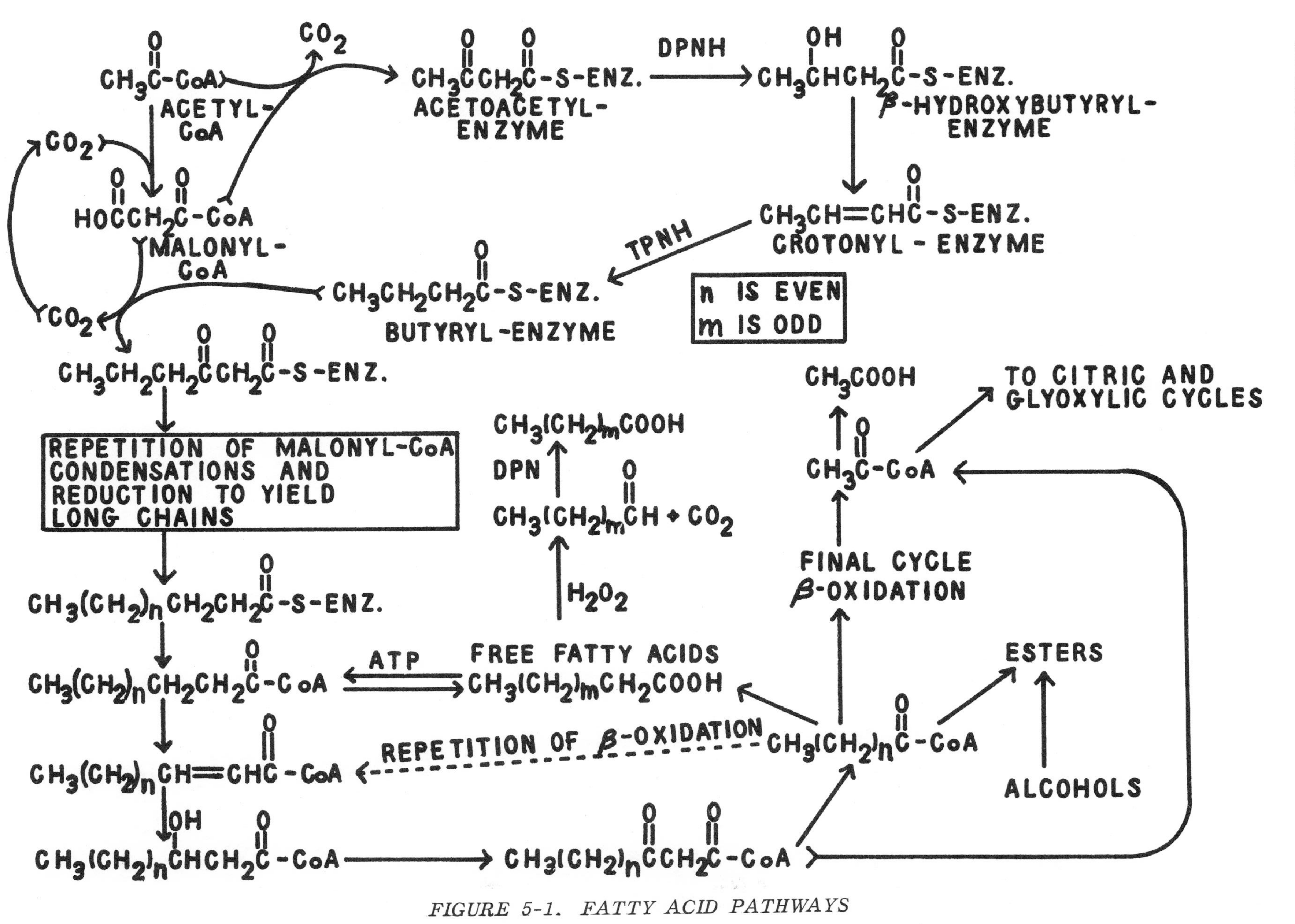

FIGURE 5-1. FATTY ACID PATHWAYS

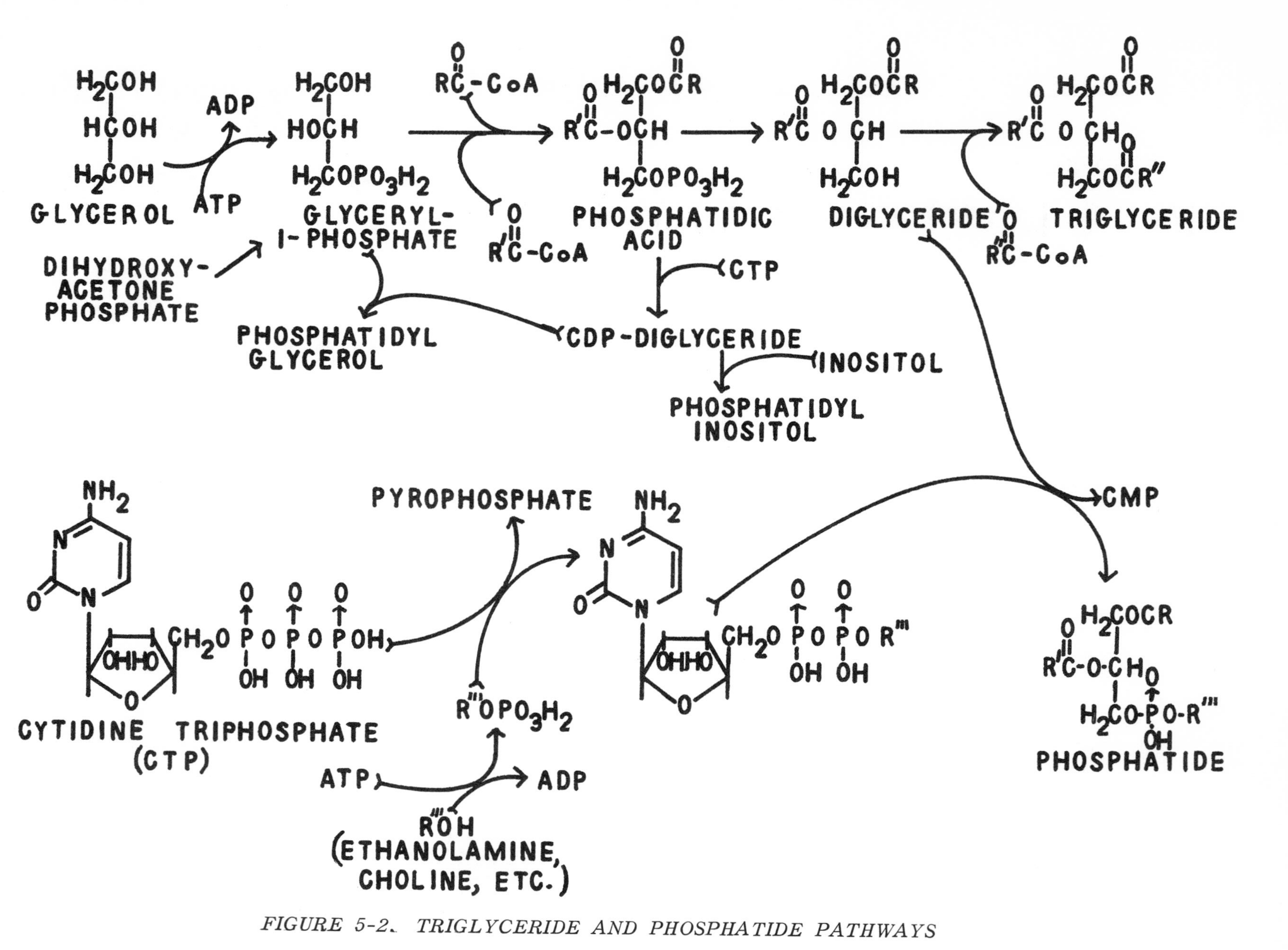

FIGURE 5-2. TRIGLYCERIDE AND PHOSPHATIDE PATHWAYS

3. The pathway of biosynthesis for the unsaturated fatty acids of higher plants is still obscure. In yeast it is well established that saturated acids are directly dehydrogenated to form the unsaturated ones (46), but in higher plants it appears that there may be separate pathways for the saturated and unsaturated acids (47, 48).
4. Phosphatidylserine is made by an exchange of serine for the ethanolamine moiety of phosphatidylethanolamine. Phosphatidylserine can also be decarboxylated directly to phosphatidylethanolamine. Phosphatidylethanolamine can be directly methylated to form lecithin. Thus, interconversions of these three types of phospholipids can occur without complete breakdown and resynthesis.
5. Practically nothing is known regarding biosynthesis of the sphingolipids and glycolipids although Benson *et al.* (16) have suggested that glycolipid sulfonic acids may be made by the oxidative splitting of a disulfide. Photosynthesizing *Chlorella* fix labelled CO_2 into glycolipids much more rapidly than into triglycerides (49).
6. The α-oxidation of long chain fatty acids seems to be a reaction peculiar to higher plants and is catalyzed by a peroxidase in the presence of other enzyme systems which can generate hydrogen peroxide. It is one way to account for the occasional appearance of long chain aliphatic compounds with an odd number of carbon atoms. See (50) for further details.

GENERAL REFERENCES

Cowan, J. C. and Carter, H. E., "Lipids" in Organic Chemistry 3 178, H. Gilman ed., John Wiley, N. Y., 1953.
Deuel, H. J., The Lipids 3 vols., Interscience Publishers, N. Y., 1951-1957.
Gunstone, F. D., An Introduction to the Chemistry of Fats and Fatty Acids, John Wiley, N. Y., 1958.
Hanahan, D. J., Lipide Chemistry, John Wiley, N. Y., 1960.
Hilditch, T. P., The Chemical Constitution of Natural Fats 3rd ed., John Wiley, N. Y., 1956.
Holman, R. T., Lundberg, W. O., and Malkin T. Progress in the Chemistry of Fats and Other Lipids. Pergamon Press, N. Y., Vol. 1 (1954)-Vol. 7 1960.
Kreger, D. R., "Wax" in Ruhland 10 249.
Lovern, J. A., The Chemistry of the Lipids of Biochemical Significance, 2nd ed., John Wiley, N. Y. (1957).
Mader, H., "Cutin" in Ruhland 10 270.
Mader, H., "Kork" in Ruhland 10 282.
Steiner, M. editor, The Metabolism of Fats and Related Compounds, Ruhland, 7.
Warth, A. H., The Chemistry and Technology of Waxes, 2nd ed., Reinhold, N. Y., 1956.

BIBLIOGRAPHY

1. Zill, L. P. and Harmon, E. A., Biochim. Biophys. Acta 57 573 (1962).
2. Downing, D. T., Revs. Pure Appl. Chem. 11 196 (1961).
3. Bohlmann, F. and Mannhardt, H. J., Fortscher. Chem. Org. Naturstoffe, 14 1 (1957).
4. Meade, E. M., Prog. Chem. Fats Other Lipids 4 45 (1957).
5. Gunstone, F. D., Prog. Org. Chem. 4 1 (1958).
6. Jones, E. R. H. Proc. Chem. Soc. 1960 199.
7. Kates, M., Biochim. Biophys. Acta 31 315 (1960).
8. Benson, A. A. and Strickland, E. H., Biochim. Biophys. Acta 41 328 (1960).
9. Woolley, D. W., J. Biol. Chem. 147 581 (1943).
10. Wagenknecht, A. C., Lewin, L. M. and Carter, H. E., J. Biol. Chem. 234 2265 (1959).
10a. LePage, M., Mumma, R. and Benson, A. A., J. Am. Chem. Soc. 82 3713 (1960).
11. Carter, H. E., Celmer, W. D , Lands, W. E., Mueller, K. L. and Tomizawa, H. H., J. Biol. Chem. 206 613 (1954).
12. Carter, H. E., Celmer, W. D., Galanos, D. S., Gigg, R. H., Lands, W. E. M., Law, J. H., Mueller, K. L., Nakayama, T., Tomizawa, H. H., and Weber, E., J. Am. Oil Chemists Soc. 35 335 (1958).

13. Bennet-Clark, T., Chem. and Mode of Action of Plant Growth Substances, Proc. Symposium, London 1955 284.
14. Sperry, W. M., editor, Fed. Proc. 16 816 (1957).
15. Hörhammer, L. and Wagner, H., Deut. Apothek.-Ztg. 97 893 (1957).
16. Benson, A. A., Daniel, H. and Wiser, R., Proc. Nat. Acad. Sci. U. S., 45 1582 (1959).
17. Miyano, M. and Benson, A. A., J. Am. Chem. Soc. 84 59 (1962).
18. Carter, H. E., Hendry, R. A., Nojima, S., Stanacev, N. Z., Biochim. Biophys. Acta 45 402 (1960).
19. Hawthorne, J. N. and Chargaff, E., J. Biol. Chem. 206 27 (1954).
20. Folch, J., Lees, M. and Stanley, G. H. S., J. Biol. Chem. 226 497 (1957).
21. Zill, L. P. and Harmon, E. A., Biochim. Biophys. Acta 53 579 (1961).
22. McGuire, T. A. and Earle, F. R., J. Am. Oil Chemists Soc. 28 328 (1951).
23. Schlenk, H., Prog. Chem. Fats Other Lipids 2 243 (1954).
24. Carter, H. E., Ohno, K., Nojima, S. Tipton, C. L. and Stanacev, N. Z., J. Lipid Res. 2 215 (1961).
25. Beerthuis, R. K. and Keppler, J. G., Nature 179 731 (1957).
26. Marinetti, G. V., J. Lipid Res. 3 1 (1962).
27. Cole, L. J. N. and Brown, J. B., J. Am. Oil Chemists Soc. 37 359 (1960).
28. Wren, J. J., J. Chromatog. 4 173 (1960).
29. Carroll, K. K., J. Lipid Res. 2 135 (1961).
30. Lands, W. E. M. and Dean, C. S., J. Lipid. Res. 3 129 (1962).
31. Zetsche, F. and Rosenthal, G., Helv. chim. Acta 10 346 (1927).
32. Legg, H. V. and Wheeler, R. V., J. Chem. Soc. 1925 1412.
33. __________ J. Am. Oil Chemists' Soc. 38 534-736 (1961).
34. Cormier, M., Jouan, P. and Girre, L., Bull. soc. chim. biol. 41 1037 (1959).
35. Sulya, L. L. and Smith, R. R., Biochem. Biophys. Res. Comms. 2 59 (1960).
36. Chayen, R. and Linday, E. M., J. Chromatog. 3 503 (1960).
37. Ballance, P. E. and Crombie, W. M., Biochem. J. 69 632 (1958).
38. Sweeley, C. C. and Moscatelli, E. A., J. Lipid Research 1 40 (1959).
39. James, A. T., Methods of Biochemical Analysis 8 1 (1960).
40. Mangold, H. K. and Kammereck, R., Chem. and Ind. 1961 1032.
41. Vioque, E. and Holman, R. T., J. Am. Oil Chemists' Soc. 39 63 (1962).
42. Pitt, G. A. J. and Morton, R. A., Prog. Chem. Fats Other Lipids 4 227 (1957).
43. Stumpf, P. K. and Bradbeer, C., Ann. Rev. Plant Physiol. 10 197 (1959).
44. Zill, L. P. and Cheniae, G. M., Ann. Rev. Plant Physiol. 13 225 (1962).
45. Kennedy, E. P. Fed. Proc. 20 934 (1961).
46. Bloch, K., Barnoowsky, P., Goldfine, H., Lennarz, W. J., Light, R., Norris, A. T. and Scheuerbrandt, G., Fed. Proc. 20 921 (1961).
47. Barron, E. J. and Stumpf, P. K., J. Biol. Chem. 237 PC 613 (1962).
48. James, A. T., Biochim. Biophys. Acta 57 167 (1962).
49. Ferrari, R. A. and Benson, A. A., Arch, Biochem. Biophys. 93 185 (1961).
50. Martin, R. O. and Stumpf, P. K., J. Biol. Chem. 234 2548 (1959).

Chapter 6
MISCELLANEOUS UNSAPONIFIABLE LIPIDS

The compounds grouped together in this chapter are very different in most chemical properties, but similar in the fact that they are soluble in lipid solvents rather than in water and not saponified by alkali. The anthraquinones fit the above description, however, they normally occur in plants not free but as water-soluble glycosides. All of the compounds included appear to be biosynthetically related in being derived by condensation of several molecules of acetate (or, more specifically, malonyl-coenzyme A). Thus they are also closely related to the long chain fatty acids discussed in Chapter 5. Speculation regarding biosynthesis of all such polyacetate compounds may be found in articles by Birch (1, 2). Because of the diversity of properties shown by compounds in this chapter discussions of isolation, characterization and biosynthesis are included under each separate section rather than for the chapter as a whole.

LONG CHAIN HYDROCARBONS ALCOHOLS AND KETONES

The most familiar long-chain aliphatic compounds are the fatty acids discussed in Chapter 5, and it is not often realized that they are only one representative of this class of plant constituents. The normal, aliphatic hydrocarbons found in plants usually have an odd number of carbon atoms, and it seems evident that they are derived by loss of carbon dioxide from even-carbon fatty acids:

$$CH_3(CH_2)_nCOOH \rightarrow CH_3(CH_2)_{n-1}CH_3 + CO_2$$

Tracer experiments have supported this pathway (3). The lowest natural member of this group, n-heptane, occurs as a constituent of the turpentine from several species of pine. The turpentines of *Pinus jeffreyi* and *P. sabiniana* are nearly pure n-heptane and contain no terpene hydrocarbons. Higher molecular weight hydrocarbons are often found in plant cuticle and pollen waxes where their chainlength generally falls in the range C_{25} - C_{37}. Commercial candelilla wax from *Euphorbia* spp. contains 50-60% n-hentriacontane ($C_{31}H_{64}$). Cuticle waxes of several common fruits have n-nonacosane ($C_{29}H_{60}$). The unsaponifiable material in olive oil contains hydrocarbons ranging from C_{13} - C_{28}. Unsaturated, normal, aliphatic hydrocarbons occur more rarely but are known. The horsetail, *Equisetum palustre,* contains a hydrocarbon with the empirical formula $C_{21}H_{42}$ -- thus one double bond (4); Costus oil *(Saussurea lappa)* has aplotaxene (heptadeca-1, 8, 11, 14-tetraene) (5); and five acetylenic hydrocarbons have been found in *Coreopsis* spp. (6). These latter compounds are interesting because of the widespread occurrence of acetylenic derivatives in the *Compositae.* All five of the coreopsis compounds are C_{13} hydrocarbons. One was shown to have the following structure:

$$CH_2 = CH - CH = CH - C \equiv C - C \equiv C - C \equiv C - CH = CHCH_3$$

Similar compounds seem to occur in other composites as well, and some contain a benzene ring at one end of the aliphatic chain, e.g.:

$$-C\equiv C-C\equiv C-CH=CHCH_3$$

Several of these highly unsaturated, conjugated compounds show light absorption in the visible region and may therefore be classed as plant pigments which are similar in color and other properties to some carotenoids.

Long-chain aliphatic alcohols and ketones are also frequent constituents of plant waxes. The alcohols almost always have an even number of carbons like the fatty acids, whereas the ketones have an odd number like the hydrocarbons. Long-chain alcohols which occur in the form of esters are discussed in Chapter 5. The unesterified alcohols are particularly common in the leaf waxes of monocots but also appear in other types of plant waxes. Unsaturated, long chain alcohols are uncommon in plants, but a few have been reported. Sugar cane wax is unusual in containing polymeric, long chain aldehydes (7). Some examples of the occurrence of these compounds are summarized in Table 1. Long-chain acetylenic alcohols and ketones are of interest because of their pronounced pharmacological effects. The first acetylenic compound to be isolated from plants, carlina oxide from *Carlina acaulis*, is strongly toxic to animals and also bacteriocidal.

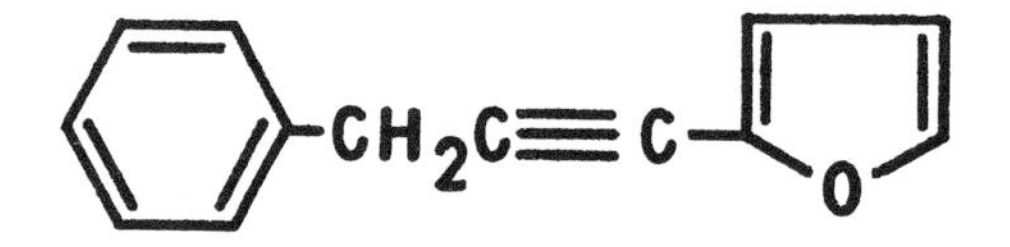

It appears related to an acetylenic alcohol found as an acetate in *Coreopsis:*

$$-C\equiv C-C\equiv C-CH=CHCH_2OH$$

Both of these aromatic compounds could be derived by ring closure from a C_{13} alcohol also found as an acetate in *Carlina acaulis:*

$$CH_2=CHCH=CH-C\equiv C-C\equiv C-C\equiv CCH=CHCH_2OH$$

The roots of several umbelliferous plants owe their great toxicity to long-chain acetylenic alcohols, of which the following are examples:

$$HOCH_2CH_2CH_2C\equiv C-C\equiv C(CH=CH)_3\overset{\overset{OH}{|}}{C}HCH_2CH_2CH_3$$

cicutoxin *(Cicuta virosa)*

$$HOCH_2CH=CHC\equiv C-C\equiv CCH=CHCH=CHCH_2CH_2\overset{\overset{OH}{|}}{C}HCH_2CH_2CH_3$$

oenanthotoxin *(Oenanthe crocata)*

TABLE 1.

Compound	Structure	Source
octanol	$CH_2(CH_2)_6CH_2OH$	fruit of *Heracleum gigantum*
dodecanol	$CH_3(CH_2)_{10}CH_2OH$	cuticle wax of *Rhamnus purshiana*
hexacosanol (ceryl alcohol)	$CH_3(CH_2)_{24}CH_2OH$	many cuticle waxes
octacosanol	$CH_3(CH_2)_{26}CH_2OH$	several cuticle waxes
triacontanol (melissyl alcohol)	$CH_3(CH_2)_{28}CH_2OH$	several cuticle and leaf waxes
takakibyl alcohol	$CH_3(CH_2)_{42}CH_2OH$	*Sorghum vulgare*
10-nonacosanol	$CH_3(CH_2)_8CHOH(CH_2)_{18}CH_3$	apple cuticle wax
11-eicosenol	$CH_3(CH_2)_7CH=CH(CH_2)_9CH_2OH$	*Simmondsia chinensis*
15-nonacosanone	$CH_3(CH_2)_{13}CO(CH_2)_{13}CH_3$	*Brassica* spp.

Long-chain acetylenic ketones are also found in several plants and are apparently less toxic than the alcohols. Two examples follow:

$$CH_3C{\equiv}C-C{\equiv}C-C{\equiv}CCH=CH\ CH_2CH_2\overset{O}{\overset{\|}{C}}CH_2CH_3$$

artemisia ketone *(Artemisia vulgaris)*

$$CH_3CH=CH-C{\equiv}C-C{\equiv}CCH=CHCH=CHCH_2CH_2\overset{O}{\overset{\|}{C}}CH_2CH_2CH_3$$

oenanthetone *(Oenanthe crocata)*

Unfortunately the name "artemisia ketone" has also been given to a terpenoid from the same plant (cf. Chap. 8).

All of these long-chain compounds show physical properties similar to the fatty acids but are less polar and less soluble in the common lipid solvents. The C_{24} alcohol is soluble in benzene and chloroform at room temperature, but the longer chain alcohols and ketones dissolve in these solvents only when hot and then only to a limited degree. The aliphatic hydrocarbons may be dissolved in such solvents as petroleum ether or carbon disulfide.

Isolation of these compounds is usually carried out by solvent extraction, steam distillation or fractional distillation at low pressures. Heating operations should, however, be avoided in isolation of the highly unsaturated, acetylenic compounds which are often very unstable. The formation of urea adducts is a characteristic property of compounds with long, aliphatic carbon chains and may be used to separate them from other compounds (e.g. sterols) with similar solubility. To some extent this method may also be used for the separation of different classes of aliphatic compounds since they differ in the ease with which the adducts are formed and decompose. Completely saturated hydrocarbons react most readily and form the most stable complexes whereas the conjugated acetylenic compounds may show practically no tendency to complex formation. Oxygenated derivatives react less readily than corresponding hydrocarbons. Urea inclusion methods are also discussed in Chapters 5 and 8 where methods are described in more detail and references given. Final purification is effectively carried out by adsorption chromatography on alumina using such solvents as petroleum ether or benzene. Since these compounds are not colored or fluorescent, bands of them on a column may be detected by using alumina impregnated with morin and observing quenching bands in ultraviolet light (8), or fractions may be collected arbitrarily and each one analyzed.

Characterization of these long-chain aliphatic compounds is made difficult by their low reactivity. Even the alcohols and ketones react only slowly with usual hydroxyl and carbonyl reagents. A method which combines identification of the components with a partial separation was developed by Chibnall *et al.* (9). In this procedure an unsaponifiable lipid mixture is heated with phthalic anhydride in pyridine to form acid phthalates of the alcohols. Esters of the primary alcohols are precipitated by pouring the reaction mixture into dilute hydrochloric acid and, after removal of excess reagents, are converted to sodium salts which are insoluble in water. The original primary alcohols may be regenerated by saponification. After removal of the sodium salts, excess pyridine, and phthalic anhydride, any residue (which would contain hydrocarbons, ketones and sodium salts of the secondary hydrogen phthalates) is dissolved in ether and crystallized from boiling alcohol. Ketones and hydrocarbons separate out. Sodium salts of the secondary alcohol phthalates remain dissolved in alcohol but may be precipitated by adding benzene and then crystallized from ethanol-benzene (4:1). Ketones may be separated from hydrocarbons by reacting them with hydroxylamine to form oximes which are more soluble than the hydrocarbons in ether-acetone.

Kaufmann and Kessen (10) have described a procedure whereby long-chain aliphatic alcohols are converted to urethanes and these chromatographed on paper impregnated with undecane, using acetic acid/acetonitrile 3:2 as the mobile phase. Spots were detected by forming mercury complexes and showing up the mercury with hydrogen sulfide.

Gas chromatography has recently demonstrated its great usefulness in separating and identifying leaf wax hydrocarbons (11, 12). The hydrocarbons can first be separated as a group from oxygenated compounds by chromatography on alumina (12).

Spectral measurements have limited usefulness for characterization of these compounds. Where conjugated unsaturation is present, it may be detected by ultraviolet spectra as described in Chapter 5. Infrared spectroscopy may be used to determine whether hydroxyl or carbonyl groups are present. X-ray crystallography has been very useful in proving the structure of certain natural, long-chain alcohols, but discussion of this specialized technique is beyond the scope of this book.

There is no real biochemical evidence regarding the biosynthetic pathways of long-chain, aliphatic hydrocarbons, alcohols and ketones; but it seems evident that they are closely related to the fatty acids, whose biosynthesis is well studied. It is likely that the alcohols and hydrocarbons are made respectively by reduction and decarboxylation of the fatty acids. The few ketones known may possibly be made by decarboxylation of keto acids since, like the hydrocarbons, they have an odd-numbered carbon chain. It is usually believed that following each two-carbon addition in the build-up of fatty acids, reduction of the β-carbonyl group occurs to form a saturated acid (cf. Chapter 5). If all the steps in this reduction are not carried out, keto compounds, hydroxyl compounds, or unsaturated compounds would result. If chain building went on through several stages without reduction, a β-polycarbonyl system might result, i. e.:

$$RCH_2\overset{O}{\overset{\|}{C}}CH_2\overset{O}{\overset{\|}{C}}CH_2\overset{O}{\overset{\|}{C}}CH_2C\text{-S-Enzyme}$$

Partial reduction could then give rise to polyhydroxy or polyunsaturated systems. Acetylenic bonds could be introduced by dehydration of the enol form of a carbonyl compound:

$$RCH_2\overset{O}{\overset{\|}{C}}CH_2\overset{O}{\overset{\|}{C}}OH \rightarrow RCH=\overset{OH}{\overset{|}{C}}CH_2\overset{O}{\overset{\|}{C}}OH \rightarrow RC\equiv CCH_2\overset{O}{\overset{\|}{C}}OH$$

The above speculation provides reasonable pathways of synthesis for most natural compounds in this group although there are occasional discrepancies such as the occurrence of even-carbon chain hydrocarbons or the appearance of oxygen attached to a carbon which would be expected to come from the methyl group of acetic acid. Obviously much research is needed in this area of biochemistry.

PHLOROGLUCINOL DERIVATIVES

A variety of natural products contain the phloroglucinol nucleus in their structure.

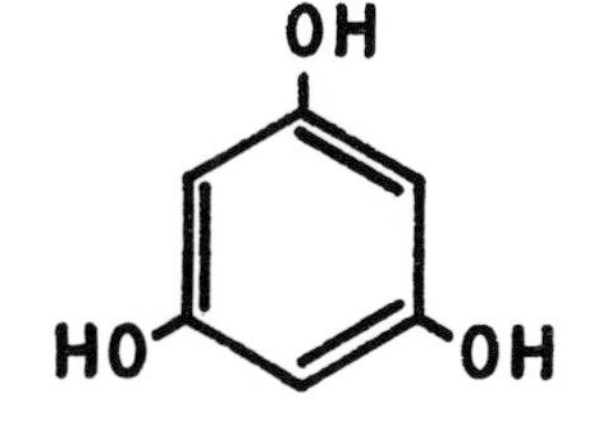

phloroglucinol

The most familiar of such compounds are the flavonoids discussed in Chapter 9. According to the hypothesis of Birch (1, 2) all compounds containing this nucleus may be regarded as derived from three molecules of acetic acid, and this scheme has been corroborated using labelled acetate for the phloroglucinol nucleus of the flavonoids.

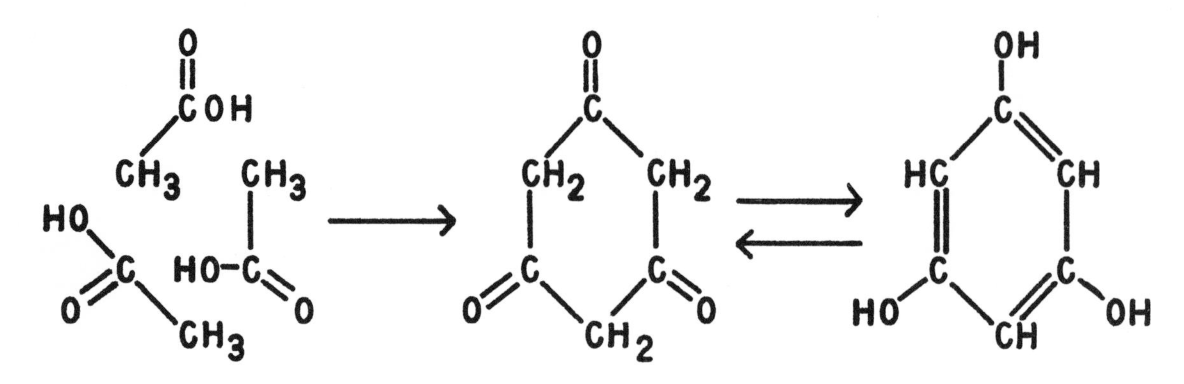

As indicated above phloroglucinol may be represented as a tautomeric triketone, and many reactions of phloroglucinol derivatives are best understood by reference to this ketone structure.

Old reports of the widespread occurrence of free phloroglucinol in plants have not been confirmed, and most such reports are questionable since the tests used give a positive result for complex phloroglucinol derivatives as well as for the compound itself. The simplest, natural phloroglucinol derivatives are a group of cyclic triketones (phloroglucinol tautomers) which are widespread in ferns of the family *Pteridaceae* but also found in essential oils of some angiosperms. Plants containing such compounds have been used for centuries as antihelmintic drugs, and the compounds have also been shown to possess insecticidal and bacteriocidal activity (13). The bitter substances found in hops *(Humulus lupulus)* have isoprenoid side chains attached to the phloroglucinol nucleus, or to a cyclopentatrione ring (14) which can also be regarded as derived from 3 acetate units. These compounds are important for their antimicrobial action as well as the flavor which they give to beer. A general review on natural phloroglucinol derivatives has been presented by Hassall (15). Some examples of these compounds and their natural occurrence are given in Table 2.

The essential oil of *Backhousia angustifolia* contains compounds obviously related to the above structures but lacking one phenolic hydroxyl group, e.g.:

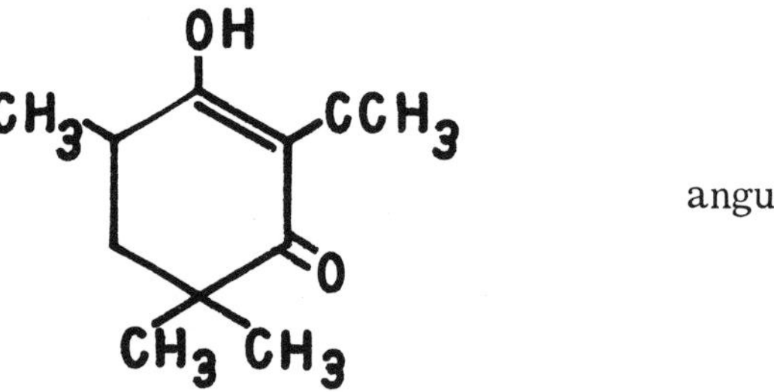

angustione

Several generalizations can be made regarding these structures:

1. All three hydroxyl groups of the phloroglucinol nucleus are never free. In some cases loss of available hydrogens stabilizes the keto form; frequently one hydroxyl group is methylated.

TABLE 2. SOME NATURALLY OCCURRING PHLOROGLUCINOL DERIVATIVES

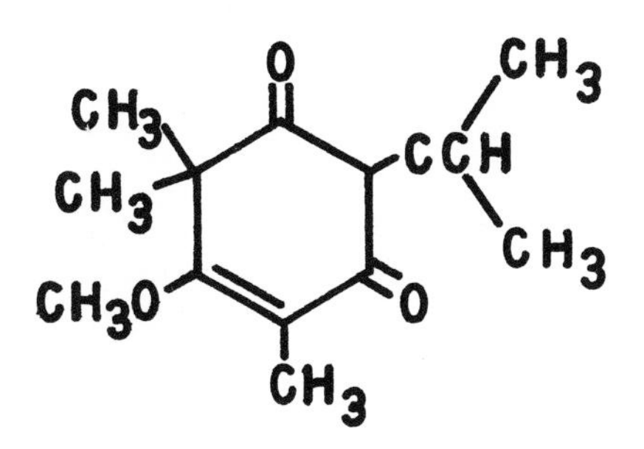

tasmanone (essential oil of *Eucalyptus risdoni*)

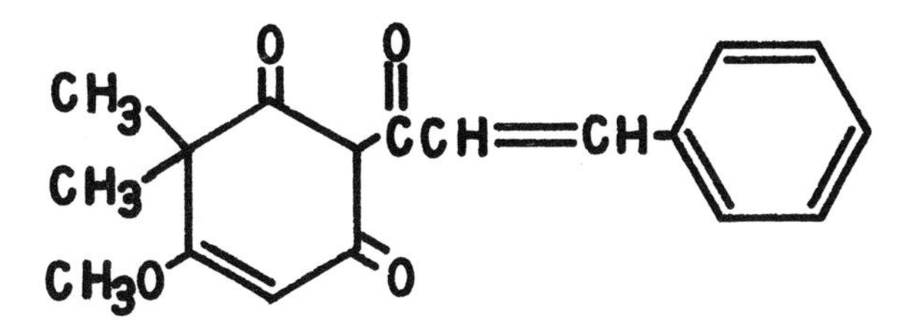

ceroptene (coating on fronds of *Pityrogramma triangularis*)

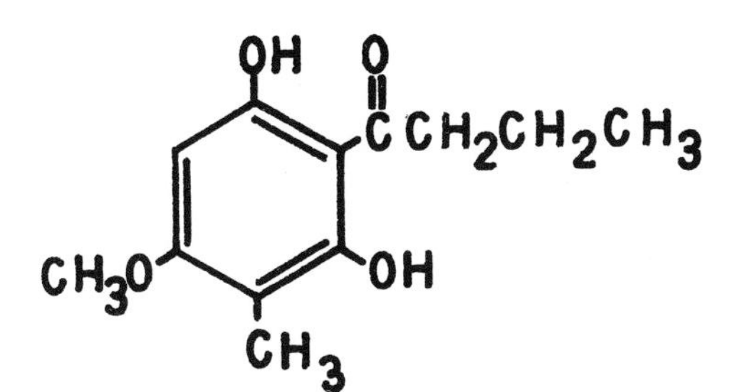

aspidinol (rhizomes of *Aspidium* spp.)

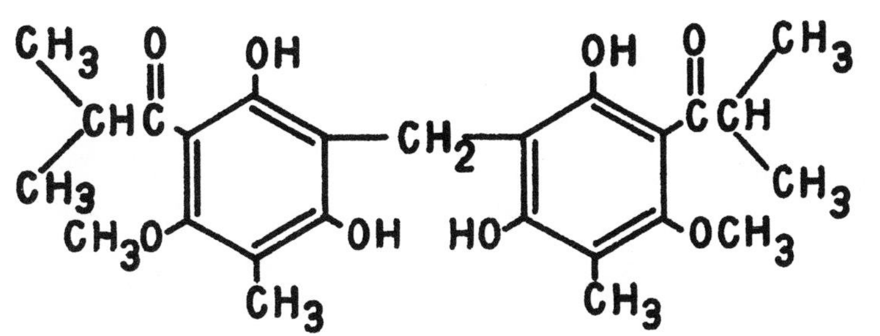

α-kosin (flowers of *Hagenia abyssinica*)

Table 2. Continued

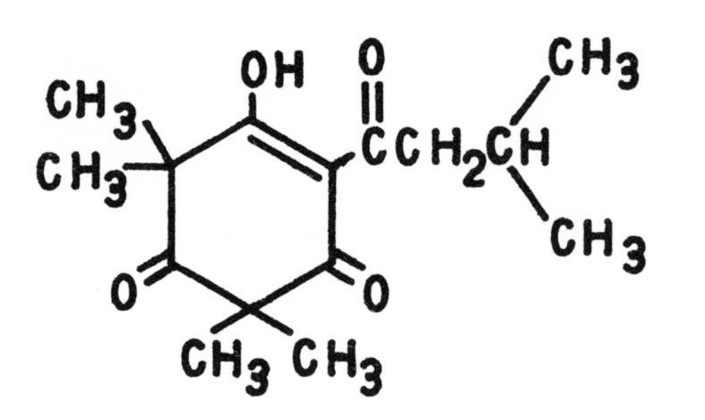

leptospermone (essential oil of *Leptospermum* spp.)

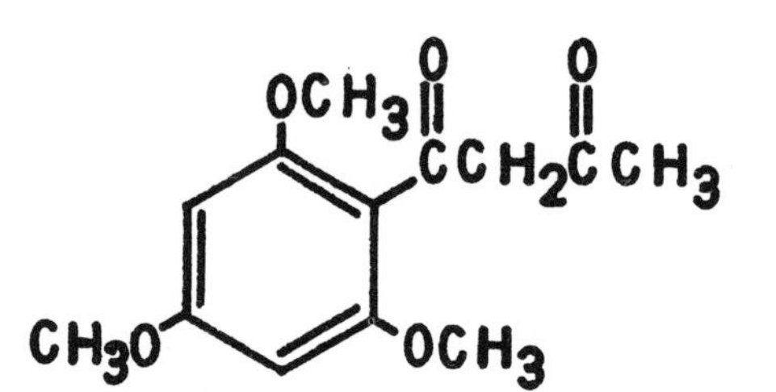

eugenone (essential oil of *Eugenia caryophyllata*)

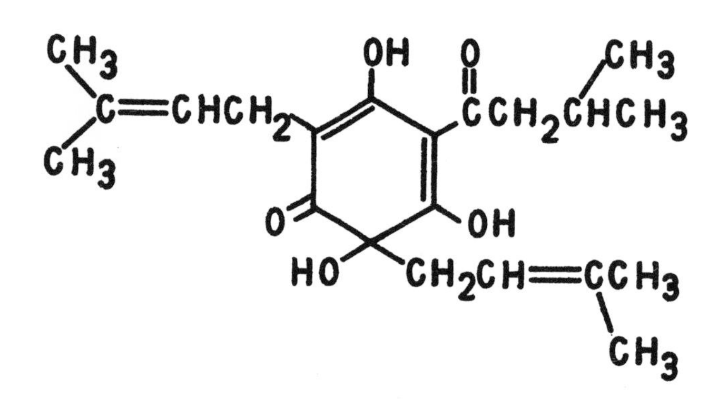

humulone *(Humulus lupulus)*

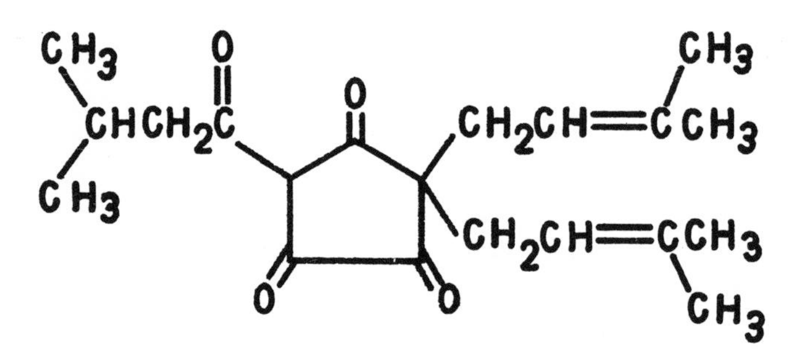

hulupone *(Humulus lupulus)*

2. An acyl group is always present at C-2.
3. Extra methyl groups are common, often giving the superficial appearance of a terpenoid structure.

The simple phloroglucinol derivatives may be extracted from plant tissues using organic solvents such as ether and then further purified by taking advantage of their phenolic properties -- e. g. extraction from organic solvents with sodium hydroxide solution. Purification of hop constituents of this type has been achieved using countercurrent distribution between phosphate buffer and iso-octane (16).

These phloroglucinol derivatives are for the most part colorless, crystalline compounds, although some (e. g. ceroptene) are yellow pigments. Those that have a free phenolic hydroxyl group show typical phenol reactions such as giving a color with ferric chloride. Heating with sodium hydroxide and zinc dust causes reductive removal of the 2-acyl group, and the resulting derivatives give a red color with vanillin-conc. hydrochloric acid. Identification of these derivatives has been an important procedure in structure determination. The infrared and ultraviolet spectra of 2-acyl-cyclohexane-1, 3-diones have been discussed by Chan and Hassall (17). They generally have one absorption maximum in the range 223-233 mμ and another at 271-293 mμ. Godin (18) has separated crude filicin from male fern *(Aspidium)* into several different phloroglucinol derivatives using paper chromatography in an aqueous solvent containing sodium carbonate and sodium sulfite. Spots were revealed by the diazonium reaction. Phloroglucinol derivatives of *Dryopteris* were separated on buffered filter paper impregnated with formamide and a benzene/chloroform solvent (19).

Details of the biosynthesis of these phloroglucinol derivatives are completely obscure especially with regard to the origin of C-methyl groups. Birch (2) has made important suggestions in this area which should be tested by experiment.

CHROMONES

The chromone nucleus with its numbering system is as follows:

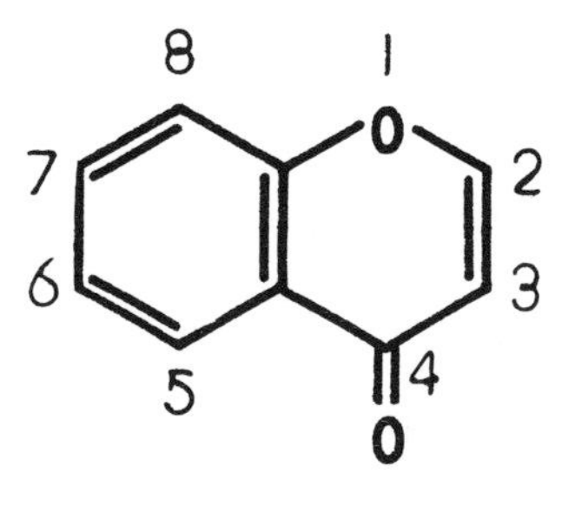

Naturally-occuring chromones generally have a methyl group at C-2 and are oxygenated at C-5 and C-7. Thus despite their overall resemblance to the carbon skeleton of the coumarins (Chapter 4), they may be regarded as derived from the condensation of five molecules of acetic acid. The coumarins, on the other hand, are probably derived by the shikimic acid pathway which rarely results in oxygenation at C-5:

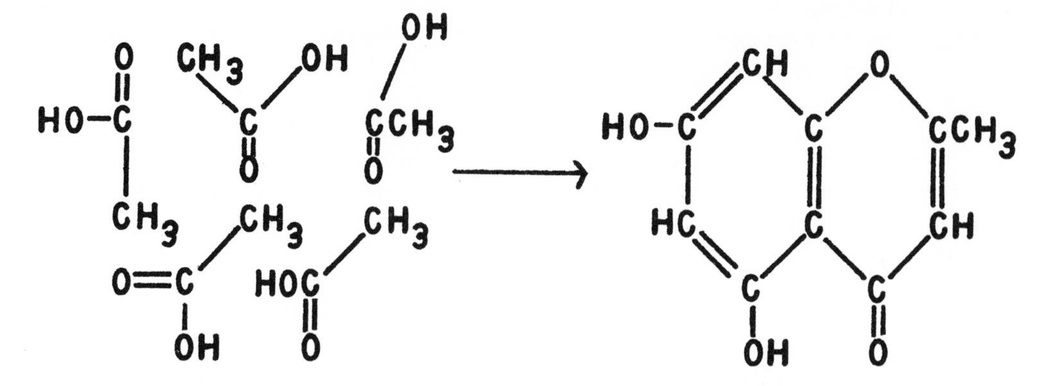

However, it is possible that chromones could be formed by the addition of an acetate unit to a phenylpropane intermediate (20). Tracer experiments should settle this point.

Analogous to the furanocoumarins are furanochromones with the following basic structure:

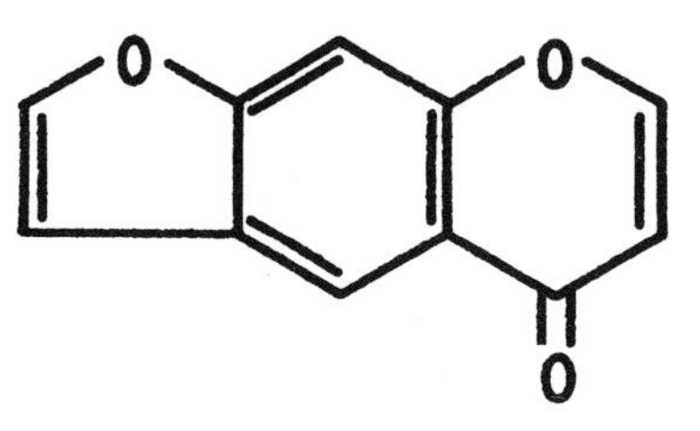

Some structures of a few natural chromones are shown below:

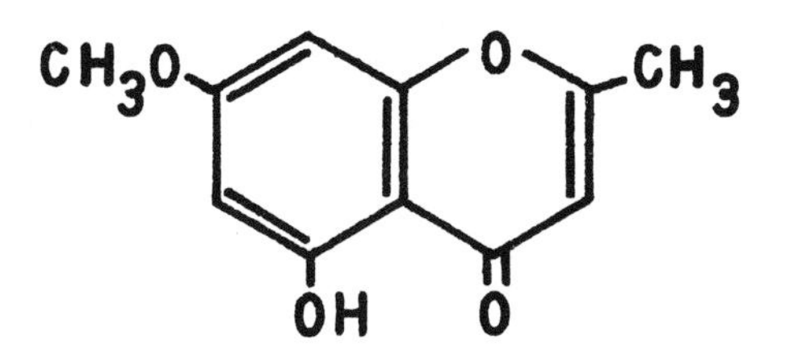

eugenin *(Eugenia caryophyllata)*

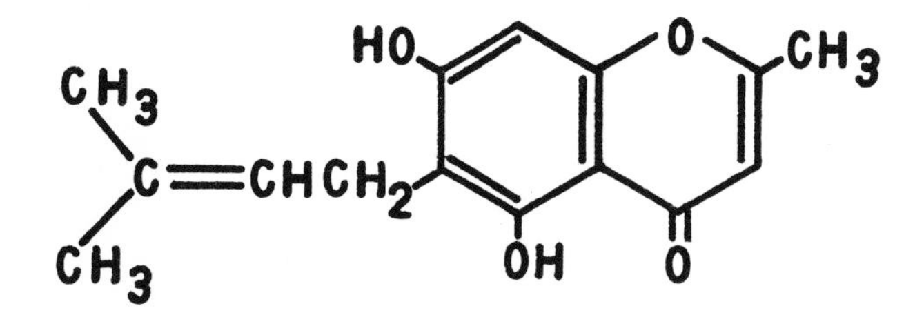

peucenin *(Peucedanum ostruthium)*

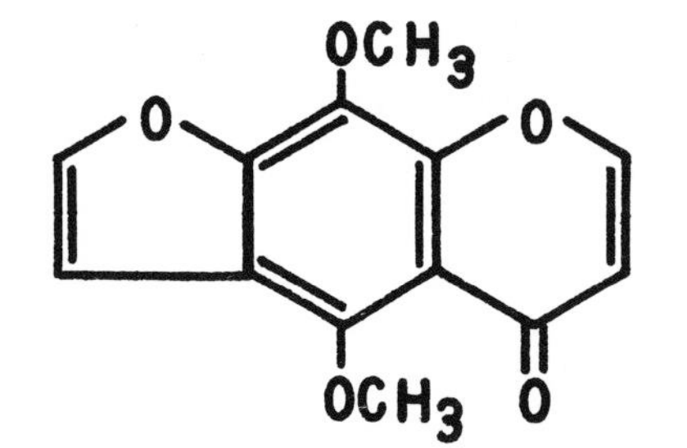

khellin *(Ammi visnaga)*

There is an obvious resemblance of these structures to the 2-acylphloroglucinols discussed in the previous section of this chapter (e. g., compare eugenone and eugenin). Naturally occurring chromones have been reviewed by Schmid (21) and the furanochromones by Huttrer and Dale (22). Both groups together contain only about a dozen compounds.

The chromones are of interest as the active ingredients of several plants used for centuries in folk medicine. Khellin is valuable as an antispasmodic and for relieving the pain of renal colic, dental caries, angina pectoris, etc. Its primary action may be as a vasodilator.

Chromones are extracted from dried plant material using such solvents as ether, chloroform, or acetone. They may be crystallized directly from these solvents or purified by chromatography on magnesium oxide or neutral, deactivated alumina. Chromones with phenolic hydroxyl groups can be extracted from ether solution with dilute, aqueous sodium hydroxide. Chromone glycosides are extracted by methanol.

Chromones are usually colorless but form yellow-orange oxonium salts in the presence of strong mineral acids. This color reaction is useful for indicating the presence of chromones, but proof of structure rests on degradation and identification of split products. The ultraviolet absorption spectrum of chromones usually shows a main band at about 295 mμ with weaker absorption at about 250 mμ. Substitution at C-8 or presence of the furan ring may increase the absorption maximum to as much as 340 mμ (23). Paper chromatographic separation of chromones can be made using water/2-propanol mixtures as the solvents.

NAPHTHOQUINONES

A large number of naphthoquinones are found in nature as yellow-red plant pigments. Theoretically some of these might be synthesized by polyacetate condensations as follows:

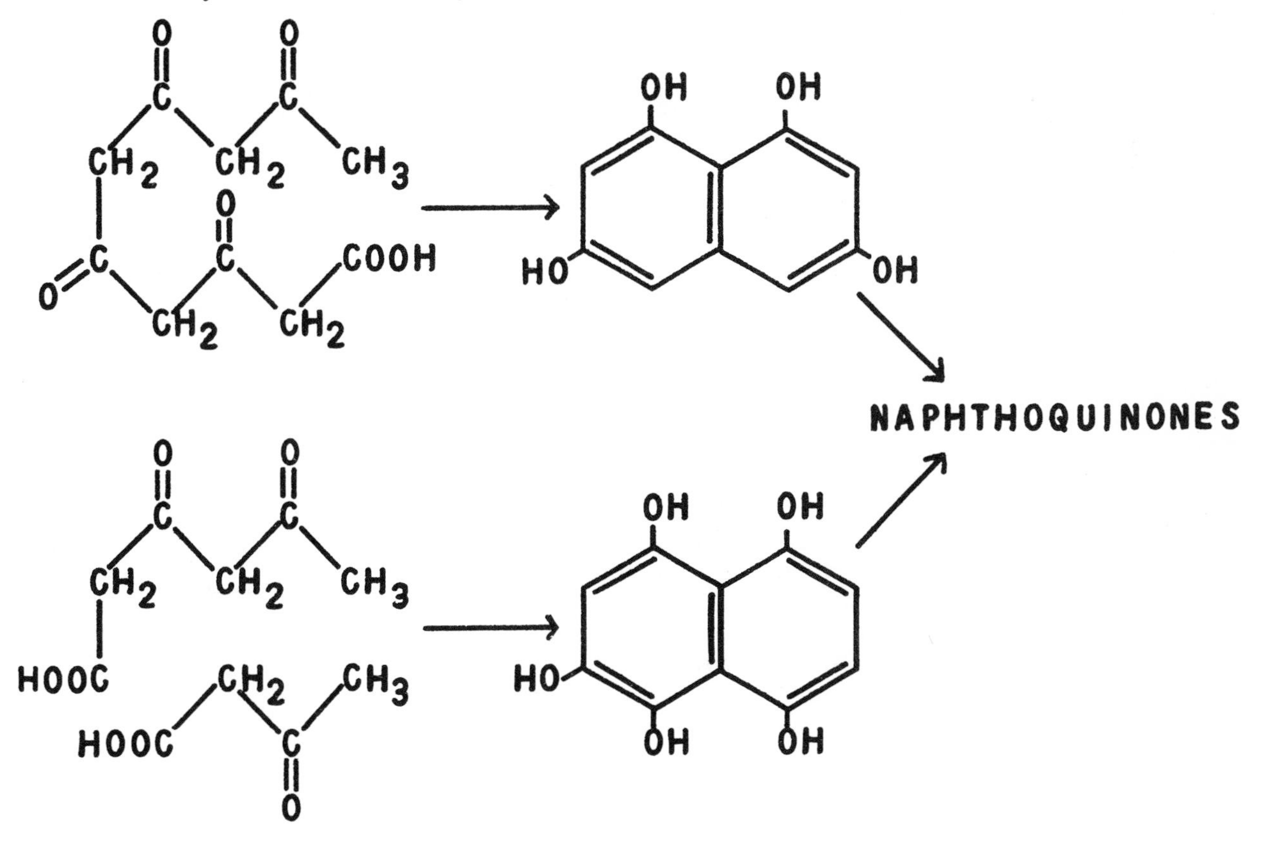

However, none of the natural naphthoquinones have the oxygenation pattern that would be predicted by either of the condensations shown. If a polyacetate pathway is followed in nature, loss and migration of hydroxyl groups must occur at some stage in the process. In spite of this discrepancy, and for want of any better theory, natural naphthoquinones are included in this chapter (except for vitamin K which because of its isoprenoid nature is found in Chapter 8). Ideas on the biosynthesis of naphthoquinones are reviewed by Neelakantan and Seshadri (24).

A few examples of naphthoquinones are given in Table 3 with their natural occurrence.

All of these quinones are crystalline materials ranging in color from yellow to red and easily soluble in such organic solvents as benzene. Some of them are toxic and antimicrobial; plants containing them have been used as drugs and poisons since prehistoric times (e.g. chimaphilin, plumbagin, eleutherin). Others have been equally important as dyestuffs. Lawsone is the chief ingredient of henna; lapachol is extracted from various woods and used for dyeing cotton; alkannin is the coloring matter obtained by alkaline treatment of the root of *Alkanna tinctoria* (dyer's bugloss). At least a few of these compounds do not exist as such in plants but are formed during the extraction process. Thus the native form of alkannin is an ester of angelic acid with the hydroxyl group of the side chain; juglone is formed by hydrolysis and oxidation of 1-hydrojuglone-4-β-D-glucoside. Plumbagin is formed by hydrolysis and oxidation of dianellin, a yellow naphthol glycoside of *Dianella laevis* (25). Although we have grouped these napthoquinones as unsaponifiable lipids, they should not be subjected to the procedure of saponification, since treatment with alkali in the presence of air frequently brings about oxidative decomposition.

The naphthoquinones may be extracted from plant tissues with benzene or other nonpolar solvents. The 1, 4-quinones are often steam distillable and may be removed from many other lipids by this procedure. Another property which may be used in their separation from other lipids is their solubility in weakly basic aqueous solutions such as sodium carbonate or bicarbonate. 1, 2-quinones are not steam distillable, but are soluble in solutions of sodium bisulfite. Final purification may be achieved with chromatography on inactivated alumina or weaker adsorbents.

The properties of naphthoquinones used in their isolation may also be put to good use in their characterization. Thus, a steam distillable, yellow-red solid which is soluble in benzene or sodium carbonate solution but insoluble in water is very likely to be a 1, 4-naphthoquinone. Additional indications are given by color reactions and spectra. 1, 4-naphthoquinones give yellow solutions in benzene, changing to red in alkali. 1, 2-quinones are usually red rather than yellow when crystalline or dissolved in benzene; in alkali they become blue-violet. If a double bond in a side chain of a 1, 4-quinone is conjugated with bonds in the quinone ring, the color reactions shown are like those of 1, 2-quinones. Other characteristic color reactions are given with concentrated sulfuric acid. Measurement of absorption spectra shows maxima at about 250 mμ for 1, 4-quinones and one or more longer wavelength bands depending on what substituents are present. The basic nucleus absorbs at about 330 mμ. When oxygen substitution is present there are other maxima toward the red, sometimes nearly to 600 mμ; and the 330 maximum may not be apparent. 1, 2-naphthoquinone has the same ultraviolet absorption bands as the 1, 4-quinone but additional bands at about 400 and 530 mμ. As with the 1, 4-quinones, the positions of all bands except the lowest are greatly influenced by oxygen substitution on the rings. Characterization of 1, 4-naphthoquinones is discussed by Sawicki and Elbert (25). If hydroxyl groups are not present at C-2, the naphthoquinones react with o-aminothiophenol to yield red-blue colors. If C-2 hydroxyl groups are present, there is no reaction with this reagent, but a color reaction is given with o-phenylenediamine.

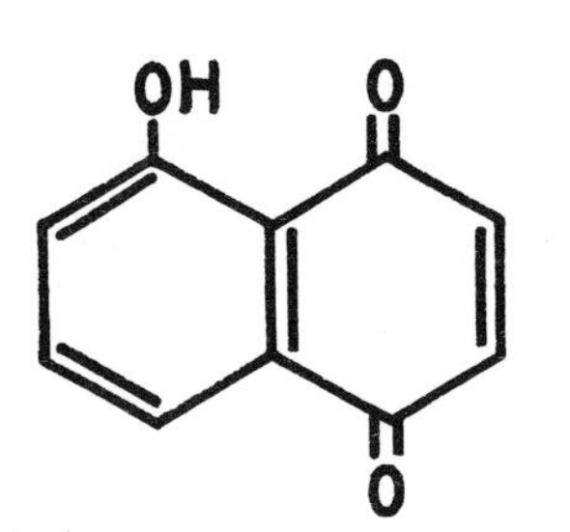

juglone *(Juglans regia)*

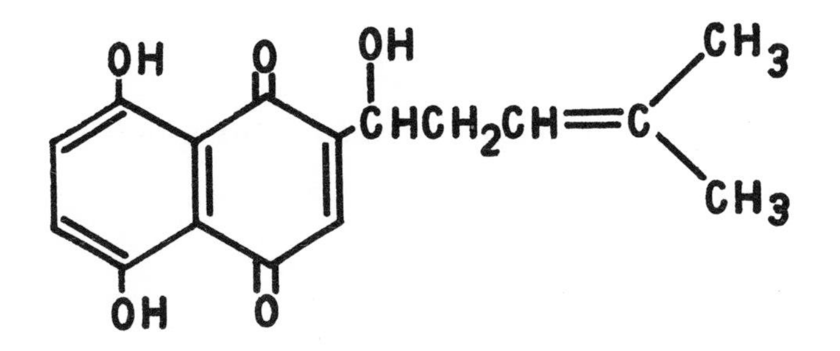

alkannin *(Alkanna tinctoria* and other *Boraginaceae)*

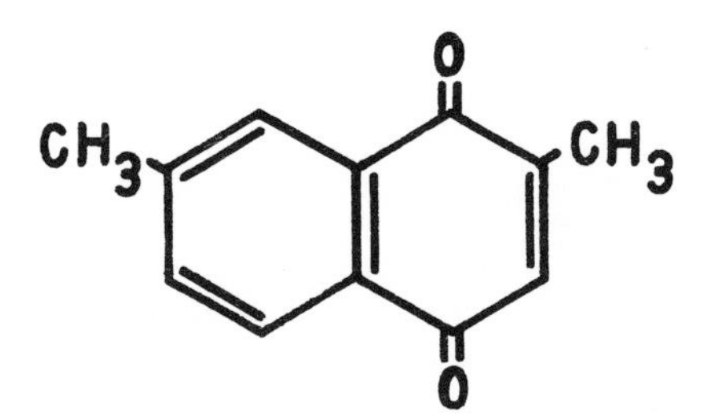

chimaphilin (Several species of the *Ericaceae*)

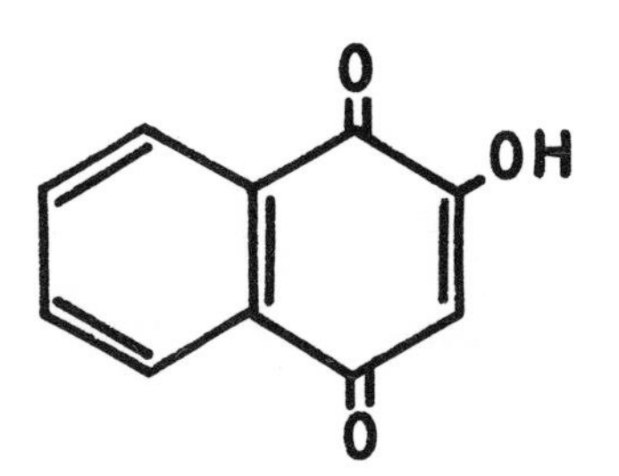

lawsone *(Lawsonia alba)*

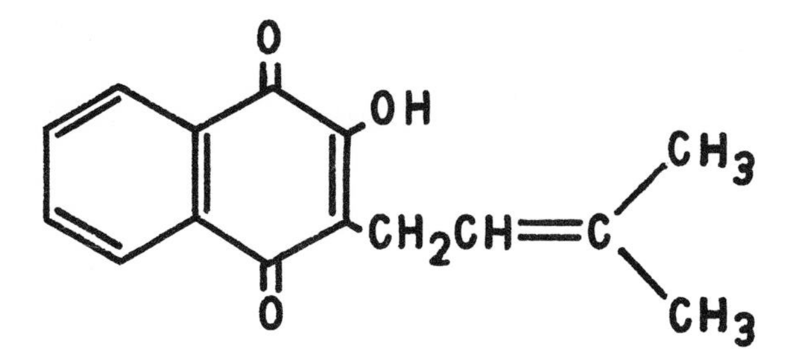

lapachol (*Tecoma* spp.)

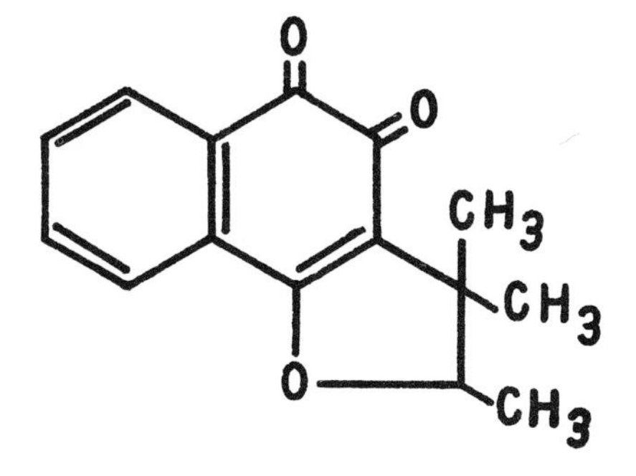

dunnione *(Streptocarpus dunni)*

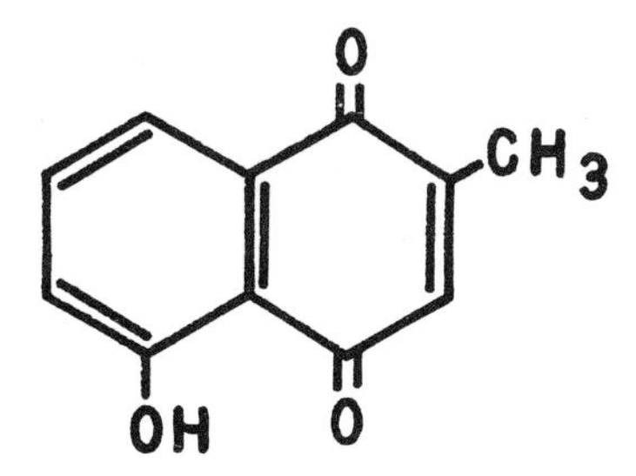

plumbagin
(*Plumbago* and *Drosera* spp.)

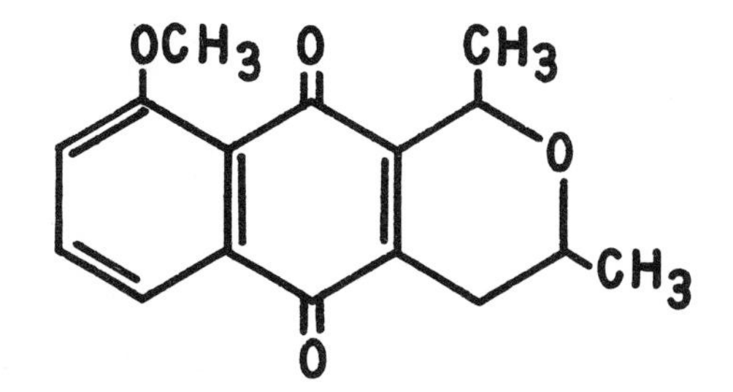

eleutherin *(Eleutherine bulbosa)*

ANTHRAQUINONES

The largest group of natural quinones is made up of anthraquinones. Some of them have been important as dyestuffs and others as purgatives. The plant families richest in this type of compound are the *Rubiaceae, Rhamnaceae* and *Polygonaceae*. The fundamental anthraquinone structure is shown below with the ring-numbering system:

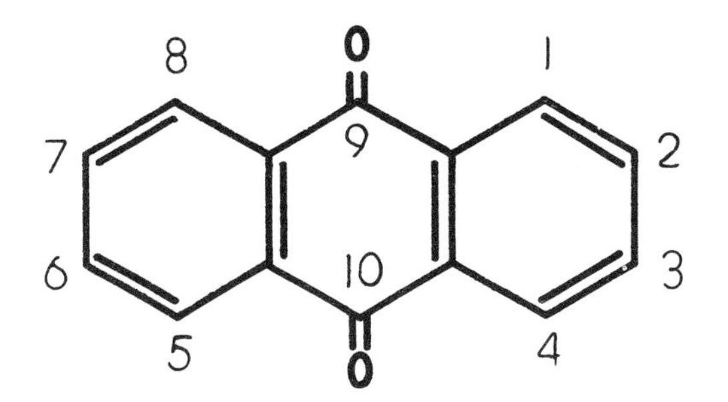

Most anthraquinones from higher plants are hydroxylated at C-1 and C-2, although anthraquinone itself has been reported to occur in various plant tannin extracts (27), and 2-methylanthraquinone is known to be a constituent of teak wood. The hydroxylated anthraquinones probably do not often occur in plants as such but rather glycosides. Treatment of the plants to obtain the commercially desirable products has the effect of hydrolyzing the glycosides, and in some cases producing additional oxidative changes. Since the free anthraquinones are the products usually dealt with, some typical structures will be considered in Table 4 followed by a general discussion of the native glycosides. All of these anthraquinones are high-melting crystalline compounds soluble in the usual organic solvents. They are usually red in color but different ones range from yellow to brown. They dissolve in aqueous alkali with the formation of red-violet colors.

The problem of the form in which these anthraquinones actually exist in plants remains a knotty one, and there are apparently several possibilities. Since the native precursors generally break down readily under the influence of enzymes or extraction procedures, reports of the appearance of free anthraquinones must be regarded cautiously. However, in some cases sufficient pains have been taken to assure that the simple compounds are true natural products. Many of the anthraquinones occur as glycosides with the sugar residue linked through one of the phenolic hydroxyl groups. Several different sugars are found in such glycosides. Thus, alizarin occurs as a 2-primoveroside (ruberythric acid); rubiadin from madder (*Rubia tinctoria)* as a 3-glucoside and from *Galium* spp. as a 3-primoveroside; morindone from *Coprosma australis* as a 6-rutinoside and from *Morinda persicaefolia* as a 6-primoveroside.

In many cases it appears that the native glucosides have as their aglycones a reduced form of the anthraquinone, known as anthrone. The sugars in these reduced glycosides may be linked as usual through phenolic oxygens in the outside rings or they may be attached at C-9 to the enol form of anthrone, anthranol:

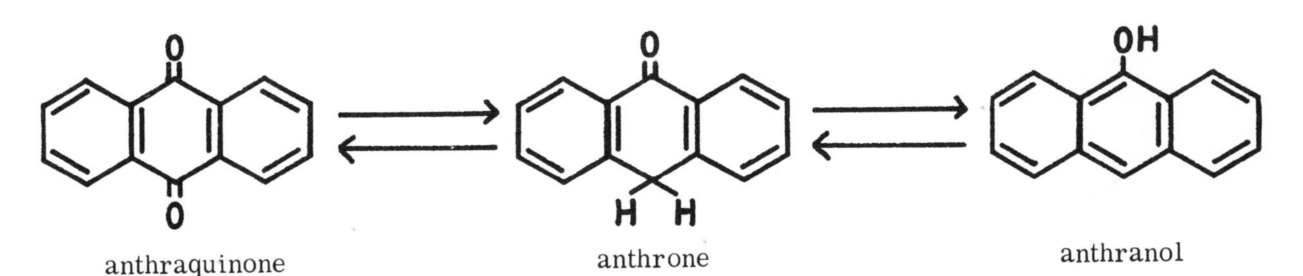

anthraquinone anthrone anthranol

TABLE 4. SOME NATURALLY OCCURRING ANTHRAQUINONES

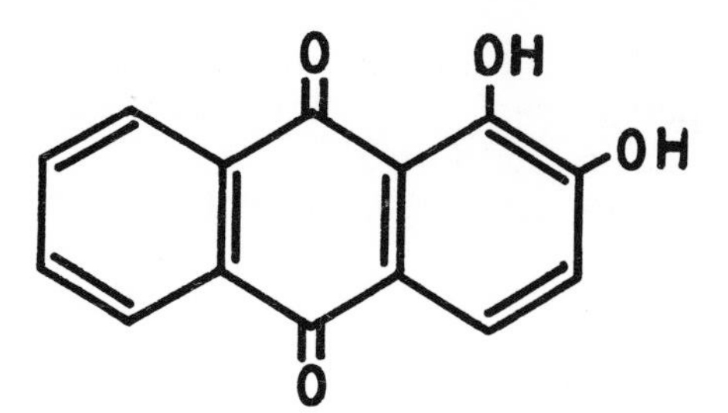

alizarin *(Rubia tinctorum)*

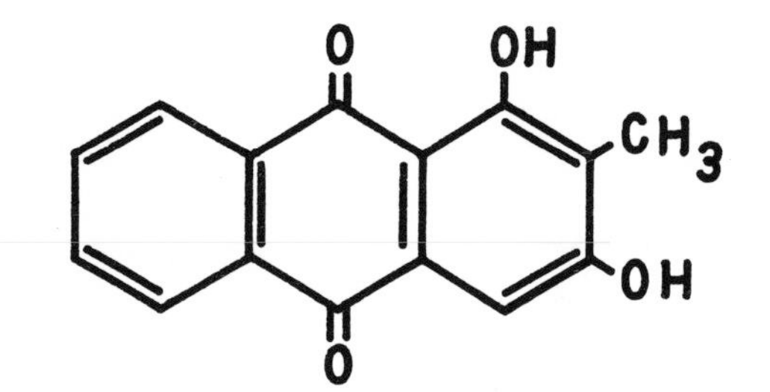

rubiadin
(*Rubia* and *Galium* spp.)

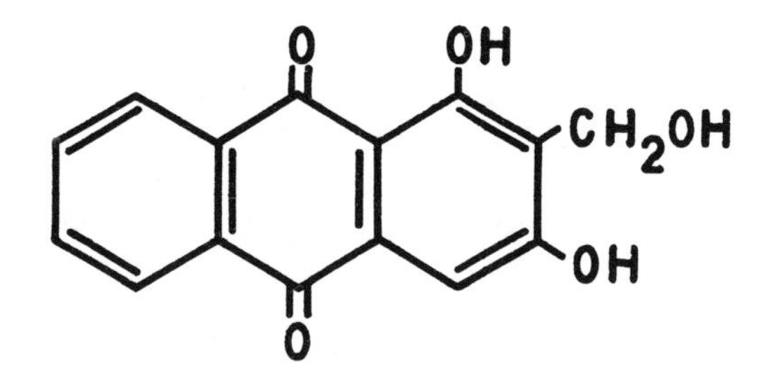

lucidin
(*Coprosma* spp.)

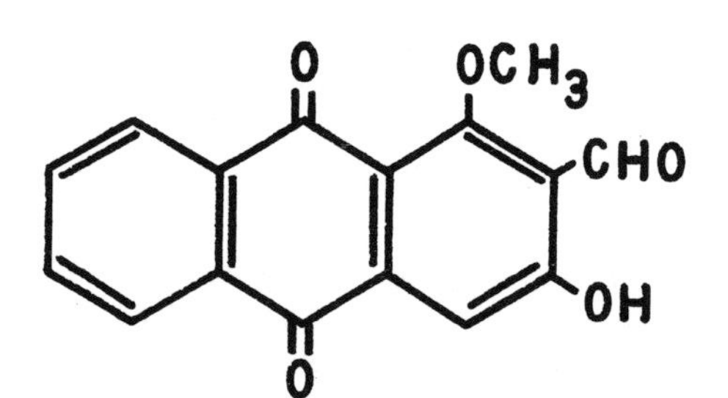

damnacanthal
(*Damnacanthus* spp.)

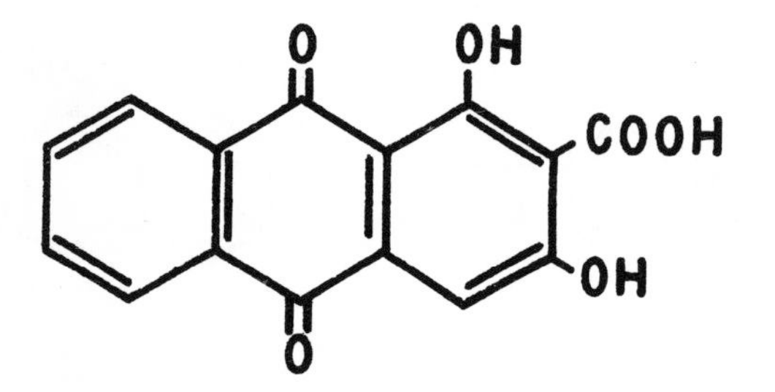

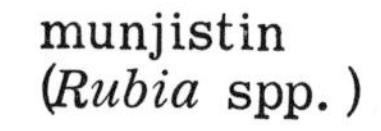
munjistin
(*Rubia* spp.)

Table 4. Continued

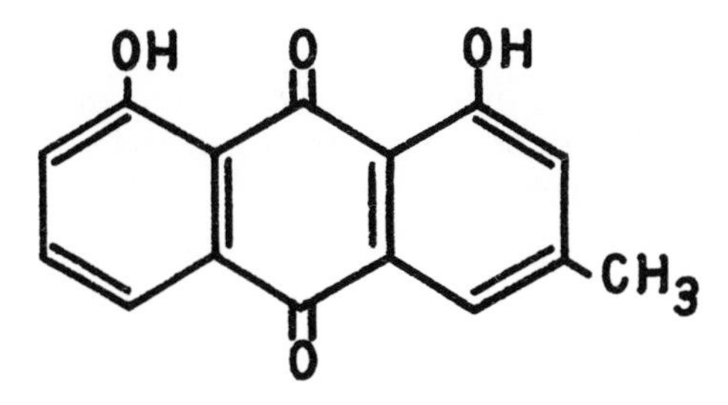

chrysophanol, chrysophanic acid
(*Rheum* and *Rumex* spp.)

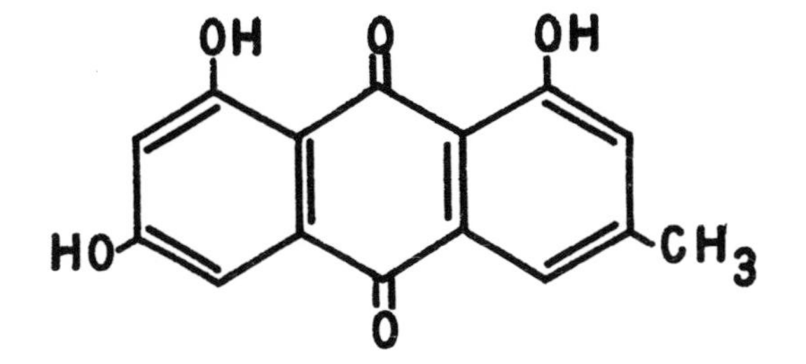

emodin, frangula-emodin
(*Rheum* and *Rumex* spp.)

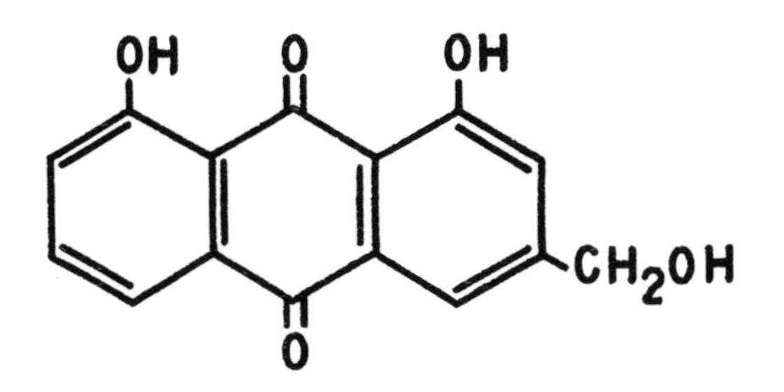

aloe-emodin
(*Aloe, Rheum* and *Rhamnus* spp.)

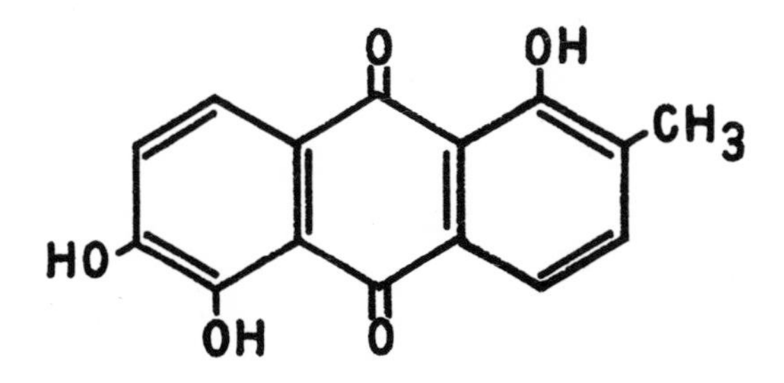

morindone
(*Morinda* spp.)

copareolatin *(Coprosma aerolata)*

Enzymatic (or chemical) hydrolysis of a C-9 glycoside of anthranol is followed by oxidation of the anthrone to an anthroquinone if oxygen is present. If the sugar is linked at some other position, anthranol glycosides may be directly oxidized to anthraquinone glycosides.

Although aloe-emodin occurs in *Rheum* spp. as an ordinary glycoside, in aloes it is found as barbaloin, an unusual compound in which a glucose-like group is linked by a carbon-carbon bond to a partially reduced anthraquinone (anthrone):

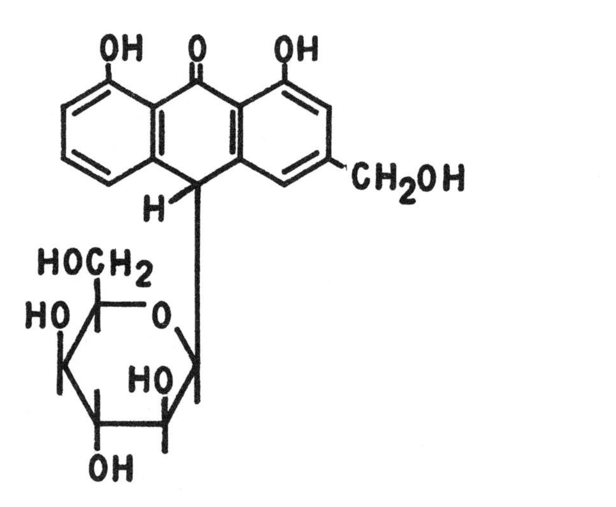

barbaloin

Other compounds apparently similar to barbaloin occur in other species of aloes. Unlike glycosides they are stable toward acid hydrolysis, but may be split with ferric chloride to form aloe-emodin (28).

Still more complex are the sennosides, the active cathartics of senna. These compounds are dianthrones. One of them, sennidin, has the following structure:

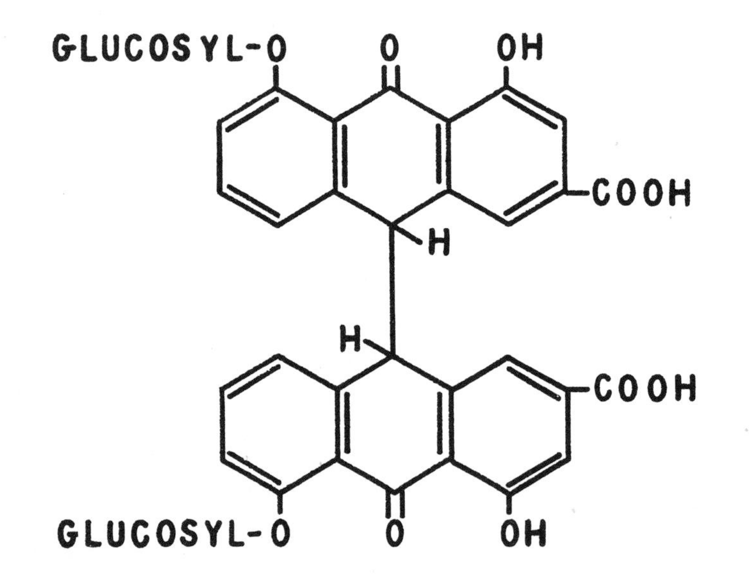

The chemistry of the sennosides has been reviewed by Stoll and Becker (29). It seems at least possible that other anthraquinones are derived from such natural precursors by exidative splitting. For instance the native glycosides of *Rheum frangula* bark (cascara) may be dianthrone glycosides which are oxidized on storage to form aloe-emodin and its glycosides (30).

The foregoing discussion illustrates some of the complexity which may be involved in studying anthraquinone derivatives as they occur naturally in plants. Adding to the problem is the fact that more than one type of derivative may be present, and frequently the nature of the constituents varies with the age of the plant. For example, in the common rhubarb *(Rheum undulatum)* young leaves contain mostly anthranol glycosides whereas older leaves have glycosides of anthraquinones.

The physiological activity of several of these anthracene derivatives has made them important cathartics for many hundreds of years. Only recently has it been shown that the free anthraquinones or the glycosides are ineffective, and the pharmacologically important compounds are free anthranols. The fact that pharmacopeias recommend storage of purgative plants for periods up to one year before use is explained by the necessity for slow hydrolysis of the glycosides to free anthranols. If storage is too long, however, the anthranols are oxidized to anthraquinones. Anthraquinones are active as cathartics only because they are reduced to anthranols by intestinal bacteria. Nothing is known regarding any function of these various anthracene derivatives in plants. The case with which the reaction anthraquinone⇌anthrone may be brought about in the laboratory has raised the possibility that these compounds may somehow participate in hydrogen transfer or oxidation-reduction reactions.

Isolation procedures depend on whether free aglycones or the various glycosidic derivatives are desired. For the first, extraction of the plant with rather non-polar solvents such as ether or benzene is effective. The sugar derivatives, however, are extracted using water, ethanol, or water-ethanol mixtures. If anthrones or anthranols are to be isolated, care must be taken to avoid their oxidation by oxygen in the air. This oxidation is particularly rapid in alkaline solutions and leads to the formation of dianthrones and polyanthrones as well as to anthraquinones. After extraction a solution of glycosides may be concentrated under reduced pressure to obtain crude crystals. These crude crystals may then be purified by repeated crystallization from acetone-water. The glycosides on heating with acetic acid or dilute (e. g. 5%) alcoholic HCl are readily hydrolyzed within one hour at 70°. After hydrolysis a 1:1 mixture of ethanol-benzene is added and then diluted with 0.5% aqueous HCl. A layer of benzene separates containing the aglycones. The aglycones obtained by hydrolysis or direct extraction of plant materials may be purified by extraction from benzene into dilute alkali and precipitation with acid. (Aglycones with free carboxyl groups can be extracted from benzene using sodium bicarbonate solution and a second extraction with sodium hydroxide used to remove any less acidic substances.) This crude precipitate is crystallized from benzene or alcohol. Purification of the aglycones by column chromatography is successful if rather weak adsorbents are used for example magnesium oxide, polyamide, or calcium phosphate. Some indication as to the nature of the compounds is given by the way they migrate when chromatographed on magnesium oxide (31). Thus, ortho-dihydroxy phenols are not eluted with even as strong an eluant as acetic acid.

For identification of anthraquinone derivatives the Bornträger reaction is routinely used. Some of the unknown material is boiled in dilute, aqueous potassium hydroxide for a few minutes. This not only hydrolyzes glycosides but also oxidizes anthrones or anthranols to anthraquinones. The alkaline solution is cooled, acidified, and extracted with benzene. When the benzene phase is separated and shaken with dilute alkali, the benzene loses its yellow color and the alkaline phase becomes red if quinones are present. The test is not specific for anthraquinones; naphthoquinones also give a positive reaction. If partially reduced anthraquinones are present, the original solution does not turn red immediately on making alkaline but turns yellow with green fluorescence and then gradually becomes red as oxidation occurs. If desired, the oxidation may be hastened by adding a little 3% hydrogen peroxide. The Bornträger reaction can also be made the basis of a quantitative colorimetric determination. Direct spectral observations of a benzene solution may also be made for characterization of anthracene derivatives. Anthraquinones show a broad absorption peak at about 440 mμ whereas the reduced forms absorb at about 360 mμ with no significant absorption at 440. 1, 4-dihydroxyanthraquinones fluoresce in acetic acid solution. The colors given with alcoholic magnesium acetate solutions are characteristic of different hydroxylation patterns (32). *Meta* hydroxyls give an orange color, *para* a purple color, and *ortho* violet.

Proof that an isolated compound has the anthracene nucleus may be obtained by dry distillation in the presence of zinc dust. This drastic treatment breaks down anthraquinone or anthrone derivatives to anthracene which distills over and may be identified by its melting point (216° C.). Methylated derivatives form 2-methylanthracene (m. p. 245°). These hydrocarbons are easily distinguished from naphthalene (m. p. 80°) which is formed from a napthoquinone.

Characterization of anthraquinone derivatives by means of paper chromatography and electrophoresis has been developed recently by several workers. Paper electrophoresis methods are described by Core and Kirch (33) and Siesto and Bartoli (34). Betts *et al.* (35) have chromatographed the glycosides and free anthraquinones on paper. In all of these methods using migration on paper, spots may be detected by spraying with 0. 5% magnesium acetate in methanol and heating at 90° C. for five minutes. Characteristic colors appear, as described above (32).

The pathways for biosynthesis of anthracene derivatives in plants are still only speculative but generally believed to involve polyacetate condensations possibly as follows (36, 37):

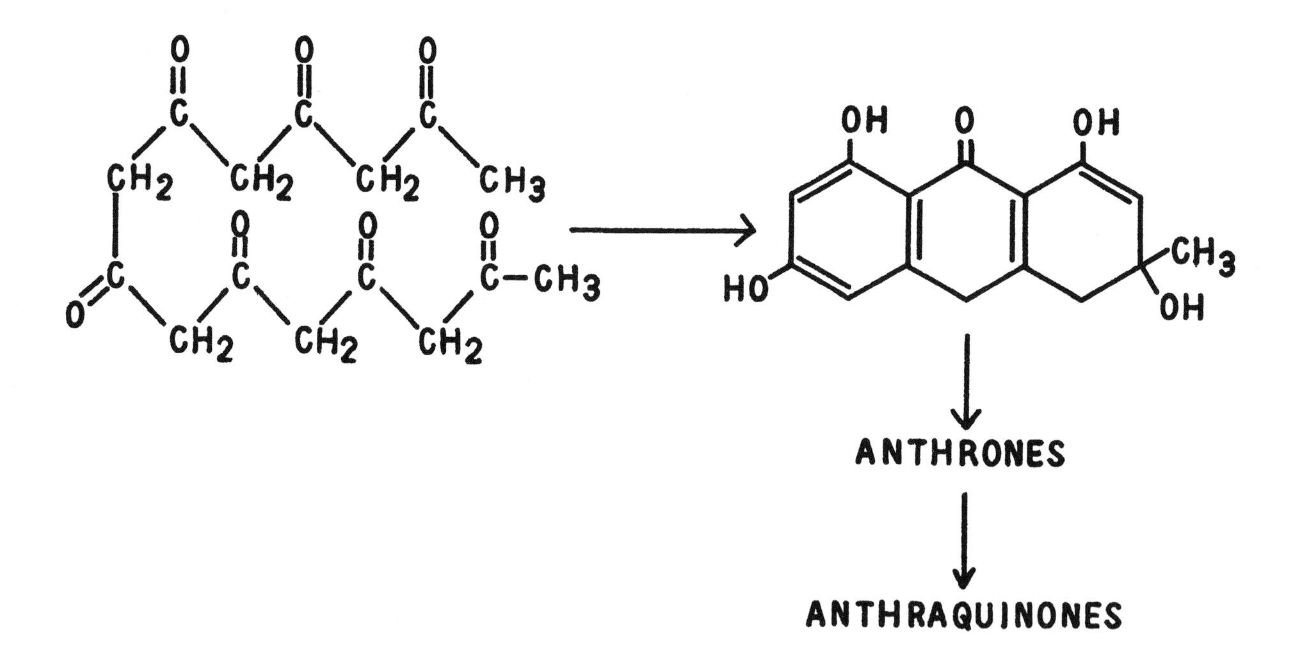

It will be seen that such a scheme accounts perfectly for the structure of emodin. For other compounds loss or rearrangement of hydroxyl groups and oxidation or removal of the methyl group are required. Hegnauer (38) has suggested that several different biosynthetic pathways may be followed, some possibly involving phenylpropane-type intermediates.

OTHER POLYNUCLEAR QUINONES

A very few phenanthraquinones are known to occur in higher plants, and their structures are not established with certainty. Three substances known as tanshinones have been isolated from the root of *Salvia miltiorrhiza* and shown to have carbon skeletons similar to the diterpenoid, abietic acid. They may therefore be isoprenoid rather than polyacetate derivatives. Another phenanthrene compound is denticulatol from the root of *Rumex chinensis*. Suggested structures for these compounds are given below. More details may be found in the book of Thomson listed under general references for this chapter.

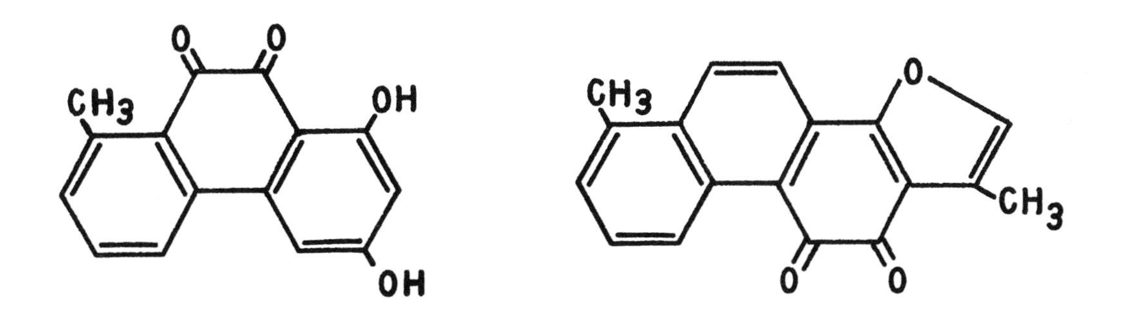

denticulatol tanshinone I

One of the most interesting quinones both chemically and physiologically is the substance hypericin which is found in petals, stems, and leaves of St. John's Wort *(Hypericum perforatum)* and other members of the *Hypericaceae*. Animals eating these plants become highly sensitized to light as a result of this compound becoming concentrated in the skin. The biochemistry of this sensitization is unknown. Possibly the actual irritants are peroxides formed in the presence of light. Other species of *Hypericum* contain a second, similar pigment named pseudohypericin; and buckwheat *(Fagopyrum)* also contains a related photosensitizing pigment named fagopyrin. All of these compounds have been reviewed by Brockman (39, 40). The structure of hypericin is given below:

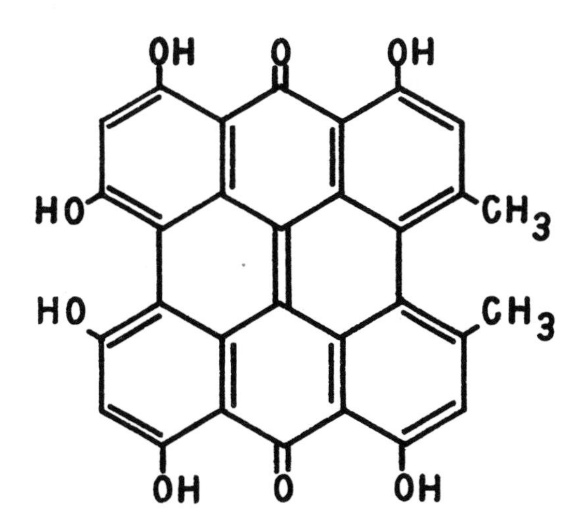

hypericin

Pseudohypericin apparently has - $CHOHCH_3$ groups rather than methyl attached to the 2 and 2' positions. Fagopyrin is more complex. On hydrolysis it forms hypericin and two other groups with the empirical formula $C_6H_{11}ON$. These groups may be attached by ether linkages. It seems likely that these pigments exist in plants in a more complex form which is broken down during extraction.

Hypericin is very dark red and only slightly soluble in organic solvents. In sulfuric acid it is green with a red fluorescence. In aqueous sodium hydroxide, unlike the anthraquinones, it also gives a green solution. Hypericin is isolated from dried flowers of *Hypericum perforatum* by first extracting with ether to remove carotenoid pigments and then extracting the hypericin with methanol. Methanolic HCl is added to give an HCl content of 2.5% and the solution allowed to stand at 0° C. for two days. Crystalline hypericin separates out. It is washed with boiling benzene and methanol and crystallized from pyridine solution by adding methanolic HCl. This crystalline preparation is contaminated with pseudohypericin unless the plant used contained only hypericin. Pyridine is the best solvent for hypericin, and in pyridine solution it shows absorption bonds at 519, 557 and 603 mμ. Kučera (41) has developed a paper chromatographic method for determination of hypericin in plants.

The structure of hypericin is obviously similar to that of the dianthrones (e.g. sennidin). Emodin anthrone is a minor constituent of *Hypericum* plants and it seems likely that hypericin is formed by ring closure between two such molecules. A careful search has revealed the presence in the plants of several presumed intermediates in the conversion of emodin anthrone to hypericin. The closure of the 4 - 4' and 5 - 5' rings is catalyzed by light; and by working in the dark a dehydrodianthrone of the following structure could be isolated:

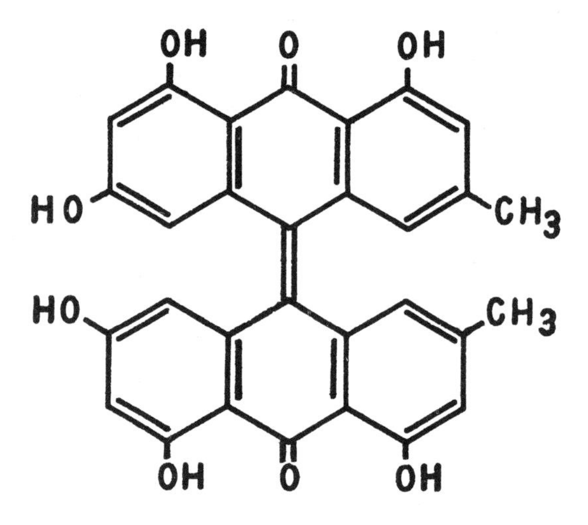

This is evidently derived from two molecules of emodin anthrone and is converted by light into hypericin. The first ring-closure at 5 - 5' gives rise to protohypericin.

GENERAL REFERENCES

Bohlmann, F. and Mannhardt, H. J., "Acetylenverbindungen im Pflanzenreich" Fortschr. Chem. Org. Naturstoffe 14 1 (1957).

Deuel, H. J., The Lipids 1 pp. 305-319, 372-383, 402-404, Interscience Publishers, N. Y., 1951.

Hoffmann-Ostenhof, O., "Ein und zweikernige Chinone" in Paech and Tracey 3 359.

Hoffmann-Ostenhof, O., "Vorkommen und biochemisches Verhalten der Chinone" Fortschr. Chem. Org. Naturstoffe 6 154 (1950).

Meara, M. L., "Fats and Other Lipids" in Paech and Tracey 2 317.
Schmid, W., "Anthraglykoside and Dianthrone" in Paech and Tracey 2 317.
Schwarze, P. "Phenole und Chinone", in Ruhland 10 507.
Sörensen, N. A., "Some Naturally Occurring Acetylenic Compounds", Proc. Chem. Soc. 1961 98.
Thomson, R. H., Naturally Occurring Quinones, Academic Press, N. Y. 1957.
Thomson, R. H., "Quinones: Structure and Distribution", in Comparative Biochemistry 3 pp. 631-725, M. Florkin and H. S. Mason, eds., Academic Press, New York, 1962.
Warth, A. H., The Chemistry and Technology of Waxes, 2nd ed., Reinhold, N. Y., 1956.

BIBLIOGRAPHY

1. Birch, A. J., Proc. Chem. Soc. 1962 3.
2. Birch, A. J., Fortschr. Chem. Org. Naturstoffe 14 186 (1957).
3. Sandermann, W. and Schweers, W., Chem. Ber. 93 2266 (1960).
4. Glet, E. and Gutschmidt, J., Deut. Apoth. Ztg. 52 265 (1958). (Chem. Abstr. 31 3206.)
5. Romaňuk, M., Herout, V. and Šorm, F., Chem. listy 52 1965 (1958).
6. Sörensen, J. S. and Sörensen, N. A., Acta Chem. Scand. 12 756 (1958).
7. Lamberton, J. A. and Redcliffe, A. H., Austral, J. Chem. 13 261 (1960).
8. Brockmann, H. and Volpers, F., Chem. Ber. 80 77 (1947).
9. Chibnall, A. C., Piper, S. H., Pollard, A., Smith, J. A. B., and Williams, E. F., Biochem. J. 25 2095 (1931).
10. Kaufmann, H. P. and Kessen, G., Z. Physiol. Chem. 317 43 (1959).
11. Mazliak, P., Compt. rend. 252 1507 (1961).
12. Eglinton, G., Hamilton, R. J., Raphael, R. A. and Gonzalez, A. G., Nature 193 739 (1962).
13. Nilsson, M., Acta Chem. Scand. 13 750 (1959).
14. Spetsig, L. O. and Steninger, M., J. Inst. Brewing 66 413 (1960).
15. Hassall, C. H., Prog. Org. Chem. 4 115 (1958).
16. Howard, G. A. and Tatchell, A. R., J. Chem. Soc. 1954 2400.
17. Chan, W. R. and Hassall, C. H., J. Chem. Soc. 1953 803.
18. Godin, S., Experientia 14 208 (1958).
19. Penttilä, A. and Sundmann, J., J. Pharm. Pharmacol. 13 531 (1961).
20. Geissman, T. A. in Ruhland 10 543.
21. Schmid, H., Fortschr. Chem. Org. Naturstoffe 11 124 (1954).
22. Huttrer, C. P. and Dale, E., Chem. Revs. 48 543 (1951).
23. Sen, K. and Bagchi, P., J. Org. Chem. 24 316 (1959).
24. Neelakantan, S. and Seshadri, T. R.,J. Sci. Indust. Res. (India) 20 448 (1961).
25. Batterham, T., Cooke, R. G., Duewell, H. and Sparrow, L. G., Austral. J. Chem. 14 637 (1961).
26. Sawicki, E. and Elbert, W. C., Anal. Chim. Acta 23 205 (1960).
27. Kirby, K. S. and White, T., Biochem. J. 60 583 (1955).
28. Hay, J. E. and Haynes, L. J., J. Chem. Soc. 1956 3141.
29. Stoll, A. and Becker, B., Fortschr. Chem. Org. Naturstoffe 7 248 (1950).
30. Hörhammer, L., Wagner, H. Köhler, O., Arch. Pharm. 292 591 (1959).
31. Briggs, L. H., Nicholls, G. A. and Patterson, R. M. L., J. Chem. Soc. 1952 1718.
32. Shibata, S., Takido, M. and Tanaka, O., J. Am. Chem. Soc. 72 2789 (1950).
33. Core, A. C. and Kirch, E. R., J. Am. Pharm. Assoc. 47 513 (1958).
34. Siesto, A. J. and Bartoli, A., Farmaco, Ed. Prat. 12 517 (1951) (Chem. Abstr. 52 12323 (1959).
35. Betts, T. J., Fairbairn, J. W. and Mital, V. K., J. Pharm. Pharmacol. 10 436 (1958).
36. Neelakantan, S. and Seshadri, T. R., J. Sci. Ind. Res. (India) A19 71 (1960).
37. Friedrich, H., Planta Medica 7 383 (1959).
38. Hegnauer, R., Planta Med. 7 344 (1959).
39. Brockmann, H., Fortscher. Chem. Org. Naturstoffe. 14 141 (1957).
40. Brockmann, H., Proc. Chem. Soc. 1957 304.
41. Kučera, M., Československ. farm. 7 436 (1958) (Chem. Abstr. 53 7507 (1960)).

Chapter 7
VOLATILE ALCOHOLS AND CARBONYL COMPOUNDS

A large variety of volatile alcohols, aldehydes, ketones and esters is found in plants though usually in very small amounts. These compounds, despite their low concentration, are of great aesthetic and commercial interest because of the contribution they make to the flavor and odor of foods, flowers, perfumes, etc. In terms of total amount terpenoids are the most important flavor and odor constituents of plants; but because of their special pathway of biosynthesis, they are treated separately in Chapter 8. The compounds discussed in the present chapter have the same types of functional groups as many of the terpenoids, but their carbon chains show much less branching and are often completely unbranched. As minor constituents of essential oils they add distinctive characteristics to products which are predominantly terpenoid; as flavor and odor constituents of fruits and flowers they may be much more significant. Their role in the plant may lie in their attractiveness to insect pollinators and animal seed-disseminators. The compound 2-hexenal ("leaf aldehyde") is largely responsible for the distinctive odor of crushed leaves. It is also reported to act as an antibiotic, wound hormone, and seed germination stimulant (1).

All of the straight chain alcohols up to C_{10} have been found in plants either free or esterified. A few branched chain and unsaturated alcohols are also known. Aliphatic aldehydes up to C_{12} have been found and ketones up to C_{13}. Unlike the fatty acids there seems to be no preference for even-carbon chains among these compounds. Branching, if present, is usually confined to a single methyl group near the end of the chain. Secondary alcohols are rather common, but they usually have their hydroxyl groups at C-2, and never farther removed from the end of a chain than C-3. The ketones are almost without exception methyl ketones. The esters usually have lower fatty acids comprising their acyl groups, but sometimes aromatic acids are present. Acids of the citric acid cycle, or closely related acids, are never found in esters---possibly because coenzyme A derivatives are not involved in their metabolism. To illustrate the complexity of some fruit flavors, Table 1 lists some flavor constituents which have been found in apples (2), pineapples (3) and strawberries (4). Table 2 lists some other compounds of this type with examples of their natural occurrence.

ISOLATION

The volatile components of fruits and flowers are present in such minute amounts that tremendous quantities of starting material are necessary for the isolation of any workable quantity of product. Because of their volatility these compounds are also difficult to isolate, and they are frequently converted *en masse* to non-volatile derivatives which can then be fractionated.

Three general methods are available for removing volatile components from plants: distillation, solvent extraction, and aeration. Distillation (or steam distillation) at atmospheric pressure may bring about some decomposition. Distillation under reduced pressure and lower temperatures may permit enzymatic degradations to proceed causing

TABLE 1. VOLATILE FLAVOR CONSTITUENTS OF SOME FRUITS

Apples	Pineapples	Strawberries
ethyl acetate	methyl iso-caproate	iso-amyl alcohol
ethyl propionate	ethyl acetate	amyl alcohol
ethyl butyrate	ethyl iso-caproate	ethanol
ethyl valerate	methyl iso-valerate	1-propanol
propyl acetate	ethyl iso-valerate	ethyl butyrate
propyl propionate	methyl valerate	iso-butyl alcohol
propyl valerate	methyl caprylate	2-pentanol
acetic acid	ethyl acrylate	1-hexanol
formic acid	acetaldehyde	*trans*-2-hexenol-1
propionaldehyde	methyl β-methylthiolpropionate	ethyl iso-valerate
propyl butyrate	methyl propyl ketone	iso-amyl acetate
		ethyl caproate
		1-hexyl acetate
		trans-2-hexenyl-1 acetate

changes in constituents of the tissue. If oxidative reactions are a problem, distillation can be carried out in a nitrogen atmosphere. Solvent extraction methods are usable in special cases especially for the less polar compounds. Some of the lower molecular weight volatile compounds are too soluble in water to be extracted efficiently by organic solvents. In the aeration process only compounds evolved into the air are isolated by passing a stream of air over the plant material for a long period of time and condensing any entrained substances in cooled receivers; or the stream of air may be passed through reagents which react with at least some of the compounds to produce non-volatile derivatives.

A mixture of volatile substances isolated by one of the above procedures may be fractionated by distillation or chromatography. Chromatographic separations can be made on liquid partition columns or by gas chromatography. Alternatively, derivatives of different components of the mixture may be used to separate them. Thus aldehydes and ketones form water-soluble bisulfite compounds from which other components may be removed by solvent extraction. They may also be converted to solid 2, 4-dinitrophenylhydrazones, and remaining volatile compounds removed by distillation. Aldehydes form water-insoluble derivatives with dimedone. Ketones do not react with this reagent. Alcohols can be converted into solid urethanes by reaction with isocyanates or into 3, 5-dinitrobenzoates by reaction with 3, 5-dinitrobenzoyl chloride. Remaining volatile compounds are then removed by distillation. Esters cannot be separated as such by chemical means since derivatives formed represent either the alcohol or the acid portion of the ester rather than the intact compound. After the various types of derivatives have been prepared, they are usually separated by chromatographic procedures as described below under "Characterization". In a few cases it is possible to recover the original compounds from purified derivatives, but there is usually no reason to do this.

TABLE 2. SOME VOLATILE ALCOHOLS AND CARBONYL COMPOUNDS FOUND IN PLANTS

Compound	Occurrence
CH_3OH methanol	widespread, usually as esters
CH_3CH_2OH ethanol	widespread, free or as esters
$CH_3CH(CH_3)CH_2OH$ iso-butyl alcohol	fruits, free or as esters
$CH_3CH_2CH = CHCH_2CH_2OH$ *cis*-3-hexenol-1	free in many leaves and flowers
$CH_3(CH_2)_5CH(OH)CH_3$ 2-octanol	geranium oil (*Pelargonium* spp.)
CH_3CHO ethanal, acetaldehyde	many fruits
$CH_3(CH_2)_4CHO$ hexanal, caproaldehyde	*Eucalyptus* spp.
$CH_3(CH_2)_{10}CHO$ dodecanal, lauraldehyde	citrus fruits
$CH_3C(=O)CH_3$ acetone	many essential oils
$CH_3C(=O)(CH_2)_5CH_3$ 2-octanone	rue (*Ruta* spp.)
$CH_3C(=O)C(=O)CH_3$ diacetyl, 2, 3-butandione	raspberries (*Rubus idaeus*)

CHARACTERIZATION

Identification of isolated volatile alcohols and carbonyl compounds can be carried out by standard procedures of qualitative organic analysis if enough material is available, but usually it is not.

There are many common spot tests and color reactions to indicate the presence of alcohols, aldehydes, ketones, and esters. Detailed information on procedures may be found in any text book of qualitative organic analysis. Primary and secondary alcohols form xanthates by reaction with carbon disulfide and solid sodium hydroxide. The xanthates treated with molybdic acid give a violet color which is extractable into chloroform. Aldehydes and ketones form insoluble red precipitates when treated with a dilute (0.4%) solution of 2, 4-dinitrophenylhydrazine in dilute sulfuric acid. Aldehydes give a pink color with Schiff's reagent (reduced rosaniline hydrochloride), but ketones do not. Esters react on heating with hydroxylamine in hot alkaline solution. When this solution is cooled and made acidic, the hydroxamic acids which have been formed give a purple color with ferric chloride solution.

Characterization of a mixture can also be performed by chromatographic methods. Most useful in this regard is probably gas chromatography since it has a high resolving power, and the compounds involved are readily volatile. The fractions may be collected separately as they pass from the column by bubbling into chilled carbon disulfide or by using a liquid air trap, but the amounts obtainable are minute. They may be identified to some extent by their rates of migration on columns of different materials, or enough material may be obtained to permit identification by infrared spectroscopy or mass spectrometry. For details of such methods see references (5) and (6).

Rather than attempt characterization of the volatile compounds as such, it is often more convenient to form various derivatives which can be purified and identified. Some of these derivatives are mentioned under "Isolation Methods". If derivatives of pure compounds have been prepared, they may be identified by physical properties such as absorption spectra or melting points. More often mixtures of derivatives must be fractionated and the compounds separately identified. Alcohol dinitrobenzoates have been separated on columns of silicic acid-celite developed with petroleum ether/ethyl ether mixtures (7). Dinitrobenzoates can also be chromatographed on paper using heptane/methanol as the solvent (8). Partial identification can be made by R_f value. Dinitrophenylhydrazones of the aldehydes and ketones can be separated on columns (silicic acid or bentonite) using such solvents as hexane, ethyl ether, chloroform, and benzene, or mixtures of them (9). They may also be separated on paper using heptane/methanol as the solvent (10). The dinitrophenylhydrazones give a pale yellow spots on paper, but they may be intensified by spraying with 10% sodium hydroxide. The absorption spectra of dinitrophenylhydrazones may be used to identify them by comparing spectra with those of known phenylhydrazones in neutral and alkaline solution (11). An ester can be hydrolyzed and the alcohols and acid characterized separately by paper chromatography or other means (cf. Chapter 3). Another procedure is to form derivatives directly from the ester without previous saponification. For example, by heating with 3, 5-dinitrobenzoyl chloride and sulfuric acid, a dinitrobenzoate of the alcohol portion may be prepared and characterized. By treating with alkaline hydroxylamine the acid portions can be converted to hydroxamic acids and these chromatographed in butanol/acetic acid/water, 4:1:5. (12). The hydroxamic acid spots are detected by spraying with ferric chloride in water-saturated butanol.

METABOLIC PATHWAYS

There is no direct evidence regarding the routes of biosynthesis for the compounds discussed in this chapter. It seems likely from their straight-chain, aliphatic structures that they are related to the fatty acids, long-chain alcohols, etc. (Chapters 5 and 6). On the other hand the presence of branched chains, odd numbers of carbon atoms, and oxygen atoms at unexpected positions indicates that considerably more clarification is needed. In studies on the origin of banana aroma, Hultin and Proctor (13) added various possible substrates to a crude enzyme preparation from bananas and concluded that valine might be a precursor of volatile terpenoids, and oleic acid of straight-chain aldehydes and ketones such as 2-hexenal and 2-pentanone.

GENERAL REFERENCES

Guenther, E., The Essential Oils 6 vols., D. Van Nostrand Co., Inc., N. Y. (1948-1952).
Meigh, D. F. "Volatile Alcohols, Aldehydes, Ketones and Esters" in Paech and Tracey 2 403.
Moncrieff, R. W., The Chemical Senses 2nd ed., John Wiley, N. Y., 1951.

BIBLIOGRAPHY

1. Schildknecht, H. and Rauch, G., Z. Naturforsch. 16b 422 (1961).
2. Henze, R. E., Baker, C. E., and Quackenbush, F. W., J. Agr. Food Chem. 2 1118 (1954).
3. Haagen-Smit, A. J., Kirchner, J. G., Prater, A. N., and Deasy, C. L., J. Am. Chem. Soc. 67 1646 (1945).
4. Corse, J. and Dimick, K. P., Flavor Research and Food Acceptance 1958 302 (Chem. Abstr. 53 5534 (1959).
5. Ikeda, R. M., Rolle, L. A., Vannier, S. H., and Stanley, W. L., J. Agric. Food Chem. 10 98 (1962).
6. Attaway, J. A., Wolford, R. W., and Edwards, G. J., J. Agric. Food Chem. 10 102 (1962).
7. Holley, A. D. and Holley, R. W., Anal. Chem. 24 216 (1952).
8. Meigh, D. F., Nature 169 706 (1952).
9. Gordon, B. E., Wopat, F., Burnham, H. D., and Jones, L. C., Anal. Chem. 23 1754 (1951).
10. Meigh, D. F., Nature 170 579 (1952).
11. Roberts, J. D. and Green, C., J. Am. Chem. Soc. 68 214 (1946).
12. Thompson, A. R., Austral. J. Sci. Res. B4 180 (1951).
13. Hultin, H. O. and Proctor, B. E., Food Technol. 16 108 (1961).

Chapter 8
TERPENOIDS AND STEROIDS

The diverse compounds covered in this chapter are not traditionally grouped together but are usually put under such categories as essential oils, sterols, alkaloids, pigments, cardiac glycosides, etc. Only from a consideration of recent biosynthetic studies is it evident that they may be reasonably grouped together as compounds whose basic skeletons are all derived from mevalonic acid or a closely related precursor. To be sure, this biosynthetic unity does not imply any functional unity or, indeed, any detailed unity in chemical properties, which depend more on functional groups than on carbon skeleton.

As the structures of this group of compounds were elucidated, it became apparent that many of them could be regarded as built up of isoprene or iso-pentane units linked together in various ways and with different types of ring closures, degrees of unsaturation, and functional groups.

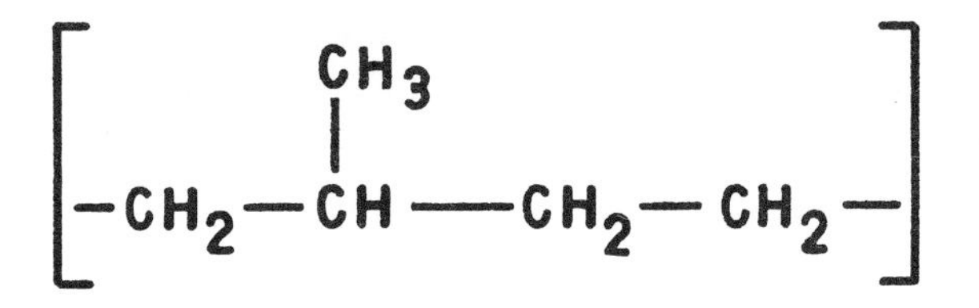

iso-pentane unit

The commonest arrangement appeared to be "head-to-tail":

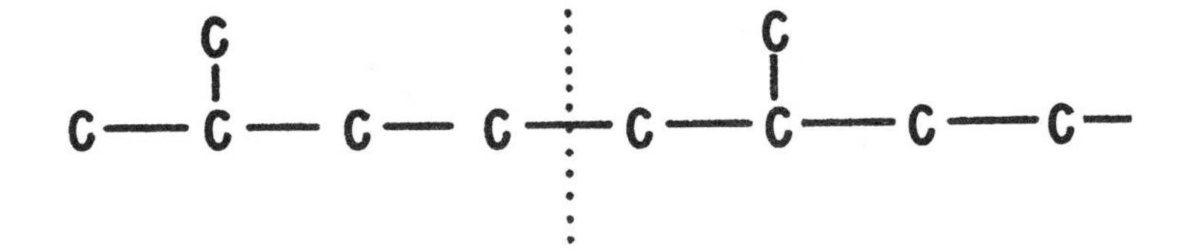

and this head-to-tail rule was regarded as so general that the correctness of proposed structures could be judged by seeing whether they conformed to it. As more compounds have been discovered, both types of possible exceptions have been found to this isoprene rule-----i.e. isoprenoid-type compounds have been found which do not contain even numbers of isoprene units, and compounds have been found where the head-to-tail arrangement is not followed. Individual cases will be discussed below, but they do not destroy the great utility of the isoprene rule as a working hypothesis. However, there is grave danger in supposing that any molecule which can be shown on paper to contain an isoprene residue is actually formed by reactions similar to those of terpene biosynthesis. For instance, the flavonoids can be dissected into two isoprene residues plus hypothetical C_3 and C_2 units:

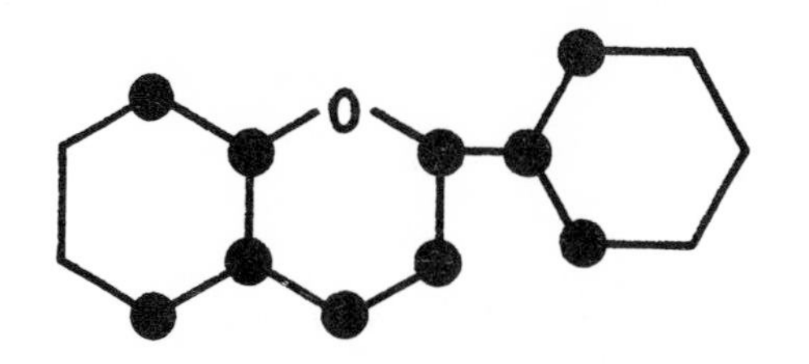

yet their biosynthesis is completely separate from that of the terpenoids and involves no isoprenoid-type intermediates. Decisions as to the proper placement of such compounds must await the results of biochemical studies.

Most compounds discussed in this chapter are considered to have their basic structures built up entirely of isoprenoid units. Other classes of plant constituents occasionally have isoprenoid side chains attached to obviously non-isoprenoid central structures. The placement of such compounds is clearly arbitrary, but some examples may be seen among the flavonoids (calophyllolide, rotenone), aromatics (galbanic acid) and porphyrins (chlorophyll).

The fundamental isoprenoid building pattern is one of the most widespread in natural products. Every living organism apparently contains some compounds built on this basis. All of these may be regarded as evolutionary modifications of a primeval mevalonic acid pathway. The adaptive importance of these different ramifications, however, remains almost completely obscure. There seems merit in the possibility that some of these compounds merely represent ways of disposing of excess acetate. In other cases more specific funtions appear reasonable and will be mentioned in the appropriate places. It is a general observation that lower terpenoids are rather restricted to phylogenetically young plant groups while carotenoids and steroids are more widespread.

HEMITERPENOIDS

Isoprene itself does not occur free in nature, but several five-carbon compounds are known with the isoprene skeleton. These include simple alcohols, aldehydes, and acids as well as the unusual sugar apiose (q. v.). They may occur free or as esters and ethers. Some examples are given in Table 1. Their chemistry is simple and requires no additional discussion here. The natural occurrence and chemistry of tiglic and angelic acids has been reviewed by Buckles *et al.* (1).

MONOTERPENOIDS

The monoterpenoids appear to be built of two isoprene residues and normally have ten carbon atoms, although rare examples are known of compounds which seem constructed on this general principle but have lost one or more carbon atoms. Both cyclic and open-chain compounds are known. In fact almost every possible arrangement of ten carbon atoms seems to occur in nature. Only some of the more common examples can be given here as illustrations. The term "terpenoid" is preferred for reference to all compounds built of isoprene units, regardless of the functional groups present while "terpene" refers specifically to hydrocarbons. Over one hundred different monoterpenoids have been isolated from plants. They are the major components of many essential oils and as such have great economic importance as flavors, perfumes and solvents. They are characteristically colorless, water-insoluble, steam distillable liquids having a fragrant odor. Some are optically active. Study of their chemistry is complicated by the difficulty of obtaining pure compounds from the complex mixtures in which they usually occur and by the readiness with which they undergo rearrangement.

TABLE 1. SOME HEMITERPENOIDS

Compound	Source
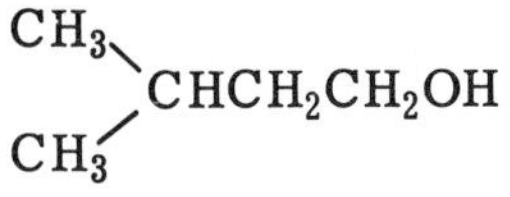 CH_3 \ $CHCH_2CH_2OH$ CH_3 / *iso*-Amyl Alcohol	as an ester in essential oils of *Mentha, Eucalyptus, Ribes,* etc.
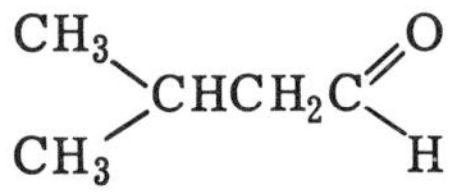 CH_3 \ //O $CHCH_2C$ CH_3 / \ H *iso*-Valeraldehyde	in essential oil of *Eucalyptus, Eugenia, Santalum,* etc.
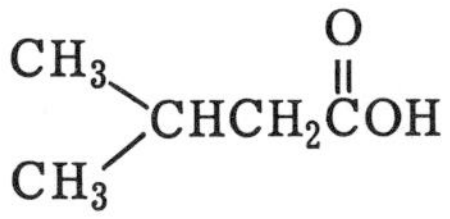 O CH_3 \ ‖ $CHCH_2COH$ CH_3 / *iso*-Valeric Acid	widespread, e.g. in *Valeriana* spp.
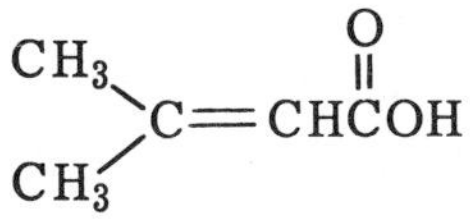 O CH_3 \ ‖ $C=CHCOH$ CH_3 / Senecioic Acid	*Senecio kaempferi* and elsewhere
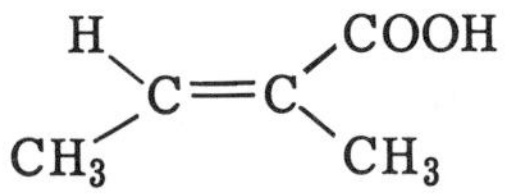 H \ / COOH $C=C$ CH_3 / \ CH_3 Tiglic Acid	widespread, e.g. *Geranium* spp.
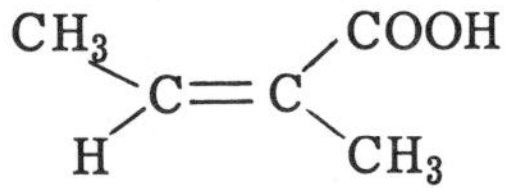 CH_3 \ / COOH $C=C$ H / \ CH_3 Angelic Acid	widespread, e.g. *Archangelica officinalis*
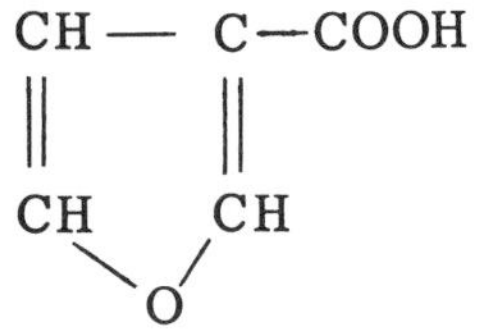 CH — C—COOH ‖ ‖ CH CH \ / O β-Furoic Acid	*Phaseolus multiformis*

The distribution of monoterpenoids in economically important essential oils is surveyed in the treatise of Guenther (see General References). The majority of these compounds occur widely and are not characteristic of particular plants or plant groups. It is rare for a single plant to contain only one terpenoid, but one may be predominant. Although the presence of monoterpenes is best documented in the seed plants, there are scattered reports of the occurrence of terpene-containing volatile oils throughout the plant kingdom down to the bryophytes and even fungi (2, 3). More information on the terpenes of lower plants would be welcome.

Most investigators are of the opinion that the function of most lower terpenoids in plants may be described as ecological rather than physiological. Many of them inhibit the growth of competing plants and may also be insecticidal. The possible ecological significance of terpenoids (and other secondary plant constituents) is well demonstrated by Fraenkel (4).

Structures of some open-chain monoterpenoids are given in Table 2. They have been chosen to illustrate a variety of double bond locations, functional groups, and deviations from the usual head-to-tail isoprene rule. Terpenoid alcohols frequently are found as esters rather than free alcohols.

It will be noted that opportunity for geometrical isomerism exists in geraniol and geranial. Their isomers, nerol and neral, occur in nature; and a mixture of geranial and neral, known as citral, constitutes 80% of the commercially valuable lemon grass oil.

Considerations of sterochemistry become especially important with the cyclic terpenoids and increase in complexity in the higher terpenoids and steroids. Most cyclic terpenoids may be regarded as cyclohexane derivatives, so a brief summary of cyclohexane sterochemistry will be given at this point. A full review of this subject is presented in an article by Orloff (5). A cyclohexane ring whether it is free or bonded to another ring cannot be planar as it is normally pictured in structural formulas, but as a result of C-C bond angles assumes a puckered shape or conformation. Geometrically the conformation may be pictured either as a "boat" form or "chair" form:

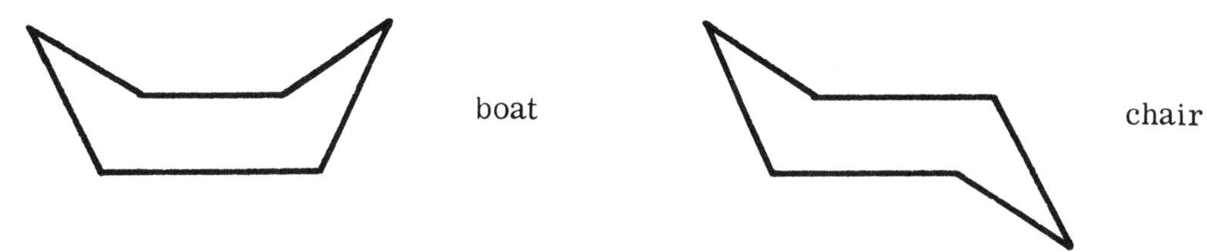

Except in special cases this geometrical possibility does not result in the appearance of actual pairs of isomers since the two forms are readily interconvertible. However, the chair form is considered to represent the preferred conformation. In a fixed molecule the two remaining carbon valences are not equivalent. This is best observed in a molecular model but is indicated diagrammatically as follows:

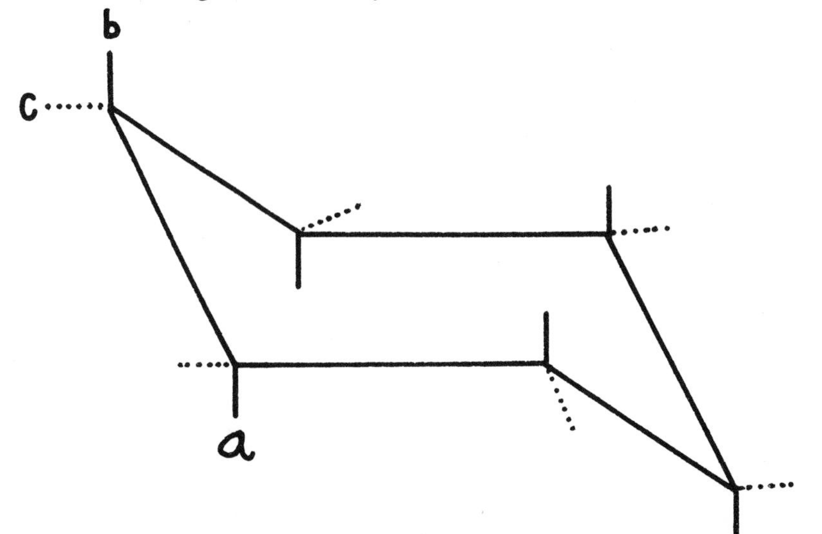

TABLE 2. OPEN-CHAIN MONOTERPENOIDS

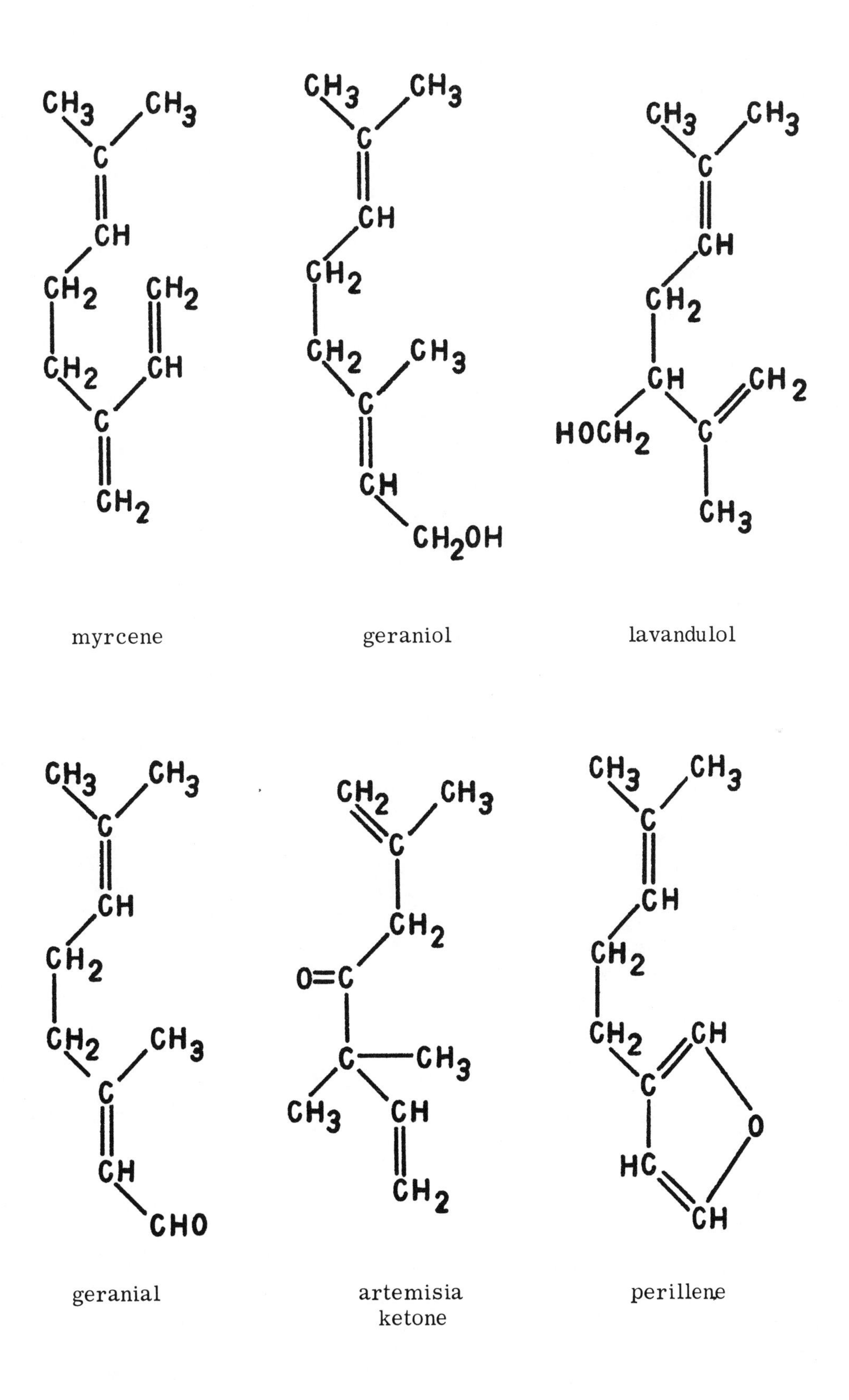

myrcene geraniol lavandulol

geranial artemisia ketone perillene

The bonds which extend roughly perpendicularly to the ring are known as axial or polar. The others are named equatorial and are more nearly coplanar with the ring. Experience with a molecular model will show that the ring may readily be flipped so that all axial bonds become equatorial and *vice versa;* therefore with an unsubstituted ring the distinction is of no significance. However, when substituent groups are present, they are more easily accommodated in equatorial positions and therefore tend to stabilize the conformation which has the bulkiest groups equatorial. The final consequence of conformational analysis to be mentioned here is that groups on adjacent carbons are described as *cis* if one is axial and the other equatorial, or *trans* if they are both either axial or equatorial. In the above figure a and b are *trans* whereas a and c are *cis*. These generalizations become important when considering the chemistry of these compounds, the differences between compounds, and possible routes of biosynthesis. The great majority of monocylic monterpenoids have the so called p-menthane skeleton:

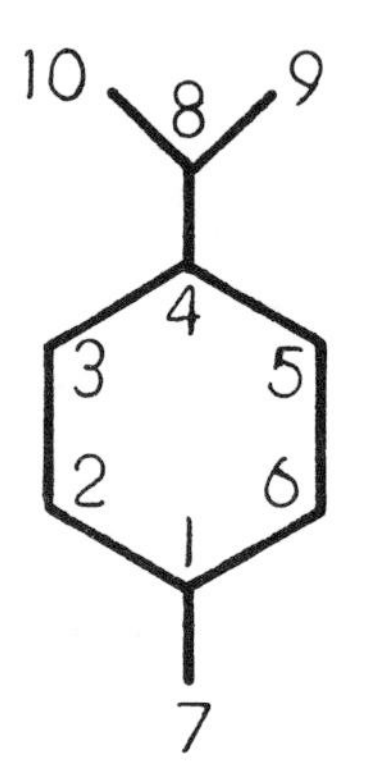

Variations are introduced into this basic structure by double bonds and functional groups. The most important compound of this group because of its widespread occurrence and commercial value is limonene. It is the chief constituent of citrus fruit oils but occurs in many other essential oils as well. A few other monocyclic compounds lacking the p-menthane structure also are known. Some examples are shown in Table 3. The sources given are intended only to be typical. Most of the compounds are widely distributed. Asymmetric carbon atoms are pointed out by asterisks, but generally both isomers are known in nature either from two different plants or sometimes both from the same plant. The (+), (-) mixture of limonenes is known commercially as dipentene. The ionones and irone are important perfumery materials which closely resemble the monocyclic monoterpenoids in structure but have additional carbon atoms:

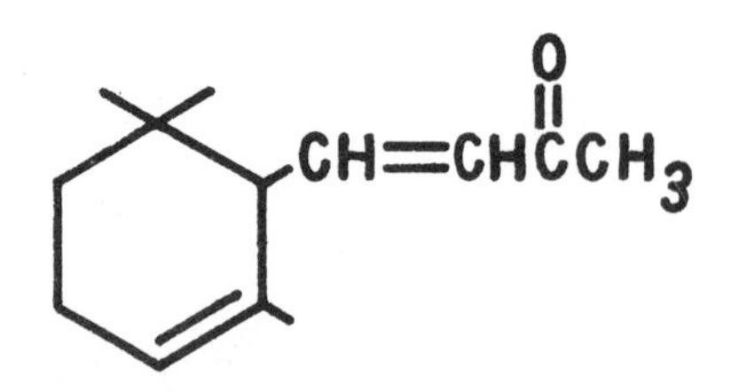

α-ionone *(Boronia megastigma)*

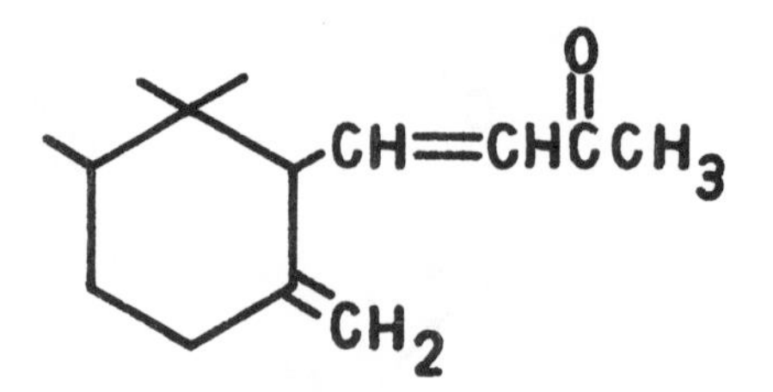

irone *(Iris florentina)*

TABLE 3. SOME MONCYCLIC MONOTERPENOIDS, STRUCTURES AND OCCURRENCE

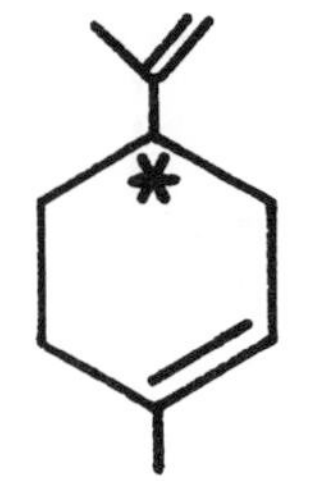

limonene (*Citrus* spp.)

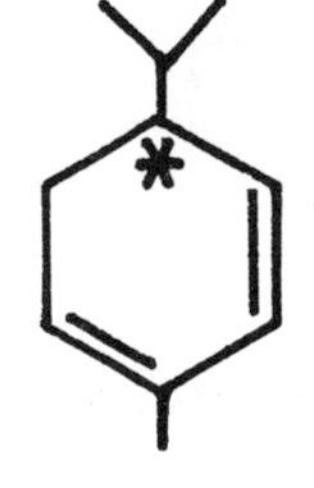

α-phellandrene (*Eucalyptus* spp.)

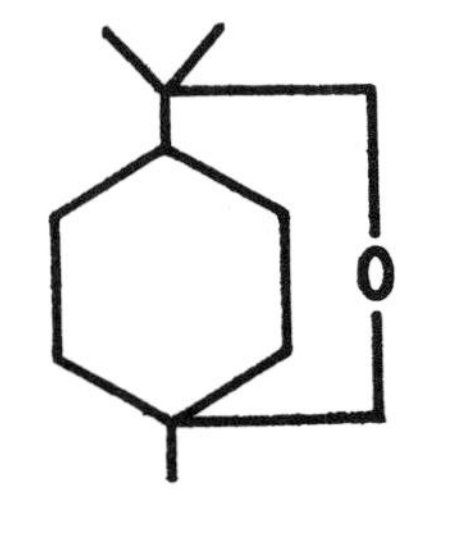

1:8 cineole (*Artemisia maritima*)

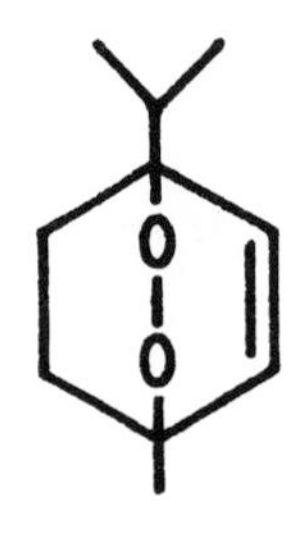

ascaridole (*Chenopodium ambrosioides*)

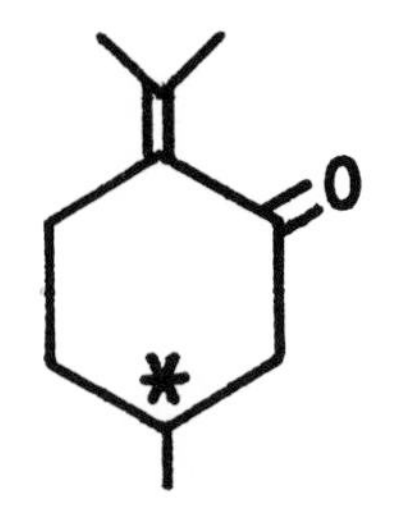

pulegone (*Mentha pulegium*)

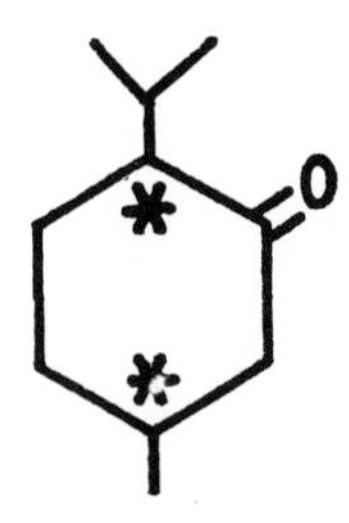

menthone (*Mentha piperita*)

Table 3. Continued

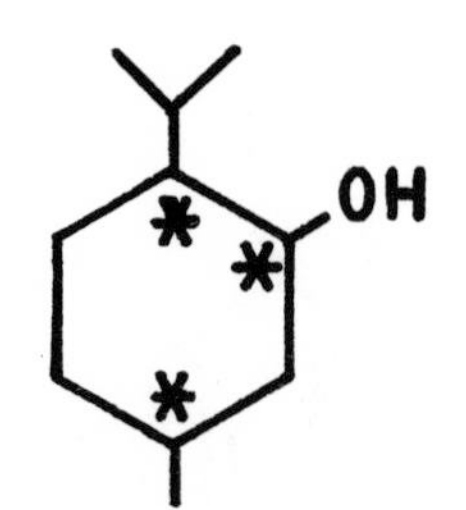

menthol *(Mentha piperita)*

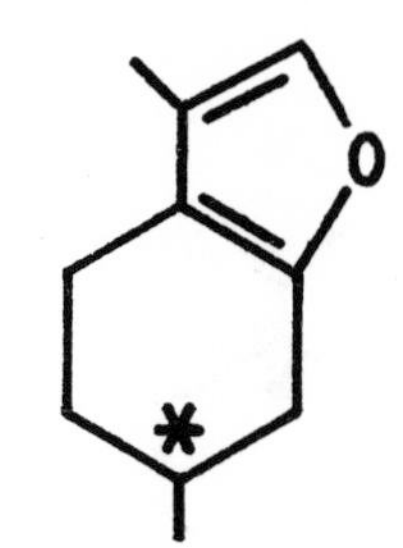

menthofuran *(Mentha piperita)*

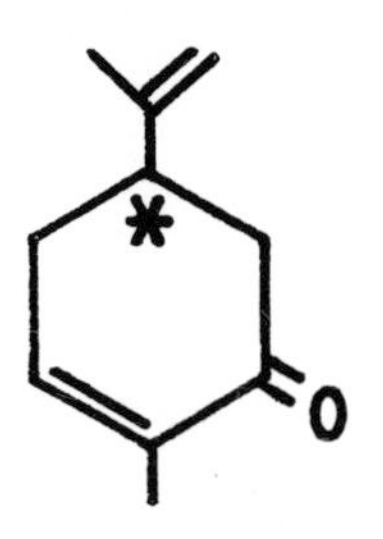

carvone *(Carum carvi)*

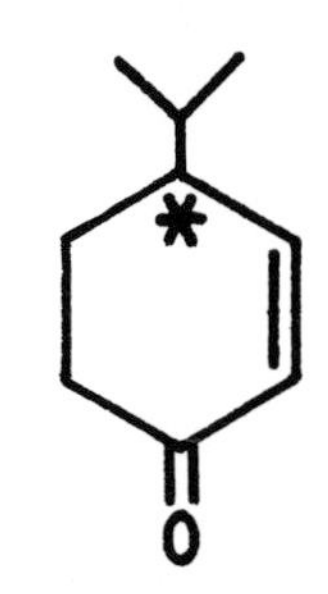

cryptone *(Eucalyptus* spp.*)*

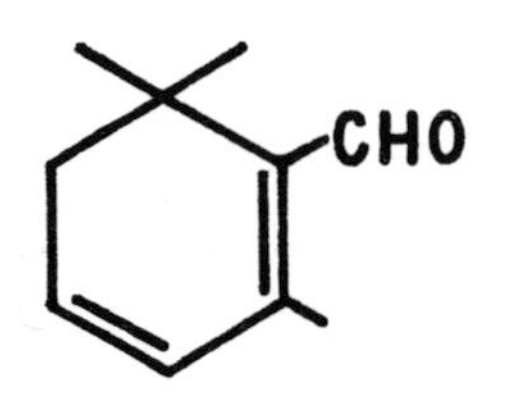

safranal *(Crocus sativus)*

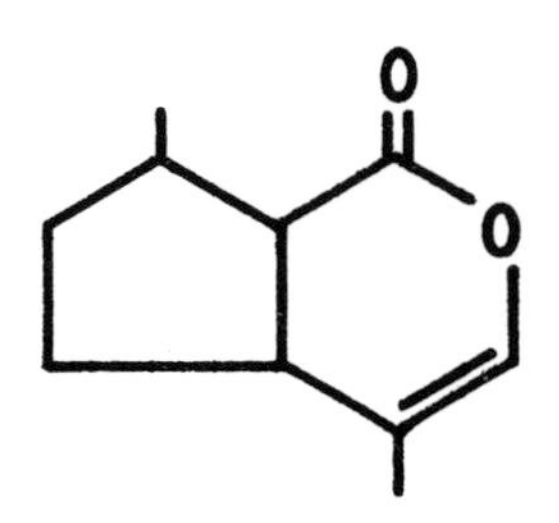

nepetalactone *(Nepeta cataria)*

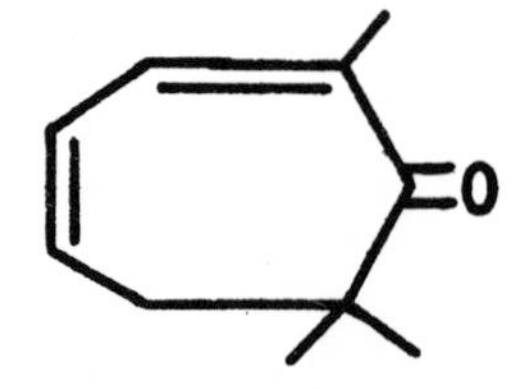

eucarvone *(Asarum sieboldi)*

The bicyclic monoterpenoids are divided into seven classes according to their carbon skeletons. These are as follows:*

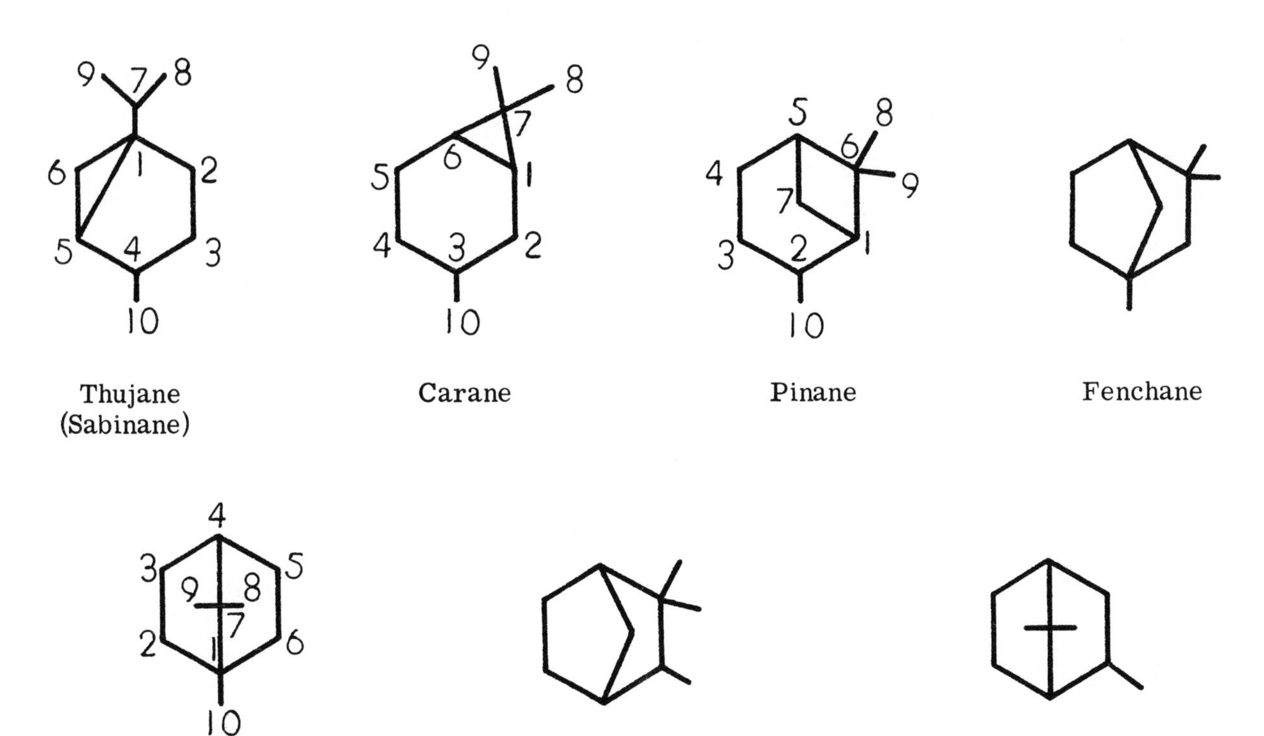

Thujane (Sabinane) Carane Pinane Fenchane

Camphane (Bornane) *iso*-Camphane *iso*-Bornylane

These forms are easily visualized as derived from the monocyclic compounds by additional ring closures. The best known of this group (and possibly of all the terpenoids) is α-pinene, the chief component of turpentine. The structure of it and of a few of the other more important bicyclic monoterpenoids are given in Table 4.

Although usually classed as aromatic compounds, some constituents of essential oils are clearly related to the terpenoids. For example p-cymene and thymol found in oil of thyme are respectively:

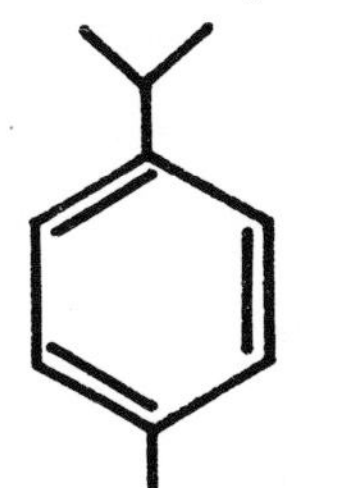

and

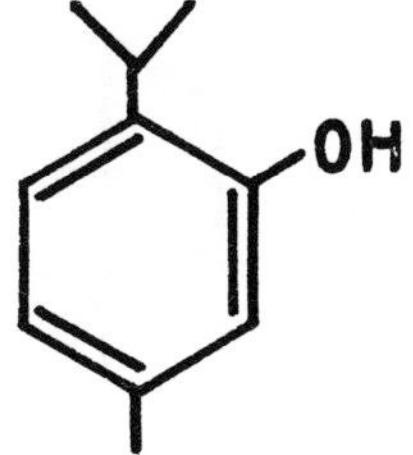

*It has been proposed (6) to name the last three structures as, respectively, 2,2,3-trimethylnorbornane, 1,3,3-trimethylnorbornane, and 2,7,7-trimethylnorbornane.

TABLE 4. BICYLIC MONOTERPENOIDS, STRUCTURE AND OCCURRENCE

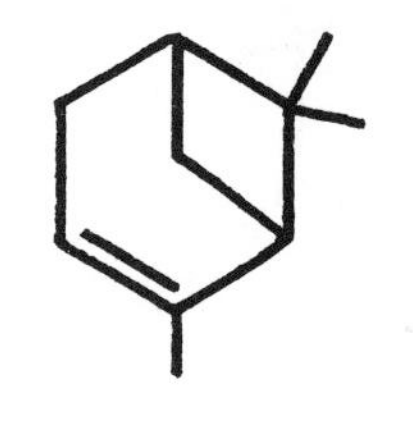

α-pinene *(Pinus* spp.)

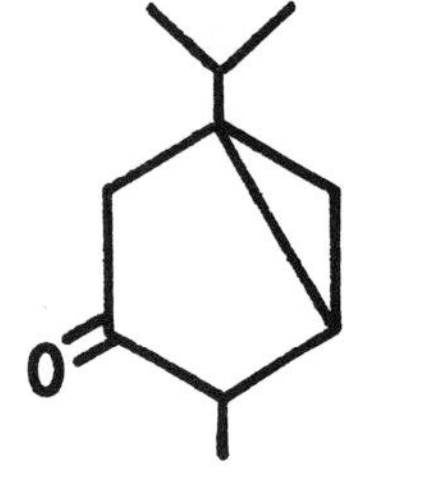

thujone *(Thuja* spp.)

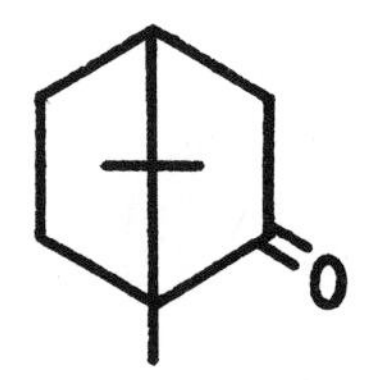

camphor *(Cinnamomum camphora)*

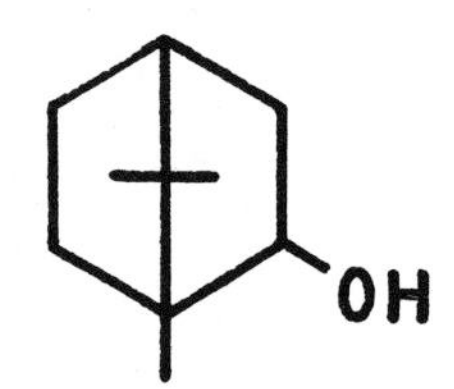

borneol *(Dryobalanops aromatica)*

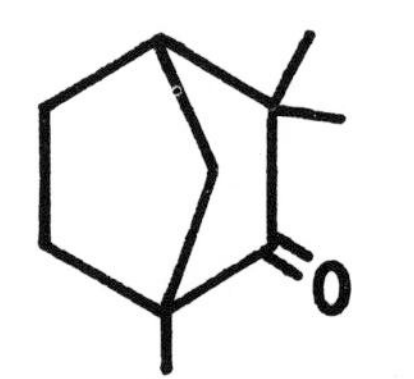

fenchone *(Foeniculum vulgare)*

Gossypol of cotton is:

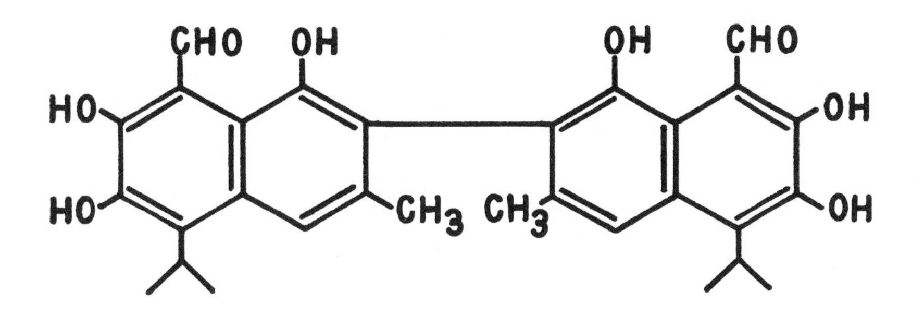

SESQUITERPENOIDS

The sesquiterpenoids are C_{15} compounds, usually regarded as derived from three isoprene residues. Like monoterpenoids they are found as constituents of steam-distillable essential oils. The general utility and occasional exceptions to the isoprene rule which were mentioned earlier apply also in this group of compounds.

The most important member of the acyclic sesquiterpenoids is the widely-distributed alcohol farnesol:

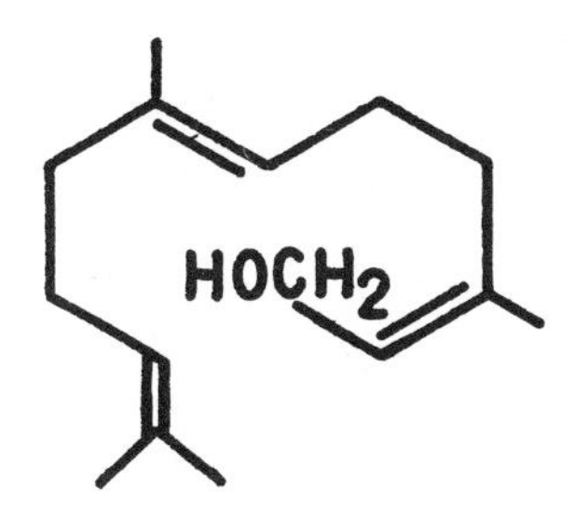

Its pyrophosphate is a key intermediate in terpenoid biosynthesis. Certain furanoid terpenoids are also classed as aliphatic since they are not carbocyclic. Examples of this type are ngaione and myoprone from the essential oils of *Myoporum* spp.

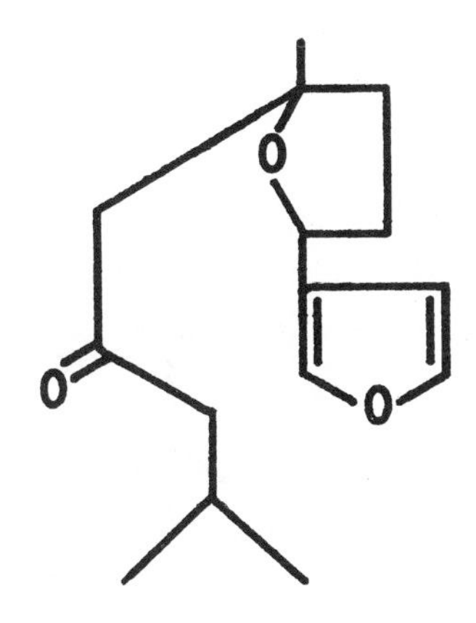

ngaione

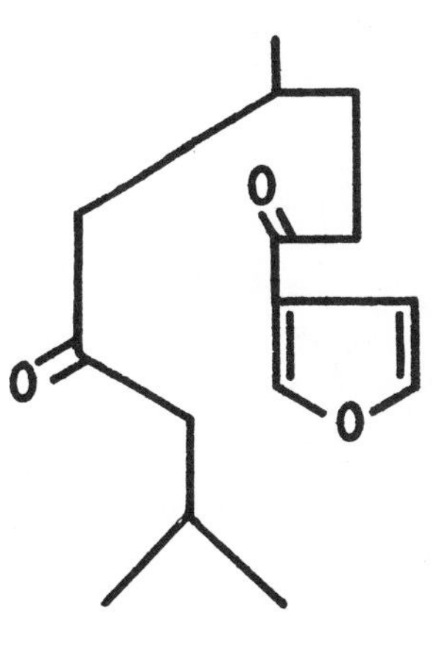

myoporone

Most of the monocyclic sesquiterpenoids have the skeleton shown below with variations in double bond location and functional groups. Some examples of this type are shown in Table 5.

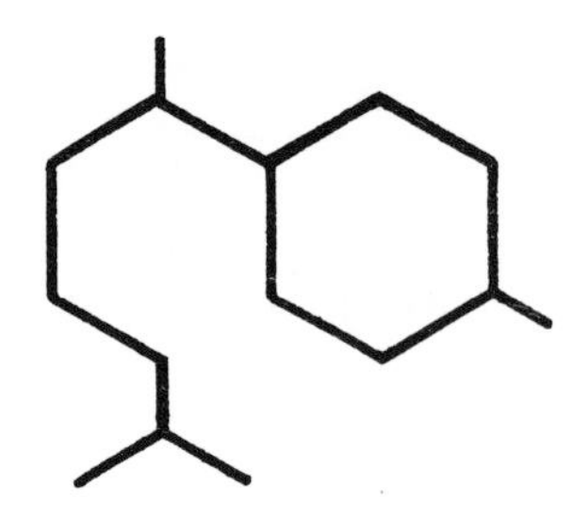

There are other more unusual monocyclic structures found among the sesquiterpenoids. Some of these cannot be conveniently constructed from isoprene residues. Presumably rearrangements and oxidation play a part in their formation from isoprenoid precursors. A few examples are given in Table 6.

Most of the bicyclic sesquiterpenoids can be divided into naphthalene types and azulene types according to which of these two aromatic structures they give on dehydrogenation. Further subdivision takes into account the locations of substituent groups on the rings. Low temperature distillation may be sufficient to convert some azulenogenic terpenoids into azulenes, and it is generally believed that the azulenes themselves never occur in nature, although this is open to some question (7, 8, 9).

Napthalenic:

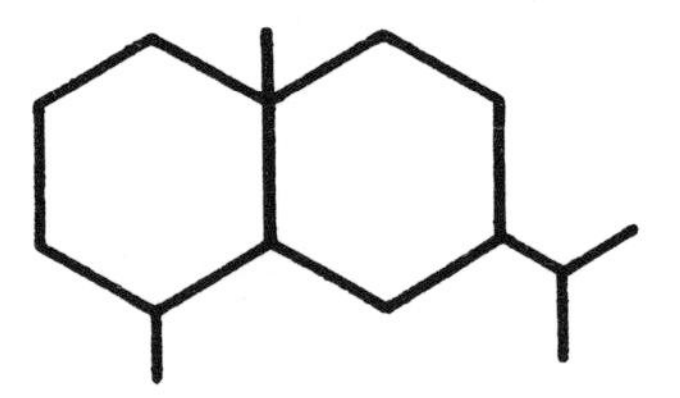

eudalene type

cadalene type

Azulenic:

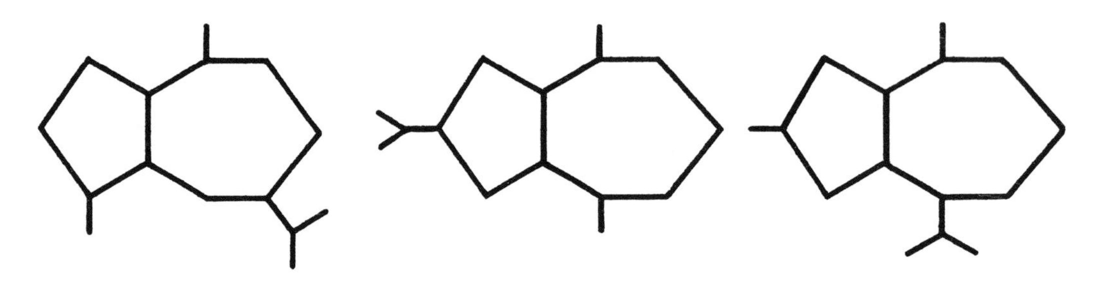

guaiazulene type vetivazulene type zierazulene type

Some specific examples are shown in Table 7.

TABLE 5. MONOCYCLIC SESQUITERPENOIDS, STRUCTURES AND OCCURRENCE

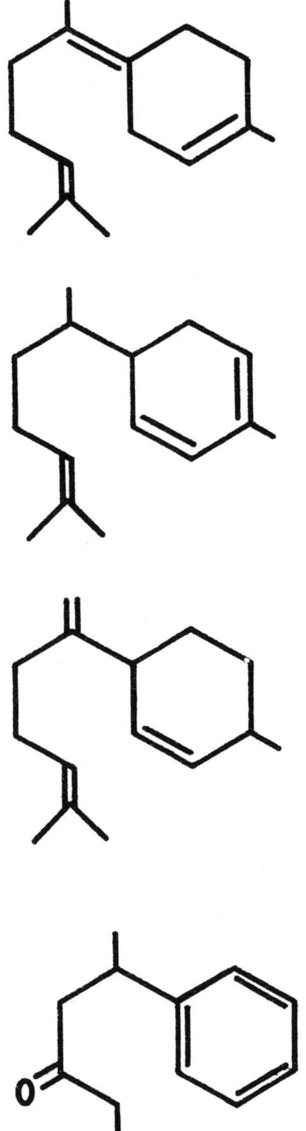

γ-bisabolene (widely distributed)

zingiberene *(Zingiber officinale)*

lanceol *(Santalum lanceolatum)*

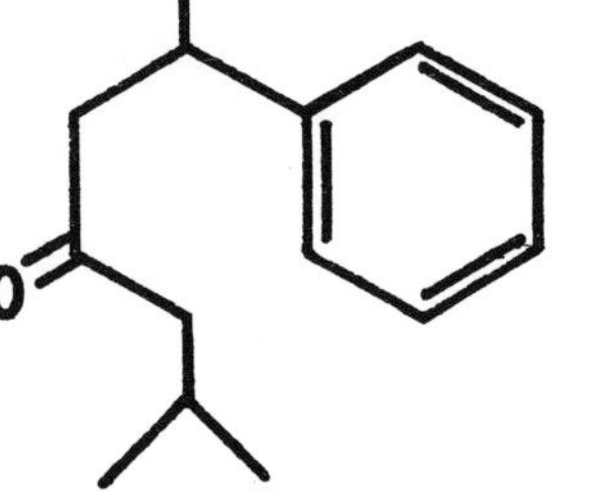

ar-turmerone *(Curcuma longa)*

perezone *(Trixis pipitzahuač)*

TABLE 6. UNUSUAL SESQUITERPENOID STRUCTURES

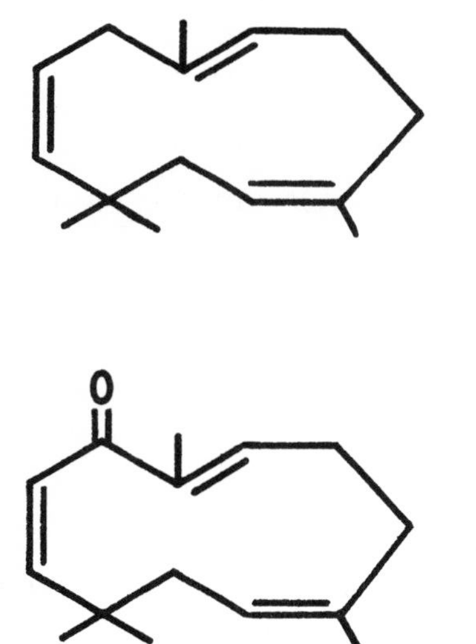

humulene *(Humulus lupulus)*

zerumbone *(Zingiber zerumbet)*

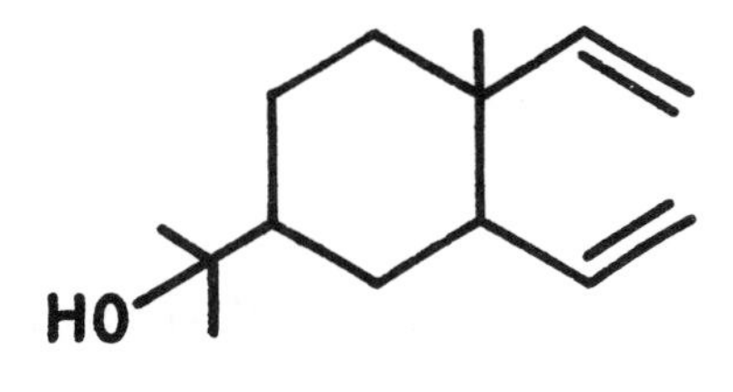

elemol *(Canarium luzonicum)*

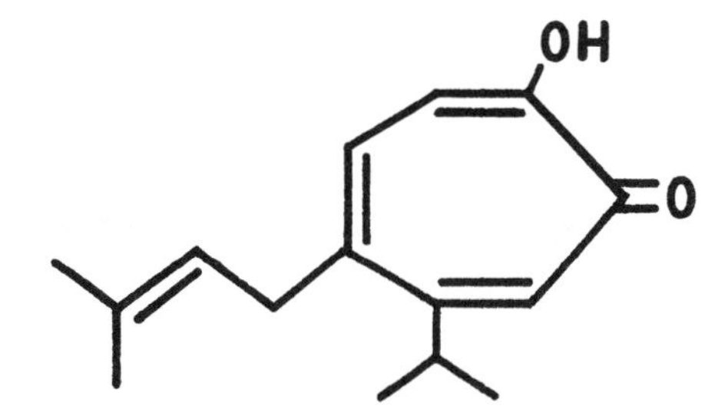

nootkatin *(Cupressus macrocarpa)*

TABLE 7. BICYCLIC SESQUITERPENOIDS, STRUCTURES AND OCCURRENCE

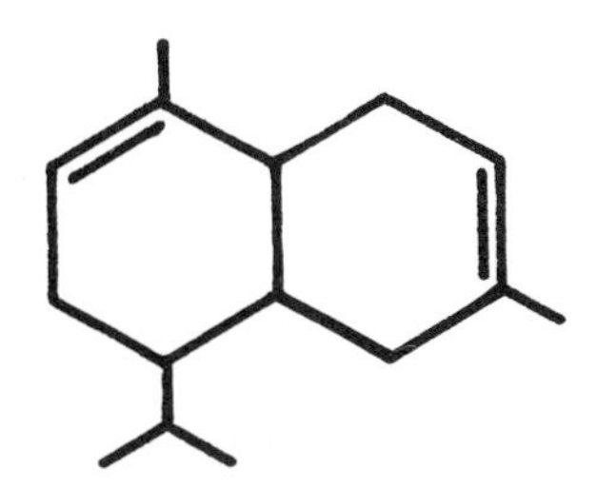

α-cadinene (*Cedrus* spp.)

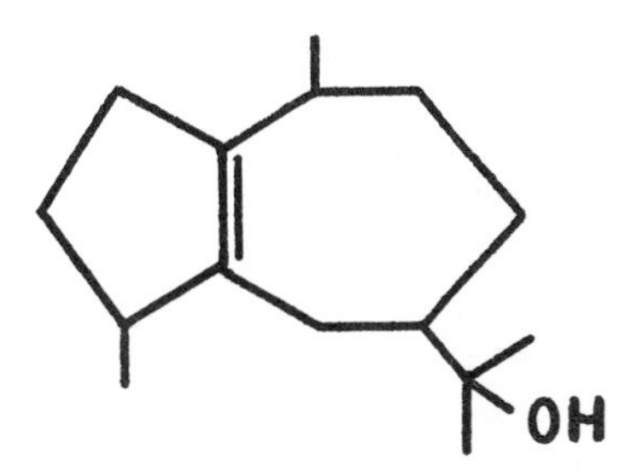

guaiol (*Guaiacum officinale)*

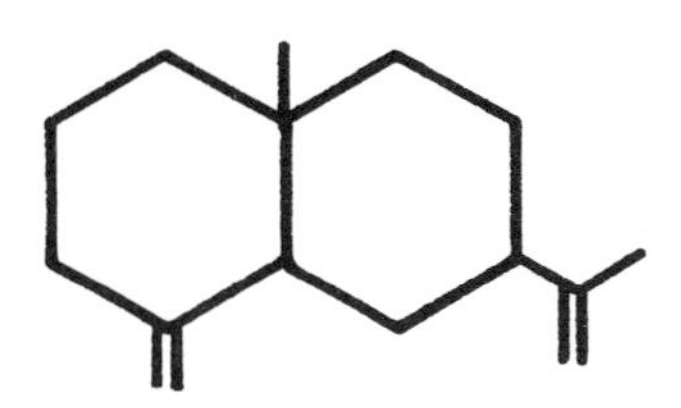

β-selinene *(Apium graveolens)*

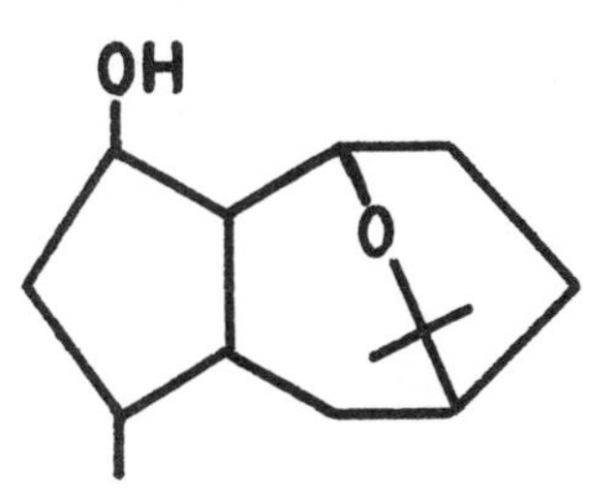

kessyl alcohol
(Valeriana officinalis)

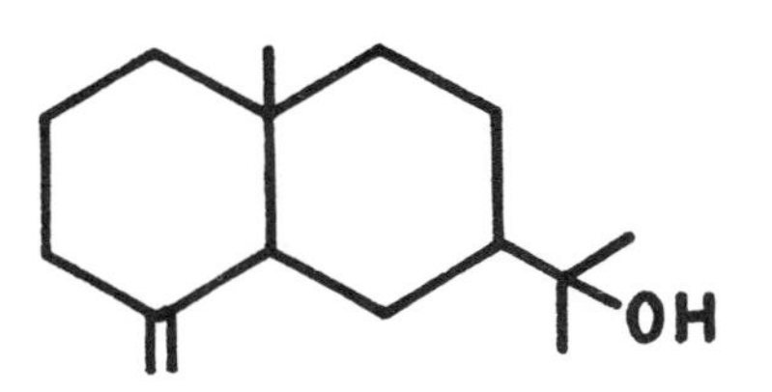

eudesmol *(Eucalyptus piperita)*

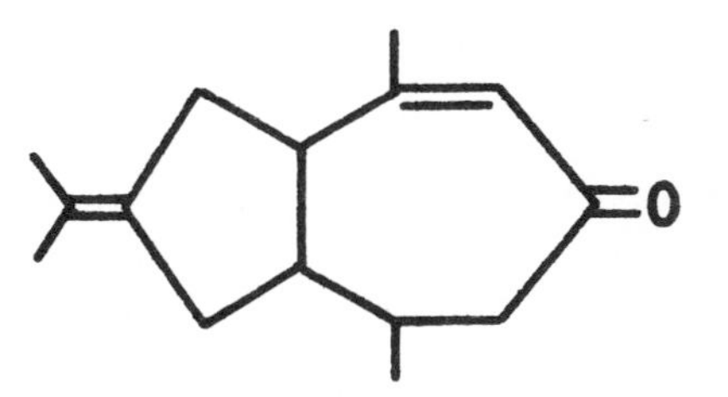

vetivone *(Vetiveria zizanioides)*

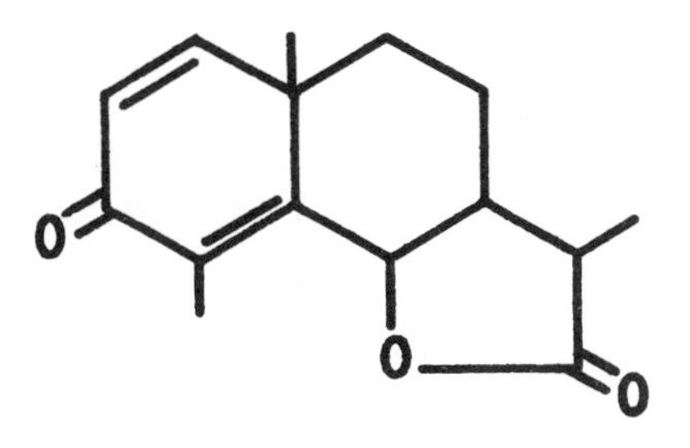

santonin *(Artemisia* spp.)

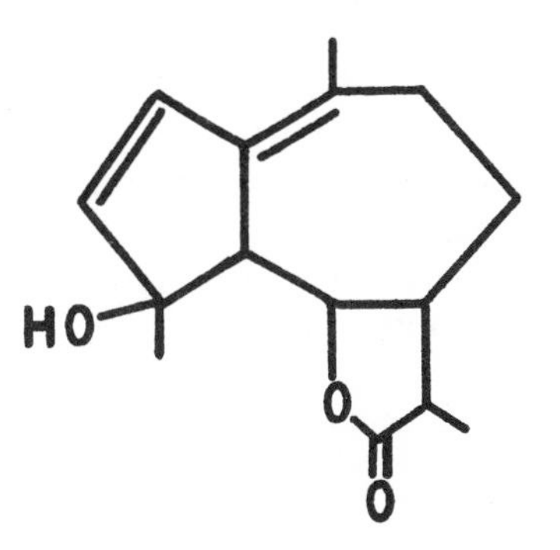

artabsin *(Artemisia absinthium)*

Additional examples of bicyclic and tricyclic sesquiterpenoids are also shown in Table 8 to indicate some of the more unusual structures that are found. One of the most interesting of these is iresin whose bicyclofarnesol type structure is similar to that of many diterpenoids but otherwise unknown among the sesquiterpenoids (10). Acorone is the only naturally occuring spirane so far discovered.

DITERPENOIDS

The diterpenoids are C_{20} compounds which may be formally regarded (with some exceptions) as derived from four isoprenoid residues. Because of their high boiling points they are not usually found in volatile oils of plants although a few of the lower boiling ones may be. They are found in resins and in the resinous high boiling fractions remaining after distillation of essential oils. The rosin remaining after distilling pine turpentine, for instance, is rich in diterpenoids. Their great complexity and difficulty of separation has resulted in only a relatively few completely known structures in this group compared to the vast number which probably occur in nature. As with the lower terpenes, hydrocarbons, alcohols, ethers and acids are all known in this group. The only important acyclic member is the alcohol phytol which forms a part of the chlorophyll molecule.

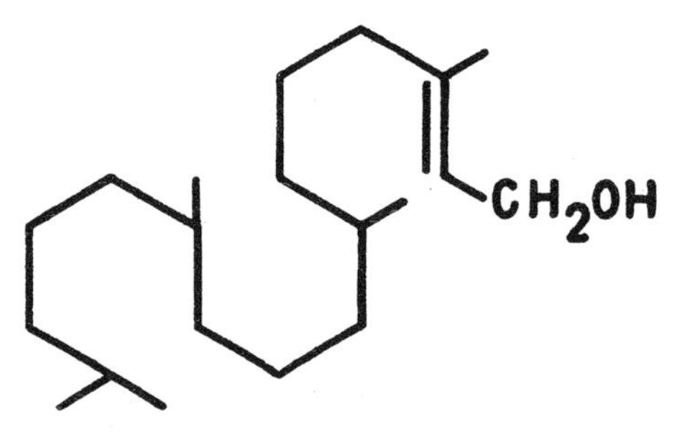

phytol

Many of the cyclic diterpenoids may be regarded as derived from phytol by ring closures, but others do not show the head-to-tail type of linkage. Some examples are given in Table 9. Diterpenoids have been reviewed by Tsutsui and Ashworth (11).

TRITERPENOIDS

Since C_{25} terpenoids are not found in nature, there is a great increase in complexity on going from the diterpenoids to the C_{30} triterpenoids. Only a few of them have been highly purified and have had their structures completely determined. Triterpenoids are widely distributed in plant resins, cork, and cutin. The so-called resin acids are triterpenoid acids frequently associated with polysaccharide gums in gum resins. Triterpenoid alcohols occur both free and as glycosides. Many of the glycosides are classed as saponins (q. v.). Triterpenoid hydrocarbons and ketones are also known. Triterpenoids are reviewed by Jeger (12).

The only important acyclic triterpenoid is the hydrocarbon squalene which was first isolated from shark liver oils but is also found in some plant oils (e. g. olive oil). Since it is presumed to be an intermediate in steroid biosynthesis, it must be made at least in small amounts by all organisms which synthesize steroids.

TABLE 8. UNUSUAL SESQUITERPENOID STRUCTURES

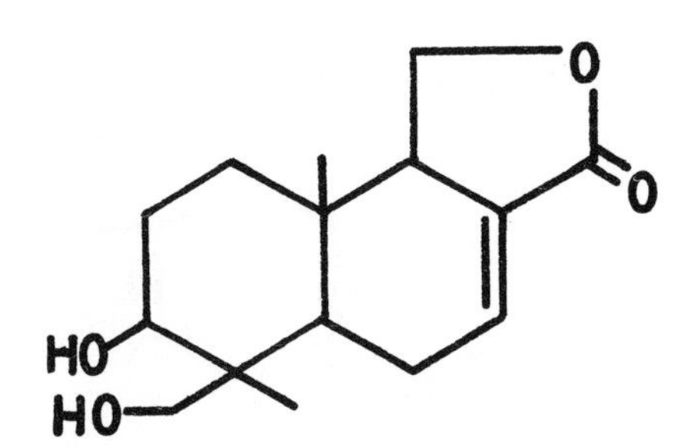

iresin *(Iresine celosiodes)*

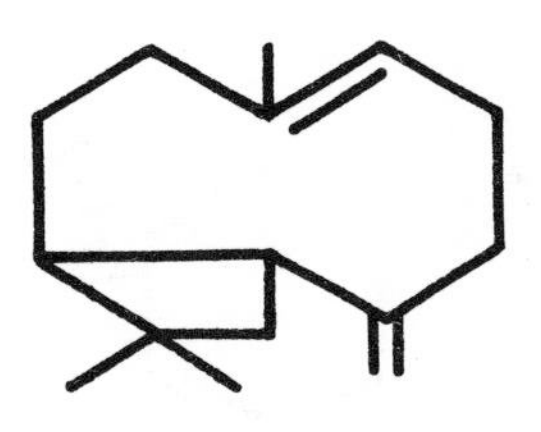

caryophyllene *(Eugenia caryophyllata)*

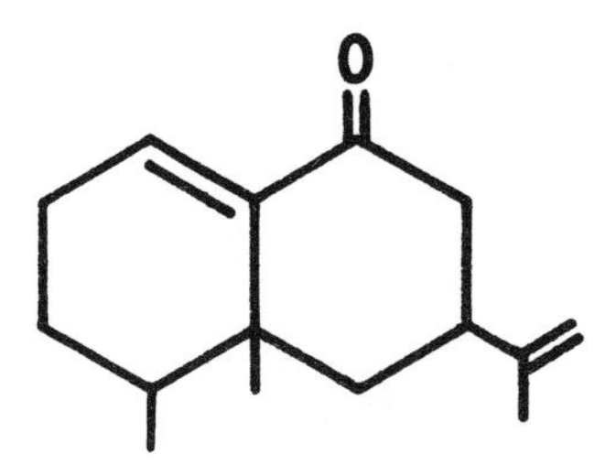

eremophilone *(Eremophilia mitchelli)*

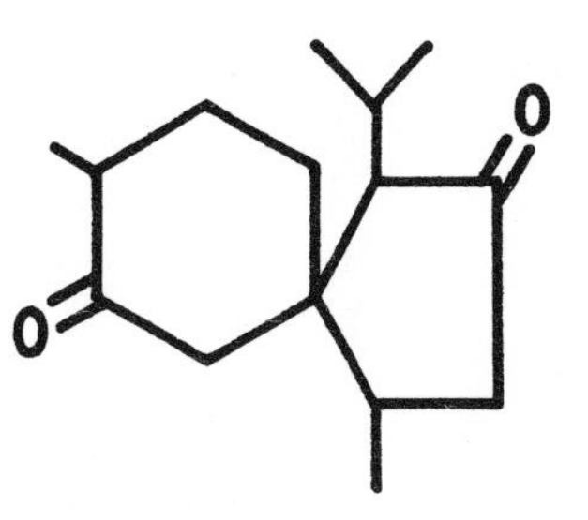

acorone *(Acorus calamus)*

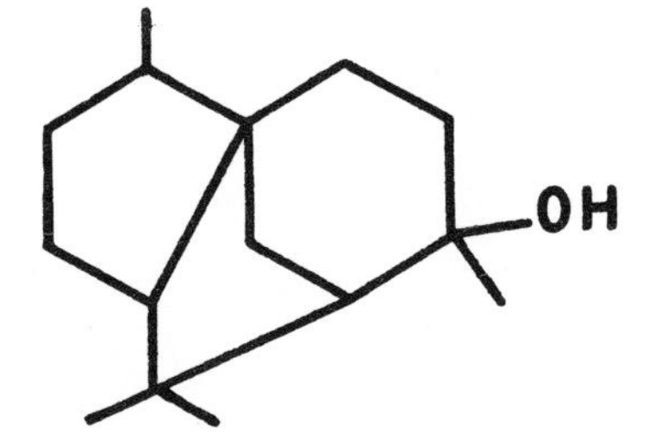

cedrol (*Cedrus* spp.)

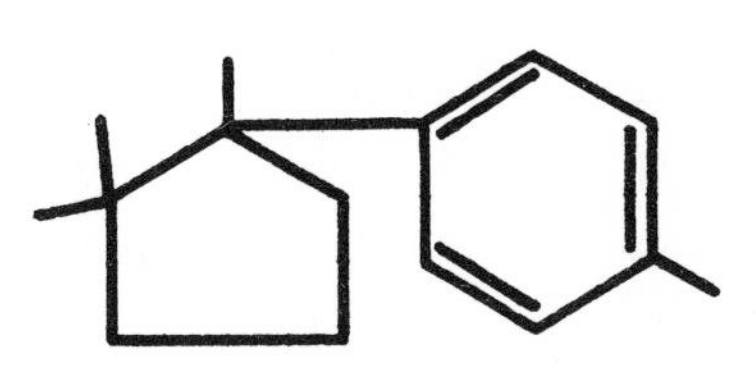

cuparene *(Cupressus* spp.)

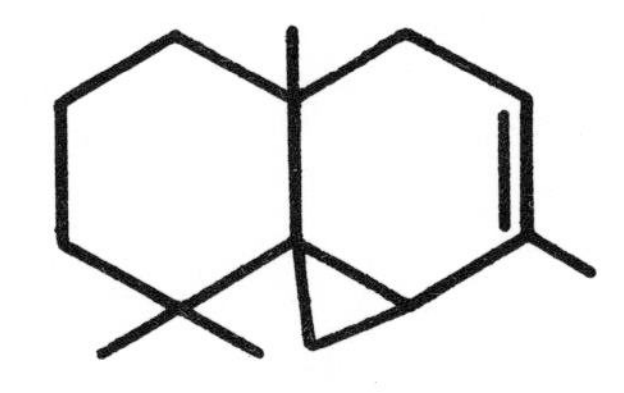

thujopsene *(Thuja* spp.)

TABLE 9. CYCLIC DITERPENOIDS, STRUCTURES AND OCCURRENCE

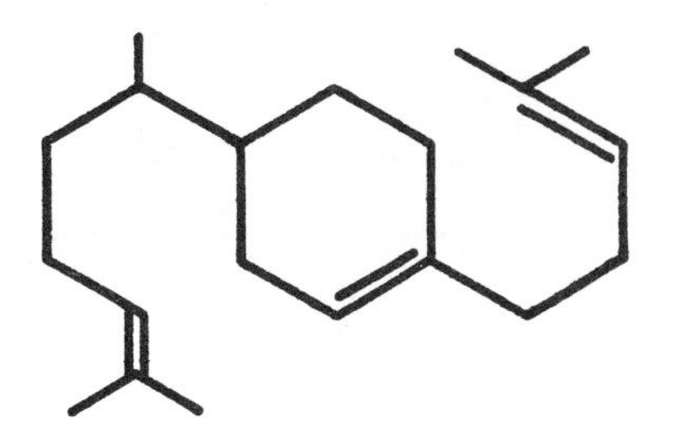

α-camphorene *(Cinnamonum camphora)*

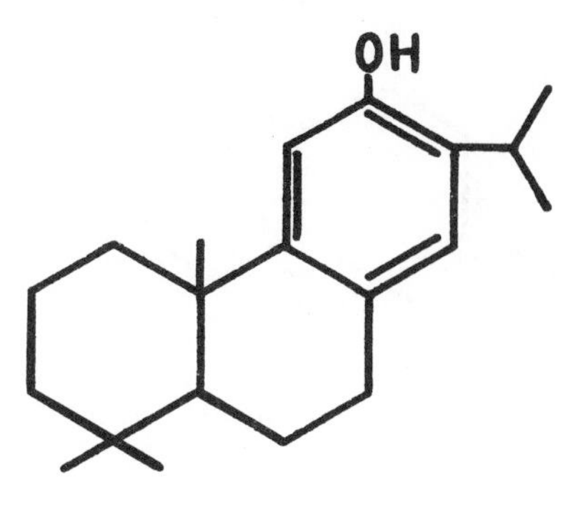

ferruginol *(Podocarpus ferrugineus)*

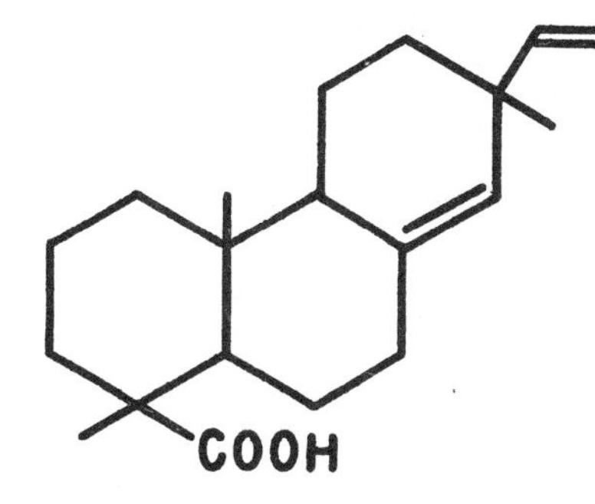

dextro-pimaric acid *(Pinus maritima)*

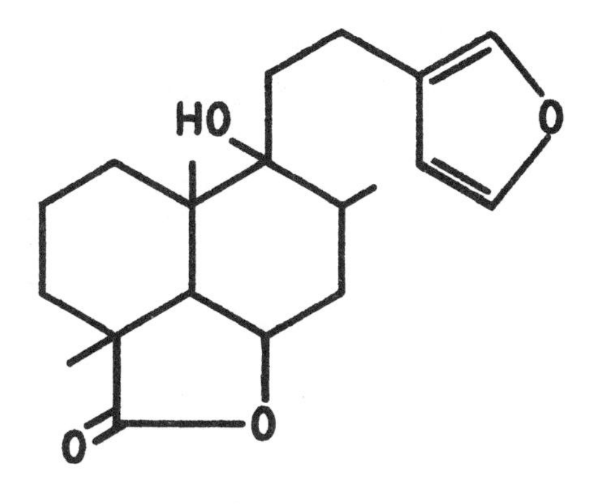

marrubin *(Marrubium vulgare)*

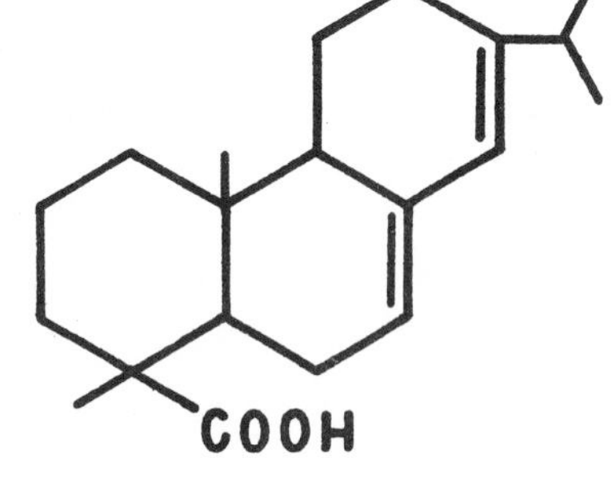

abietic acid *(Pinus palustris)*

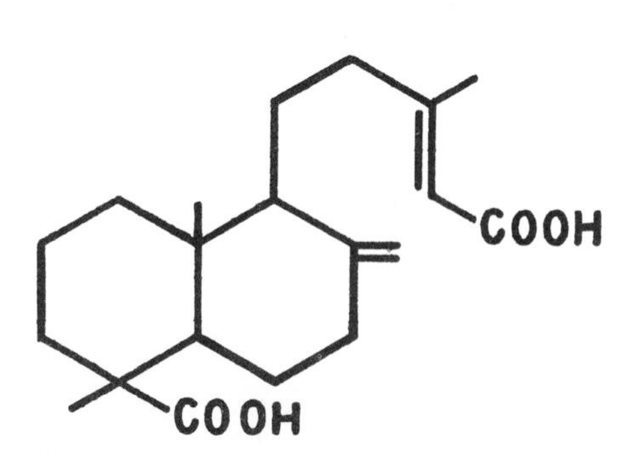

agathic acid *(Agathis alba)*

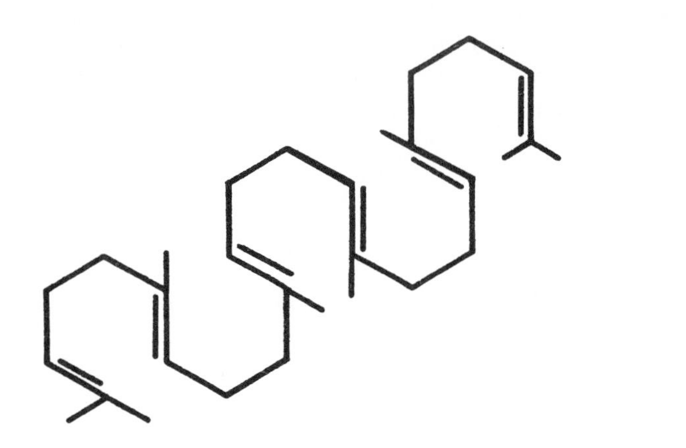

squalene

No triterpenoids so far have been found to have monocyclic or dicyclic structures. Tricyclic ones are rare. Several tetracyclic triterpenoids are known. They are of interest chiefly because of their resemblance and probable biogenetic relationship to the steroids. For a long time some of them were thought to be sterols, and this misconception is reflected in their names. The best known of these compounds is lanosterol which occurs in wool fat, yeast, and some higher plants (e.g. *Euphorbia electa)*. Like squalene, it appears to be an intermediate in steroid biosynthesis. Other tetracyclic triterpenoids are the alcohol euphol from *Euphorbia* spp. and the so-called elemi acids of *Canarium commune*. The tetracyclic triterpenoids are reviewed by Jones and Halsall (13).

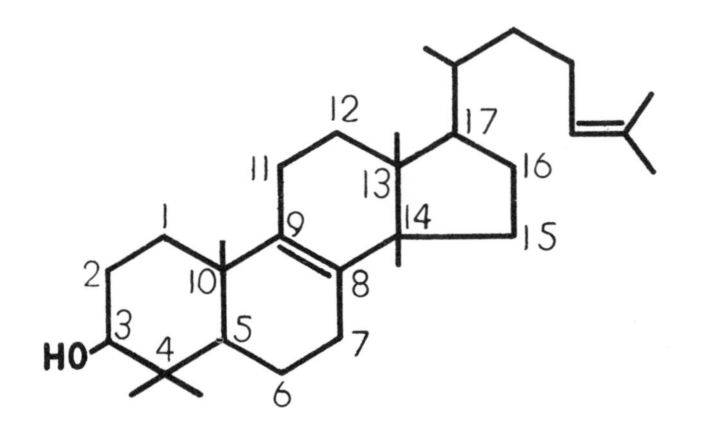

lanosterol

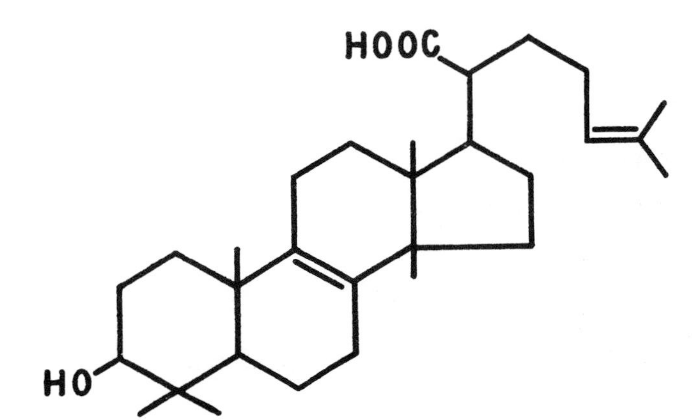

elemadienolic acid

The most important and widely distributed triterpenoids are the pentacyclic compounds. They have been found in plants as primitive as *Sphagnum* (14) but are most common among the seed plants, both free and as glycosides (see also under "Saponins"). The nonglycosidic triterpenoids are frequently found as excretions and in cuticle where they may have a protective or waterproofing function. Zimmerman (15) has proposed the interesting generalization that monohydroxy triterpene alcohols are not accompanied by pigments in the plant whereas triterpene diols occur along with carotenoids, and triterpene acids with flavonoids.

Three basic ring skeletons are recognized, derived from three hypothetical hydrocarbons.

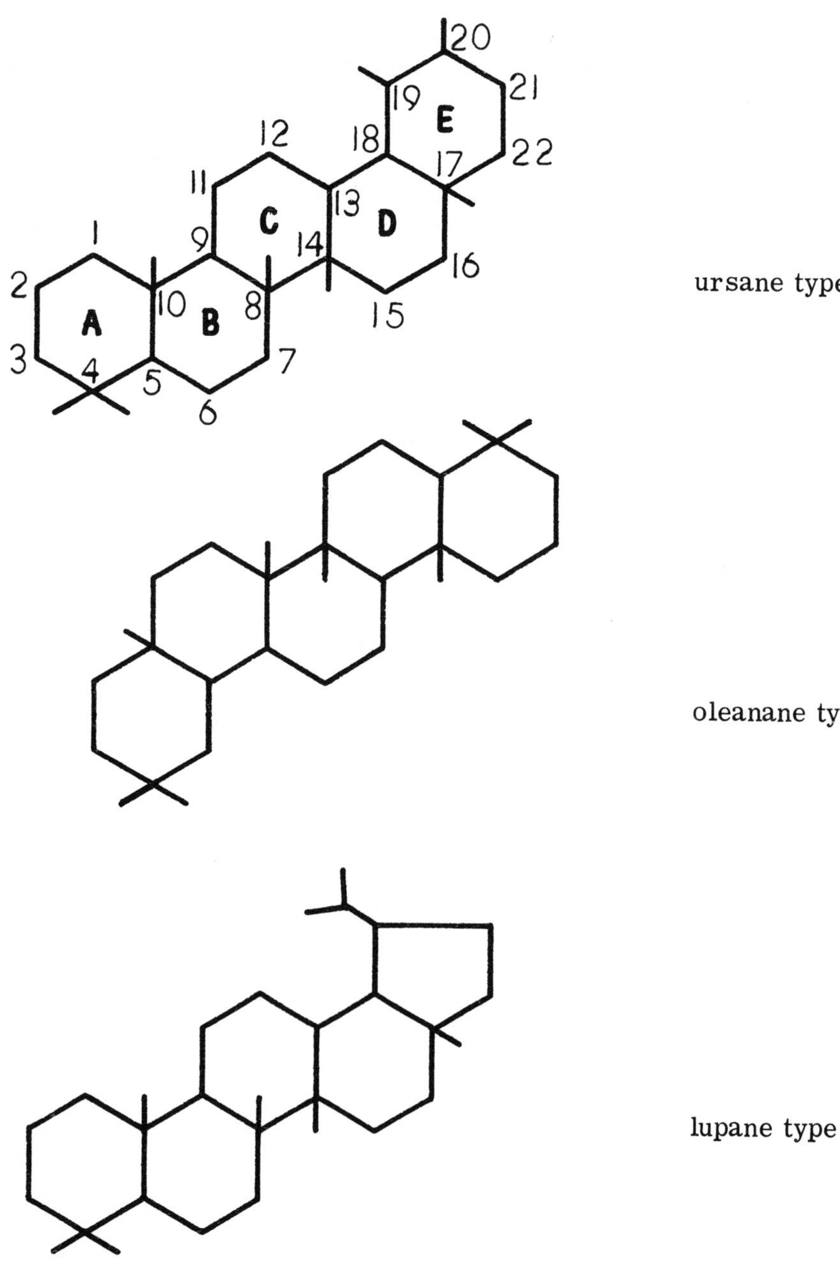

ursane type

oleanane type

lupane type

Some specific compounds with their occurrence are given below. All known members of this group are oxygenated at C-3 usually as alcohols but some as ketones. They are distinguished from each other by unsaturations, additional hydroxyl groups, and frequently carboxyl groups. Stereochemical differences also play an important role in this group, but their consideration is beyond the scope of this book, and no configurations are indicated in the accompanying formulas. The β-amyrin type structure is most common and occurs in both primitive and advanced plants. Interesting correlations between plant classification and triterpenoid structures are presented by Brieskorn (16).

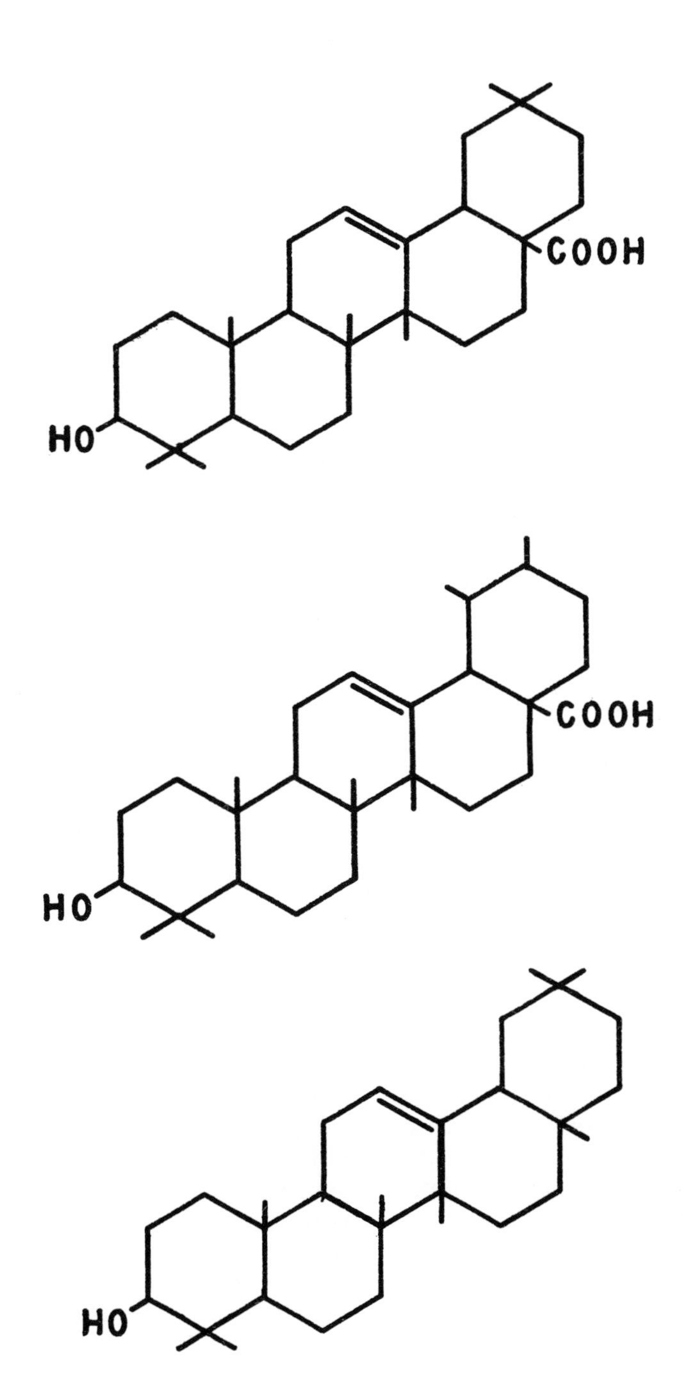

oleanolic acid (widely distributed, e.g. *Olea europaea)*

ursolic acid (in waxy coating of many leaves and fruits, e.g. *Arctostaphylus uvaursi)*

β-amyrin (resins, latex and waxes of many plants, e.g. *Canarium commune)*

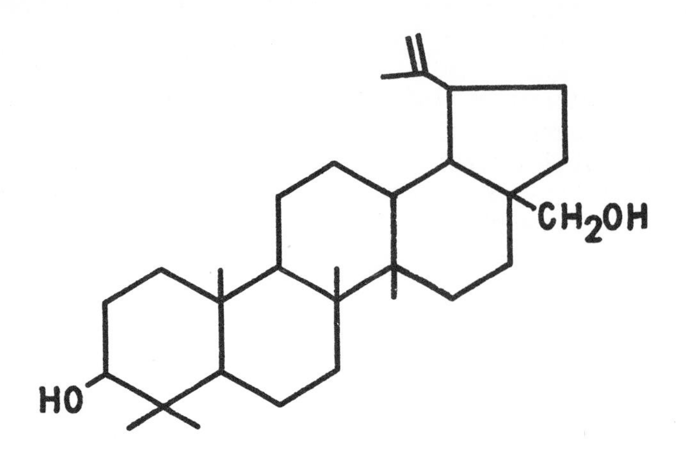

betulin (bark of *Betula alba*)

STEROLS

The fundamental steroid nucleus is the same as that of lanosterol and other tetracyclic triterpenoids, but only two methyl groups are attached to the ring system, at positions 10 and 13. The eight-carbon side chain found in lanosterol is also present in many steroids, especially from animal sources; but most plant steroids have one or two additional carbon atoms. The name "sterol" applies specifically to steroid alcohols; but since practically all plant steroids are alcohols with a hydroxyl group at C-3, they are frequently all called sterols. The steroid numbering system is as follows:

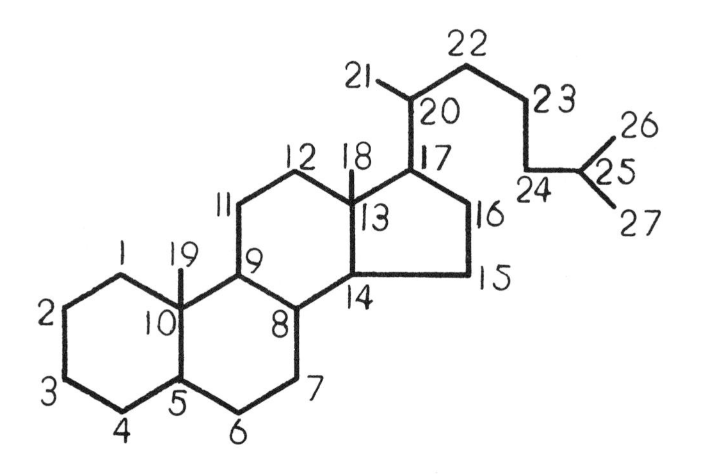

Steroids occur throughout the plant kingdom as free sterols and their esters in many lipids and as more complex derivatives to be discussed in sections to follow. In plants they have no known function although they have profound importance in animal metabolism as hormones, coenzymes, bile acids and provitamin D. Certain animal steroids have been shown to influence plant growth strongly, but whether presently unknown plant steroids may act similarly is an open question (17). The steroid alkaloid tomatine (see below) may be somehow related to flowering since its concentration may be photoperiodically controlled in the same way as the flowering response (18). Cholesterol, the most common animal steroid, has not been found in plants; but there is no sharp distinction between plant and animal steroids, since other members of the group are found in both kingdoms. Pregnane type steroids have recently been found in plants (19).

Classification of sterols is done on the basis of their optical rotations. This is not purely arbitrary but reflects important structural differences as summarized in Table 10.

TABLE 10.

Specific Rotation	Structural Type	Example
greater than -90°	conjugated double bonds in ring B	ergosterol
-70° to -50°	double bonds at 5, 6 and 22, 23	stigmasterol
-45° to -30°	double bond at 5, 6	β-sitosterol
-25° to +10°	double bond at 7, 8 and possibly 22, 23 also	α-spinasterol
+10° to +30°	completely saturated ring system	stigmastanol
+40° to +50°	double bond at 8, 9 and possibly in side chain also	zymosterol
greater than +50°	not a sterol	lanosterol

Sterols of the zymosterol type are known in the fungi but have not been established yet in any higher plants. The stigmasterol type is most characteristic of higher plants. Structures and occurrence of some plant steroids are shown below. A thorough survey of plant sterols is given by Bergmann (20).

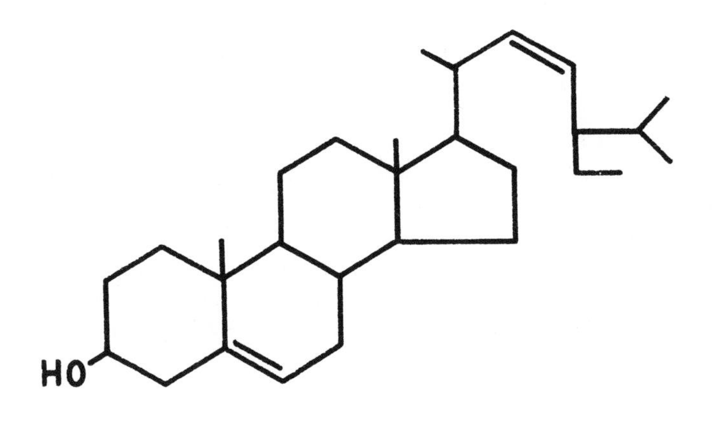

stigmasterol *(Glycine max)*

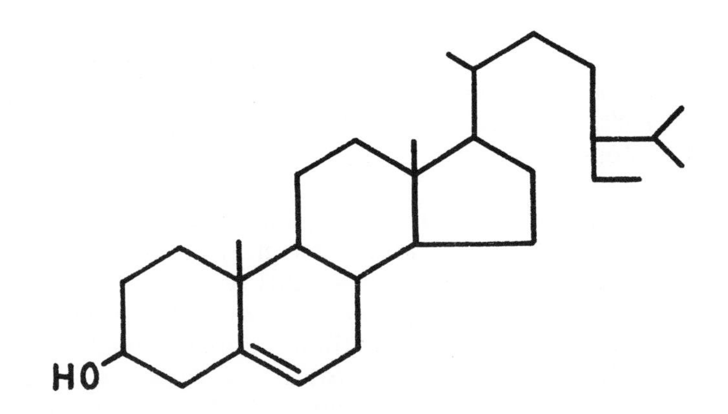

β-sitosterol *(Pinus spp.)*

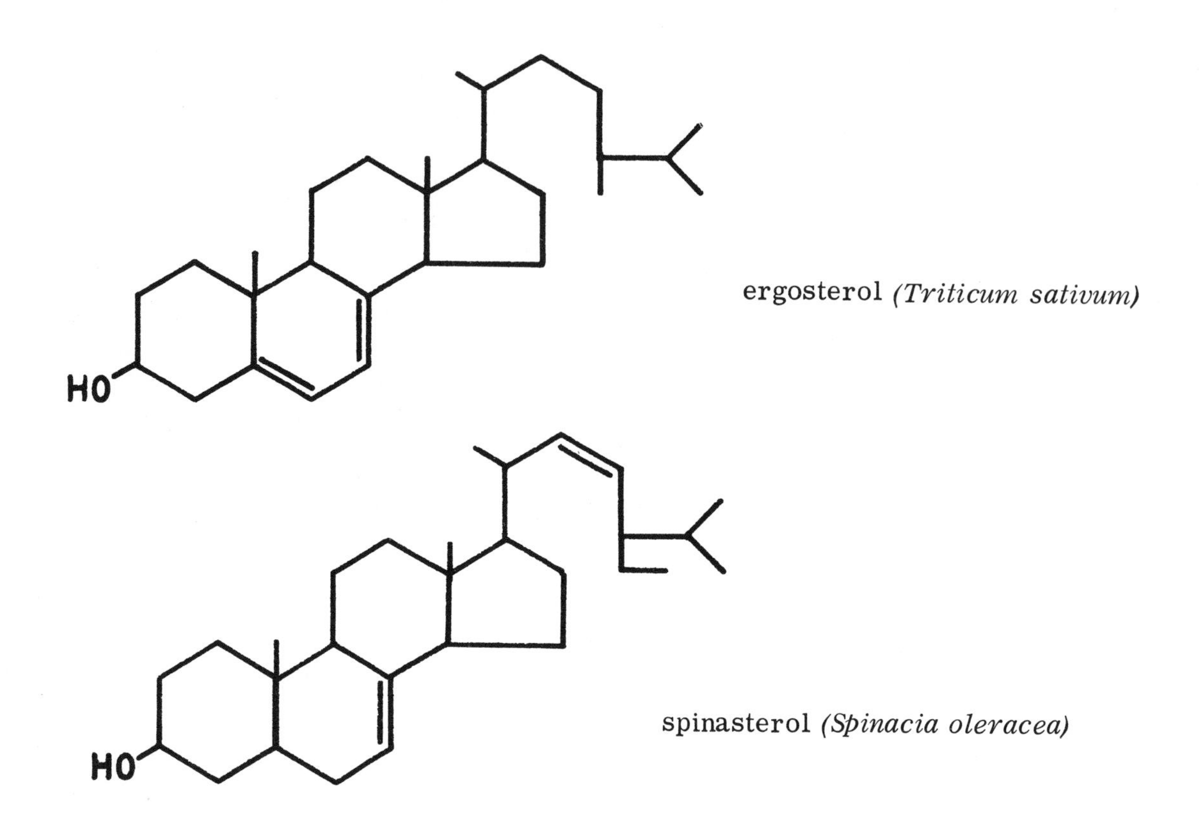

ergosterol *(Triticum sativum)*

spinasterol *(Spinacia oleracea)*

Nomenclature of the steroids is complicated by the necessity of distinguishing between possible sterochemical configurations. In the vast majority of plant steroids the rings are all joined to one another by *trans* linkages (see page 122). The result of this is that the entire ring system is coplanar and substituent groups extend perpendicularly to the plane of the rings. The methyl group at C-10 is defined as sticking up. Any group *trans* to it is described as α and groups *cis* to it β. Steroids with the A/B ring juncture *trans* may therefore be described as 5α, since the hydrogen on C-5 is below the plane. All natural sterols have the C-3 hydroxyl group and the C-17 side chain β. A greater variety of configurations is found in the tetracyclic triterpenoids which closely resemble the steroids in other respects (see above). Other nomenclature rules may be found in the general references.

STEROLINS AND SAPONINS

As has been mentioned previously, many terpenoid and steroid alcohols exist in nature not as free alcohols but as glycosides. Names have been assigned to certain types of these glycosides--"sterolins" "saponins", "cardiac glycosides", etc. The cardiac glycosides and glycosyl alkaloids will be considered in later sections.

Sterolins or sterol glycosides are widespread in unrelated plant species. They are found along with free sterols in the unsaponifiable lipid fraction but may be distinguished from free sterols by their much higher melting points and low solubility in such fat solvents as ethyl ether. They are distinguished from saponins (see below) by their insolubility in water and lack of toxicity to animals. The first sterolin to be discovered was ipuranol of *Ipomoea purpurea*. It is a β-sitosterol glycoside. Similar glycosides of the higher plant sterols are also known; but as β-sitosterol is the most widely distributed plant sterol, so its glycosides are the commonest sterolins.

The saponins were originally named because of their soap-like characteristics. They are powerful surface active agents which cause foaming when shaken with water and in low concentration often produce hemolysis of red blood cells. In very dilute solution they are quite toxic to fish, and plants containing them have been used as fish poisons for hundreds of years. They have also been implicated as a contributing cause of bloat in cattle on some forage crops. Certain saponins have become important in recent years because they may be obtained in good yields from some plants and are used as starting material for the synthesis of steroid hormones to be used in medicine. The saponins have no known function in plants but have been shown to stimulate the growth of pea embryos (17).

Two types of saponins are recognized--glycosides of triterpenoid alcohols, and glycosides of a particular steroid structure described as having a spiroketal side chain. Both types are soluble in water and ethanol but insoluble in ether. Their aglycones, called sapogenins, are prepared by acid or enzymatic hydrolysis and without the sugar residues have the solubility characteristics of other sterols. A few of the steroidal sapogenins are distinguished by having a *cis* A/B ring juncture. Steroidal saponins are most common in the families *Liliaceae, Amaryllidaceae* and *Dioscoraceae.*

The spiroketal steroid nucleus has the following structure:

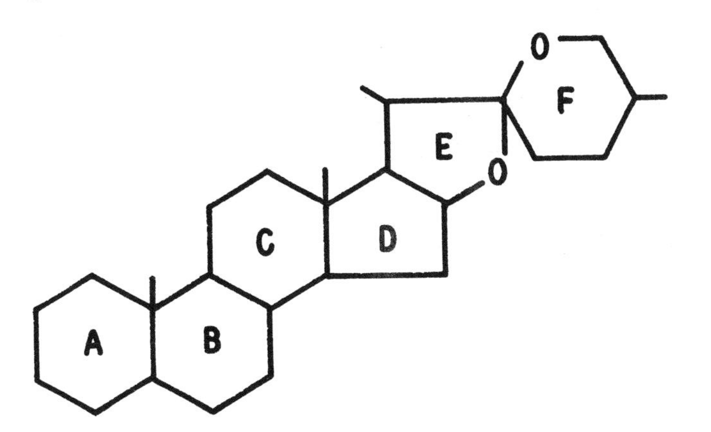

Rings E and F contain the same basic carbon skeleton as common animal steroids but lack the extra carbon atoms found in most plant sterols.

The triterpenoid saponins may have as their aglycones such compounds as oleanolic acid which also occur uncombined with sugars. In some cases though, the aglycones are known only as sapogenins. Oleanane-type sapogenins are much more common than either ursane or lupane types.

Some sapogenin structures are given in Table 11. Glycosylation is generally at C-3. Several different monosaccharides are usually present as an oligosaccharide. Uronic acids may also be present. For example, digitonin is derived from digitogenin plus an oligosaccharide composed of 1 xylose, 2 glucose, and 2 galactose units. Several different saponins may all have the same sapogenin but different sugars.

CARDIAC GLYCOSIDES

The cardiac glycosides, cardenolides, or heart poisons bear a structural resemblance to the steroid saponins and have the same solubility and foaming characteristics. They are distinguished from other steroid glycosides by an unsaturated lactone ring attached at C-17, a *cis*-juncture of rings C and D, a 14β hydroxy group, and by the peculiar sugars composing them.

TABLE 11. SOME SAPOGENINS, STRUCTURES AND OCCURRENCE

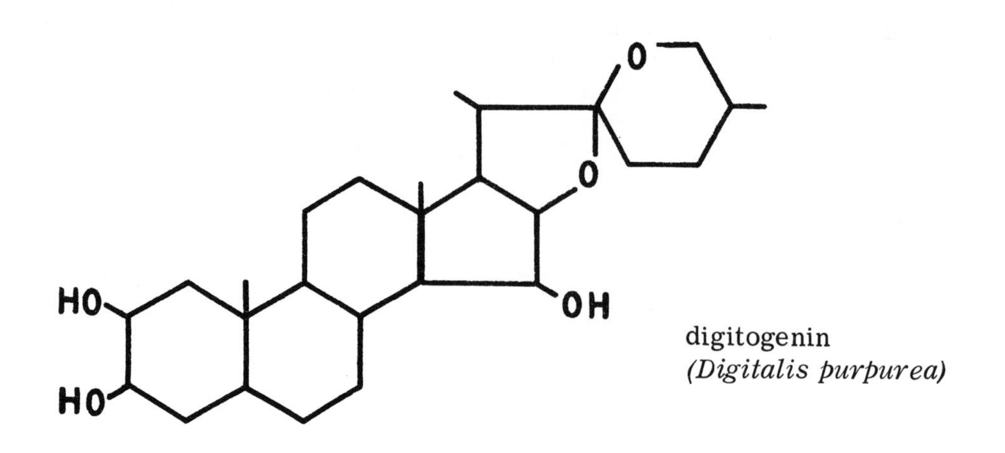

digitogenin
(Digitalis purpurea)

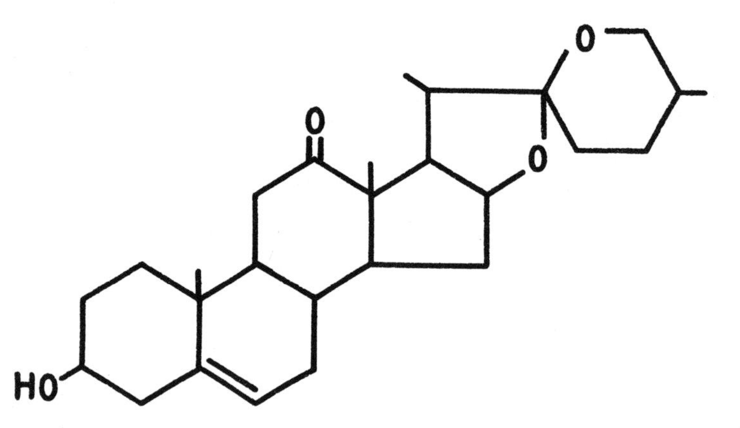

hecogenin (*Agave* spp.)

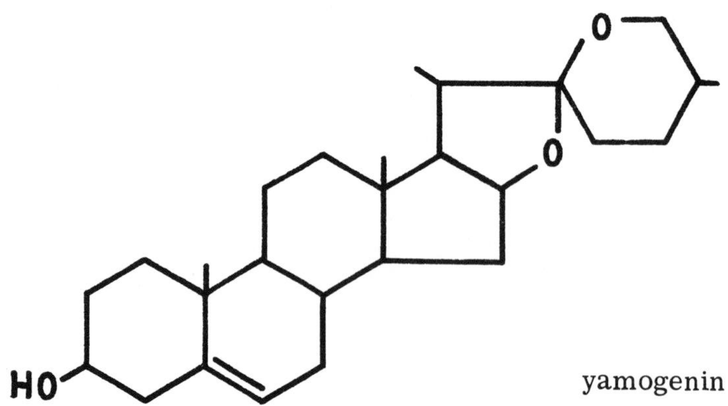

yamogenin *(Dioscorea* spp.*)*

Table 11. Continued

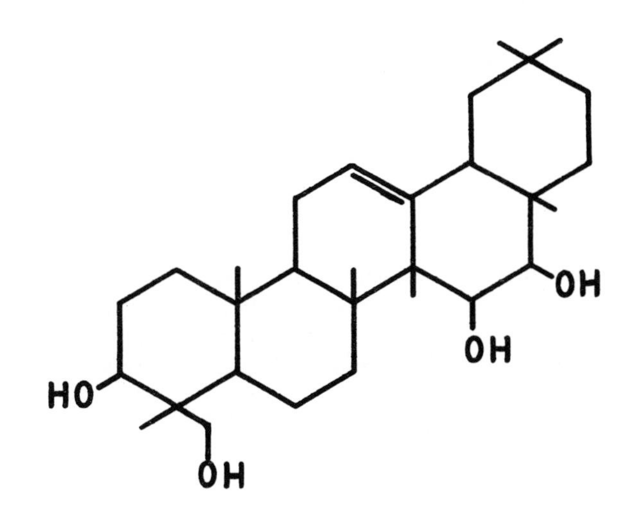

soyasapogenol A (*Soja* spp.)

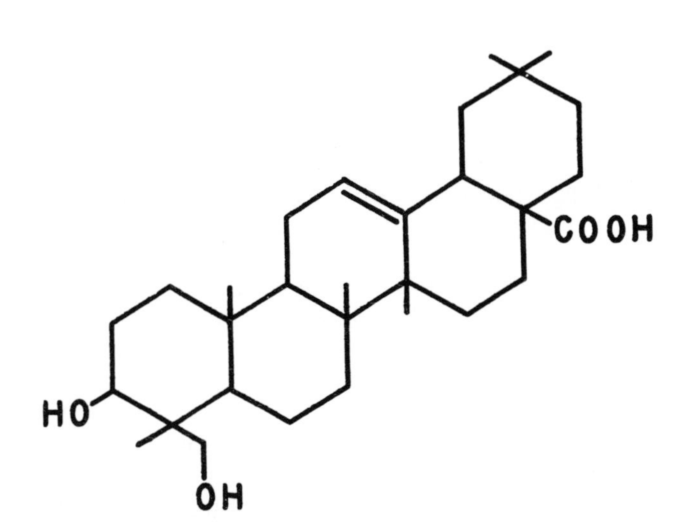

hederagenin *(Hedera helix)*

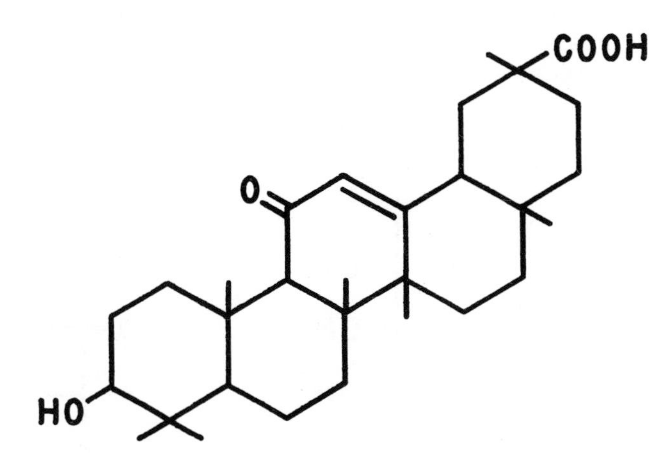

glycyrrhetic acid
(Glycyrrhiza glabra)

The usual basic nucleus is as follows:

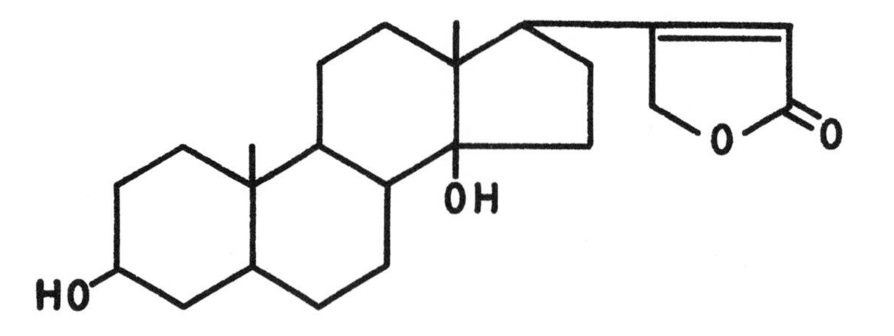

Other substituent groups may be present, for example additional hydroxy groups at C-1, 11, 12, 16, and 19. The sugars are always linked at C-3. Some members have an aldehyde group rather than a methyl group at C-19, and many have a *cis* A/B ring fusion. The so-called scilladienolides of squill and hellebore have a six-membered lactone ring:

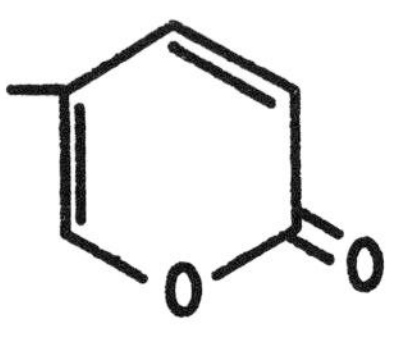

The cardiac glycosides are found in several quite unrelated plant families such as *Apocyanaceae, Liliaceae, Moraceae,* and *Ranunculaceae.* Plants containing them have been used since prehistoric times as arrow and ordeal poisons. The glycosides have a specific cardiotonic effect. The aglycones are poisonous but have no specific effect on heart muscle.

The chief commercial source is the genus *Digitalis* (family Scrophulariaceae). Several species of this genus are used, and active material is extracted from seeds, leaves and roots. It will be recalled that this same genus is the source of the steroid saponin, digitonin.

By the usual methods of preparation some degradation occurs, both by enzymatic and non-enzymatic hydrolysis of some of the sugar residues and ester groups which may be present. Thus what were originally believed to be the three active glycosides of *Digitalis,* digitoxin, gitoxin, and digoxin are known to be derived from the actual natural products (the digilanides, A, B, and C) by loss of a glucose residue and an acetyl group. The same aglycone or genin may be present in different plants but joined with different sugars. Structures of some of the rare sugar components are given below:

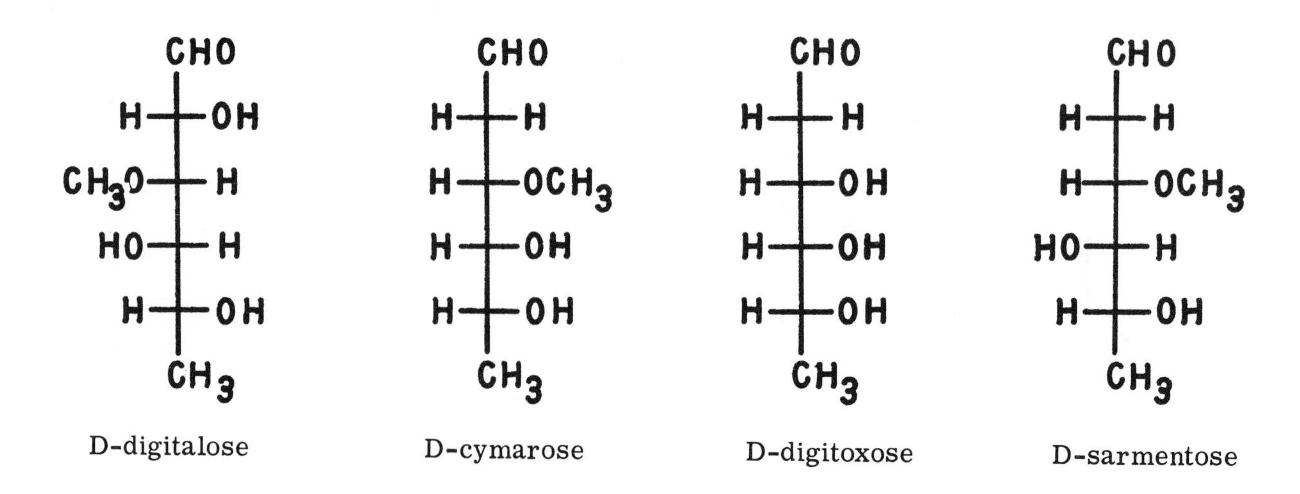

D-digitalose D-cymarose D-digitoxose D-sarmentose

The heart poisons of *Calotropis procera* cannot truly be called glycosides since instead of a sugar residue they have methylreductic acid. This compound is, however, closely related to the sugars:

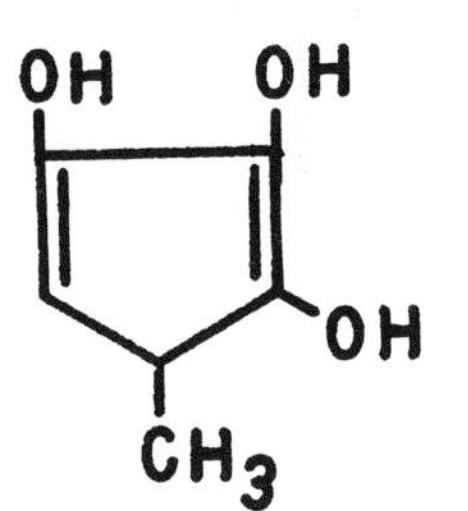

Examples of some cardiac glycosides with their occurrence are given below. The name of the aglycone follows the name of the glycoside.

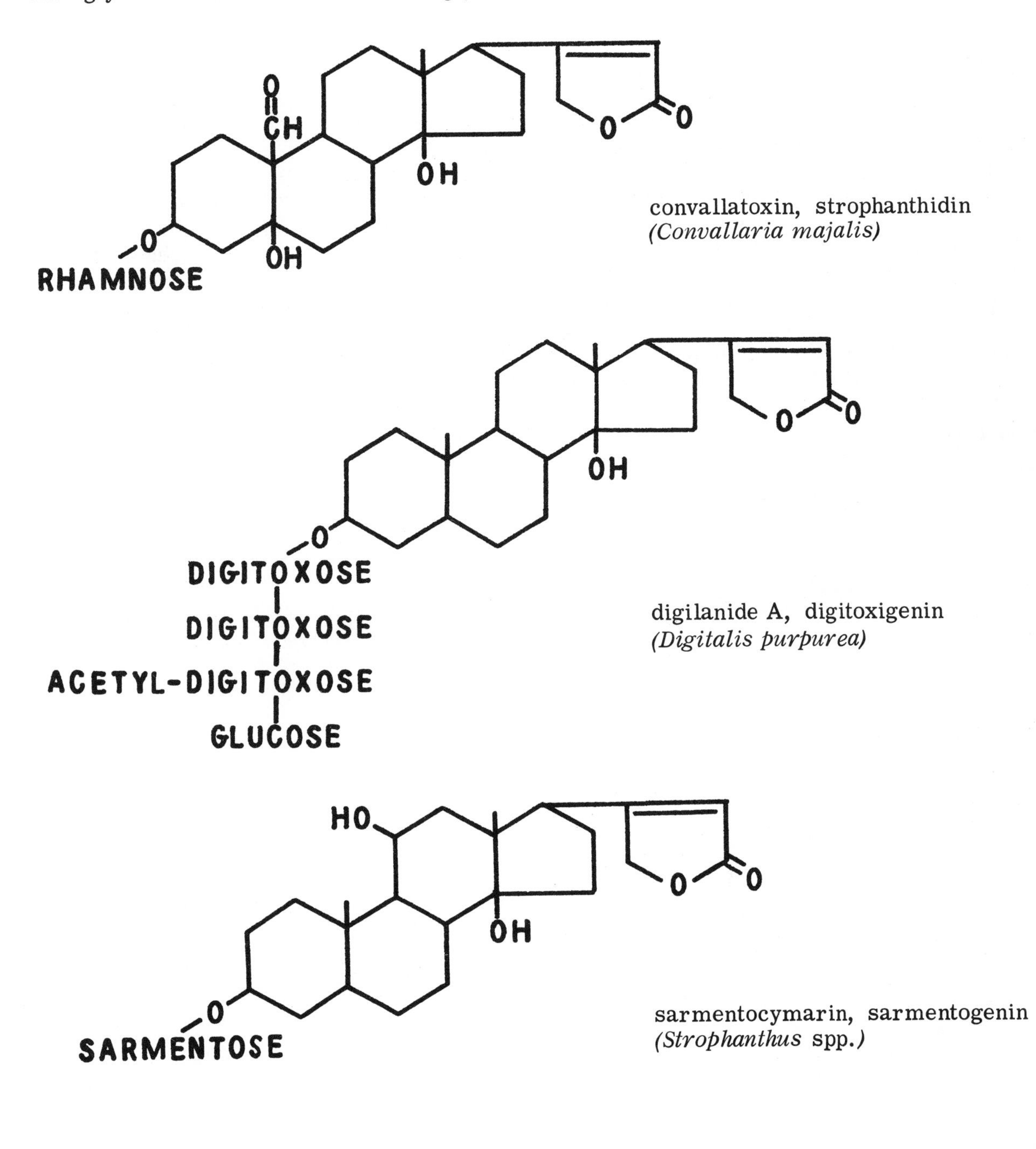

convallatoxin, strophanthidin
(Convallaria majalis)

digilanide A, digitoxigenin
(Digitalis purpurea)

sarmentocymarin, sarmentogenin
(Strophanthus spp.*)*

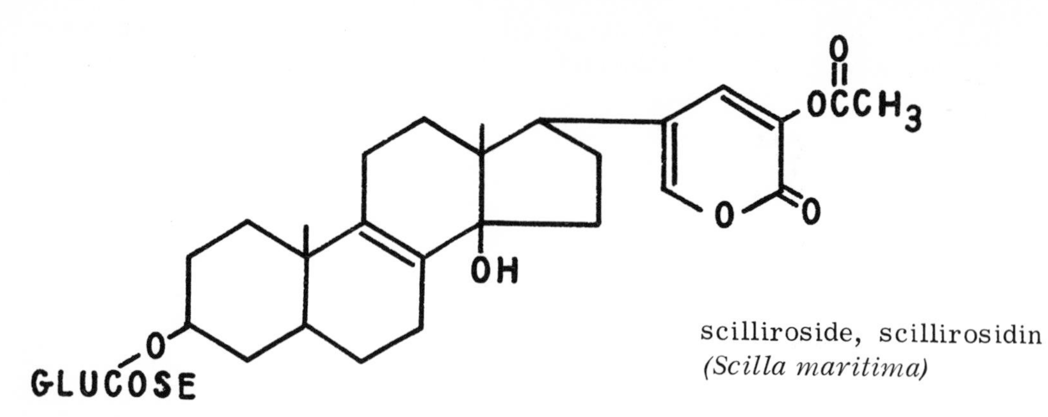

scilliroside, scillirosidin
(Scilla maritima)

Reviews of these compounds have appeared by Tamm (21, 22) and Stoll (23).

ALKALOIDS

Nitrogen-containing compounds are included in many of the groups discussed in this chapter. Such compounds possess alkaloidal properties and are normally classed with the alkaloids although their carbon skeletons clearly mark them as isoprenoid derivatives. The most important members of this group are the aconite and steroid alkaloids. The former have been reviewed by Wiesner and Valenta (24), the latter by Prelog and Jeger (25). Several complex diterpenoid alkaloids with structures similar to aconitine and veatchine occur in various species of *Aconitum, Delphinium, Taxus,* and *Garrya.* The steroid and modified steroid alkaloids normally occur as C-3 glycosides or esters. A close resemblance of such structures to the saponins is apparent; in fact solanine has saponin-like properties and is sometimes described as a nitrogen-containing saponin. Some examples of terpenoid and steroid alkaloids are shown below.

Monoterpenoid:

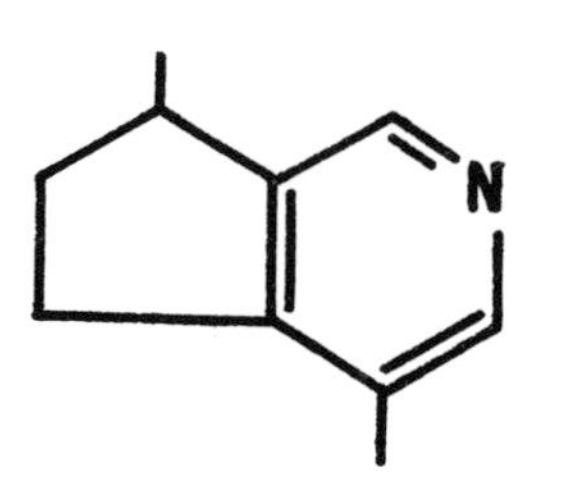

actinidine *(Actinidia polygama)*

Sesquiterpenoid:

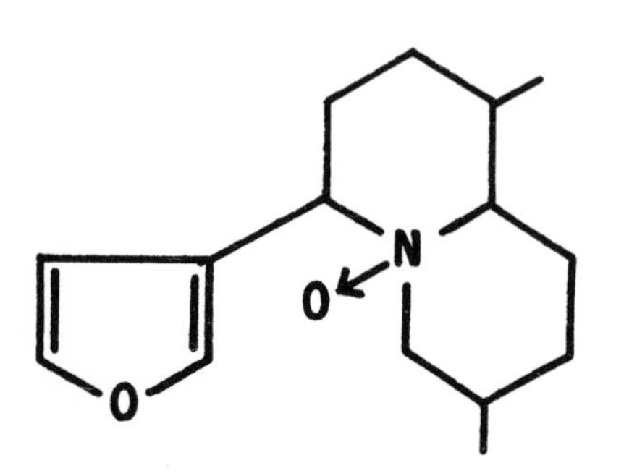

nupharidine *(Nupher kaponicum)*

Diterpenoid:

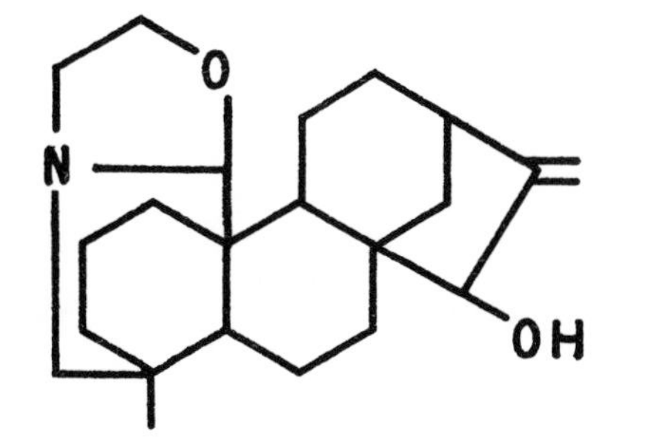

veatchine *(Garrya veatchii)*

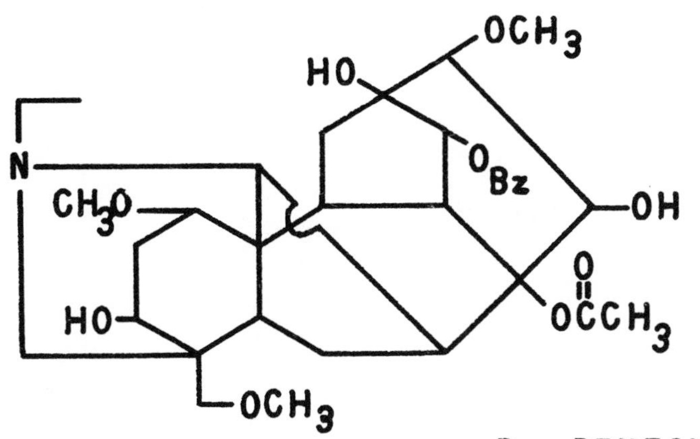

aconitine *(Aconitum* spp.*)*

Steroid:

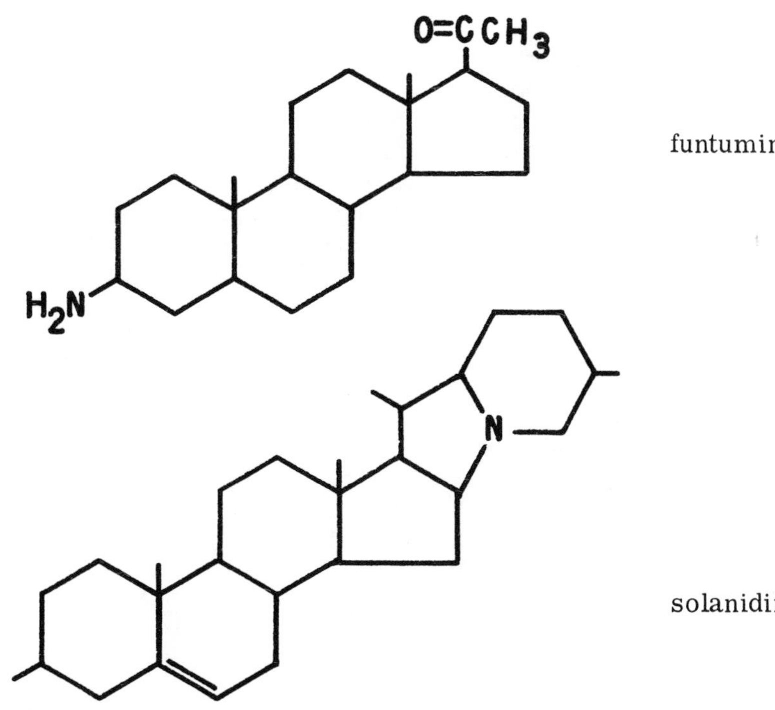

funtumine *(Funtumia latifolia)*

solanidine *(Solanum* spp.*)*

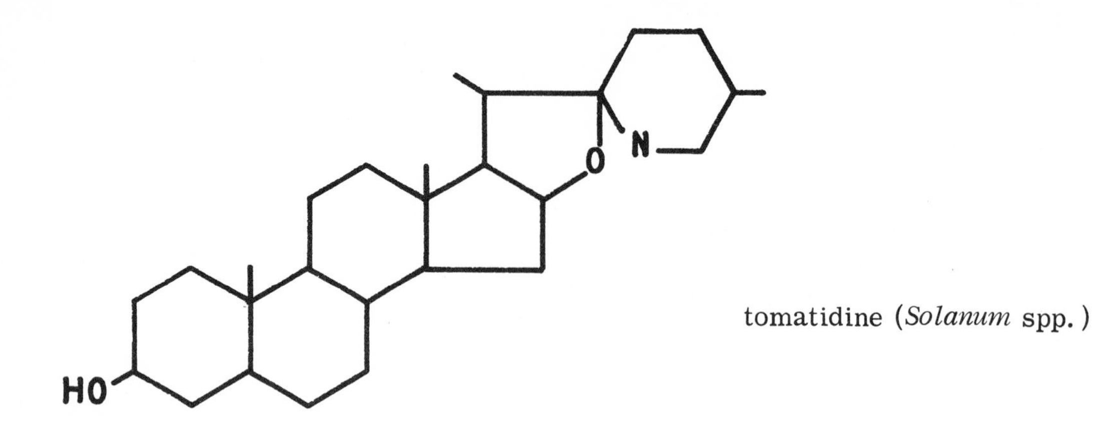

tomatidine (*Solanum* spp.)

Modified steroid:

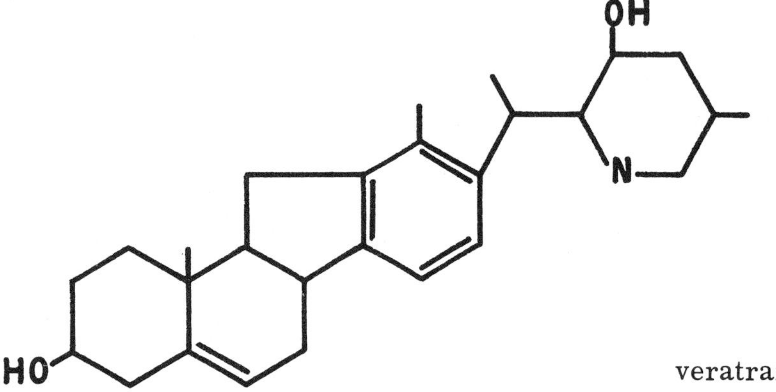

veratramine (*Veratrum* spp.)

TETRATERPENOIDS

The most familiar tetraterpenoids are the carotenoids--yellow to red, fat soluble pigments occurring throughout the plant kingdom and in many different types of tissues. About 80 of them are known. Hydrocarbon pigments are called carotenes and oxygenated derivatives are xanthophylls. Colorless tetraterpenoids are also known (e.g. phytoene, phytofluene) but have been studied much less than the carotenoids. Structurally the only difference between colored and colorless tetraterpenoids is the larger number of conjugated double bonds found in the former. The tetraterpenoids never contain large condensed ring systems. They are either acyclic, monocyclic, or bicyclic. Acyclic members may be depicted by the following skeleton:

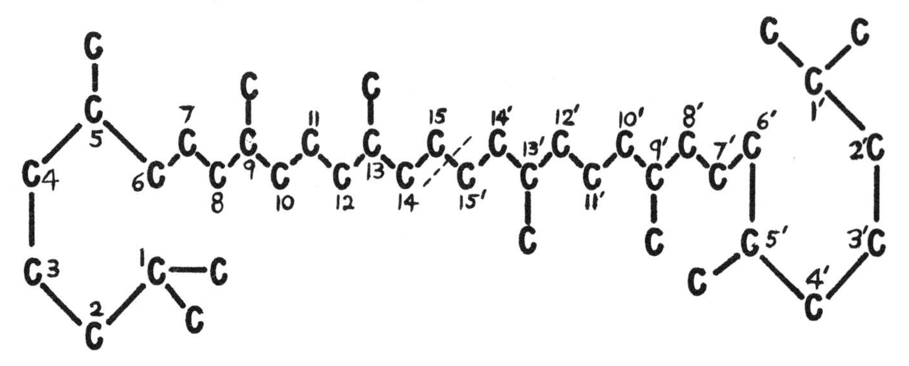

It will be noted that the molecule is symmetrical on each side of the dotted line and may be viewed as formed by joining two diterpene radicals of the phytyl type. Variations are introduced by double bonds and functional groups such as hydroxyl and carboxyl. As double bonds are added, opportunites for *cis-trans* isomerism are introduced, and many of the problems in carotenoid chemistry arise from difficulty in distinguishing and separating geometrical isomers of this type. Native carotenoids are believed to be all *trans*, but isomerization may occur on isolation.

Cyclization at one or both ends of the carbon chain gives rise to the other two fundamental types of carotenoids - i. e.:

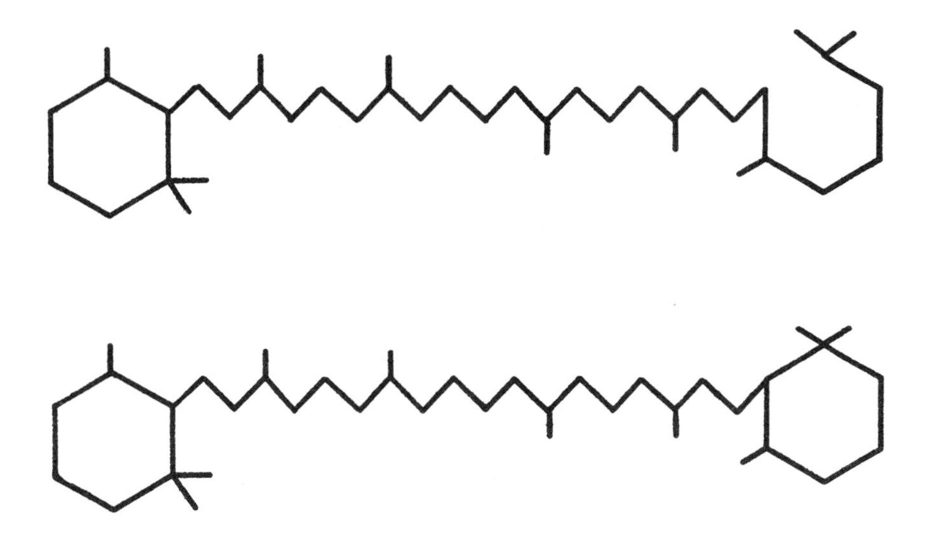

If only one β-ionone type ring is present, it is written to the left. Some other compounds (e. g. bixin, crocetin) are known which have fewer than 40 carbon atoms but are classed with the carotenoids because peculiarities in their structure suggest that they have been derived from degradation of carotenoids rather than built up from smaller units.

No general function can be assigned to the carotenoids. There is some indication that they function as light receptors for phototropism. As flower pigments they may play a role in attracting insects, but most attention has been given to their possible function as leaf chloroplast pigments. To some extent light absorbed by carotenoids can be transferred to chlorophyll and used in photosynthesis. There is also good evidence that the carotenoids protect chlorophyll against photodestruction by short wavelength light--i. e. at a wavelength of about 400 mμ where both carotenoids and chlorophylls have strong absorption maxima. Albino plants lack both carotenoids and chlorophyll under normal conditions of growth but in dim light they are able to accumulate chlorophyll. In normal light the chlorophyll is rapidly destroyed since carotenoids are not present to protect it (26).

The most widespread carotenoid is β-carotene, which may make up as much as 0. 1% of dried green leaves. Lutein is the most important leaf xanthophyll and may occur in green leaves at a greater concentration than β-carotene. Most carotenoids have the same central carbon chain as β-carotene and differ only in the portions corresponding to the two rings. Therefore in the formulas of Table 12, the complete structure is given only for β-carotene and the straight chain represented by a dotted line unless it differs from that of β-carotene.

TABLE 12. SOME CAROTENOIDS, STRUCTURES AND OCCURRENCE

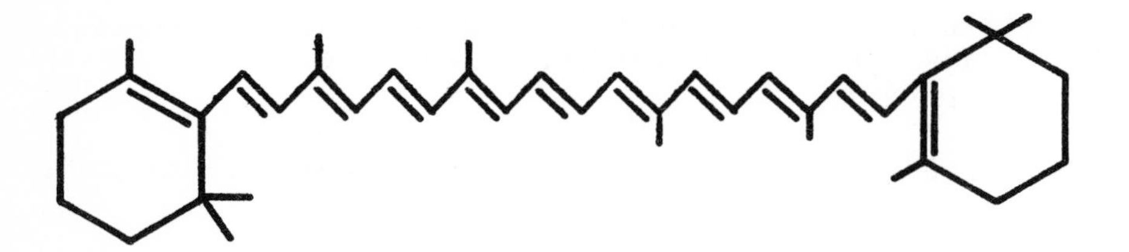

β-carotene

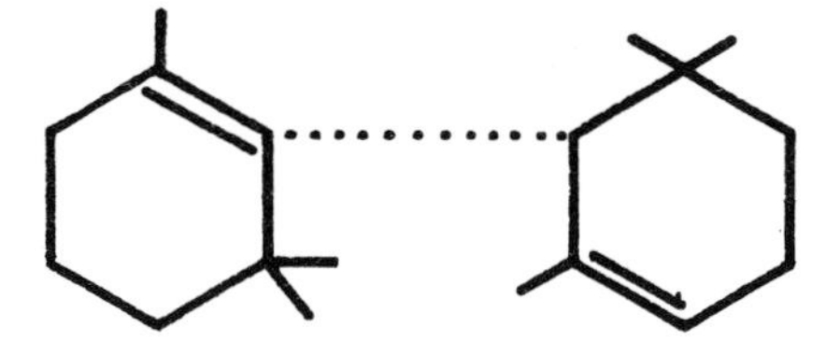

α-carotene (leaf pigment)

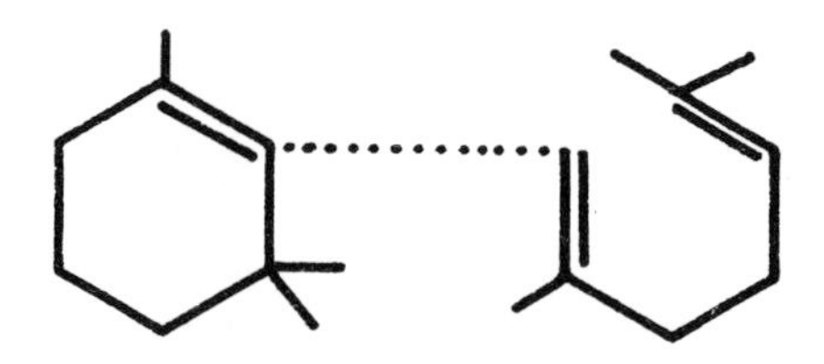

γ-carotene (flower and fruit pigment)

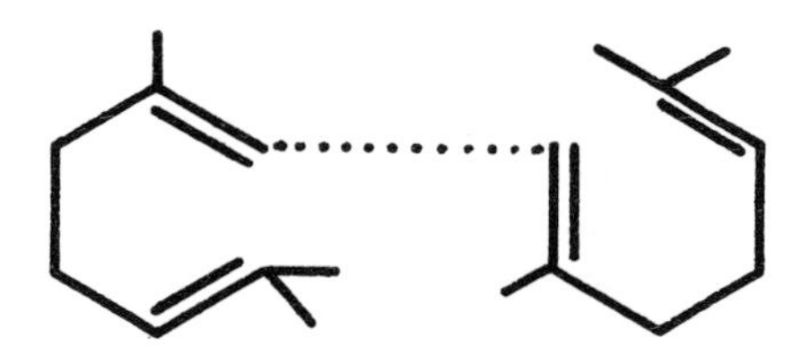

lycopene (fruit pigment)

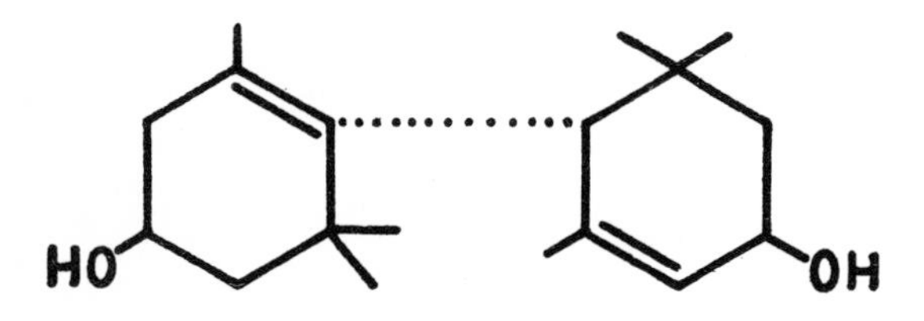

lutein (leaf pigment)

Table 12. Continued

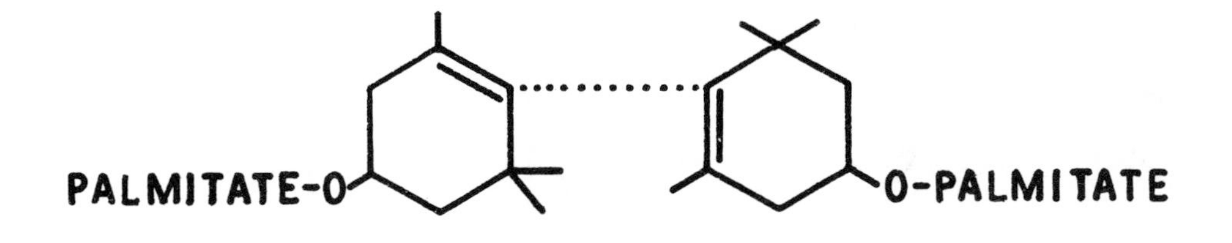

physalien, zeaxanthin palmitate (fruits)

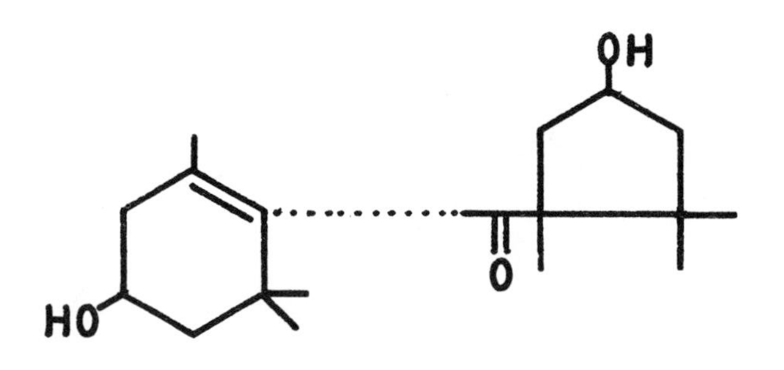

capsanthin *(Capsicum annuum)*

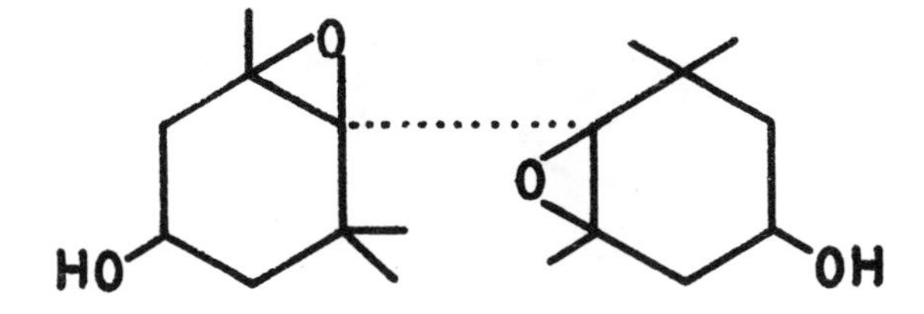

violaxanthin (flowers, fruits, and leaf)

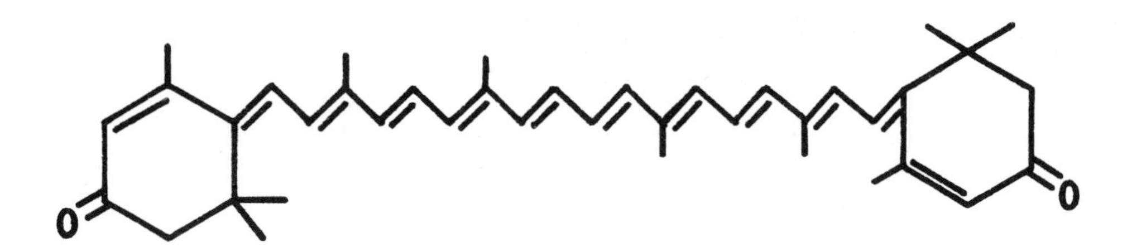

rhodoxanthin (many Gymnosperms, horsetails, club mosses)

Table 12. Continued

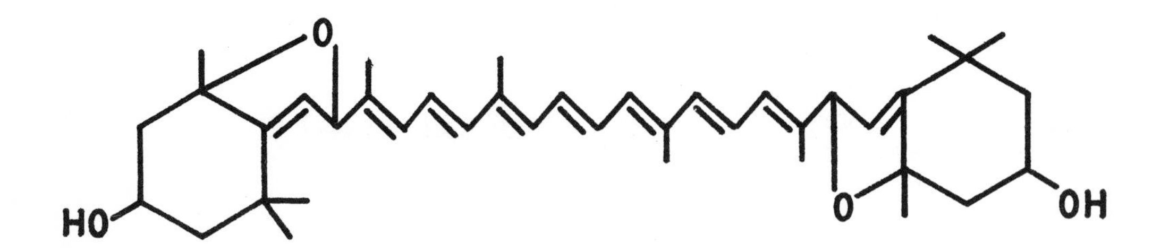

auroxanthin (flowers and fruits)

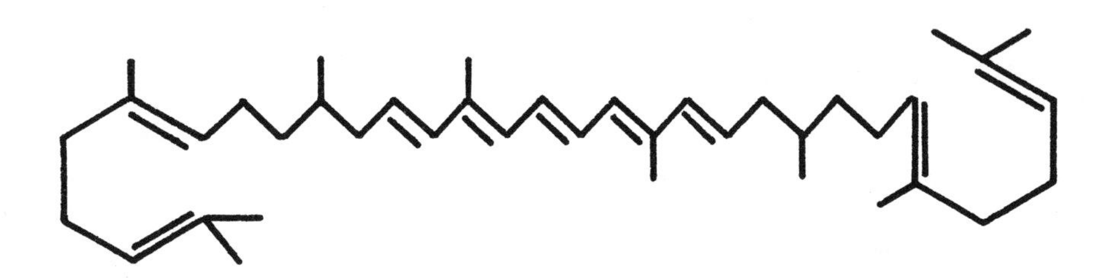

phytofluene (fruits and seeds)

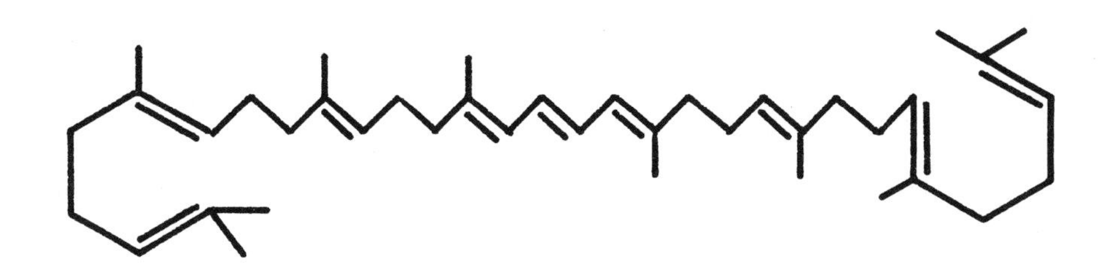

phytoene (leaves fruits, seeds)

bixin *(Bixa orellana)*

crocetin *(Crocus sativus;* as crocin, an ester of gentiobiose)

BITTER PRINCIPLES

The various bitter substances distributed through the plant kingdom constitute no chemically homogeneous group. It is commonly believed that alkaloids are usually the cause of bitterness in plants, but in many cases terpenoids have been found to be responsible. For example, both the saponins and cardiac glycosides are bitter. Bitter principles generally have been reviewed by Korte *et al.* (27) and Courtney (28). Many of the bitter terpenoids contain ketone or lactone groupings, but bitterness does not seem to be ascribable to any particular functional groups. Some bitter principles are known to be terpenoids but the complete structures are not known. The bitter principles of the *Cucurbitaceae,* cucurbitacins, are known to be triterpenoid glycosides with a ring structure like lanosterol and the following side chain at C_{17} (29, 30).

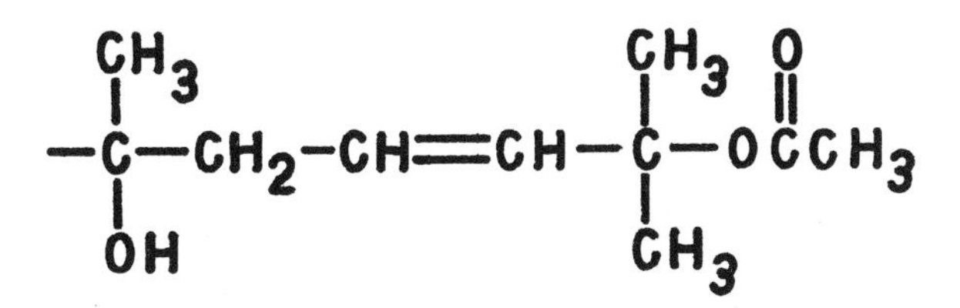

The bitterest natural product known is a diterpenoid, amarogentin, of unknown structure. Structures and occurrence of some other compounds of this nature are given in Table 13. Plumieride is shown as an example of a group of glucosides with pronounced structural similarities which are believed to be biogenetically related although they are found in quite unrelated plants (31). Other members of the group are genipin, loganin, asperuloside, aucubin, catalposide, nepetalactone, and iridodial. They often have physiological effects on mammals and microorganisms. Aucubin is responsible for the darkening observed on grinding certain plants, especially *Plantago* spp. (32).

In contrast to the terpenoid bitter principles, it should be mentioned that the sweetest natural product known is also a diterpenoid. This is a glycoside known as stevioside found in *Stevia rebaudiana.* On hydrolysis it yields three molecules of glucose. The complete structure of the aglycone, steviol, is unknown; but a tentative suggestion is as follows (33).

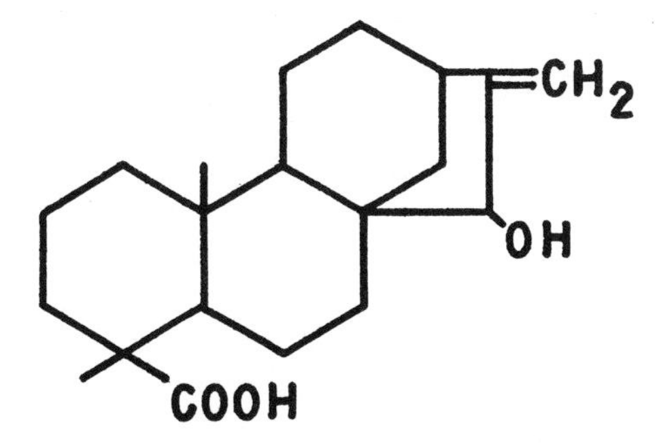

TROPONES

The basic tropone nucleus is a seven-membered ring containing a double bond system conjugated with a keto group:

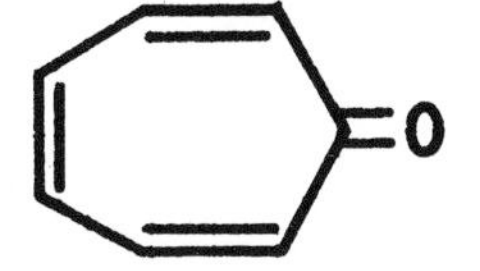

TABLE 13. SOME BITTER PRINCIPLES, STRUCTURE AND OCCURRENCE

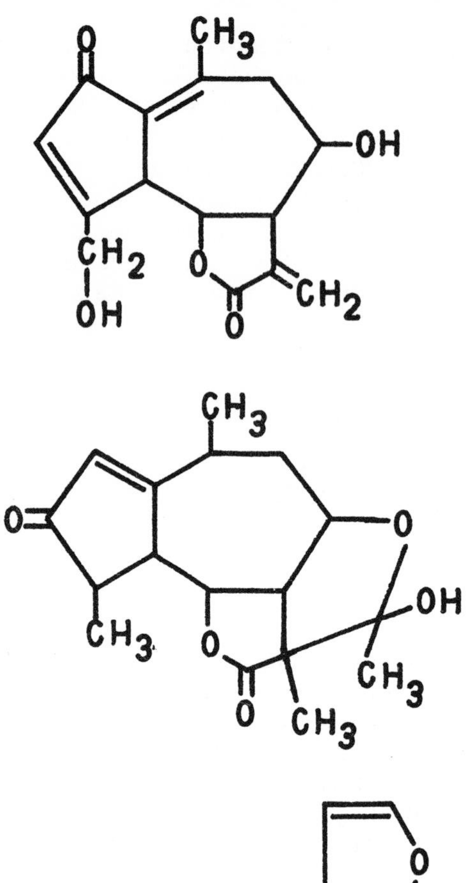

lactucin *(Cichorium intybus)*

tenulin (*Helenium* spp.)

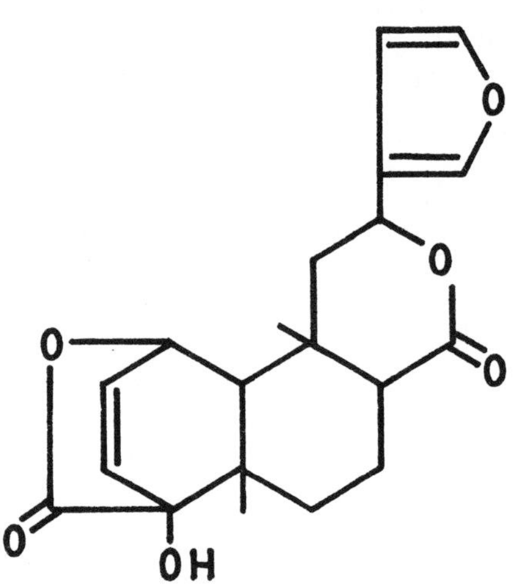

columbin *(Jatrorrhiza palmata)*

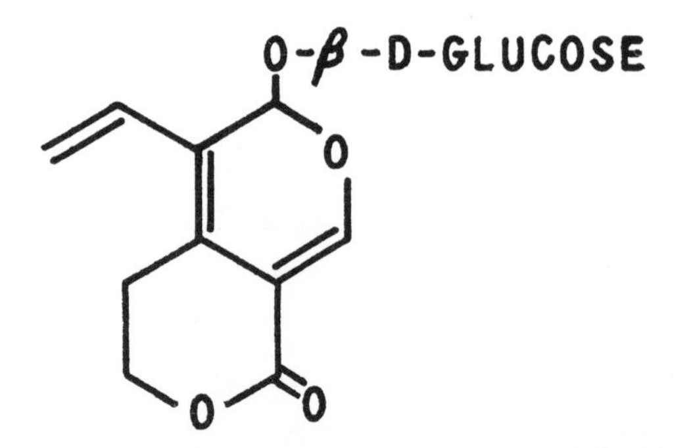

gentiopicrin *(Gentiana lutea)*

Table 13. Continued

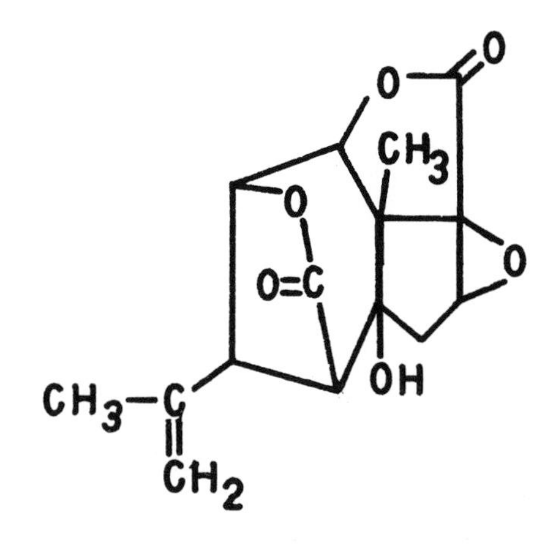

picrotoxinin *(Cocculus indicus)*

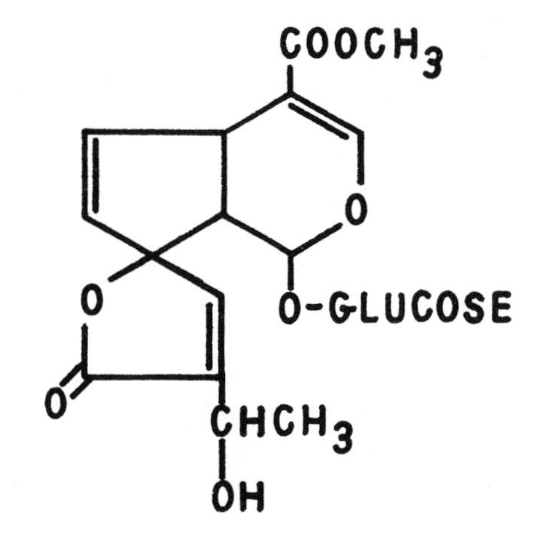

plumieride (*Plumiera* spp.)

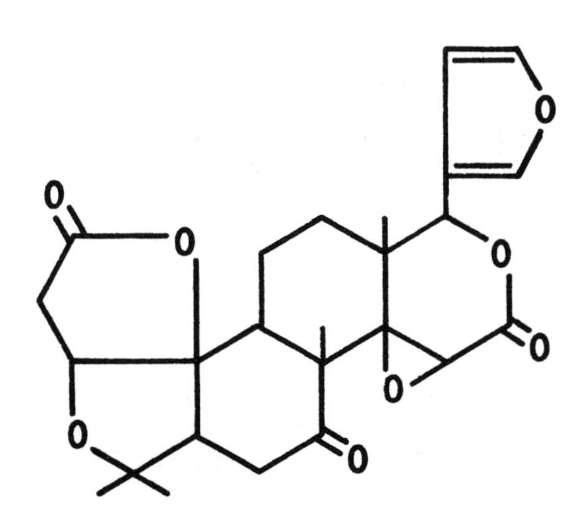

limonin (*Citrus* spp.)

CHO

GLUCOSE-O

picrocrocin *(Crocus sativus)*

The parent member of the group, tropolone, has an addition a hydroxyl group--hence the name ol - one:

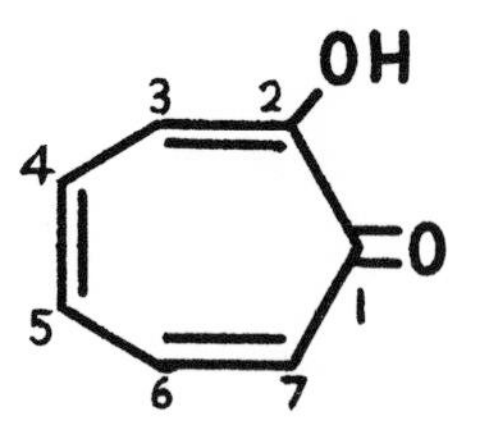

On the basis of biosynthesis there appear to be two classes of tropolones in nature, one derived from terpenoid-like precursors and the other by ring expansion of 6-membered aromatic rings. Since the common tropolones of higher plants resemble the terpenoids, they are included in this chapter. Tropolones derived from aromatic acids seem to be the predominant form in the fungi. In some cases no clear-cut decision regarding precursors is possible at present. Structures of some tropolones have already been given along with related terpenoids (e.g. eucarvone, nootkatin); and there seems no reason to set them apart. These compounds are of interest primarily because of their strong fungicidal action. In this they resemble the phenols, but their toxicity may also be attributed to their strong capacity for chelation (34). The alkaloid colchicine (q. v.) may be classed as a tropolone. Tropolones have been reviewed by Pauson (35), Erdtman (36) and Nozoe (37).

RUBBER AND OTHER HIGH POLYMERS OF ISOPRENE

Rubber is by far the most important isoprenoid derivative of molecular weight higher than the tetraterpenoids, and almost no substances are known with a molecular weight intermediate between these two. A C_{45} terpene alcohol, solanesol, has been isolated from tobacco leaves (38).

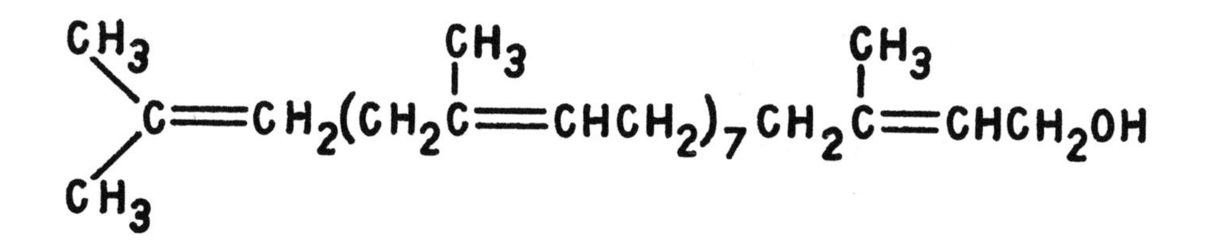

solanesol

Sporopollenine, the chief constituent of the outer layer (exine) of pollen grains, is probably a polyterpene. Practically nothing is known concerning its chemistry although its great resistance to breakdown is suggested by the survival of pollen grains for thousands of years in peat bogs.

Rubber is a polymer containing from 3000 to 6000 isoprene units. A small portion of the molecule may be represented as:

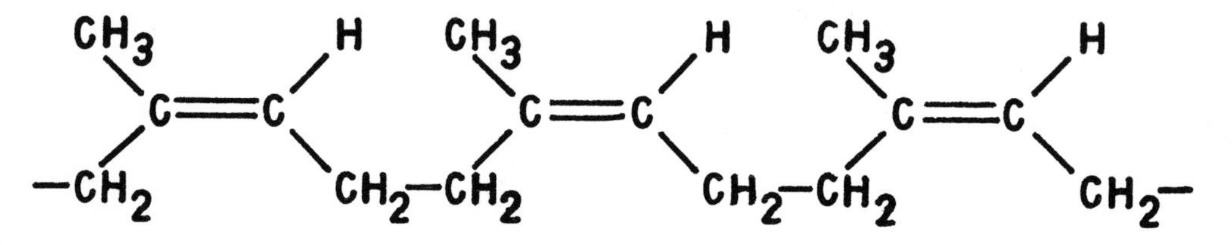

It will be noted that the sterochemistry at all the double bonds is *cis*. Gutta and balata are also high molecular weight polyisoprenes but have an all-*trans* structure. Gutta also has a lower average molecular weight than rubber. Rubber may be distinguished from gutta by its elasticity and incomplete solubility in aromatic hydrocarbons.

Although only a very few plants (e.g. *Hevea brasiliensis*, *Taraxacum* spp., guayule) offer possibilities for commercial production, rubber occurs in many dicotyledons. It is found in some plants as a component of latex and may be obtained by tapping the latex vessels. In other plants it is found throughout the tissues and can only be extracted after grinding up the plant. The plant kingdom has not been surveyed for gutta as extensively as it has for rubber, but it seems to be a general rule that no plants have both. The chief commercial sources of gutta are East Indian plants of the genera *Payena* and *Palaquium*.

MIXED TERPENOIDS

The mixed terpenoids are a miscellaneous group of compounds which seem to be built predominantly from isoprene residues but which contain additional carbon atoms or lack the required number. In some cases they may come from strictly isoprenoid precursors as the result of extensive rearrangement and/or loss of carbon atoms. The most general category to be placed in this group are the naturally occurring furans, which according to Aneja *et al.* (39), may all be regarded as derived from isoprenoid units by the loss of three carbon atoms. Some of the other compounds in this group are among the most interesting natural products from a physiological point of view.

Gibberellic acid is regarded by Birch *et al.* (40) as derived from a diterpenoid by loss of one carbon atom and rearrangement. The structure shown for this important growth substance is that produced by the fungus *Gibberella fujikuroi*. Higher plants apparently have as many as nine similar gibberellins with somewhat different structures (41, 42, 43).

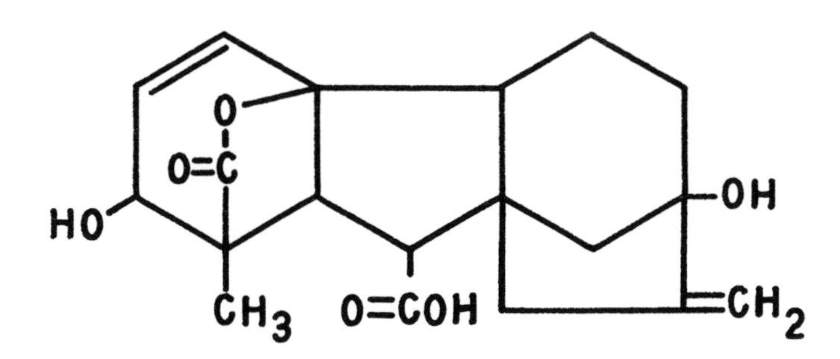

gibberellic acid

The tocopherols, or various forms of vitamin E, are important antioxidants found in various seed oils (e.g. wheat germ). The predominant member of this group is α-tocopherol. Others differ from it by having fewer methyl groups. They are all apparently interconvertible in the plant (44) and may be involved in the flowering process (45) or in growth responses (46).

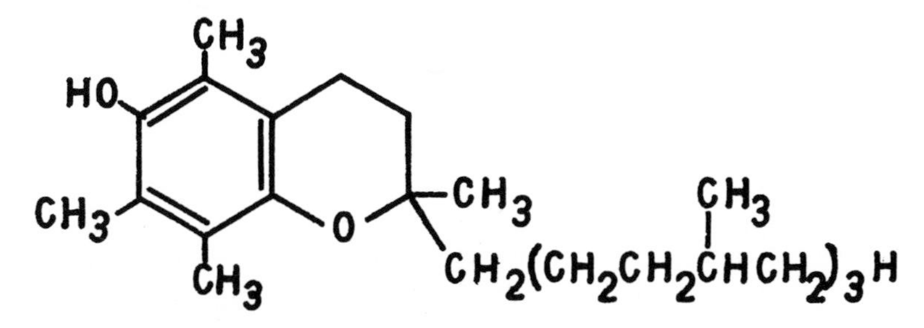

α-tocopherol

The K vitamins and ubiquinones are two naturally occurring groups of quinones which are assuming great importance in the oxidation-reduction reactions of respiration and photosynthesis. Presumably they act as hydrogen carriers through reduction to hydroquinones (47, 48). The different forms of ubiquinone (or coenzyme Q) are designated by subscripts indicating the number of isoprene residues in the side chain (e.g. UQ_9). They are found in mitochondria and may be characterized by their ability to restore succinic-cytochrome c reductase activity which has been lost by extraction with acetone.

A benzoquinone isolated from chloroplasts has been named plastoquinone and is presumed to have a function in photosynthesis (49). Recently two new quinones have been found from the same source, and they are apparently homologues of the original plastoquinone (50). For several years there has been controversy regarding the presence or absence of vitamin K_1 in chloroplasts. Problems of analysis have recently been solved and K_1 definitely shown to be present (51). There are many other naturally occurring quinones of unknown function and without isoprenoid side chains. They are discussed in Chapters 4 and 6.

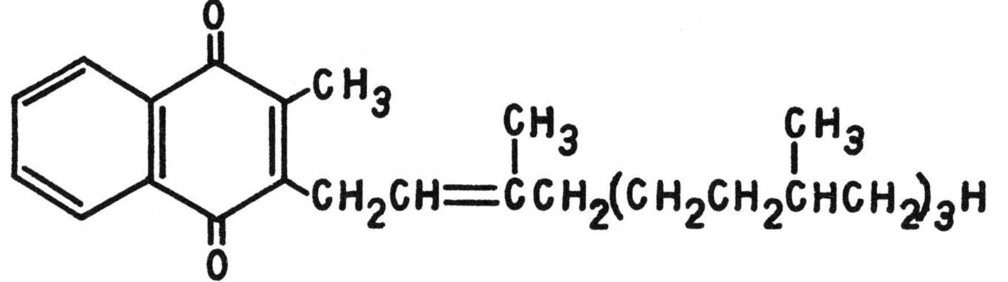

vitamin K_1

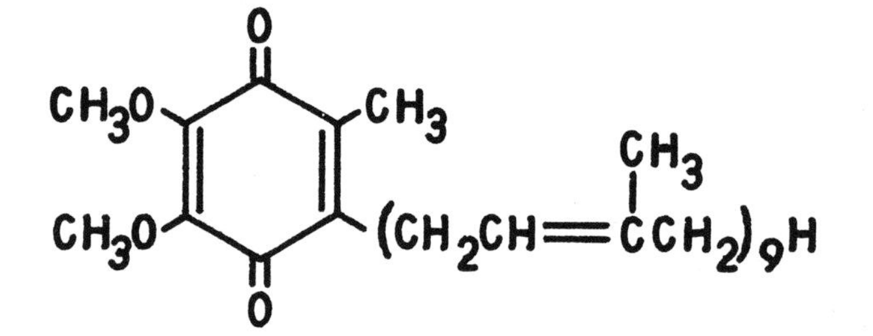

$ubiquinone_9$

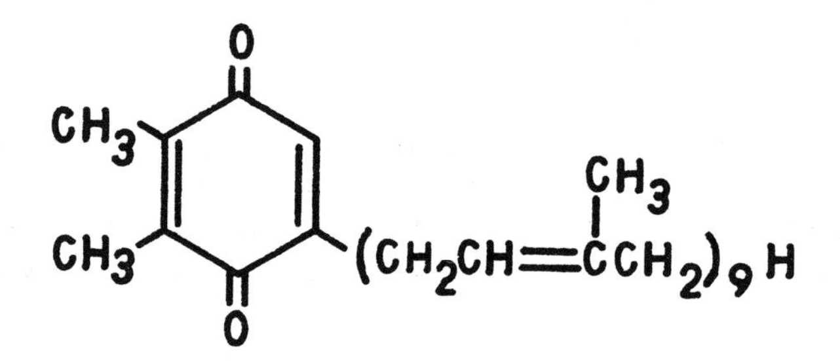

plastoquinone

The pyrethrins are a very valuable group of insecticides found only in the flowers of some members of the genus *Chrysanthemum* (52). The most important commercial source is *C. cinerariaefolium*. Four substances of very similar structure have been isolated. They are all esters; and while the acid portion of the molecule is clearly an isoprenoid structure, the keto-alcohol part is not derived either from mevalonic acid or acetate (53).

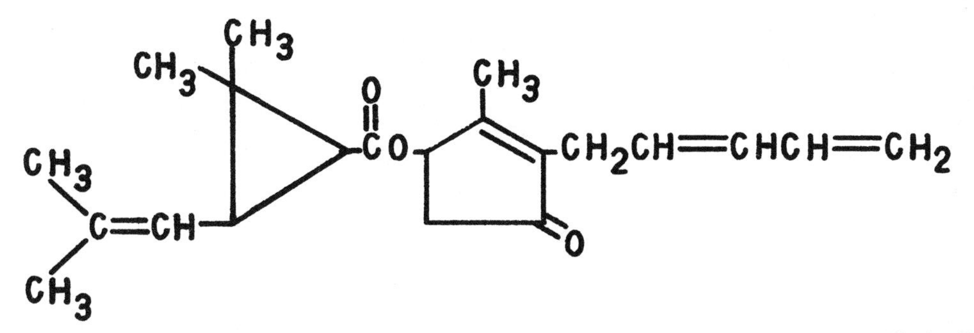

pyrethrin I

The compounds responsible for the physiological action of marihuana *(Cannabis sativa)* contain one ring having a p-menthane type structure and a second ring which does not appear to be related to the terpenoids. For example, cannabidiol is:

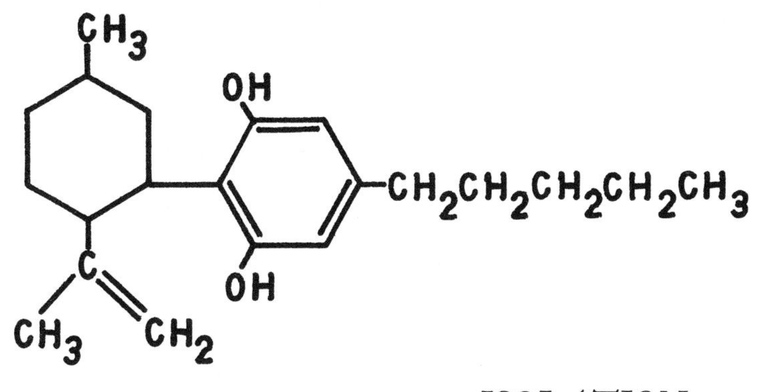

ISOLATION

It is clear from the great variety of structures found among the terpenoids and steroids that no general method of isolation can be applicable to all of them. However, a large number are decidedly non-polar compounds and may therefore be separated from polar plant constituents by extraction with such solvents as benzene or ether. Such an extract would also contain other types of lipids, esters, waxes, etc. Most of these may be removed by saponification in alcoholic alkali followed by extraction with ether. Acids and low molecular weight alcohols remain in the alkaline phase while most terpenoids and steroids will go into the ether extract along with high molecular weight alcohols, non-terpenoid hydrocarbons, etc.

A few exceptions to this general procedure must be noted. Glycosidic compounds such as the saponins and cardiac glycosides are insoluble in non-polar solvents. They are most conveniently extracted from plants with 70-95% hot ethanol and extraneous lipids removed from this solution by extraction into benzene. The order of extraction may also be reversed - i. e. lipids extracted first with ether or benzene and then glycosides extracted with hot alcohol. Some of the glycosides will precipitate when a hot alcoholic solution of them is cooled, and this may aid in separations (54). Acidic terpenoids, when present as the free acid, are soluble in non-polar solvents but on saponification will pass into the alkaline phase. Terpenoid and steroid alkaloids, of course, behave like other alkaloids in being more soluble in non-polar solvents under alkaline conditions than they are under acidic conditions. Rubber is insoluble in acetone but soluble in benzene, so a preliminary acetone extraction is used to remove contaminants if rubber is to be isolated. A general procedure for extracting and separating triterpenoids has been described by Pourrat and Hammouda (55).

Special methods of purification are applicable to various categories of compounds. The low molecular weight terpenes are usually separated by simple distillation or steam distillation. The most likely contaminants are volatile esters which may be removed by saponification. In purification of the carotenoids saponification of contaminants is carried out without heating in order to avoid degradations. The carotenoids may be separated according to their solubilities. The so-called epiphasic ones go preferentially into the petroleum ether layer when shaken with a mixture of this with methanol. Hypophasic carotenoids are those with two or more hydroxy groups. They are preferentially extracted into the methanol layer. Some monohydroxy compounds are found in both layers.

Formation of molecular complexes has found application in purifying some compounds of this group. Thiourea forms adducts with many types of branched hydrocarbon chains, depending on their molecular dimensions. Some cyclic compounds may also be accommodated. The thiourea adducts are insoluble in alcohol and non-polar solvents. They may be prepared by mixing alcoholic solutions of thiourea and the sample to precipitate the adduct, or dry material may be triturated with thiourea and a small amount of methanol. When the adduct has formed, uncombined lipids are extracted with benzene, ether, etc. The thiourea adduct is then decomposed with hot water and the desired material extracted into ether. For a general discussion of this technique see (56). Straight-chain aliphatic compounds can be removed from the branched or cyclic terpenoids by converting the former to urea complexes (57).

Complex formation is very common between various members of the steroids. This phenomenon causes difficulties in purification, but may also be put to practical use. In particular, digitonin is frequently used to precipitate sterols from alcoholic solution as insoluble digitonides. The reaction is specific for 3-β-OH sterols (as almost all natural ones are). Free sterols are then regenerated by partitioning the complex between mixtures of hot water and benzene or xylene whereupon the saponin goes to the aqueous and sterol to the organic layer. Another method used for splitting the complex involves boiling it with pyridine, cooling and adding ether to precipitate the saponin and leave sterol in solution. Conversely, this same technique may be applied to purifying many saponins by adding cholesterol to form an insoluble addition complex.

Further purification is usually carried out by column chromatography as a general technique although special methods may be available for individual examples (e.g. fractional distillation for the low molecular weight terpenoids). Purification of saponins and other glycosides is difficult and not commonly performed. These compounds are usually first hydrolyzed to their aglycones by boiling for several hours with 1-4N HCl, the aglycones extracted with benzene and purified as such (58). Alumina is the most common adsorbent used for chromatography of these compounds, with non-polar developing solvents such as petroleum ether, benzene, etc. In most cases highly active alumina is undesirable since it may cause degradative reactions. It may be neutralized with acid and a few per cent water added to lower its activity. Column chromatography of steroids is discussed by Neher (59). Sterols can be converted to colored urethanes to aid visualization of their separation on florisil columns. After separation, the original sterols are quantitatively regenerated (60). Some carotenoids are too sensitive for chromatography on even deactivated alumina and milder adsorbents such as magnesium oxide and sucrose are recommended for them. Chromatographic purification of carotenoids is extensively discussed by Strain (61). Other common adsorbents such as calcium carbonate and silica gel have been used for some of the terpenoids, cardiac glycosides, etc. Tropolones are isolated by procedures similar to those used for plant phenols, but in addition advantages can be taken of their property of forming chelate complexes (62).

CHARACTERIZATION

There is no single test which will distinguish terpenoids and steroids as a group from all other plant constituents. The closest approach to this goal is to describe them all as unsaponifiable lipids although such an operational grouping will include a few other types of compounds. There is no simple test to distinguish between the volatile terpenoids and such unsaponifiable aromatic compounds as eugenol or cinnamaldehyde. Classically hydrogenation to known cyclohexane derivatives or pyrolysis of terpenoids to form isoprene have been used to make such a differentiation. Infra-red spectra also indicate whether a compound is aromatic or aliphatic. Characterization of the lower terpenoids usually depends on their functional groups rather than on the carbon skeleton. A standardized procedure for identification of sesquiterpenes using distillation and chromatography on alumina has been developed by Pliva *et al.* (63). Paper chromatographic identification is based on recognition of functional groups. Because of their volatility and non-polar nature ordinary paper chromatography of the lower terpenoids is difficult. Carbonyl compounds may be chromatographed as their bisulfite complexes or reversed phase chromatography used with silicone impregnated paper. A method using glass strips coated with adsorbent rather than paper has been developed by Kirchner *et al.* (64). The best adsorbent layer was found to be silicic acid and the best general purpose solvent 15% ethyl acetate in hexane. Most compounds could be detected by spray reagents specific for functional groups. Unreactive materials were detected by charring with a sulfuric-nitric acid mixture and heat. This technique has been applied to terpenes of *Mentha piperita* (65). A general spot test for essential oils has been proposed by Hayashi and Hashimoto (66). They touch a spot of oil on filter paper with 20% sodium bisulfite and then with 10% antimony pentachloride in chloroform. Different constituents give rise to characteristic colors. Vapor phase chromatography will probably find increasing application for separating small quantities of volatile terpenoids. However, identification must depend on comparison with the elution time of knowns or on isolation and characterization by other techniques such as infrared spectrophotometry (67, 68).

The various structural types of the higher terpenoids and the steroids have classically been recognized by the aromatic hydrocarbons formed on dehydrogenation. Dehydrogenation is carried out either catalytically with palladium or by heating with sulfur or selenium at about 300° to form hydrogen sulfide or selenide as the other product. Yields in such reactions are usually very low; but if an identifiable product is obtained, it may be enough to determine the ring structure of the starting material. This procedure has already been mentioned in discussing the sesquiterpenoids where naphthalene and azulene types are recognized according to which of these two ring systems is produced on dehydrogenation. The azulenes are readily recognized by their blue color or specific absorption spectra. The different types of azulenes must be identified by comparison with knowns. Similarly, the tetracyclic triterpenoids yield 1, 2, 8-trimethylphenanthrene, pentacyclic terpenoids yeild picene or naphthalene derivatives, and steroids yield Diel's hydrocarbon (methylcyclopentanophenanthrene) along with several other products. It will be noticed that tertiary methyl groups are lost as a result of aromatization.

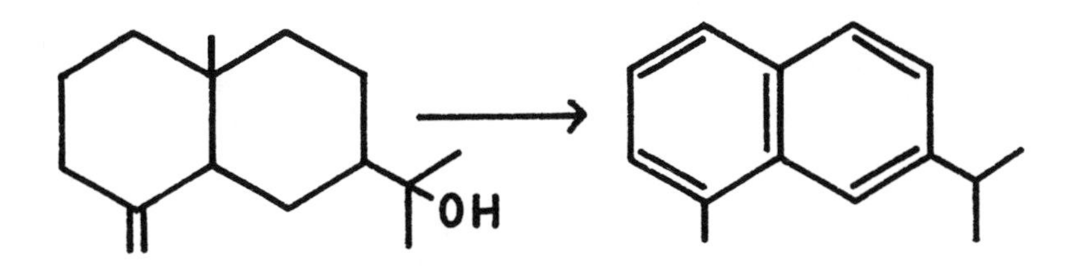

Eudesmol Eudalene

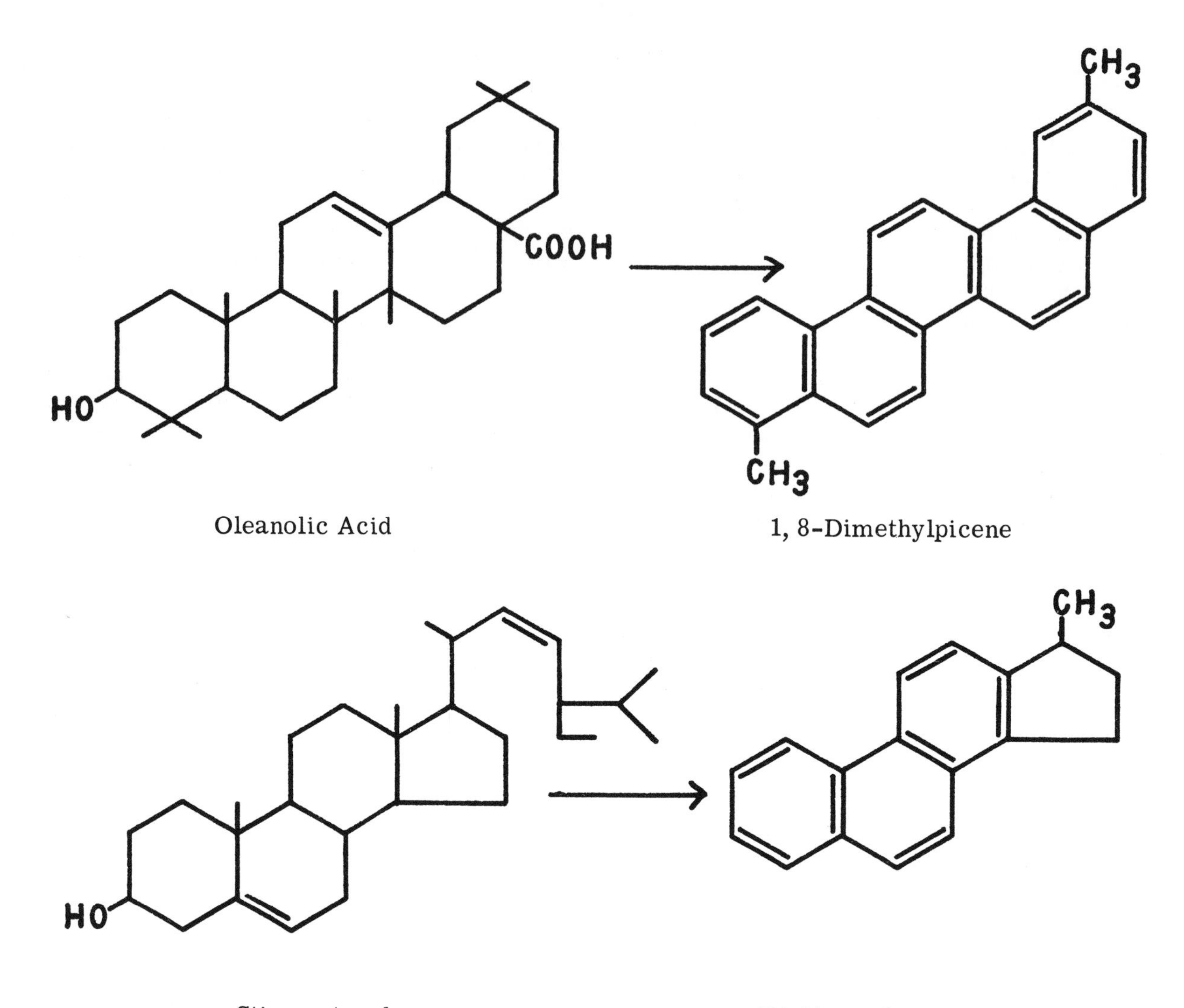

Oleanolic Acid

1, 8-Dimethylpicene

Stigmasterol

Diel's Hydrocarbon

Paper chromatography of the higher terpenoids and steroids has generally been unsuccessful by normal methods because of the non-polar nature of most of these compounds. Reversed phase chromatography has been used most widely. The paper is impregnated with such stationary phases as aluminum oxide, mineral oil, or aluminum soap, and non-polar, mobile phases used for development. Generally only rather non-specific spray reagents are available for detection of the terpenoids and steroids. One of the commonest is 10% antimony trichloride or pentachloride in chloroform, followed by heat. Table 14 summarizes some of the literature on paper chromatography of terpenoids and steroids.

Thin layer chromatography has also been usefully applied to the steroids and higher terpenoids. Silica gel is the commonly used adsorbent and analyses have been made of cardiac glycosides (80), triterpenoids (81), carotenoids (82), and benzoquinones (83). Gas chromatography can also be applied even to the rather non-volatile steroids and triterpenoids (84).

Many color reactions of the higher terpenoids and steroids have been recorded in the literature, and some of them could probably be adapted for use on paper chromatograms. One of the best known is the Liebermann-Burchard reaction on giving a blue-green color with most sterols and triterpene alcohols when they are mixed with acetic

TABLE 14. LITERATURE REFERENCES TO PAPER CHROMATOGRAPHY OF TERPENOIDS AND STEROLS

Type of Compound	Author and Reference Number
Terpenoid acids	Pasich (69)
Saponins	Sannié *et al.* (70), Pasich (71)
Steroids	Neher (59), Reineke (72), Axelrod and Pulliam (73)
Carotenoids	Šesták (74), Jensen and Jensen (75)
Cardiac glycosides	Resplandy (76), Kowalewski (77)
Ubiquinone derivatives	Lester and Ramasarma (78)
Sterols, terpenoid alcohols	Peereboom *et al.* (79)

anhydride and a drop of concentrated sulfuric acid. The mechanism and specificity of this test are discussed by Brieskorn and Herrig (85) and Cook (86). This, and some of the other common color reactions, cannot be applied to paper strips because of their destructive effect on the paper but might be used on glass fiber paper or on silica coated glass strips. The well-known Légal reaction for cardiac glycosides is given by many substances containing the grouping CH-CO and is therefore of value only for testing substances already shown to be steroids. It is also not given by the scilladienolides. Pentacyclic triterpenoids give a violet color when heated with 2, 6-di-*tert*-butyl-p-cresol in ethanol. Steroids give no color or a yellow-green one (87). Gerlach (88) has reviewed eleven well-known color reactions and recommends the reagent of Brieskorn and Briner (chlorosulfonic acid and Sesolvan NK) for specifically distinguishing between triterpenoids (red color) and steroids (brown color). Several color reactions for detecting steroids and terpenoids on chromatograms have been reviewed by Wachsmuth and Koeckhoven (89). Most saponins are readily recognized by their hemolytic property although some may be quite weak in this respect. They can be added in isotonic solution to defibrinated or citrated blood and hemolysis observed, or paper chromatograms may be sprayed with isotonically diluted blood and hemolytic zones observed. Shamma (90) has presented a useful review of diagnostic reactions which may be used to distinguish among the three basic type structures of the pentacyclic triterpenoids. A color reaction relatively specific for ubiquinone derivatives is based on their formation of a blue color with ethyl cyanoacetate and ammonia (91).

If pure compounds have been separated by chromatography or other means, determination of absorption spectra is of great value in assigning them to groups. In the ultraviolet and visible region absorption of these compounds is mostly due to the presence of conjugated double bond systems. Compounds with isolated double bonds have no absorption peaks in the visible or ultra-violet spectrum above 200 mμ.

Woodward (92) has presented rules for predicting the absorption maximum for a diene system, taking the base value of 217 mμ for a conjugated double bond and adding appropriate increments for different structural features. Measurements are generally in close agreement with predicted values. Ultraviolet and infrared spectra of over 200 sesquiterpenes are recorded by Pliva *et al.* (63). The carotenoids show strong absorption peaks in the visible usually at about 450 mμ. Many spectra of individual carotenoids will be found in the appropriate general references and in the book by Strain (61). It should be noted that the exact absorption maximum may vary slightly with the solvent used. Ultraviolet and infrared absorption spectra of steroids have been compiled by Dorfman (93) and Dobriner *et al.* (94) and infra-red spectra for many steroid sapogenins and their derivatives by Jones *et al.* (95). Diaz *et al.* (96) have recorded the absorption spectra observed on treating 16 different sapogenins with concentrated sulfuric acid. Bernstein and Lenhard (97) have correlated steroid structures with their spectra in concentrated sulfuric acid. Rubber can be distinguished from gutta by infra-red spectra. Rubber has 42% more absorption than gutta at 12μ.

Optical rotations of all known triterpenoids and steroids have been compiled by Mathieu *et al.* (98, 99).

METABOLIC PATHWAYS

There is reasonable agreement regarding the early steps in the biosynthesis of isoprenoid compounds and some scattered evidence regarding the biosynthesis of some of the major categories. These generally acceptable pathways are outlined in Figure 8-1. Almost nothing is known for certain about the details of interconversion within any of the major categories, although some working hypotheses are taken for granted in the interests of simplification.

A. It seems self-evident that cyclic compounds are made from acyclic precursors. Two warnings must however be inserted:

1. Straight chain structures which do not follow the isoprene rule may be regarded as derived from cyclic compounds by a ring scission in the middle of an isoprene residue (e. g. elemol);
2. The straight chain precursors are not necessarily known terpenoids (e. g. phytol as such, although it is the only important acyclic diterpenoid, need not be the precursor of cyclic diterpenoids. Some transient acyclic derivative may be the precursor of both phytol and the cyclic diterpenoids).

B. Compounds which do not follow the isoprene rule are considered to result from rearrangements late in the biosynthetic sequence rather than from unusual condensations early in the sequence.

A general review of this area is presented in a symposium publication (100) and an article by Wright (101). Other reviews are those of Goodwin (102) for carotenoids, Crabbé (103) for tetracyclic triterpenoids, Dutta and Narang (104) for diterpenoids, and Halsall and Theobald for sesquiterpenoids (105). It should be noted that much of the work on steroid biosynthesis has been carried out with animal tissues and fungi. Much work on carotenoid biosynthesis has been done using fungi. It is, of course, uncertain how far such results apply to the higher plants; but where evidence is available, it indicates a similarity of pathways in all organisms. Several specific areas will be discussed below.

Early in the study of terpene chemistry frequent intra-molecular rearrangements of these compounds were observed. On the basis of such observations it has been assumed that molecular rearrangements can account for many *in vivo* transformations. The most important general type of rearrangement is the Wagner-Meerwein reaction which occurs in the presence of acids. It may be pictured as resulting from the addition of hydrogen ion to a double bond to form a carbonium ion. Electrons from another part of the molecule are attracted to the positively charged carbon atom and a new bond is formed with elimination of a hydrogen ion or addition of a negative ion. This type of re-

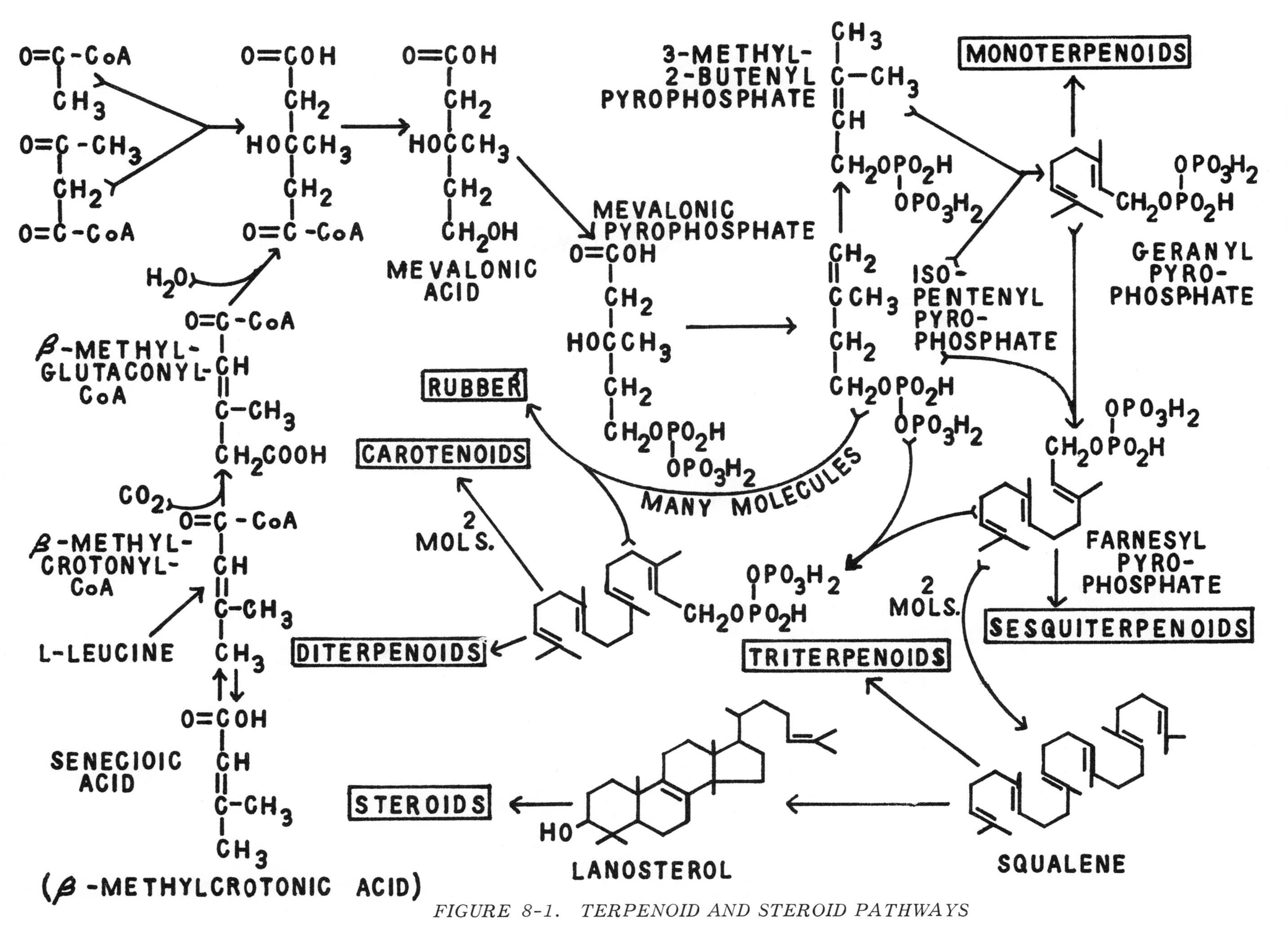

FIGURE 8-1. TERPENOID AND STEROID PATHWAYS

action is illustrated for the simple case of α-pinene which forms bornyl chloride in the presence of hydrochloric acid:

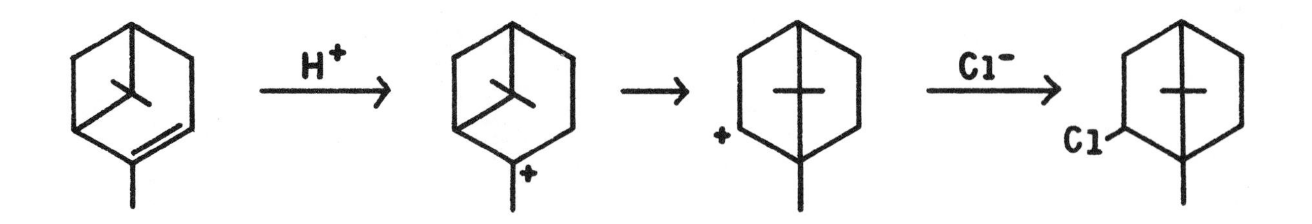

In more complicated cases several different rearrangements may occur before the final structure is attained so that profound modifications are introduced. The general references may be consulted for critical discussion of this type of reaction. It should, however, be noted here that stereochemical configuration is frequently retained, and therefore it is probably an oversimplification to picture a free carbonium ion as an intermediate.

Applications of the Wagner-Meerwein rearrangement to theories of terpene biosynthesis are very common in the literature. A simple example has been suggested by Enzell and Erdtman (106) to explain the formation of cuparene from a bisabolene type skeleton:

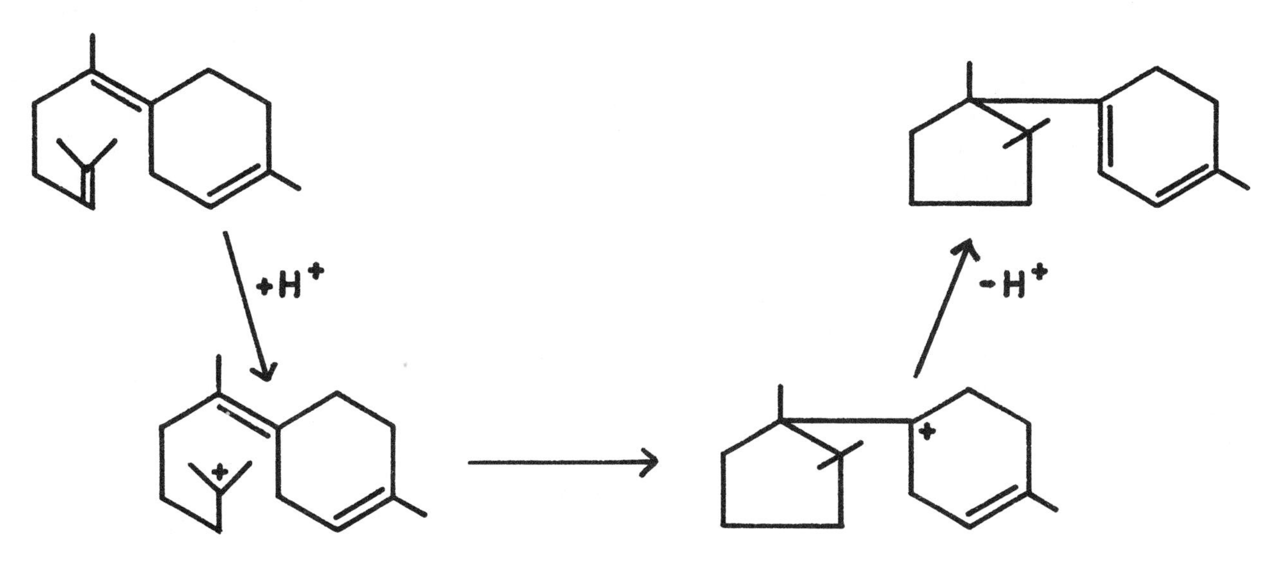

A more complex series has been used by Wenkert (107), Valenta and Wiesner (108), and Whalley (109) to account for some diterpenoid structures including the diterpenoid alkaloids (see opposite page). There is tracer evidence for a small part of this scheme in that Sandermann and Stockmann (110) have shown that from the labeling pattern abietane type compounds are formed by rearrangement of pimarane type compounds in *Pinus silvestris*.

Some type of rearrangement must be involved in formation of the pentacyclic triterpenoids since ring E and its substituents cannot be derived by any simple ring closure from a squalene-type compound. Simple rearrangements, however, can account for the conversion of any one of three basic types to the other two. Synthesis of a soybean sapogenin has been shown by Arigoni (111) to proceed from mevalonic acid-2-C^{14} with incor-

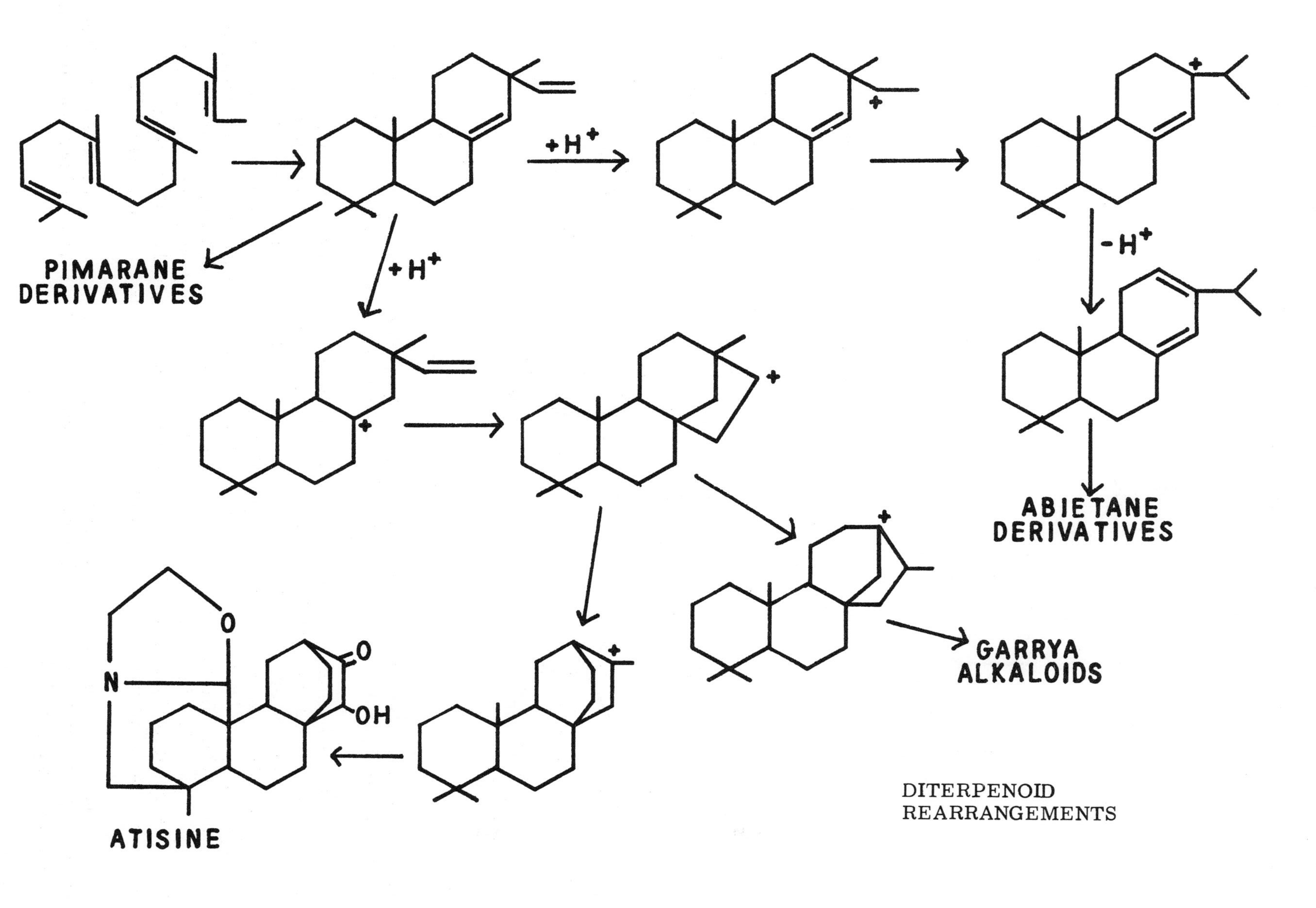

DITERPENOID REARRANGEMENTS

poration of label at the circled positions in the carbon skeleton:

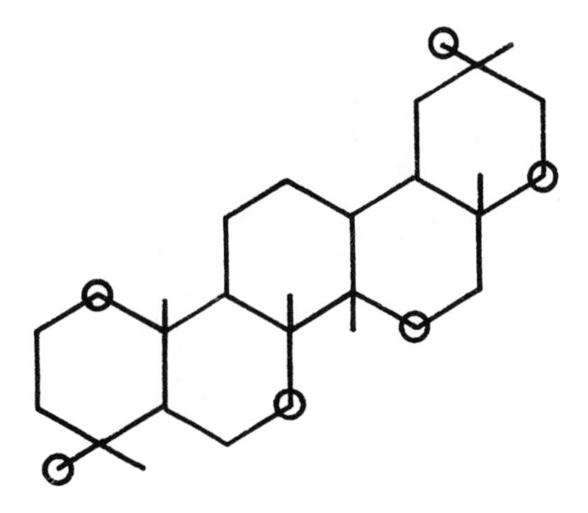

A pentacyclic compound formed from squalene might be expected to have a structure and label distribution as follows:

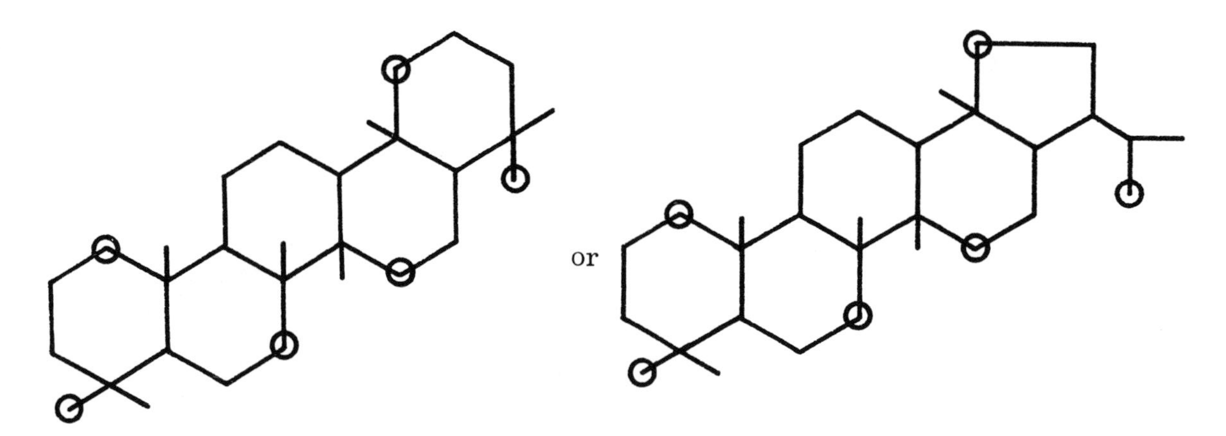

A few natural compounds of the second structure are known, and a possible mechanism of rearrangement has been proposed to account for the more usual structures (112, 113).

Other labelling experiments have shown the conversion of acetate into α-pinene (114) sterols (115), solanidine, (116), and rubber (117); the conversion of mevalonic acid into α-pinene (114), sterols (118, 119), cardiac glycosides (120, 121), triterpenoids (118, 119) and rubber (122); the conversion of β-methylcrotonic acid into pulegone (123), α-pinene (110), and rubber (117); and the conversion of iso-pentenyl pyrophosphate into rubber by fresh latex (124). Biosynthesis of the terpenoids of peppermint (*Mentha piperita)* and spearmint *(Mentha spicata)* has received considerable attention, and detailed pathways have been presented for interconversion of the various monoterpenoids in these plants (125, 126) as well as the genetic determination of the composition of the essential oils (127).

It has been interesting to find that the lactone ring of cardiac glycosides is evidently not made from mevalonic acid, but possibly is derived by the addition of two acetate units to a C_{21} steroid (19, 121).

Biosynthesis of the carotenoids has been studied much more extensively than is the case for any of the other terpenoids. Unfortunately the picture rather than being more clear as a result of a great mass of data is greatly confused by many conflicting reports. There is little doubt that the general pathways indicated in Figure 8-1 are followed (128). However, it must be noted that Goodwin (129) found very slight incorporation of mevalonic or acetic acid into the β-carotene of maize, whereas carbon dioxide was rapidly incorporated. Labelled iso-pentenyl pyrophosphate was converted into carotenoids by tomato fruit homogenates 40 times faster than mevalonic acid (130). Other experiments showing the incorporation of L-leucine can be accommodated into the accompanying scheme as a by-pass. The greatest difficulty rests on the question as to whether the various carotenoids are interconvertible or whether they arise by parallel pathways from a common (unknown) C_{40} precursor (131). Most genetic and tracer evidence favors the idea of independent pathways for the various carotenes and xanthophylls. On the basis of genetic analysis Porter and Lincoln (132) proposed a common C_{40} intermediate with three double bonds and divergence after this stage resulting from successive dehydrogenations. This proposal has since been modified slightly (131). Tracer experiments of Purcell *et al.* (133) with tomatoes have pointed to an unknown precursor with four double bonds. In order of appearance, phytofluene is one of the first compounds to contain label from mevalonic acid; lycopene is the last; and other carotenes intermediate. It must not be inferred from this that compounds early in this sequence are the actual precursors of compounds late in the sequence. Some colorless polyenes, rather than being precursors of pigments, may be formed by reduction of carotenes particularly under pathological conditions (134). Other experiments (115, 116) indicate that light stimulates synthesis of carotenes from colorless polyenes; and in addition, oxygen may be required. Some of these different requirements, the conditions of the plants used, and the particular species studied may account for discrepancies in the various pathways of carotenoid biosynthesis which have been proposed. Recent studies with isotopically labelled oxygen have shown that hydroxyl groups of xanthophylls derive their oxygen atom from the atmosphere, but in the epoxides it comes from water (135).

The introduction of nitrogen into the alkaloids of this group has not been studied. In some cases, by analogy with other alkaloids, nitrogen may be supplied to the carbon skeleton as ammonia from an amide. With the diterpene alkaloids the problem is complicated by the invariable presence of an extra two-carbon residue attached to the nitrogen. This three atom grouping might reasonably come intact from glycine.

As noted above, most of the plant sterols contain an "extra" methyl or ethyl group at C-24. In the ergosterol of yeast the additional methyl group is known to come from formate or methionine. Nothing is known regarding the source of ethyl groups; a reasonable choice might be acetate.

GENERAL REFERENCES

Arreguin, B., "Rubber and Latex" in Ruhland 10 223.
de Mayo, P., Mono-and Sesquiterpenoids, Interscience Publishers, N. Y., 1959.
de Mayo, P., The Higher Terpenoids, Interscience Publishers, N. Y., 1959.
Eastman, R. H., and Noller, C. R., "The Terpenes" in Organic Chemistry 4, ed. by H. Gilman, John Wiley, N. Y., 1953.
Fieser, L. F. and Fieser, M. Steroids, Reinhold, N. Y., 1959.
Goodwin, T. W., "Carotenoids" in Ruhland 10 186.
Goodwin, T. W., The Comparative Biochemistry of the Carotenoids, Chapman and Hall, London, 1952.
Guenther, E., The Essential Oils 6 vols., D. Van Nostrand, N. Y., 1948-1952.
Haagen-Smit, A. J., "Sesquiterpenes and Diterpenes," Fortschr. Chem. Org. Naturstoffe 12 1 (1955).

Haagen-Smit, A. J. "The Lower Terpenes" in Ruhland 10 52.
Heusner, A. "Phytosterine" in Ruhland 10 132.
Hoch, J. H., A Survey of Cardiac Glycosides, Univ. South Carolina, Columbia, S. C., 1961.
Karrer, P. and Jucker, E., Carotenoids, Elsevier, Amsterdam, 1950.
Klyne, W., The Chemistry of the Steroids, John Wiley, N. Y., 1957.
Moritz, O. "Die Terpenoide" in Ruhland 10 24.
Sandermann, W., "Terpenoids: Structure and Distribution", "Terpenoids: Metabolism", Comparative Biochemistry 3 pp. 503-590, 591-630, M. Florkin and H. S. Mason, eds., Academic Press, New York, 1962.
Shoppee, C. W., Chemistry of the Steroids, Butterworths, London, 1958.
Simonsen, J. L., The Terpenes 3 vols., 2 ed., Cambridge U. Press, 1947-1952.
Many articles in Paech and Tracey 3.

BIBLIOGRAPHY

1. Buckles, R. E., Mock, G. V. and Locatell, L., Jr., Chem. Revs. 55 659 (1955).
2. Fujita, Y., Ueda, T. and Ono, T., Nippon Kagaku Zasshi 77 400 (1956).
3. Sprecher, E., Pharmazie 13 218 (1958).
4. Fraenkel, G. S., Science 129 1466 (1959).
5. Orloff, H. D., Chem. Revs. 54 366 (1954).
6. System of Nomenclature for Terpene Hydrocarbons, American Chemical Society, Washington, D. C., 1955.
7. Nozoe, T. and Ito, S., Fortschr. Chem. Org. Naturstoffe 19 32 (1961).
8. Stahl, E., Ber. 87 202, 505, 1626 (1954).
9. Gordon, M., Chem. Revs. 50 127 (1952).
10. Rossmann, M. G. and Lipscomb, W. N., Tetrahedron 4 275 (1958).
11. Tsutsui, M. and Ashworth, E., Chem. Revs. 59 1031 (1959).
12. Jeger, O., Fortschr. Chem. Org. Naturstoffe 7 1 (1950).
13. Jones, E. R. H. and Halsall, T. G., Fortschr. Chem. Org. Naturstoffe 12 44 (1955).
14. Ives, D. A. J. and O'Neill, A. N., Can. J. Chem. 36 926 (1958).
15. Zimmerman, J., Helv. Chim. Acta 29 1455 (1946).
16. Brieskorn, C. H., Pharmazeut. Zentral. 95 235 (1956).
17. Helmkamp, G. and Bonner, J., Plant Physiol. 28 428 (1953).
18. Sander, H., Planta 52 447 (1958).
19. Tschesche, R., Angew. Chem. 73 727 (1961).
20. Bergmann, W., Ann. Rev. Plant Physiol. 4 383 (1953).
21. Tamm, C., Fortschr. Chem. Org. Naturstoffe 13 137 (1956).
22. Tamm, C., Fortschr. Chem. Org. Naturstoffe 14 71 (1957).
23. Stoll, A., Chem. and Ind. 1959 1558.
24. Wiesner, K. and Valenta, Z., Fortschr. Chem. Org. Naturstoffe 16 26 (1958).
25. Prelog, V. and Jeger, O. in the Alkaloids ed. by R. H. F. Manske and H. C. Holmes, 3 248, Academic Press, N. Y., 1953.
26. Anderson, I. C. and Robertson, D. S., Plant Physiol. 35 531 (1960).
27. Korte, F., Barkemeyer, H. and Korte, I., Fortschr. Chem. Org. Naturstoffe 17 124 (1959).
28. Courtney, J. L., Revs. Pure Appl. Chem. 11 118 (1961).
29. Lavie, D., Shvo, Y., Gottlieb, O. R. and Glotter, E., Tetrahedron Letters 1961 615.
30. Schlegel, W., Melera, A. and Noller, C. R., J. Org. Chem. 26 1206 (1961).
31. Djerassi, C., Nakano, T., James, A. N., Zalkow, L. H., Eisenbraun, E. J., and Shoolery, J. N., J. Org. Chem. 26 1192 (1961).
32. Birch, A. J., Grimshaw, J. and Juneja, H. R., J. Chem. Soc. 1961 5194.
33. Dolder, F., Lichti, H., Mosettig, E., Quitt, P., J. Am. Chem. Soc. 82 246 (1960).
34. Belleau, B. and Burba, J., Biochim. Biophys. Acta 54 195 (1961).
35. Pauson, P. L., Chem. Revs. 55 9 (1955).
36. Erdtman, H., in Paech and Tracey 3 351 (1955).
37. Nozoe, T., Fortschr. Chem. Org. Naturstoffe 13 232 (1956).
38. Kofler, M., Langemann, A., Rüegg, R., Gloor, U., Schwieter, U., Würsch, J., Wiss, O. and Isler, O., Helv. Chim. Acta 42 2252 (1959).
39. Aneja, R., Mukerjee, S. K., and Seshadri, T. R., Tetrahedron 4 256 (1958).
40. Birch, A. J., Rickards, R. W. and Smith, H., Proc. Chem. Soc. 1958 192.
41. Phinney, B. O. and West, C. A., Ann. Rev. Plant Physiol. 11 411 (1960).
42. MacMillan, J., Seaton, J. C. and Suter, P. J., Tetrahedron 18 349 (1962).

43. Brian, P. W., Hemming, H. G. and Lowe, D., Nature 193 946 (1962).
44. Green, J., J. Sci. Food Agric. 9 801 (1958).
45. Sironval, C. and El Tannir-Lomba, J., Nature 185 855 (1960).
46. Stowe, B. B. and Obreiter, J. B., Plant Physiol. 37 158 (1962).
47. Crane, F. L., Biochemistry 1 510 (1962).
48. Wolstenholme, G. E. W. and O'Conner, C. M. eds., Quinones in Electron Transport, Little, Brown and Co., Boston, 1961.
49. Crane, F. L. Plant Physiol. 34 546 (1959).
50. Kegel, L. P., Henniger, M. D. and Crane, F. L., Biochem. Biophys. Res. Comms. 8 294 (1962).
51. Kegel, L. P. and Crane, F. L., Nature 194 1282 (1962).
52. Crombie, L. and Elliott, M., Fortschr. Chem. Org. Naturstoffe 19 120 (1961).
53. Crowley, M. P., Inglis, H. S., Snarey, M. and Thain, E. M., Nature 191 281 (1961).
54. Heitz, S., Compt. rend. 248 283 (1959).
55. Pourrat, H. and Hammouda, Y., Lyon Pharm. Spec. 7 31 (1956).
56. Kobe, K. A. and Reinhart, L. R., J. Chem. Educ. 36 300 (1959).
57. Ives, D. A. J. and O'Neill, A. N., Can. J. Chem. 36 434 (1958).
58. Wall, M. E., Krider, M. M., Rothman, E. S., and Eddy, C. R., J. Biol. Chem. 198 533 (1952).
59. Neher, R., J. Chromatog. 1 122 (1958).
60. Bergmann, W. and Domsky, I. I., Ann. N Y. Acad. Sci. 90 Art. 3, 906 (1960).
61. Strain, H. H., Chloroplast Pigments and Chromatographic Analysis, Phi Lambda Upsilon, Penn. State Univ., University Park, Penna., 1958.
62. Zavarin, E., Smith, R. M. and Anderson, A. B., J. Org. Chem. 24 1318 (1959).
63. Pliva, J., Horák, M., Herout, V. and Šorm, F., Die Terpene. Teil 1. Sesquiterpene, Akademie Verlag, Berlin, 1960.
64. Kirchner, J. G., Miller, J. M., and Keller, G. J., Anal. Chem. 23 420 (1951).
65. Battaile, J., Dunning, R. L. and Loomis, W. D., Biochim. Biophys. Acta 51 538 (1961).
66. Hayashi, K. and Hashimoto, Y., Pharm. Bull. (Tokyo) 5 611 (1957). (Chem. Abstr. 52 15838.)
67. Cartoni, G. P. and Liberti, A., J. Chromatog. 3 121 (1960).
68. Zubyk, W. J. and Conner, A. Z., Anal. Chem. 32 912 (1960).
69. Pasich, B., Nature 181 765 (1958).
70. Sannié, C. S., Heitz, S. and Lapin, H., Compt. rend. 233 1670 (1951).
71. Pasich, B., Nature 190 830 (1961).
72. Reineke, L. M., Anal. Chem. 28 1853 (1956).
73. Axelrod, L. R. and Pulliam, J. E., Arch. Biochem. Biophys. 89 105 (1960).
74. Šesták, Z., J. Chromatog. 1 293 (1958).
75. Jensen, A. and Jensen, S. L., Acta Chem. Scand. 13 1863 (1959).
76. Resplandy, A., Ann. pharm. franc. 17 536 (1959). (Chem. Abstr. 54 7069 (1960).
77. Kowalewski, Z., Helv. Chim. Acta 43 1314 (1960).
78. Lester, R. L. and Ramasarma, T., J. Biol. Chem. 234 672 (1959).
79. Peereboom, J. W. C., Roos, J. B. and Beekes, H. W., J. Chromatog 5 500 (1961).
80. Steinegger, E. and van der Walt, J. H., Pharm. Acta Helv. 36 599 (1961).
81. Tschesche, R., Lampert, F. and Snatzke, G., J. Chromatog. 5 217 (1961).
82. Eichenberger, W. and Grob, E. C., Helv. Chim. Acta 45 974 (1962).
83. Barbier, M., J. Chromatog. 2 649 (1959).
84. VandenHeuvel, W. J. and Horning, E. C., J. Org. Chem. 26 634 (1961).
85. Brieskorn, C. H. and Herrig, H., Arch. Pharm. 292 485 (1959).
86. Cook, R. P., Analyst 86 373 (1961).
87. Brieskorn, C. H. and Mahran, G. H., Naturwiss. 47 107 (1960).
88. Gerlach, H., Planta Med. 6 1948 (1958).
89. Wachsmuth, H. and Van Koeckhoven, L., Anal. Chim. Acta 22 41 (1960).
90. Shamma, M., Drug Standards 27 42 (1959).
91. Shunk, C. H., McPherson, J. F., and Folkers, K. A., J. Org. Chem. 25 1053 (1960).
92. Woodward, R. B., J. Am. Chem. Soc. 64 72 (1942).
93. Dorfman, L., Chem. Revs. 53 47 (1953).
94. Dobriner, K., Katzenellenbogen, E. R. and Jones, R. N., Infrared Absorption Spectra of Steroids, Interscience Publishers, N. Y., 1953.
95. Jones, R. H., Katzenellenbogen, E., and Dobriner, K., J. Am. Chem. Soc. 75 158 (1953).
96. Diaz, G., Zaffaroni, A., Rosenkranz, G., and Djerassi, C., J. Org. Chem. 17 747 (1952).
97. Bernstein, S., and Lenhard, R. H., J. Org. Chem. 25 1405 (1960).
98. Mathieu, J. P. and Petit, A., Optical Rotatory Powers, I Steroids Pergamon Press, N. Y.
99. Mathieu, J. P. and Ourisson, G., Optical Rotatory Powers. II Triterpenoids, Pergamon Press, N. Y.
100. Ciba Foundation Symposium on the Biosynthesis of Terpenes and Sterols, Little, Brown, Boston, 1959.
101. Wright, L. D., Ann. Rev. Biochem. 30 525 (1961).
102. Goodwin, T. W., Ann. Rev. Plant Physiol. 12 219 (1961).
103. Crabbé, P., Record Chem. Prog. 20 189 (1959).
104. Dutta, P. C. and Narang, S. A., J. Indian Chem. Soc. 38 576 (1961).

105. Halsall, T. G. and Theobald, D. W., Quart Revs. 16 101 (1962).
106. Enzell, C. and Erdtman, H., Tetrahedron 4 361 (1958).
107. Wenkert, E., Chem. and Ind. 1955 282.
108. Valenta, Z. and Wiesner, K., Chem. and Ind. 1956 354.
109. Whalley, W. B., Tetrahedron, 18 43 (1962).
110. Sandermann, W. and Stockmann, H., Chem. Ber. 91 933 (1958).
111. Arigoni, D., Experientia 14 153 (1958).
112. Ruzicka, L., Experientia 9 357 (1953).
113. Eschenmoser, A., Ruzicka, L., Jeger, O. and Arigoni, D., Helv. Chim. Acta 38 1890 (1955).
114. Stanley, R. G., Nature 182 738 (1958).
115. Goodwin, T. W., Biochem. J. 69 26P (1958).
116. Guseva, A. R. and Paseshnichenko. V. A., Biokhimiya 23 412 (1958).
117. Bandurski, R. S. and Teas, J. H., Plant Physiol. 32 643 (1957).
118. Nicholas, H. J., J. Biol. Chem. 237 1476, 1480, 1485, (1962).
119. Baisted, D. J., Copstack, E. and Nes, W. R., Biochemistry 1 537 (1962).
120. Ramstad, E. and Beal, J. L., Chem. and Ind. 1960 177.
121. Gregory, H. and Leete, E. Chem. and Ind. 1960 1242.
122. Park, R. B. and Bonner, J., J. Biol. Chem. 233 340 (1958).
123. Sanderman, W. and Stockman, H., Chem. Ber. 91 930 (1958).
124. Henning, U., Möslein, E M., Arreguin, B., and Lynen, F., Biochem. Z. 333 534 (1961).
125. Reitsema, R. H., J. Am. Pharm. Assoc., 47 267 (1958).
126. Battaile, J. and Loomis, W. D., Biochim. Biophys Acta 51 545 (1961).
127. Murray, M. J., Genetics 45 925 (1960).
128. Braithwaite, G. D. and Goodwin, T. W., Biochem. J. 76 1 (1960).
129. Goodwin, T. W., Biochem. J. 70 612 (1958).
130. Varma, T. N. R. and Chichester, C. O., Arch. Biochem. Biophys. 96 265 (1962).
131. Porter, J. W. and Anderson, D. G., Arch. Biochem. Biophys. 97 520 (1962).
132. Porter, J. W. and Lincoln, R. E., Arch. Biochem. 27 390 (1950).
133. Purcell, A. E., Thompson, G. A., Jr., and Bonner, J., J. Biol. Chem. 234 1081 (1959).
134. Vogt-Beekmann, H., Z. f. Bot. 44 289 (1956).
135. Yamamoto, H. Y., Chichester, C. O. and Nakayama, T. O. M., Arch. Biochem. Biophys. 96 645 (1962).

Chapter 9
FLAVONOIDS AND RELATED COMPOUNDS

The flavonoid group may be described as a series of C_6 - C_3 - C_6 compounds. That is, their carbon skeleton consists of two C_6 groups (substituted benzene rings) connected by a three-carbon aliphatic chain.

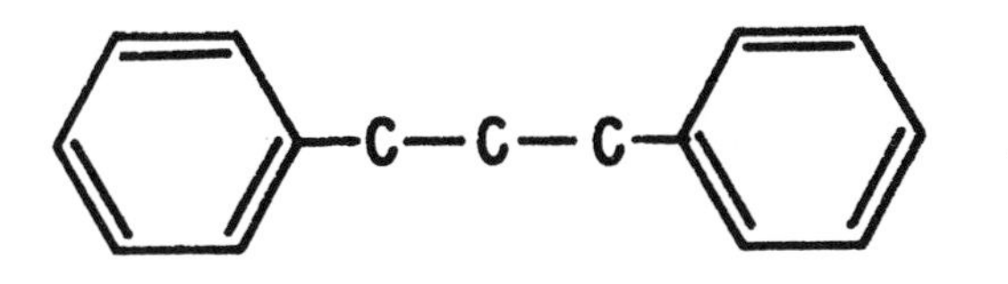

flavonoid skeleton

The different classes within the group are distinguished by additional oxygen-heterocyclic rings and by hydroxyl groups distributed in different patterns. Flavonoids frequently occur as glycosides. The largest group of flavonoids is characterized by containing a pyran ring linking the three-carbon chain with one of the benzene rings. The numbering system for these flavonoid derivatives is given below:

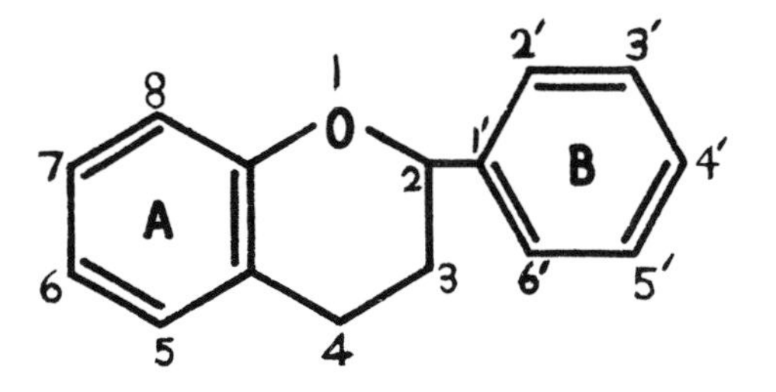

Among the typical flavonoids having the above skeleton the various types are distinguished by the oxidation state of the C_3 chain. Going from most reduced to most oxidized, the structures and their names are as follows (only the key portion of the molecule is shown):

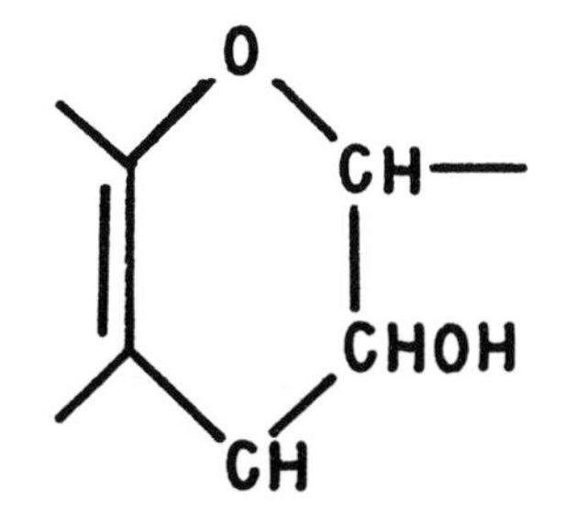

catechins

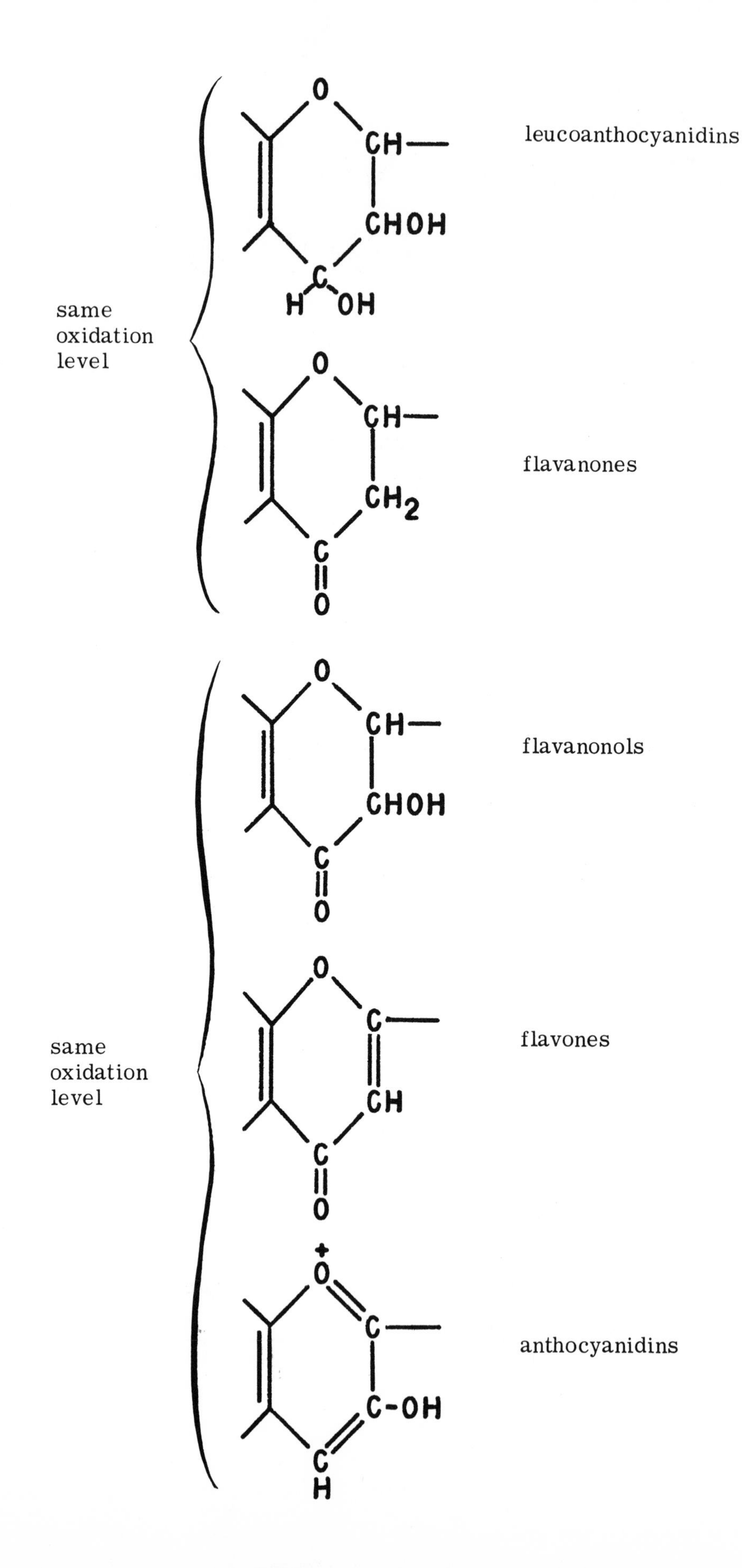

O
CH—
CHOH
C
H OH
leucoanthocyanidins
same
oxidation
level
O
CH—
CH2
C
O
flavanones
O
CH—
CHOH
C
O
flavanonols
O
C
CH
C
O
flavones
same
oxidation
level
O
C
C-OH
C
H
anthocyanidins

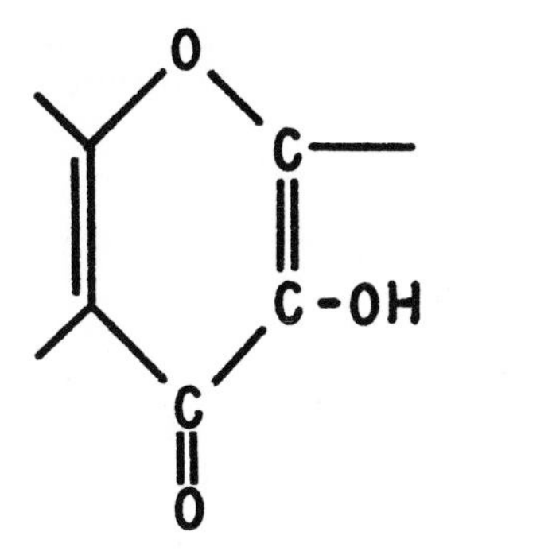

flavonols

Other variations in the C_6 - C_3 - C_6 pattern also occur and are denoted as follows:

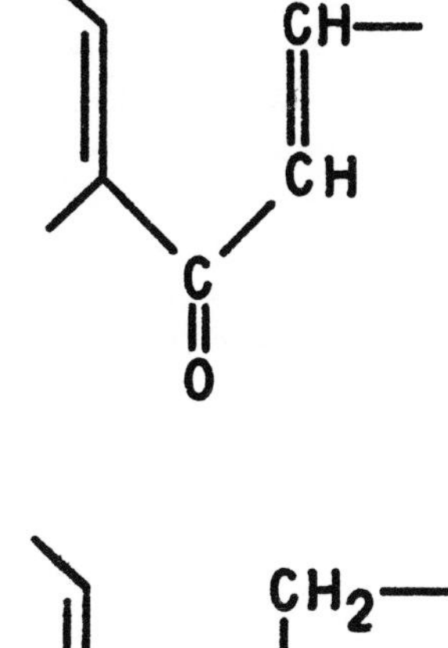

chalcones

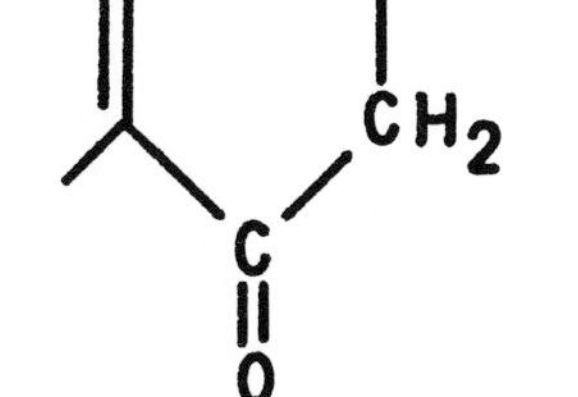

dihydrochalcones

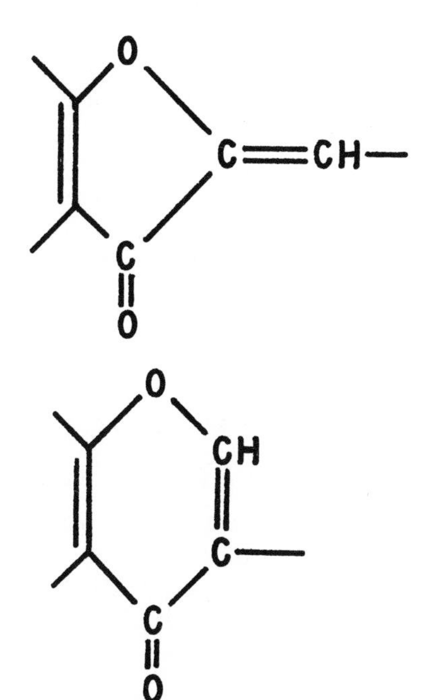

aurones

isoflavones

Although not indicated by these partial formulas, hydroxyl groups are normally present on the aromatic rings or they may be found combined as methoxyl groups or glycosides.

In addition to the flavonoids other compounds such as xanthones, condensed tannins, etc. seem to fit into a natural grouping; and they will also be discussed in this chapter.

The flavonoids include many of the most common pigments and occur throughout the entire plant kingdom from the fungi to the angiosperms. They are found both in the flowers and in the vegetative parts of the higher plants. In addition to their possible function as flower pigments in attracting pollinating birds and insects, various other roles have been suggested for them in the plant. The growth inhibitor of dormant peach buds is a flavanone, naringenin (1), which is an activator of indoleacetic acid oxidase (2). Other flavonoids inhibit the same enzyme (3) so that plant growth could be controlled by the balance between inhibiting and activating flavonoids. A possible role of flavonoids in the physiology of sexual reproduction was first indicated by the experiments of Moewus (4) which showed the sex-determining action of flavonoids of algal gametes. Later Kuhn and Löw (5) showed that the inability of two *Forsythia* varieties to cross-pollinate was related to the presence of specific flavonoids in the pollen of each one. Much more work along these lines needs to be done to determine whether the widespread occurrence of flavonoids in pollen is functional or just fortuitous. Hartshorne (6) has suggested that they may be related only indirectly to the biochemistry of sex. That is, a particular flavonoid synthesis may be possible only in the environment of one or the other sex. In connection with sexual biochemistry it is intriguing to find that certain isoflavones act as estrogens for mammals (7), and their structures may be written so as to bear a steric resemblance to those of the steroid hormones, e.g.:

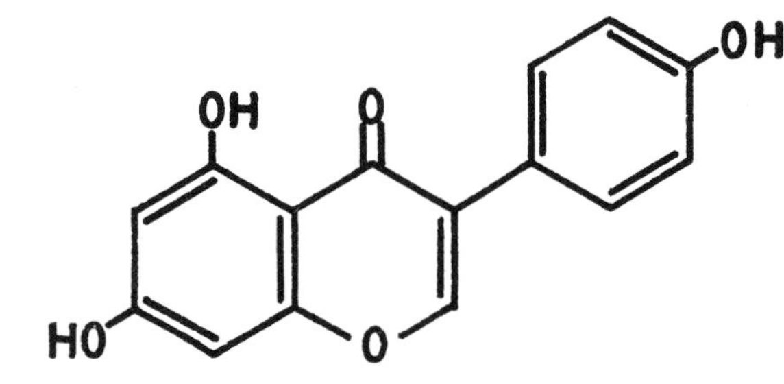

genistein

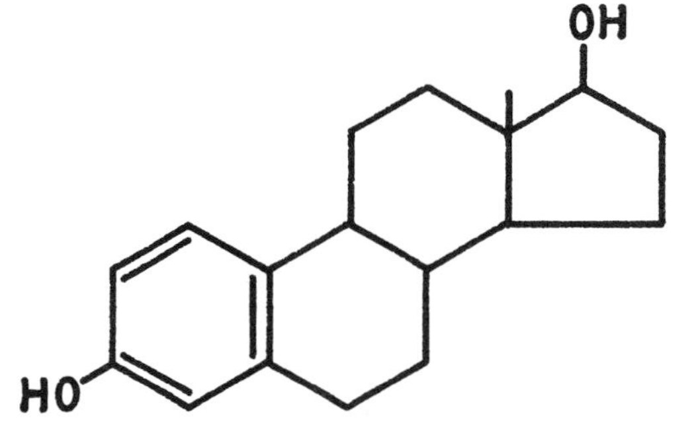

estradiol

Sandalwood contains similar estrogenic isoflavone derivatives, pterocarpin and homopterocarpin (8). To be estrogenic, an isoflavone must have a free 5-OH group (9). It has been suggested that some flavonoids act as antibiotics to protect the plant against attack by parasites. The review of Geissman (10) discusses other possible roles of the flavonoids.

CATECHINS AND LEUCOANTHOCYANIDINS

The catechins and leucoanthocyanidins are two groups which show many similarities, differing as they do in only a single, aliphatic hydroxyl group. They are all colorless compounds, existing throughout the plant kingdom but especially in the higher woody plants. Leucoanthocyanidins have been found in ferns but not in plants lower than ferns. They almost never exist as glycosides (hence the name "leucoanthocyanidin" is preferred to "leucoanthocyanin"), but some catechins may occur as esters of gallic acid. One epicatechin glucoside has been found (11) and one leucoanthocyanidin glucoside (12). Only three types of catechin are known differing in the number of hydroxyl groups in ring B. They have two asymmetric carbons (starred) and therefore 4 possible isomers:

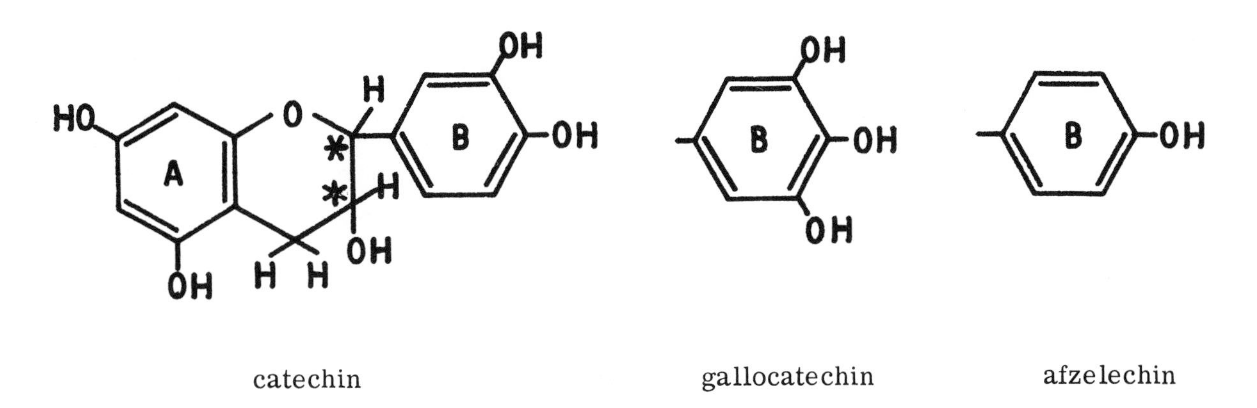

catechin gallocatechin afzelechin

The sterochemistry of these compounds has been elucidated (13). The (+) and (-) catechins have the number 2 and 3 hydrogens *trans*, whereas they are *cis* in the epicatechins. Epimerization involves inversion of the 2-aryl group rather than the 3-hydroxy group.

The leucoanthocyanidins have only recently had their structures elucidated. Although they are basically flavan-3, 4-diols, certain variations have been found. Some examples of established structures and their sources follow:

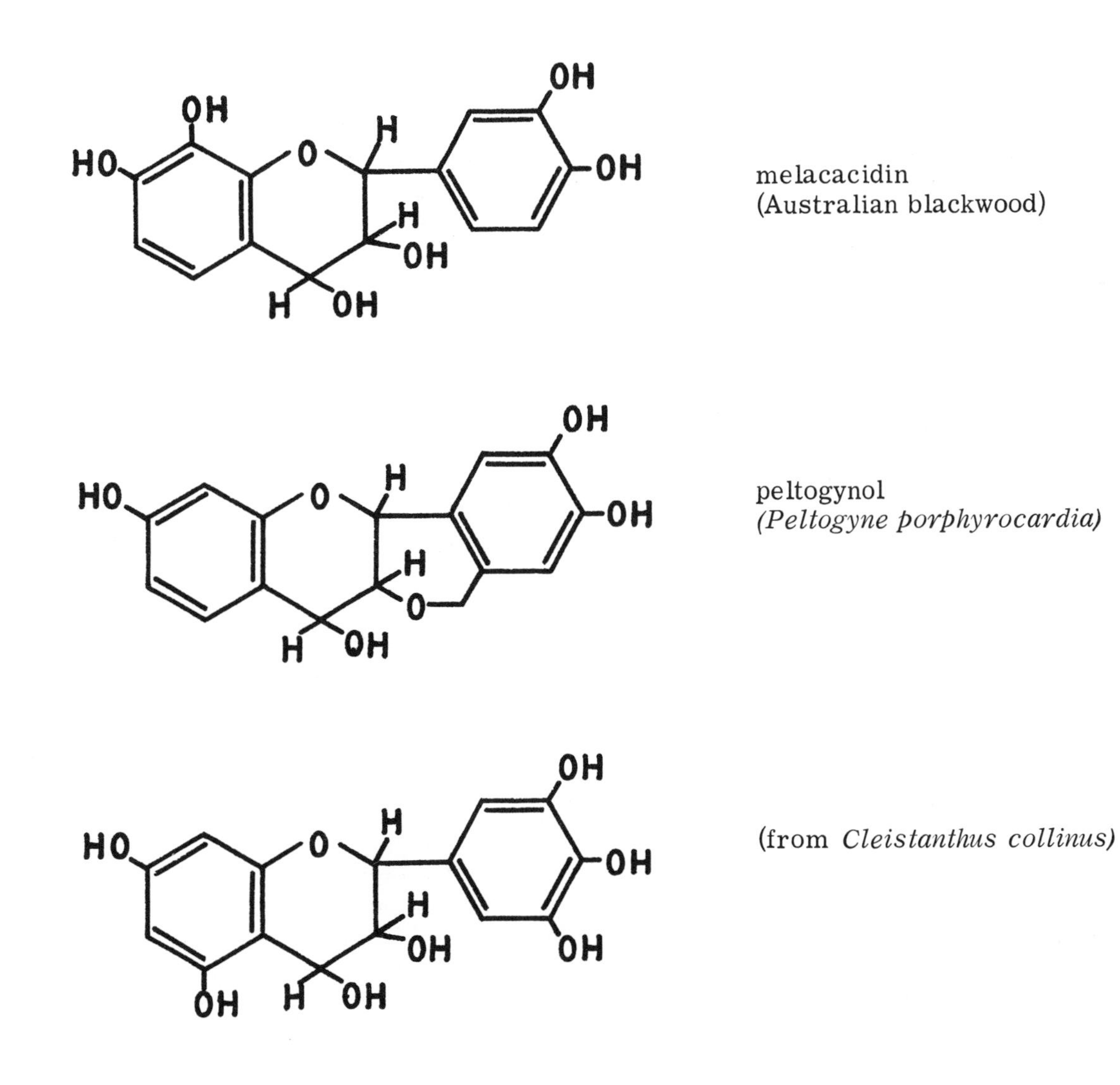

melacacidin (Australian blackwood)

peltogynol (*Peltogyne porphyrocardia)*

(from *Cleistanthus collinus)*

Although only one purified leucoanthocyanidin has been found to be a glycoside, several instances are known where they apparently exist as part of a colloidal polymer, possibly bound to a hemicellulose by glycosidic bonds. Polymers similar to some of the natural ones have also been prepared by treating the monomer with 2N HCl in the cold (14). Obviously in these no hemicellulose would be present. These polymers may be distinguished from the monomers by their insolubility in both water and ethyl acetate, whereas the monomers (and catechins) are soluble in ethyl acetate but not in water (15). The leucoanthocyanidins, by definition, are compounds which form anthocyanidins on heating with acid. The reaction is oxidative, involving loss of a hydrogen atom as well as dehydration:

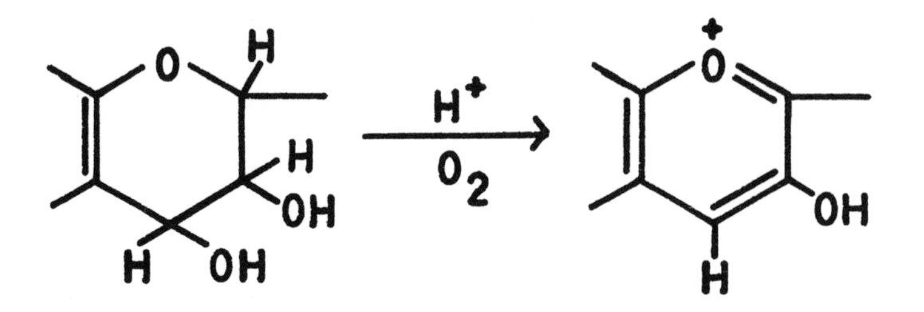

Unfortunately their name is a misnomer since even under the most carefully controlled conditions only about 25% of the theoretical yield of anthocyanidin is obtained (16). The mechanism of this reaction and other aspects of leucoanthocyanidin chemistry are reviewed by Bokadia (17). The major products on heating with acid are red-brown polymers loosely known as phlobaphenes or tannin-reds. The catechins under these conditions also form similar brown polymers. Freudenberg and Weinges (18) have shown that compounds with 4' and 7 hydroxyl groups are most susceptible to polymer formation. According to Freudenberg *et al.* (19) the initial step in formation of these polymers is a condensation between C-1 of one monomer and C-6 of another:

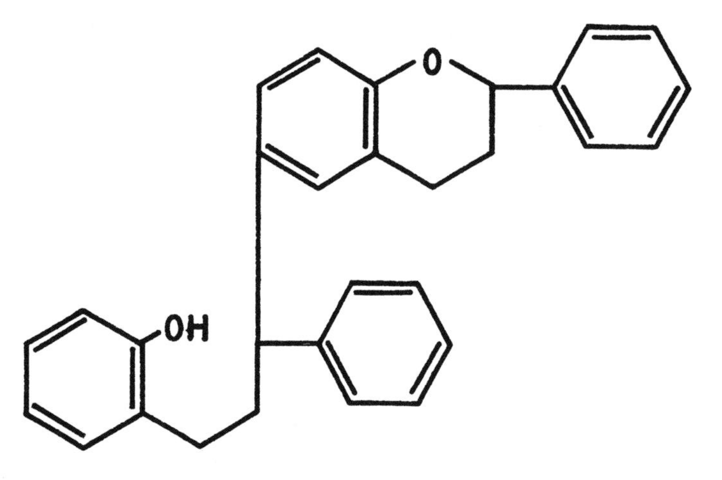

The yield of this dimer is only about 10%, so that the formation of other types of product is by no means excluded (18). Polymers of this sort involving unknown numbers of units probably constitute the group of compounds known as "condensed tannins", "phlobatannins", or "catechol tannins". They possess many of the typical tannin properties as described for the hydrolysable tannins (Chap. 4) and are very widely distributed in nature. According to Russel (20) all tannins produced by normal physiological processes in wood, bark, leaves and roots are phlobatannins. The polymeric leucoanthocyanidins may also have this type of structure (21). Oxidation of these colorless polymers on heating with acid forms the colored phlobaphenes, as well as some anthocyanidin if a 3, 4-diol structure is present and splitting of the polymer occurs. These complex and little-understood reactions are further complicated by the loose terminology which has been used. A rough summary is diagrammed as follows:

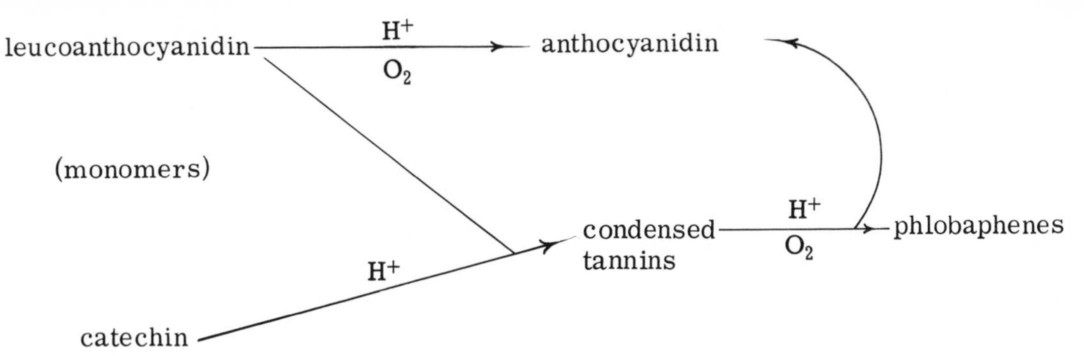

The ill-defined catechutannic acid is a dehydration product of either catechin or a catechin polymer, probably as follows:

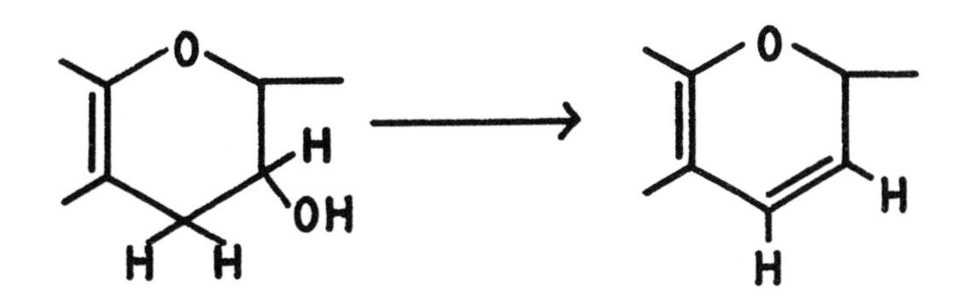

It has recently been found that not all compounds which give anthocyanidins with acid have the flavan-3, 4-diol structure, and a new class of natural products called "proanthocyanidins" has been suggested (22, 23). Some of these are found to be dimers and some polymers. One of the dimers found in *Gleditschia triacanthos* on heating with acid forms cyanidin, epicatechin, and other products. It has the structure:

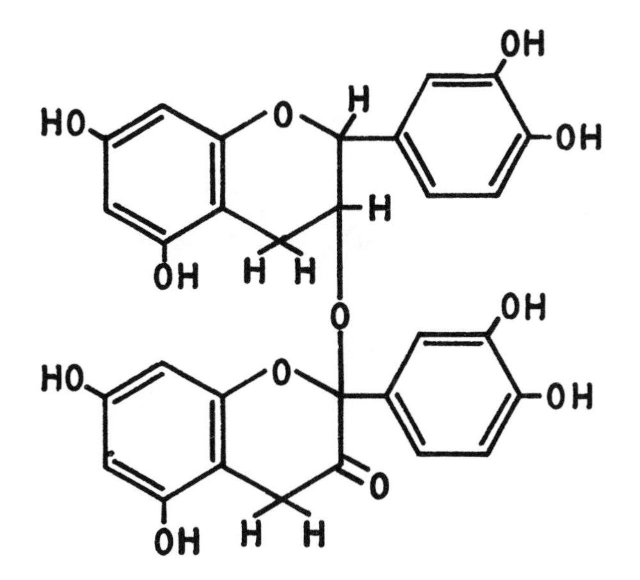

The red colors obtained on heating many plant parts with acid have been ascribed to the presence of leucoanthocyanidins. However, the phlobaphenes may be red; and humic acid, present in some leaves, also gives a red color on heating with acid (24) so that a better criterion than mere color should be applied (e. g. absorption spectra).

FLAVANONES AND FLAVANONOLS

These compounds occur in very small amounts compared with the other flavonoids. They are either colorless or only slightly yellow. Because of their low concentration and lack of color they have been largely neglected. Glycosides of the flavanones are well-known as, for instance, hesperidin and naringin from citrus fruit peels. (The corresponding aglycones are hesperetin and naringenin.) The flavanonols are probably the least known of the flavonoids, and it is not known whether they normally exist as glycosides. Pachéco (25) has made the most extensive recent study of these compounds, but his analytical procedure would have hydrolyzed any glycosidic bonds if they were present. Only about 8 flavanonols have been isolated. Unlike the leucoanthocyanins, they are stable to hot hydrochloric acid but are decomposed by warm alkali to form chalcones. According to Nord and de Stevens (26) a flavanone type of unit is probably present in bagasse lignin. It is peculiar that no condensed tannins based on the flavanones have been found since flavanones appear to be structurally as suited for polymerization as the catechins or leucoanthocyanidins. The fact that they are frequently 5- or 7-glycosides may hinder condensation at position 6 to give a polymer such as is formed from the aglyconic catechins and leucoanthocyanidins.

FLAVONES, FLAVONOLS, ISOFLAVONES

The flavones and flavonols are probably the most widely distributed of all the yellow plant pigments, although the deeper yellow colors of plants are normally due to carotenoids. Some of the flavones and flavonols are still economically important, and luteolin was probably the first dye to be used in Europe. Quercetin is one of the commonest phenolic compounds of vascular plants, followed closely by kaempferol (27). Isoflavones are much less important. Only about half a dozen of them are known (28).

These compounds are usually soluble in hot water and alcohol although a few highly methylated forms are insoluble in water. They vary in hydroxylation from flavone itself, which occurs as dust on primrose (*Primula* spp.) flowers, to nobiletin of tangerines (*Citrus nobilis*).

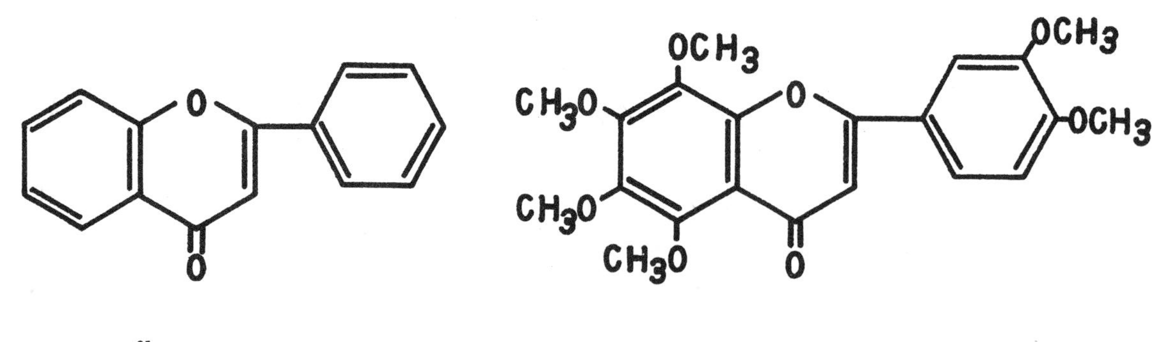

flavone nobiletin

However, the most common derivatives have 5 and/or 7 hydroxylation in ring A and 4' hydroxylation in ring B. Ring B is hydroxylated in positions 3' and 5' only if the 4' position is hydroxylated too. Rarely 2' hydroxylation is found. Additional variation is introduced by methylation of hydroxyl groups to form ethers or methylenation of neighboring hydroxyl groups to form methylenedioxy derivatives. Glycosidic sugar residues may occur in almost any position, although 4'-glycosides are rare and 6-glycosides unknown. The flaones and isoflavones are most commonly 7-glycosides and the flavonols, 3-glycosides. The usual sugars found in the glycosides are glucose, galactose and rhamnose although

TABLE 1. SOME FLAVANONES AND FLAVANONOLS, STRUCTURES AND OCCURRENCE

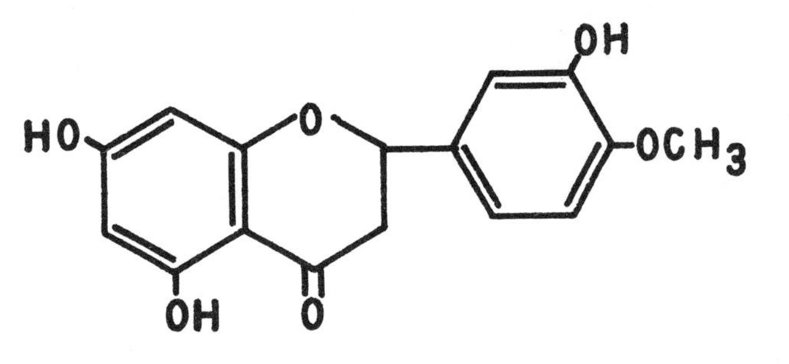

hesperetin
(citrus fruits)

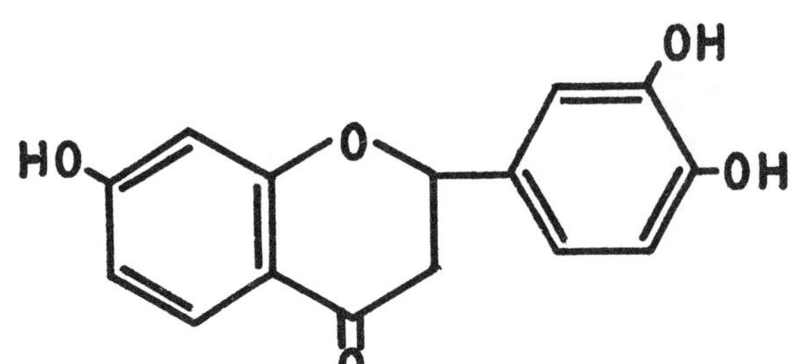

butin
(Butea frondosa)

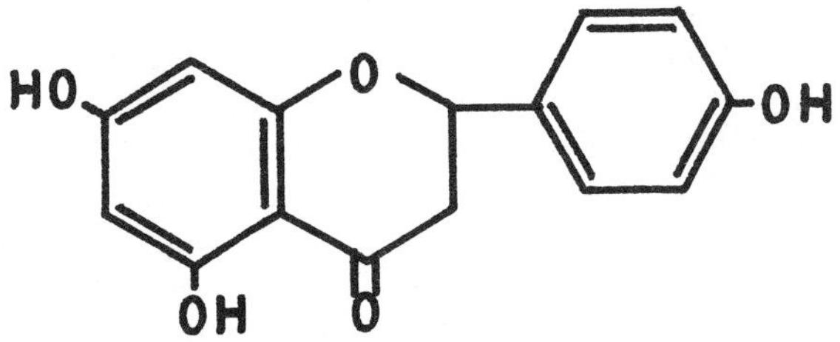

naringenin
(citrus fruits)

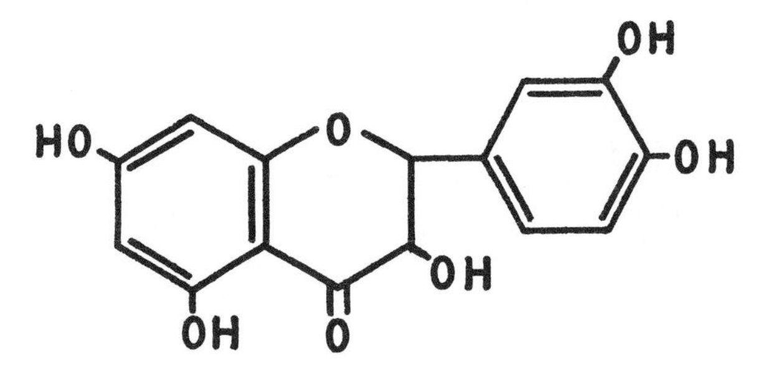

taxifolin
(Pseudotsuga taxifolia)

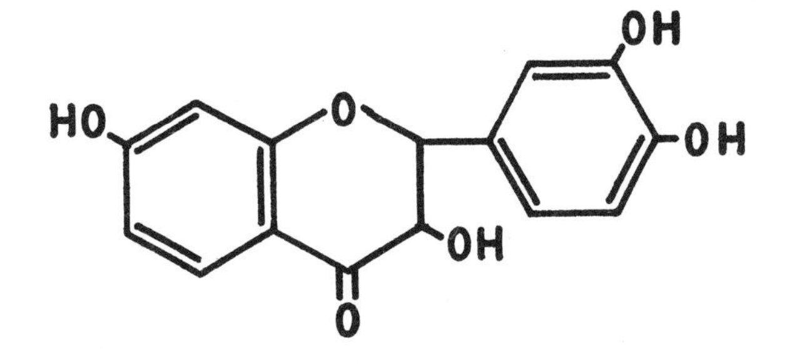

fustin *(Quebracho colorado)*

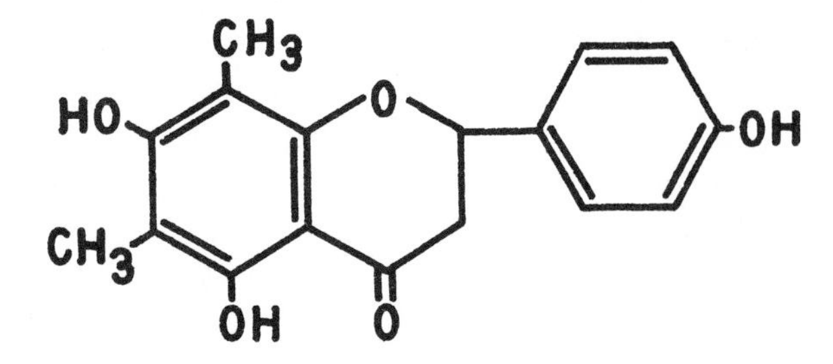

farrerol *(Rhododendron)*

others occur. Disaccharides are occasionally present in the so called "biosides". In contrast to the anthocyanins (see below) there are never two sugar residues attached to different hydroxyl groups. A few flavone-sugar derivatives are known in which the sugar is attached by a carbon-carbon bond rather than as a glycoside. The best known of these is vitexin, a glucose derivative of apigenin:

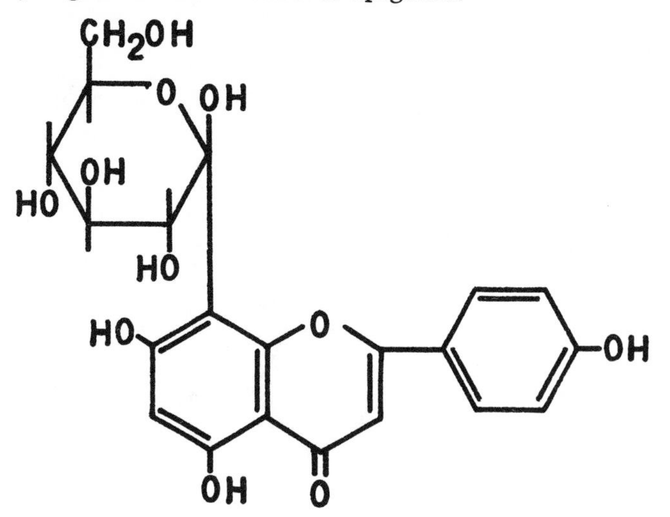

Other such compounds are cited by Whalley (29) and Hörhammer *et al.* (30). Bate-Smith and Swain have proposed the name "glycoflavonol" for such compounds (31). They might be formed by an aldol condensation between the carbonyl of the sugar and the active methylene group of an A-ring precursor like acetoacetate (see below under "Biosynthesis"). The glycosides are naturally less soluble in organic solvents and more soluble in water than the corresponding aglycones. They are also less colored than the aglycones, some being colorless when in neutral or acidic solution. However, they become bright yellow or orange in alkali and may be detected by exposing colorless plant parts to ammonia. This appearance of color is due to salt formation and assumption of a quinoid structure in ring B:

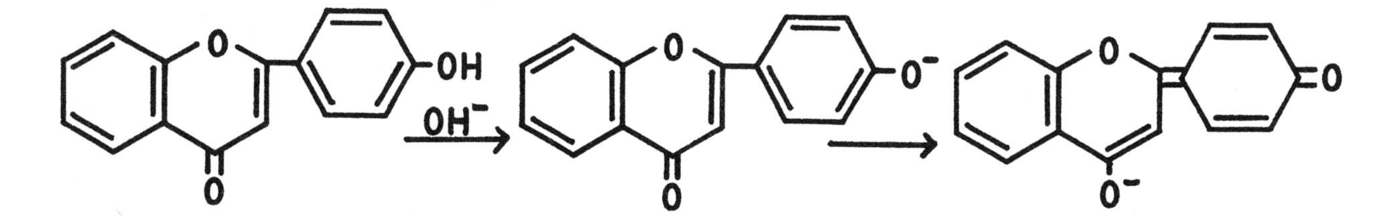

Alkaline solutions of the flavonols (but not flavones) are oxidized in the air but not so rapidly as to preclude the use of alkaline solutions in their preparation. Table 2 summarizes the hydroxylation patterns of some well-known flavones, flavonols, and isoflavones. Structures of a few other derivatives are given in Table 3 to illustrate some varieties of methylation and glycosidation which are found.

TABLE 2. HYDROXYLATION PATTERNS OF SOME FLAVONOIDS

Phenolic Hydroxyl Positions	Compounds		
	Flavones	Flavonols	Isoflavones
5, 7	chrysin	galangin	----
5, 7, 4'	apigenin	kaempferol	genistein
5, 7, 3', 4'	luteolin	quercetin	orobol
5, 7, 3', 4', 5'	----	myricetin	----
7, 3', 4'	----	fisetin	----
5, 7, 2', 4'	lotoflavin	morin	----
5, 7, 8, 3', 4'	----	gossypetin	----

ANTHOCYANINS

The anthocyanins are the common red to blue pigments of flower petals, making up as much as 30% of the dry weight in some flowers. They also occur in other parts of higher plants and throughout the plant kingdom except in the fungi. Unlike the other classes of flavonoids, they seem always to occur as glycosides except for traces of the aglycones, anthocyanidins. Hydrolysis may occur during autolysis of plant tissues or during isolation of the pigments so that anthocyanidins are found as artifacts. At the normal pH of vacuoles where they occur the anthocyanins exist as cations. They were originally thought to be oxonium compounds with the positive charge residing on the heterocyclic oxygen. It is probably more accurate to consider the molecule as a whole as possessing a non-localized charge. As the solution becomes more basic a purple color-base first appears and then a blue colored salt form:

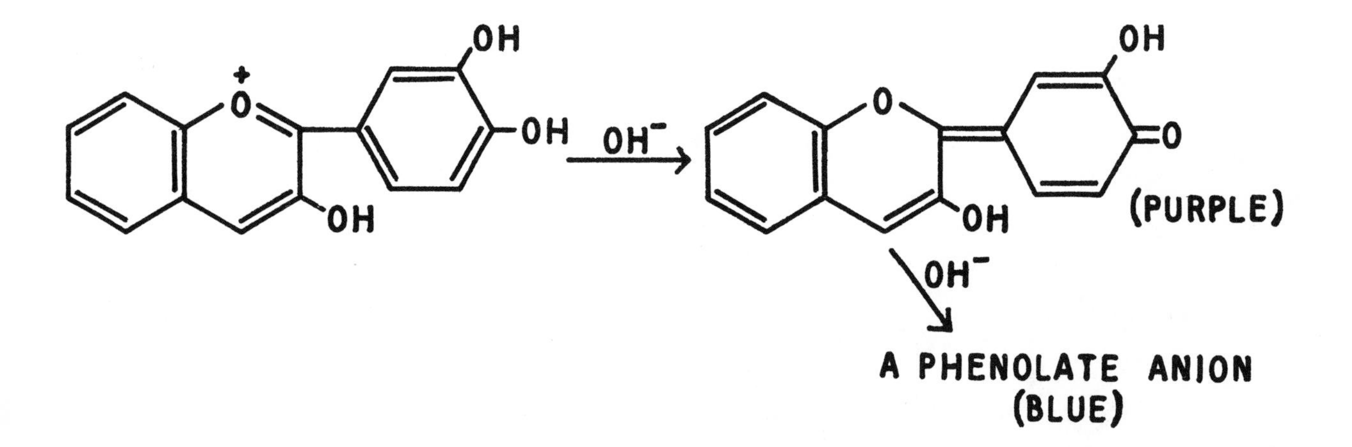

TABLE 3. SOME FLAVONES, FLAVONOLS, AND ISO-FLAVONES

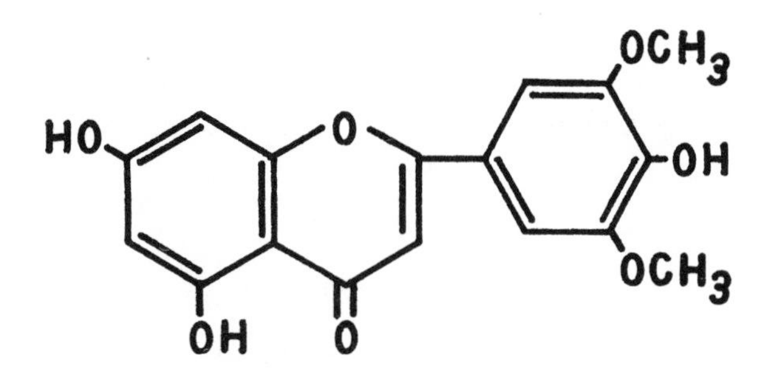

tricin (Khapli wheat)

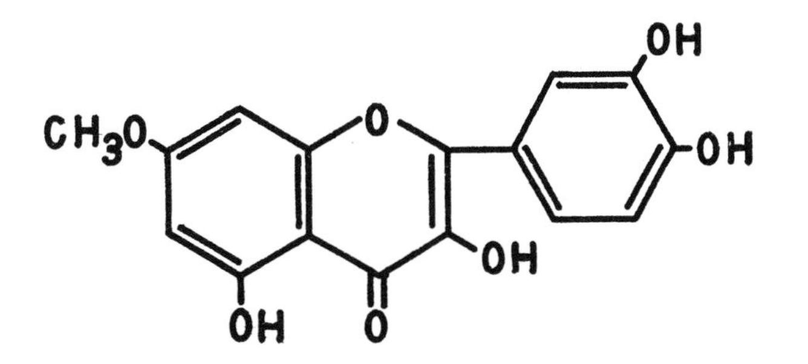

rhamnetin (*Rhamnus* spp.)

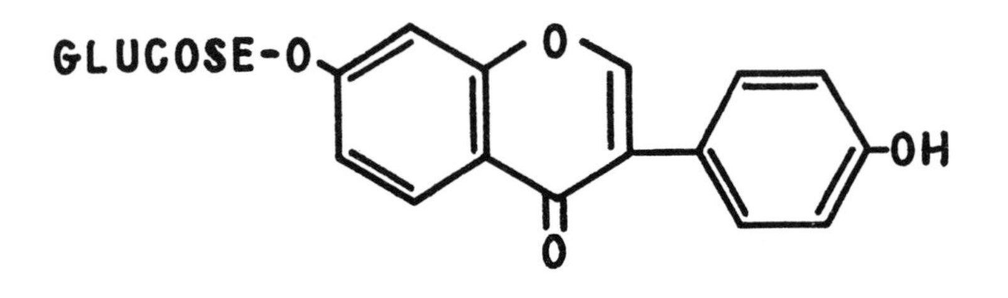

daidzin (Soy beans)

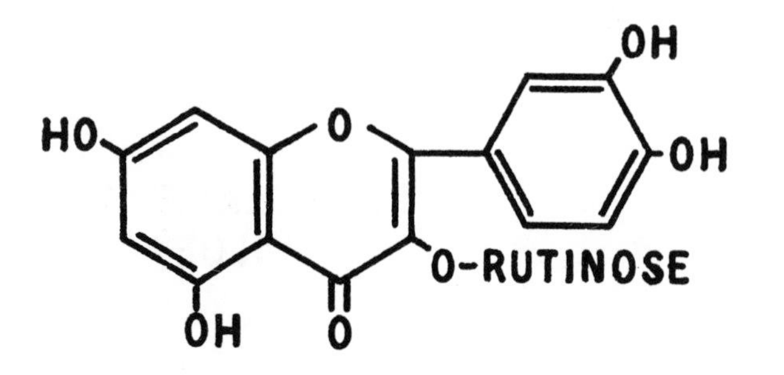

rutin (buckwheat)

Table 3. Continued

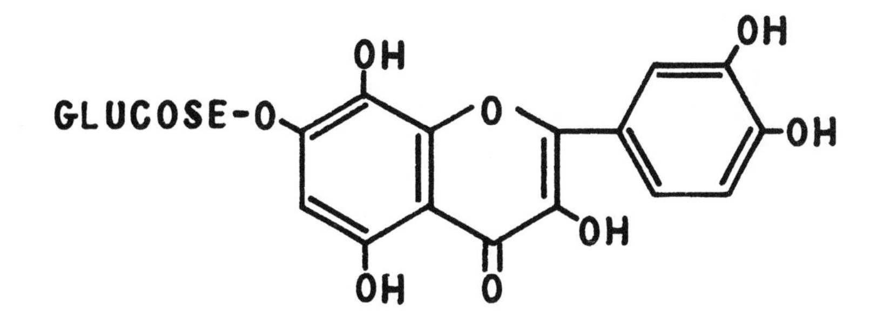

gossypitrin (cotton)

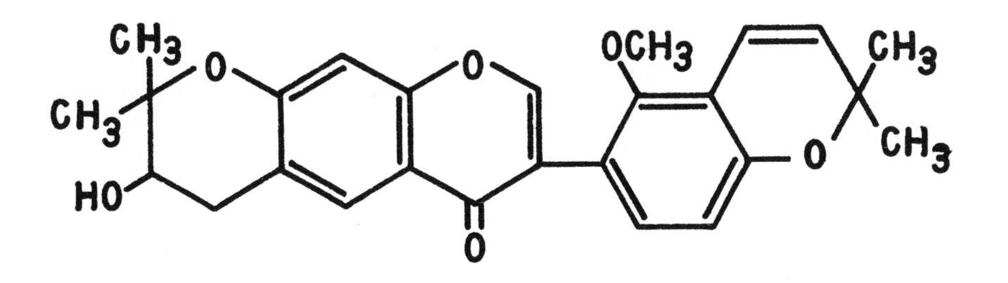

mundulone *(Mundulea sericea)*

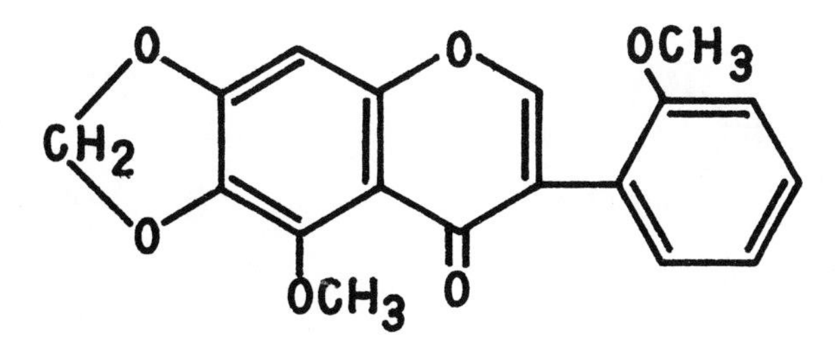

tlatancuayin *(Iresine celosioides)*

In the quinoid form they are rapidly oxidized by air and destroyed. Therefore they are most safely prepared in slightly acidic solution. Since they are both glycosides and salts, the anthocyanins are the most water-soluble of all the flavonoids. On standing or warming in neutral aqueous solution a colorless isomer ("pseudobase") is formed:

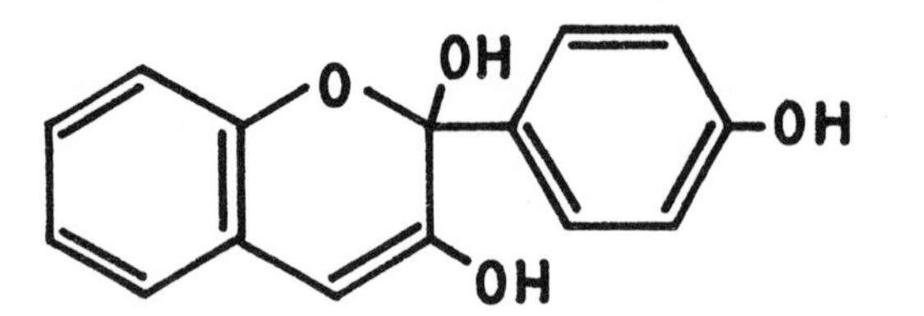

The hydroxylation patterns of the anthocyanins are very much like those of the flavones. Methylation is generally restricted to the 3' and 5' hydroxyl groups. Hirsutidin is a rare exception, having a 7-methoxyl group. Glycosylation is also more restricted in the anthocyanins than in the other flavonoids. If only one sugar is present, it is invariably in the 3-position (except for glycosides of apigenidin, which lacks a 3-hydroxyl group). If two hydroxyls are glycosylated (which never happens in the flavones) they are at the 3 and 5 positions. These 3, 5-diglycosides are the most common and best known anthocyanins. The sugars which combine seem to be the same ones used in the flavone glycosides. Sometimes acids are present esterifying hydroxyl groups of the ring itself or of the sugar.

The three basic types of anthocyanins, like the catechins, depend on the hydroxylation of ring B. All of them have 5, 7-hydroxyl (or methoxyl) on ring A.

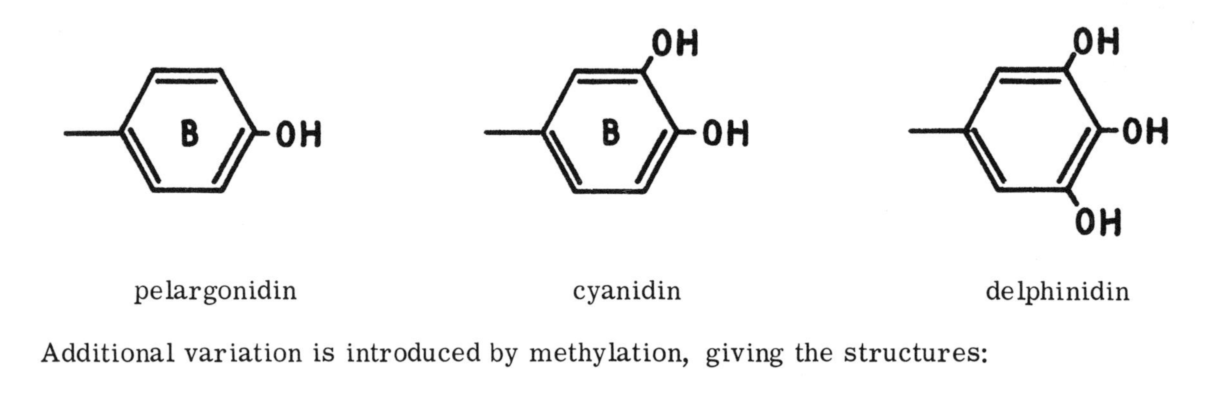

pelargonidin cyanidin delphinidin

Additional variation is introduced by methylation, giving the structures:

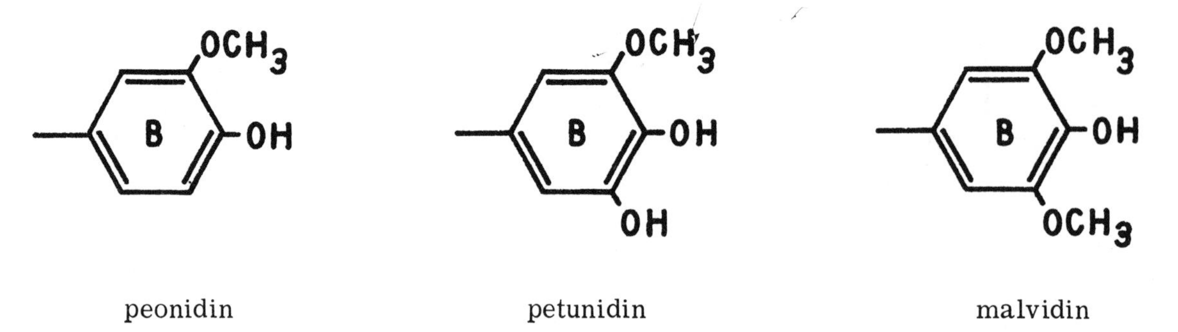

peonidin petunidin malvidin

Hirsutidin, as mentioned above, has the B ring as in malvidin with an additional 7-methoxyl group. Apigenidin has no 3-hydroxyl group:

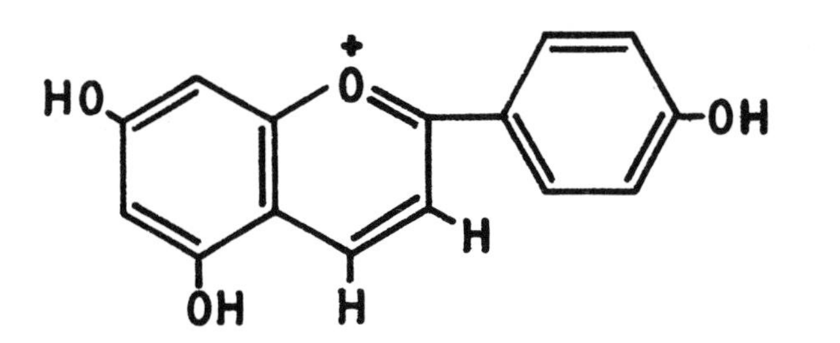

apigenidin

An example of an anthocyanin containing both sugar and acid residues is salvianin from *Salvia splendens:*

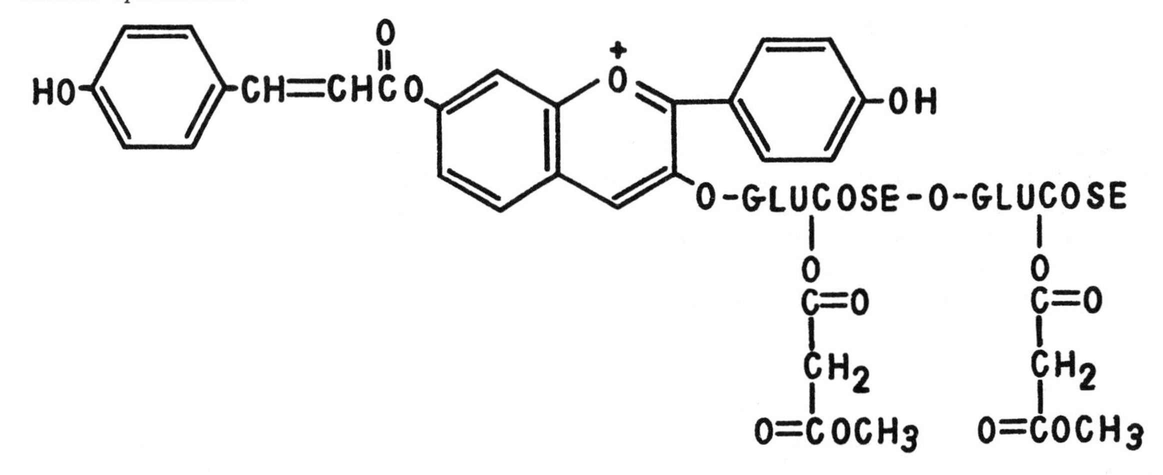

The exact locations of the methyl malonate residues is not known, but this example illustrates the possible complexity to be found in this group.

Some general rules can be given regarding the dependence of color on methylation and glycosylation. Methylation increases the redness, while increase in free hydroxyl groups or addition of a 5-glycosidic group increases the blueness. However, the dependency of color on pH and the presence of copigments and metal cations makes these rules of little value unless one is dealing with a pure pigment.

Table 5 lists some well-known anthocyanins with their particular glycosylation and sources. Many, of course, are found in more than one plant.

TABLE 5. SOME WELL-KNOWN ANTHOCYANINS

Anthocyanin	Aglycone	Glycoside	Source
pelargonin	pelargonidin	3, 5-diglucoside	dahlia, pelargonium
cyanin	cyanidin	3, 5-diglucoside	red rose
idaein	cyanidin	3-galactoside	cranberries
violanin	delphinidin	3-rhamnoglucoside	violet
peonin	peonidin	3, 5-diglucoside	red peony
oenin	malvidin	3-glucoside	blue grapes
hirsutin	hirsutidin	3, 5-glucoside	*Primula hirsuta*
gesnerin	apigenidin	5-glucoside	*Gesneria* spp.

CHALCONES AND DIHYDROCHALCONES

The numbering convention for these compounds differs from that of the flavonoids having a pyran ring:

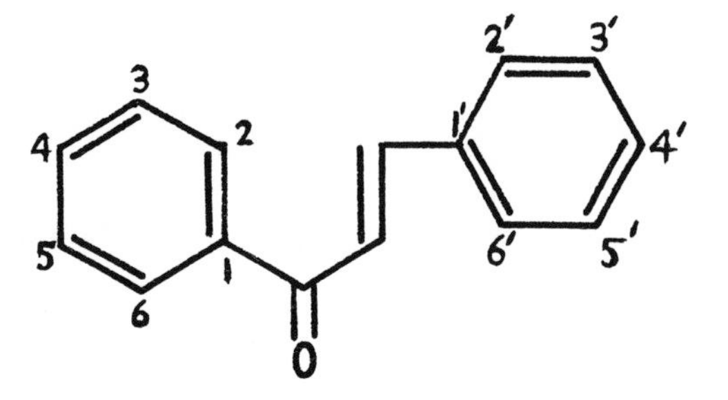

Only a few natural representatives are known, so that far-reaching generalizations about their structure are premature. However, hydroxylation patterns generally agree with those of the other flavonoids; a hydroxyl group is always present in position-2, corresponding to the hetero oxygen atom of the flavanones etc. The conversion of chalcones to flavanones in fact occurs readily in acid solution and the reverse reaction in base. This interconversion is shown for the chalcone butein and the flavanone butin:

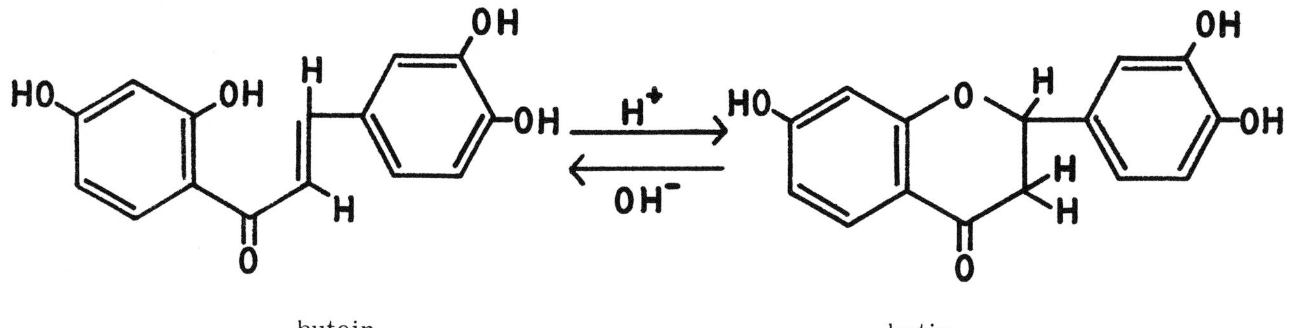

butein butin

The reaction is easily observable since the chalcones are much more highly colored than the flavanones, especially in basic solution where they are orange-red. Because of this reaction acidic hydrolysis of chalcone glycosides yields a flavanone aglycone as an artifact rather than the chalcone. This is shown for carthamin, a glycosidic pigment of the safflower.

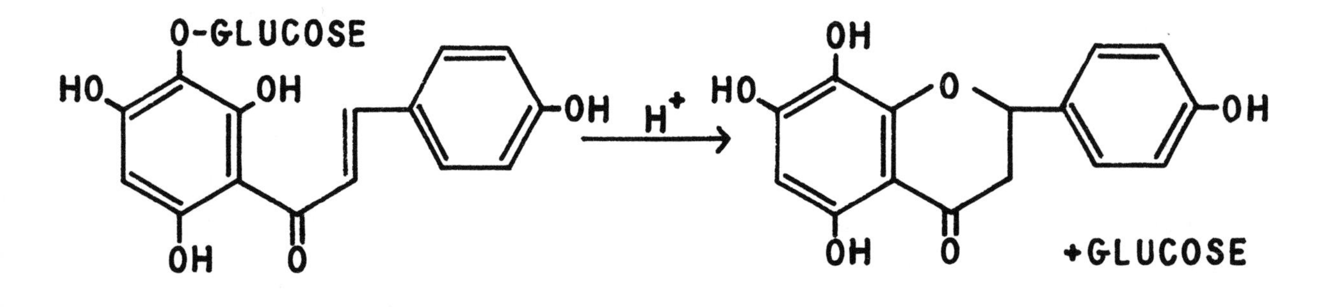

carthamin carthamidin

Isocarthamidin is also formed by a ring closure involving the 6-hydroxy group.

One of the most interesting of these rather rare compounds is phlorizin, a glucoside of the dihydro-chalcone, phloretin, which causes glycosuria in animals. Phlorizin is also a strong inhibitor of apple seedling growth (32).

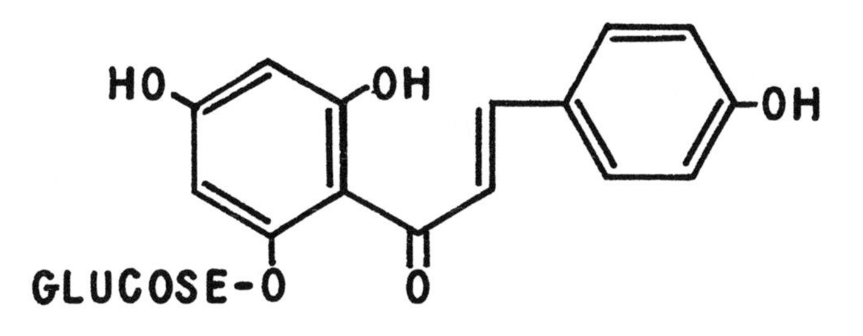

Structures of some other chalcones with their sources are as follows:

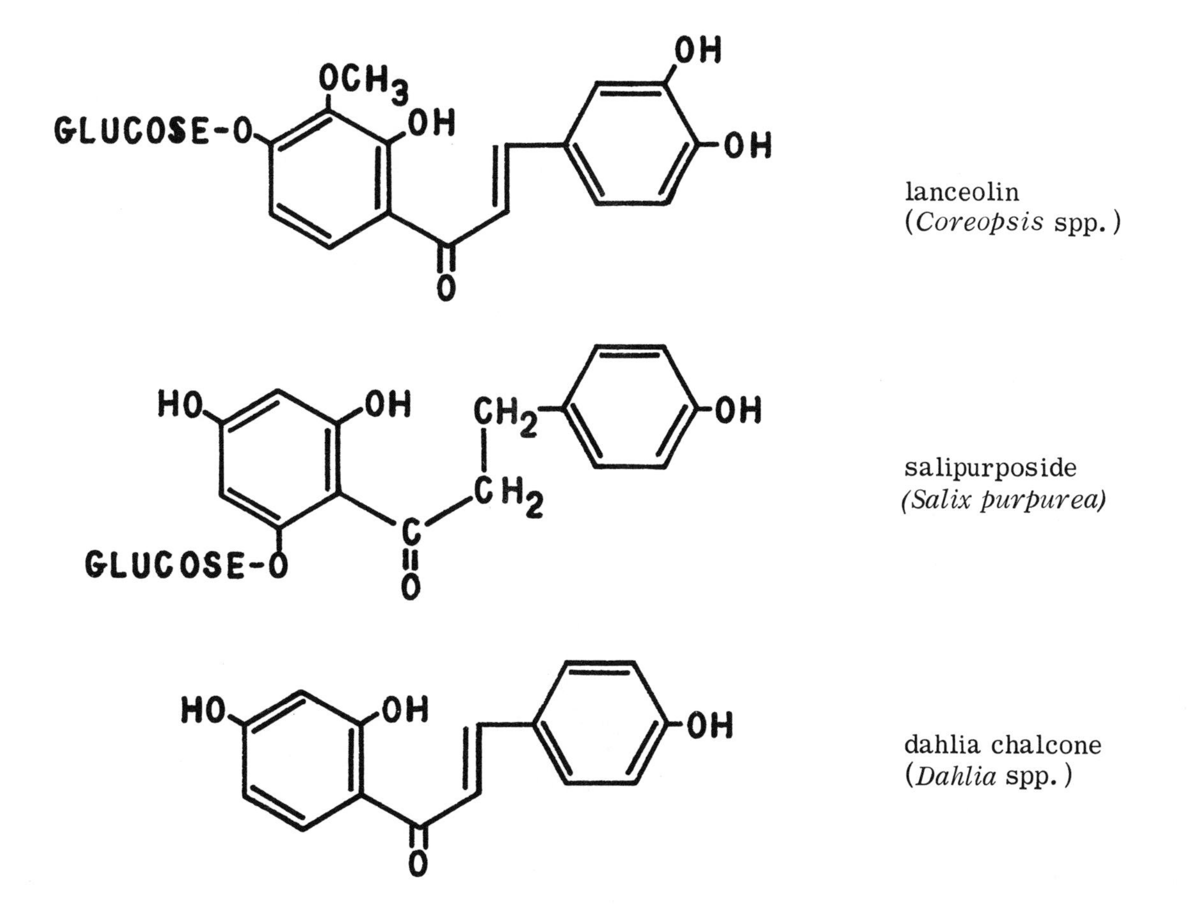

A rare example of an isodihydrochalcone is angolensin of sandalwood *(Pterocarpus angolensis)*:

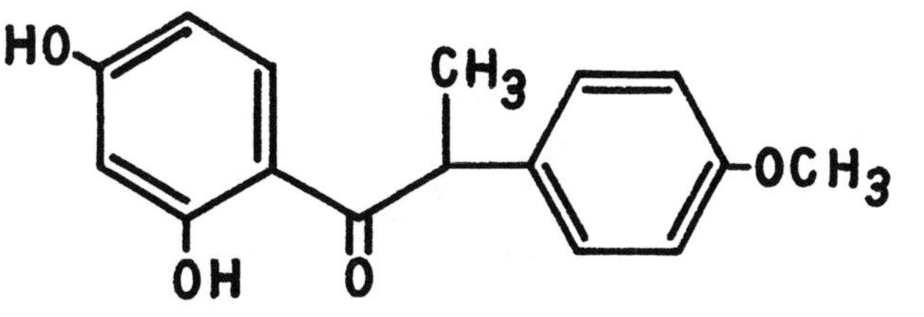

AURONES

The aurone or benzalcoumaranone ring system is numbered in the following way:

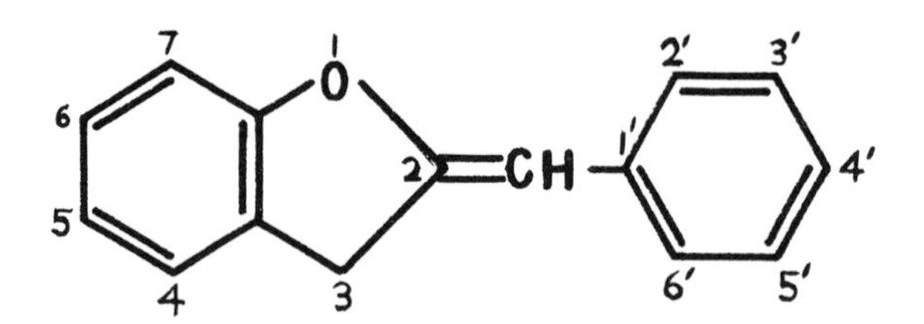

These are golden yellow pigments occurring in certain flowers. Only a few are known, but they generally possess the hydroxylation pattern of the other flavonoids as well as being found in the form of glycosides and methyl ethers. In alkaline solution they become rose-red. Some examples of aurones and their glycosides are shown in Table 6.

MISCELLANEOUS COMPOUNDS

Several unusual plant constituents appear by their structures to be biogenetically related to the flavonoids but with additional complexities. They will be mentioned briefly but fit into no widespread group.

Several compounds may be classed either with the furanocoumarins (see Chap. 4) or with the flavonoids. The most important of these is the insecticide rotenone of derris root. Its structure is written below so as to show its relationship to the isoflavones:

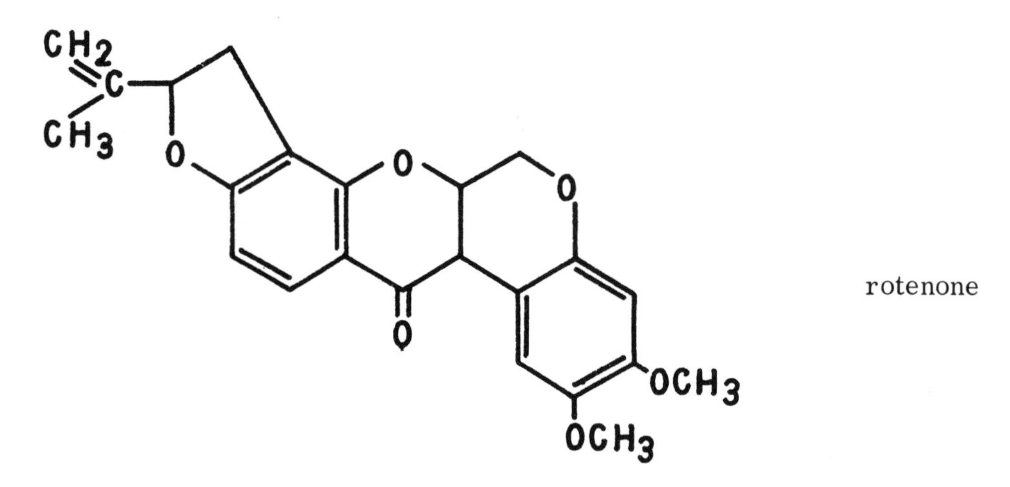

rotenone

A somewhat simpler but similar compound is found in the yam bean, *Pachyrrhizus erosus:*

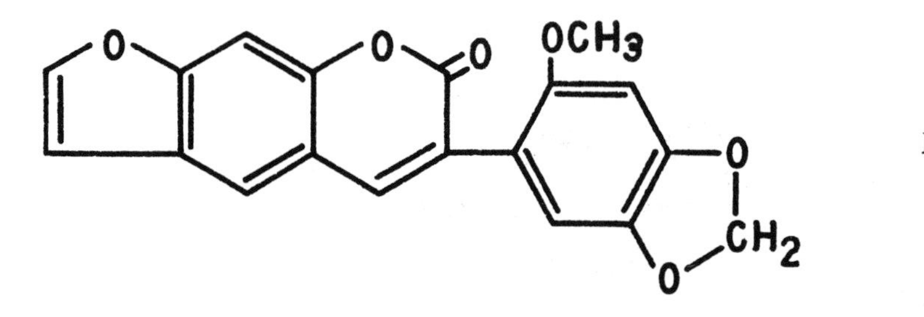

pachyrrhizin

TABLE 6. SOME AURONES, STRUCTURES AND OCCURRENCE

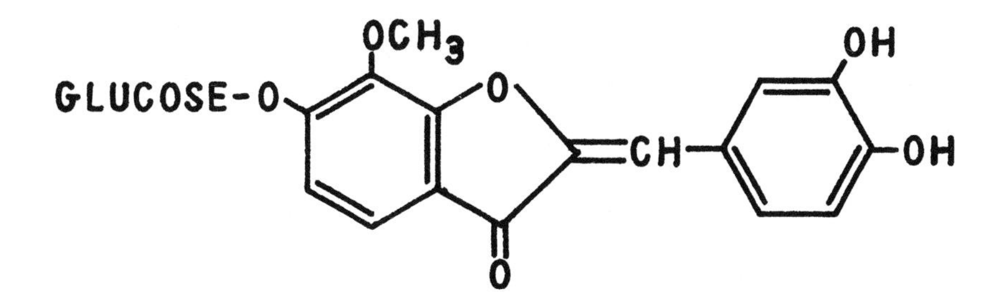

leptosin (*Coreopsis* spp.)

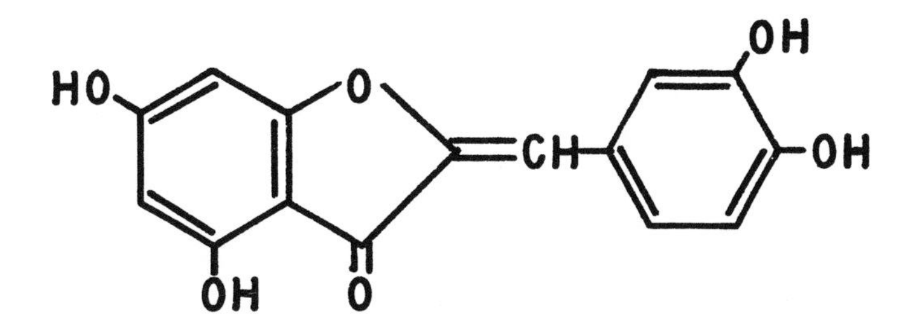

aureusidin *(Antirrhinum majus)*

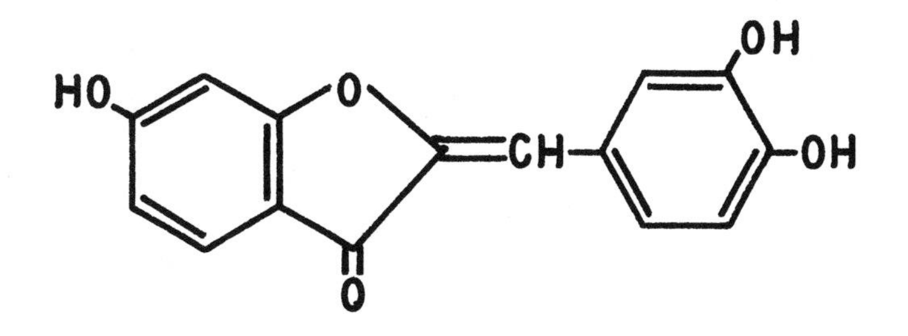

sulphuretin *(Dahlia variabilis)*

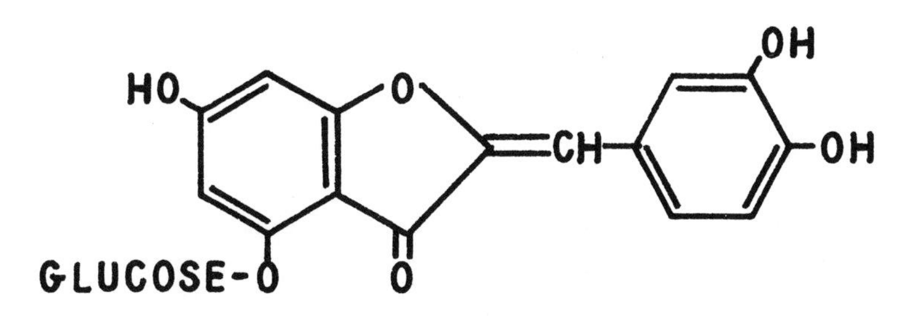

cernoside *(Oxalis cernua)*

Karanjin also has a furo ring fused to the flavonol structure:

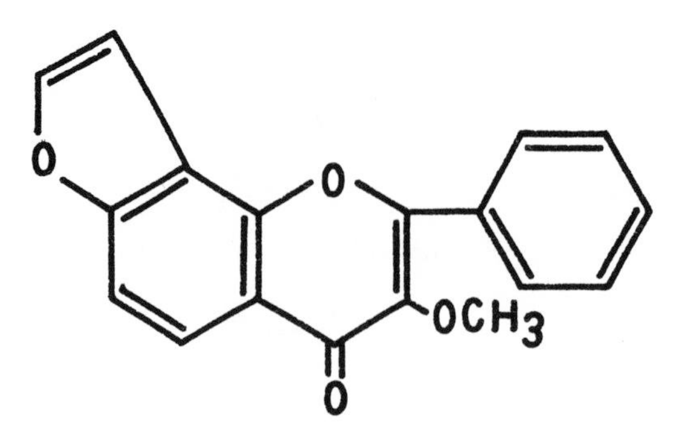

In fukugetin from *Garcinia spicata* bark an additional C_6 - C_3 group is attached to the A ring of an otherwise typical flavone:

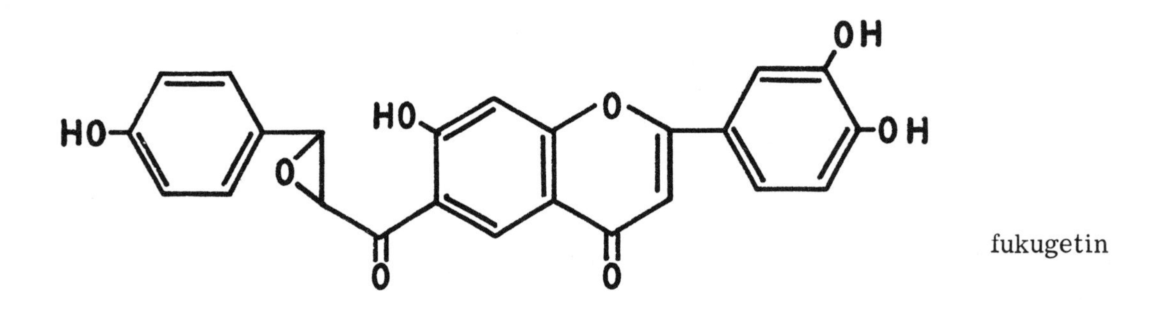

fukugetin

The dyes of Brazil wood and logwood are also similar in structure to the flavonoids. Their chemistry has been reviewed by Robinson (33). It seems possible that both of their aromatic rings could be derived from shikimic acid. If so, they do not really belong with the flavonoids.

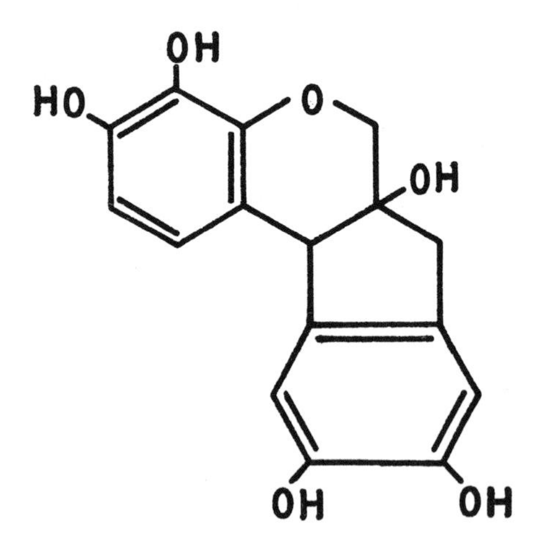

hematoxylin

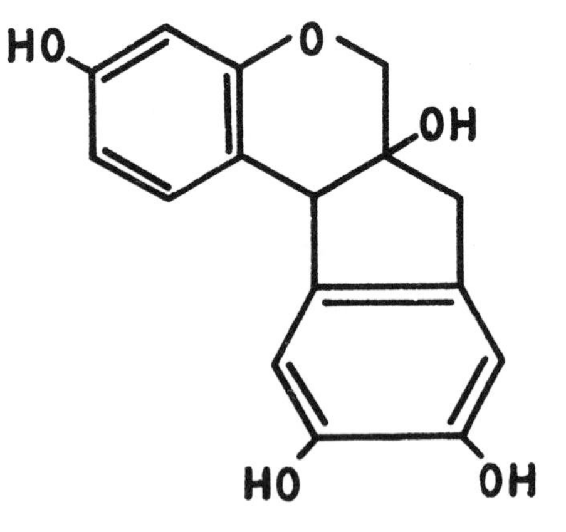

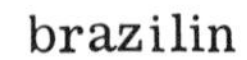

brazilin

Other substances are known with a 4-phenyl coumarin nucleus, such as calophyllolide from *Calophyllum inophyllum* (34) and dalbergin.

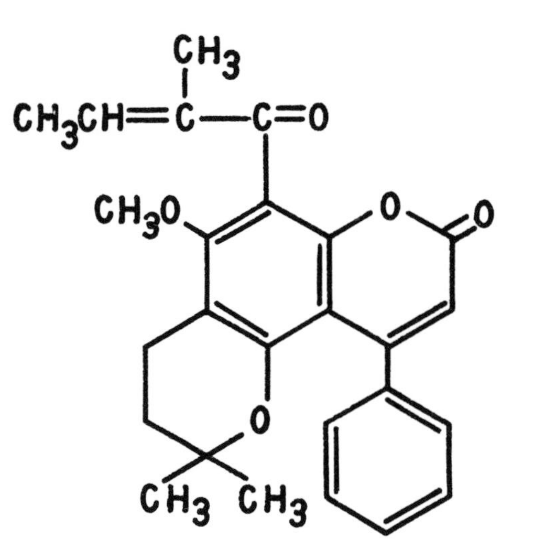

calophyllolide

Betanin, the red pigment of beets, has been the subject of controversy for many years since it contains nitrogen. Recent work indicates that betanin is structurally quite unrelated to the flavonoids, and it is therefore discussed in Chapter 14. Nitrogenous anthocyanins have been reported to occur in several other plants, but even less is known about them (see the reviews by Blank listed under General References). A 4'-amino group has been suggested as a possibility (35). Edulein from the bark of *Casimiroa edulis* has a structure completely analogous to that of the flavones but with nitrogen rather than oxygen in the heterocyclic ring (36):

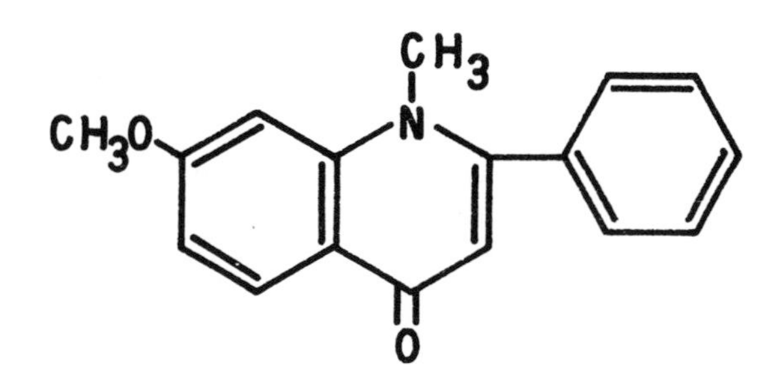

Stilbene derivatives have been found in a few unrelated plants. Structurally they represent a C_6-C_2-C_6 group. Their hydroxylation patterns strongly suggest that, like the flavonoids, one ring is formed from acetate and the other from shikimic acid (37). Their chief interest lies in their high toxicity to fungi, fish, insects and mice. They may also act as tannins, and oxidation of them can form condensed products similar to the phlobatannins (38). Some apparently occur as glycosides, but the aglycone structures are given here:

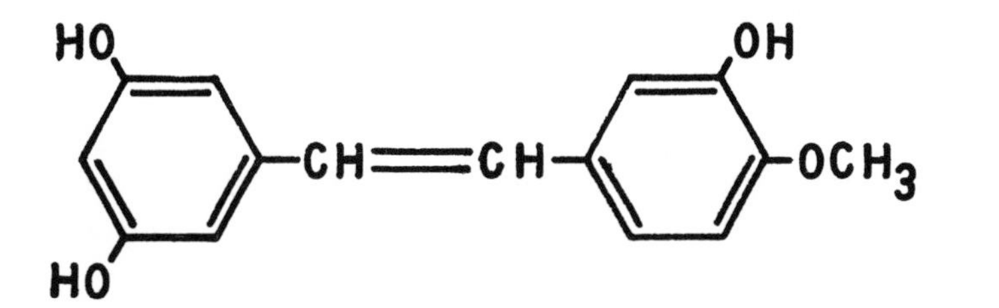

rhapontigenin (rhubarb)

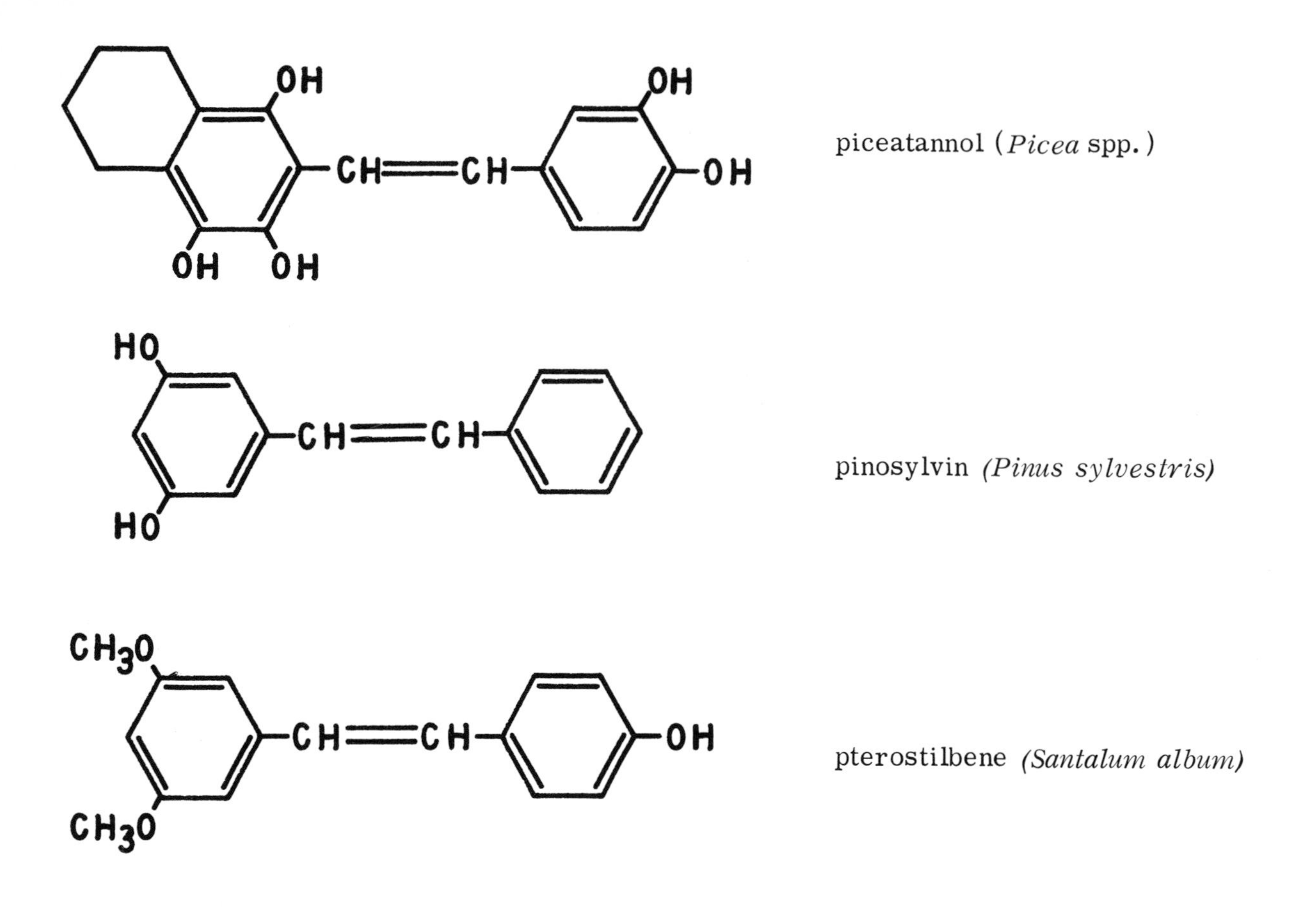

piceatannol (*Picea* spp.)

pinosylvin *(Pinus sylvestris)*

pterostilbene *(Santalum album)*

The isocoumarin, phyllodulcin (q. v.), may also be biogenetically related to the stilbenes. Stilbenes are discussed in the review of Geissman and Hinreiner (see under General References).

Benzophenone derivatives have also been found in a few plants. They may be described as a C_6-C_1-C_6 group, and like the stilbenes are included in this chapter because the hydroxylation patterns suggest a biogenetic relationship to the flavonoids. The most important members of this group are the xanthones which have been used as dyes for hundreds of years. They have the basic structure and numbering system shown below:

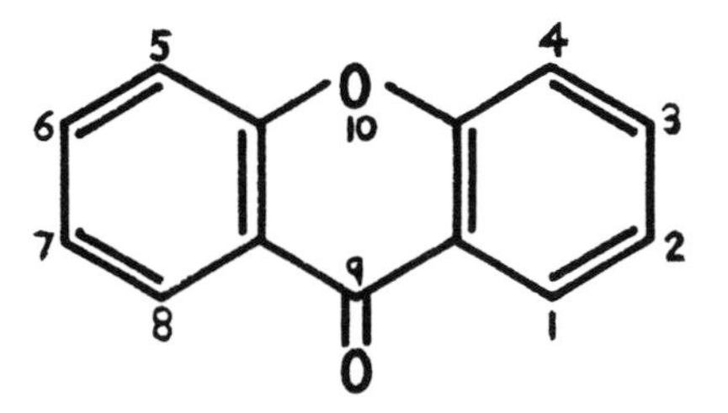

Only about a dozen xanthones are known from flowering plants (39). They are all hydroxy-derivatives. The best known xanthones are the yellow pigment gentisin of *Gentiana lutea* roots:

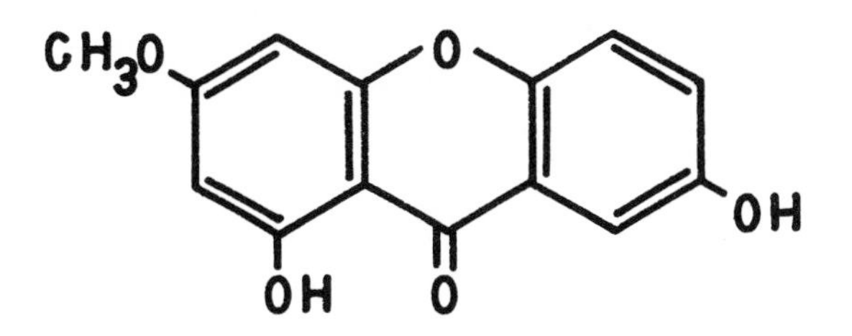

and the glycoside mangiferin from roots of *Mangifera indica:*

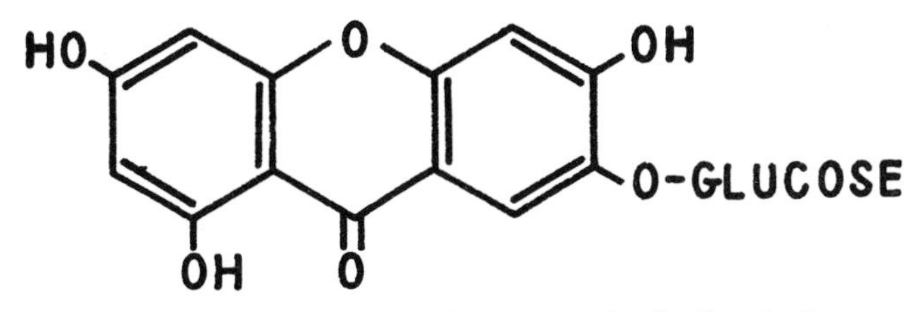

Other naturally occurring benzophenones lack the heterocyclic oxygen ring of the xanthones but are otherwise similar. Maclurin from osage orange and fustic wood has been used as a yellow dye. Various cotoin derivatives of coto bark have been used in medicine as astringents. Hydroxybenzophenone derivatives have sometimes been grouped under "condensed tannins".

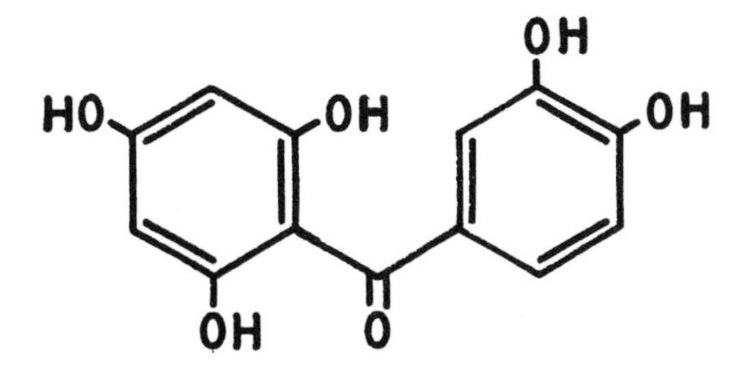

maclurin *(Maclura pomifera)*

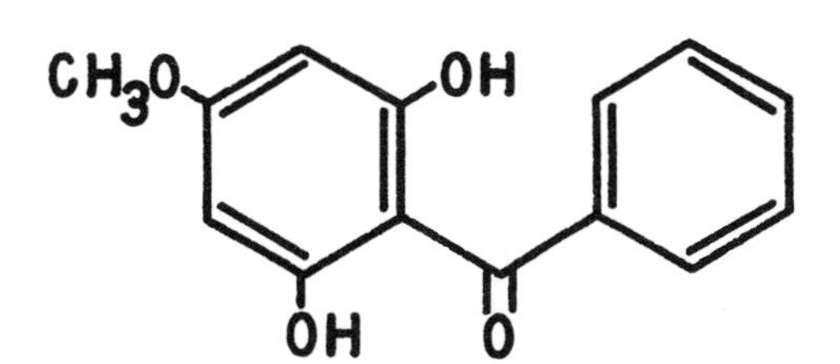

cotoin *(Aniba coto)*

One example of the so-called bis-flavones is dracorubin from dragon's blood resin of *Dracaena draco:*

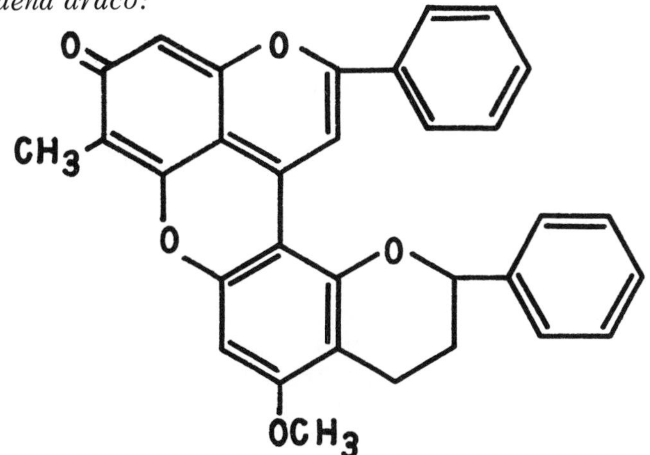

It seems to be derived from a condensation of two flavonoids but is peculiar in having no hydroxylation on either B ring or C_3 chain and in having an added methyl group on one of the A rings. Several other bis-flavonols have been isolated from leaves of *Ginkgo biloba* (40). Other types of bisflavonoids are discussed by Kawano (41).

ISOLATION

Many compounds of this group are water-soluble, especially in the glycoside forms, and they are therefore present in aqueous plant extracts. Even those which are only slightly soluble in water are sufficiently polar to be well extracted by methanol, ethanol or acetone; and these are the solvents most frequently used for extraction of the flavonoids. Re-extraction of an aqueous solution with an immiscible but rather polar organic solvent is frequently of value in separating this group from more polar compounds such as carbohydrates. Ethyl acetate is a useful solvent for dealing with catechins and leucoanthocyanidins in this way. Benzene can be used for benzophenones and stilbenes. Amyl alcohol has been extensively used for the anthocyanins. Secondary butyl alcohol is the most polar alcohol to be incompletely miscible with water; and if the aqueous extract is saturated with sodium chloride or magnesium sulfate, it is very successfulfor removing compounds of this group. Polyphenolic substances such as these are quite sensitive to air oxidation in neutral and basic solution so that it is a good practice to prepare extracts in the presence of a dilute acid (e.g. 0.1 N HCl). However, hot acid or long-standing with acid in the cold may cause hydrolysis of glycosides.

Classically, various precipitating reagents have been used for these compounds. Neutral or basic lead acetate has been particularly recommended. Flavonoids can be freed from the lead precipitate by adding dilute sulfuric acid or hydrogen sulfide leaving the lead as insoluble lead sulfate or sulfide. Other precipitating agents have been picric acid, potassium acetate, barium hydroxide, pyridine, etc. These methods have been described by Geissman (10), Freudenberg (42) and Schmidt (43).

More recently column chromatography has been used for separation of these compounds although no completely satisfactory system for all of them has been developed. Magnesol and silicic acid partition columns have been used with water-saturated ethyl acetate or ether as developing solvents (44, 45, 46). Karrer and Strong (47) used adsorption chromatography on aluminum oxide plus calcium carbonate, with water as a solvent to purify anthocyanins, although this adsorbent may cause changes in more sensitive compounds. Forsyth (48) has used a partition column of cellulose powder pulp with amyl alcohol-acetic acid-water as the mobile phase to separate polyphenols of cacao. Garber *et al.* (49) have used a similar method for anthocyanins. Ion exchange columns have been used to separate polyphenols from plant materials by Williams and Wender (50, 51) and Levin and Harris (52). Chandler and Swain (53) and Neu (54) recommend the use of polyamide (Nylon) columns for purification of flavonoids.

CHARACTERIZATION

Classically, many different color reactions and solubility properties were used to characterize the different classes of flavonoid pigments. These are well summarized in the review by Geissman (10). A few will be mentioned here.

If interfering pigments are not present, plant tissues (e.g. white flower petals) can be tested for the presence of flavones and flavonols by exposing to ammonia vapor. A yellow coloration indicate the presence of these compounds. Chalcones and aurones turn from yellow to red in this test. If an aqueous pigment extract is made alkaline, various color changes may be observed although the changes in one pigment may mask changes in another:

anthocyanins	purple→blue
flavones, flavonols, xanthones	yellow
flavanones	colorless, becoming orange-red (especially if heated)
chalcones and aurones	immediate red-purple
flavanonols	orange-brown

The reaction with ferric chloride has been widely used to identify phenolic compounds, but it is of little value in distinguishing different classes. Other things being equal, it gives a greenish color with catechol derivatives and a blue color with pyrogallol derivatives; but the "other things" are seldom equal. If a deep blue-black color appears, it is good evidence for the presence of a 3, 4, 5-trihydroxy phenol (e.g. gallocatechin) but the formation of a green color does not necessarily indicate the absence of this group nor the presence of a catechol (*ortho* dihydroxy) group.

Reduction with magnesium and concentrated hydrochloric acid produces red colors with flavonols, flavanones, flavanonols and xanthones. The red pigments are not anthocyanidins but 4, 4' *bis* anthocyanidin derivatives (55). Chalcones and aurones give immediate red colors on adding acid rather than a gradual intensification of color as reduction proceeds. Flavones give some color but much less than flavonols.

Addition of bromine water has been used to identify catechins and phlobatannins since they give a precipitate while other tannins and other flavonoids do not. At least certain leucoanthocyanidins also give a positive test with bromine water.

Boiling plant parts with 2N HCl has been used to detect catechins and leucoanthocyanidins. The former give a yellow-brown color, the latter a red color. For additional confirmation of anthocyanidins the red color may be extracted with amyl alcohol and further tests for the presence of anthocyanin applied. Pachéco (56) has adapted this method to detect flavanonols. After boiling with acid, he extracted with ether to obtain the flavanonols, which were unaffected. The flavanonols were then reduced to flavan-3, 4-diols (leucoanthocyanidins), converted to anthocyanidins with boiling acid, and the anthocycyanidins identified by paper chromatography.

Other color reactions for the flavonoids will be described below under paper chromatography since most of the spray reagents described can be equally well applied to solutions of the compounds.

Although extensive degradations for proof of structure are beyond the scope of this book, it should be mentioned that splitting with base has been a most useful technique for determining hydroxylation patterns of unknown flavonoids. Fusion with potassium hydroxide (or boiling with concentrated solutions) splits flavonoids to form a phenol from ring A and a phenolic acid from ring B. For example, from luteolin there are obtained phloroglucinol and protocatechuic acid:

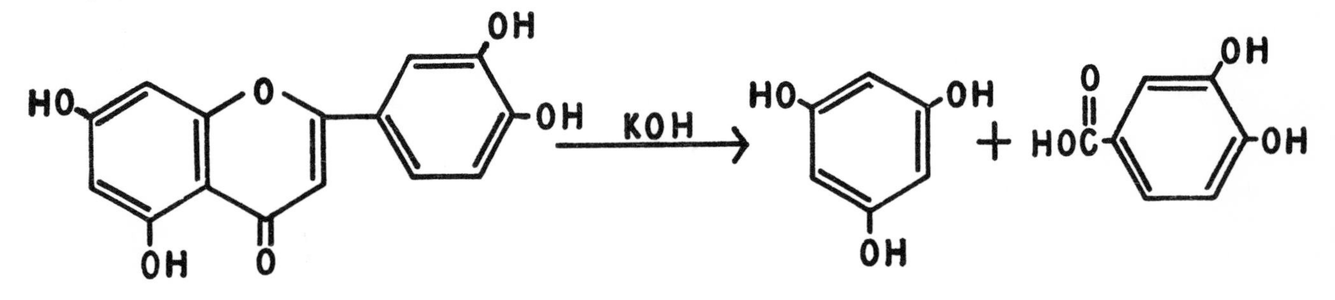

Methyl ethers are also hydrolyzed to phenols by this procedure so that the position of methoxy groups cannot be determined. However, methoxy groups are retained if 10% barium hydroxide in a hydrogen atmosphere is used for the cleavage. A longer reaction time is required for the latter method, but in some cases it is obviously preferable. Neu and Neuhoff (57) and Dunlap and Wender (58) have applied this technique to microquantities (20-40 μg) of flavonoids, using paper chromatography to identify the split products. The position of sugar attachment in glycosides may be determined by methylating all free hydroxyl groups with methyl sulfate, removing the sugar by acid hydrolysis, and locating the position of the now freed hydroxyl group. Paper chromatography can also be applied to identification of the partially methylated aglycone. Chandler and Harper (59) have developed a procedure for identifying the type and location of sugars in flavonoid glycosides. It depends on selective oxidative splitting of the glycoside and identification of the sugar residue that is released. Hydrogen peroxide splits off sugars attached at C-3 whereas permanganate or ozone releases sugars attached to an aromatic system.

Paper chromatography of flavonoids has been widely used in recent years. The most popular solvent has been butanol-acetic acid-water (4:5:1) although water is useful for moving glycosides away from aglycones. In organic solvents the R_f value decreases with hydroxylation of the molecule. Bate-Smith and Westall (60) have discussed the variables affecting chromatographic behavior of phenolic compounds, using the polyphenols of green tea. General reviews on the chromatography of flavonoids have been presented by Harborne (61) and by Roux and Maihs (62). Roux and Evelyn (63) have used chromatographic behavior to estimate molecular weights of condensed tannins.

Geissman (10) has outlined a routine procedure for examining paper chromatograms of flavonoids:

1. Note visible spots (anthocyanins, chalcones, aurones).
2. Examine in long wave ultra-violet light--some substances fluoresce (flavonols, chalcones) others absorb and appear as dark spots against the fluorescence of the paper (flavonol glycosides, anthocyanins, flavones).
3. Expose to ammonia vapor while examining in ultraviolet light--flavones and flavonol glycosides fluoresce yellow, flavonones appear pale yellow, catechins pale blue.
4. Reexamine in white light in presence of ammonia vapor--flavones appear yellow, anthocyanins blue-gray, chalcones and aurones orange-red.

A few other spray reagents are worthy of mention. Diazonium salts react with all phenols to give colored azo dyes. The diazonium salts that have been used most frequently are prepared from benzidine, p-nitroaniline, or sulfanilic acid. Paranitrobenzenediazonium fluoborate is especially convenient since it is a stable compound that can simply be dissolved in water before use. Compounds other than phenols may react (e.g. histamine), but not many of them are likely to be encountered in flavonoid preparations.

Flavanones and flavanonols may be detected because they show up as purple spots when sprayed with 4% Rhodamine B in 0.1N HCl. Flavones and flavonols do not react (64).

The vanillin-hydrochloric acid reaction is valuable for identifying phloroglucinol or resorcinol derivatives which do not have a carbonyl group next to the ring (e.g. catechins and leucoanthocyanidins). This reagent gives a pink color with such compounds (65).

The phlobaphene reaction of catechins and leucoanthocyanidins is best applied to paper by spraying with p-toluenesulfonic acid and heating (66). The former give brown spots, the latter pink. Other flavonoids may also have their colors intensified by this reagent without heating.

Hörhammer and Müller (67) have recommended a zirconium oxychloride reagent to distinguish flavonols from flavones. The 3-glycosides of flavonols do not react with this reagent and may therefore be distinguished by chromatogramming before and after hydrolysis and applying this reagent. Spada and Cameroni (68) identified a 3-glucoside of myricetin in this way.

By combining spectrophotometric methods with paper chromatography, it is frequently possible to make a positive identification of a flavonoid aglycone or glycoside in all its structural detail. The amount of material in a chromatogram spot can be enough for spectral measurements and frequently it is not even necessary to elute the spot. All of the flavonoids have a more or less intense absorption band at about 220-270 mμ and another strong band at a longer wavelength. Additional weaker bands may also be present. Approximate locations of the long wavelength band for different flavonoids are as follows:

anthocyanins	500-530 mμ
flavones and flavonols	330-375 mμ
chalcones and aurones	370-410 mμ
flavanones	250-300 mμ
leucoanthocyanidins and catechins	ca. 280 mμ
iso-flavones	250-290 mμ (very weak)

Detailed presentation if spectral curves are given in the review of Geissman (10) which also lists extensive references to other papers. The infra-red spectra of many different flavonoids have recently been presented by Inglett (69).

Addition of alkali causes characteristic spectral shifts with most flavonoids. Sodium acetate and sodium ethylate have been used for this purpose (70, 71). Flavonols with free hydroxyl groups in positions 3 and 4' are decomposed by alkali, and this can be followed by the decrease in absorption at the long wavelength band. Sodium acetate causes a shift of the short wavelength band to shorter wavelengths if a free 7-hydroxyl group is present. Other examples are given in the review by Geissman (10). Harborne (72, 73) has given a full description of the procedures for identifying anthocyanins by a combination of spectrophotometric methods with paper chromatography.

Various methods have been developed for locating hydroxyl groups on the flavonoids by utilizing reagents which produce spectral shifts with different hydroxylation patterns. Jurd (74) has presented a method for detecting *ortho* dihydroxyl compounds by adding borate which, by complexing with such groups, produces characteristic shifts in the long wavelength band. Hörhammer and Hänsel (75) have used boron complexes in a similar way for analysis of flavones, flavonols and chalcones. Aluminum chloride has also been applied as a useful complexing agent. Roux (76) has measured absorption spectrum of spots on chromatograms before and after treatment with 0.2% aluminum chloride and used the spectral shifts for identification of structures. Shifts of 20 or more mμ are characteristic of *ortho* dihydroxyl compounds. Flavanones can be distinguished from isoflavones by the differences in spectral shifts which they show with aluminum chloride (77).

METABOLIC PATHWAYS

The primary precursors of the flavonoids proper are known beyond any doubt as a result of many tracer experiments. Still unknown are the precursors of the less common substances covered in this chapter such as xanthones, stilbenes, etc., although from their structures they probably have similar precursors. Also unknown are the more specific pathways by which one type of flavonoid is formed rather than another. Speculation on these matters is presented in the reviews of Geissman and Hinreiner (78), Bogorad (79), and Grisebach and Ollis (80). The diagram here attempts to present what seem to be likely pathways.

Tracer experiments by several workers have established that the B ring of flavonoids comes from shikimic acid:

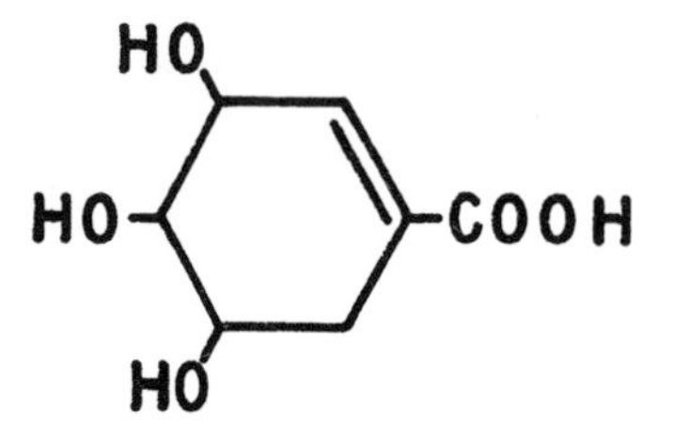

The A ring is formed by head-to tail grouping of three acetate molecules. The aliphatic three-carbon chain is probably added to ring B before ring A is formed to produce a C_6 - C_3 compound. This broad picture of flavonoid biosynthesis has been shown to hold for quercetin (81, 82), cyanidin (83), phlorizin (84), and catechins (85). It presumably applies also to other flavonoids. More generally, it is presumed that all aromatic rings having *ortho* hydroxyl groups arise from shikimic acid and all aromatic rings with *meta* hydroxyl groups arise from acetate. The tracer experiments have ruled out formation of ring A from inositol or phloroglucinol as has sometimes been suggested. They have also shown that such C_6-C_3 compounds as phenylalanine, cinnamic acid and ferulic acid (85) are efficient precursors of the C_6(B)-C_3 portion of flavonoids. The accumulation of p-coumaric acid esters in flower buds of *Antirrhinum majus* and their disappearance as the colored flowers develop also points to p-coumaric acid as a pigment precursor (87).

It is frequently observed that in a given species all of the different flavonoids have the same ring hydroxylation pattern, differing in methylation, glycosylation and the structure of the C_3 portion (88). Such an observation suggests that there is a common C_{15} intermediate that is converted to the different flavonoids after the ring hydroxylation pattern has been established. In fact there is a good likelihood that the hydroxylation of ring B is established in a C_6-C_3 intermediate before ring A is added to it. There is controversy as to whether the different classes of flavonoids are formed by completely divergent pathways from a single precursor or whether interconversion of the flavonoid classes can occur without mediation of a common precursor. The question has been raised particularly with regard to the leucoanthocyanidins and anthocyanidins. It seems quite possible that some plants carry out this conversion whereas in other plants the two classes arise as end products of parallel pathways (89,90,91). Seshadri (92) has argued for the key importance of flavanonols in the biosynthesis of other flavonoids. Grisebach and Patschke (93, 94) have shown that chalcones are converted to flavanones, aurones, anthocyanidins, flavonols, and isoflavones.

It is widely accepted that isoflavones are produced from flavones by migration of the phenyl group from C-2 to C-3. This view has been supported by the experimental work of Grisebach and Doerr (95) who fed carboxyl-labelled phenylalanine to *Trifolium pratense* and isolated an isoflavone with label at C-4. On the other hand Seshadri (92) has suggested that a branched C_6-C_3 compound may undergo initial condensation with ring A. Possibly different plants use different biosynthetic routes.

Nothing has been said to indicate the point where methylation or glycosylation occurs. It is usually assumed that these steps are the last in the sequence, and the genetic experi-

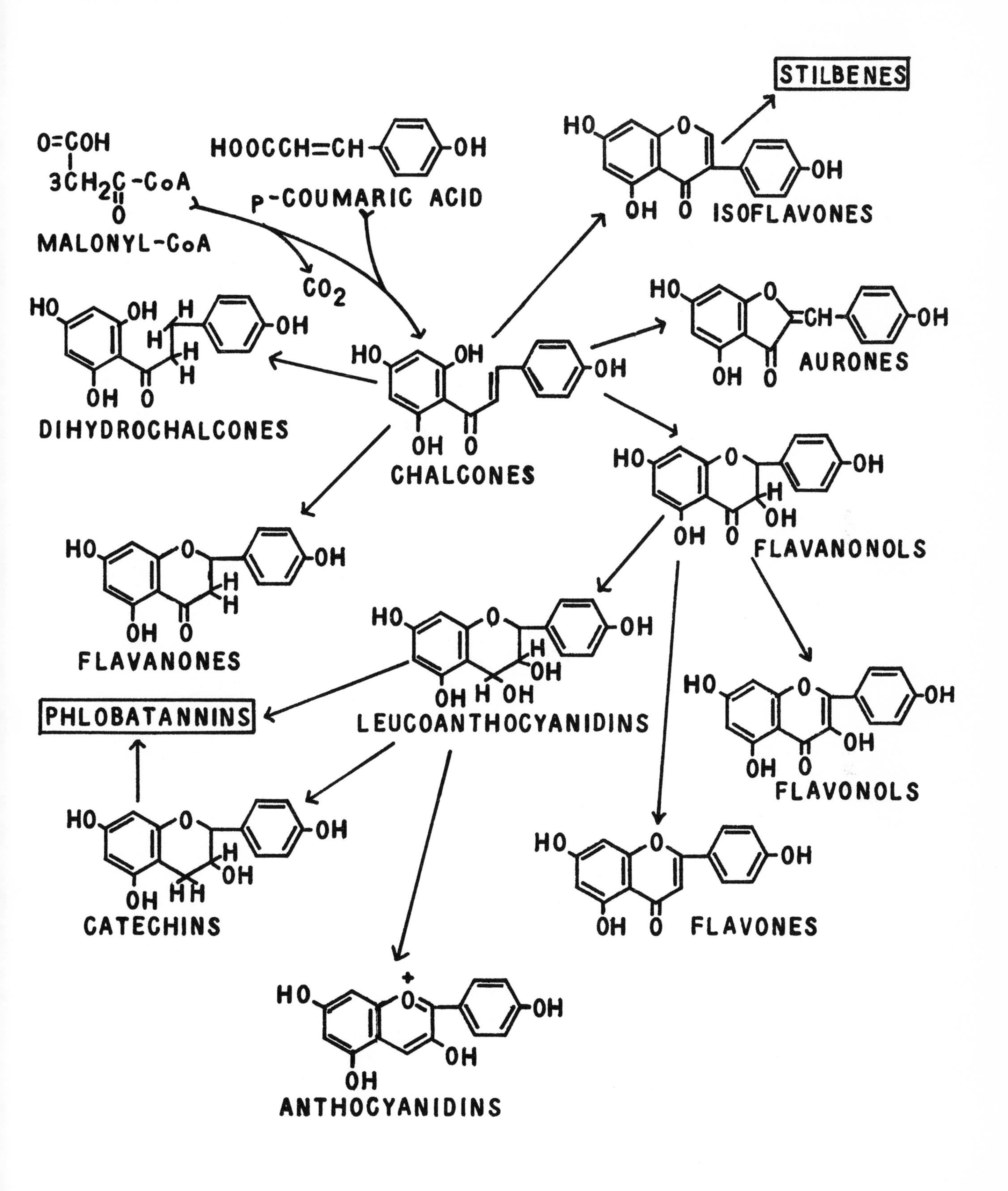

FIGURE 9-1: FLAVONOID PATHWAYS

ments of Harborne (96) support this idea. If one assumes a conversion of leucoanthocyanidins to anthocyanins, it is indicative that the former are never glycosylated while the latter always are. By analogy with the methoxy groups of other natural products (pectin, alkaloids) it is probable that methionine serves as a methyl donor for the flavonoids and related compounds. However, no tracer experiments have been carried out to support this.

Biosynthesis of the phlobatannins has not been investigated by the tracer technique. The consensus is that they are formed by polymerization of catechin or leucoanthocyanidin monomers (97). Since the exact structure of the phlobatannins is unknown, different mechanisms for the condensation have been suggested. Freudenberg's condensation (see p. 178) is non-oxidative. Others have proposed an oxidative condensation either nonenzymatic or catalyzed by a peroxidase or phenol oxidase. These oxidative mechanisms have been studied by Hathway (98, 99, 100, 101) who favors a quinoid structure for the polymer:

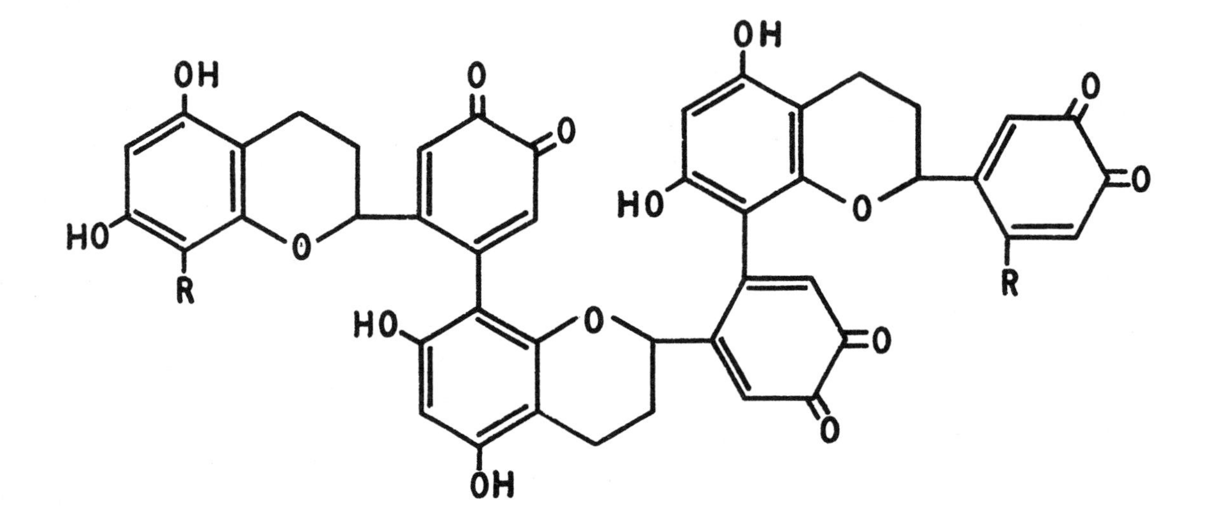

Hathway believes that the formation of phlobatannins is normally catalyzed by phenol oxidase of the cambium but may also be nonenzymatic. Herz (102) has found that peroxidase of blood can catalyze a similar conversion. Roux and Evelyn (103) suggest that the cambium furnishes precursors which are converted to specific condensed tannins in other parts of the plant - even in the central (dead?) heartwood.

GENERAL REFERENCES

Bate-Smith, E. C. "Flavonoid Compounds in Foods" Advances in Food Research 5 261 (1954).

Bentley, K. W., The Natural Pigments, Interscience Publishers, N. Y., 1960.

Blank, F. "The Anthocyanin Pigments of Plants", Bot. Rev. 13 241 (1947).

Blank, F. "Anthocyanins, Flavones, Xanthones", in Ruhland 10 300.

Freudenberg, K., Tannin, Cellulose, Lignin, Springer, Berlin, 1933.

Freudenberg, K. and Weinges, K. "Catechine, andere Hydroxyflavane und Hydroxyflavene", Fortschr. Chem. Org. Naturstoffe 16 1 (1958).

Freudenberg, K. and Weinges, K., "Systematik und Nomenklatur der Flavonoide" Tetrahedron 8 376 (1960).

Geissman, T. A., "Anthocyanins, Chalcones, Aurones, Flavones and Related Water-Soluble Plant Pigments", Paech and Tracey, 3 450.

Geissman, T. A., ed., The Chemistry of Flavonoid Compounds, Macmillan, New York, 1961.

Geissman, T. A. and Hinreiner, E., "Theories of the Biogenesis of Flavonoid Compounds", Bot. Rev. 18 77 (1952).
Schmidt, O. T., "Naturliche Gerbstoffe" in Paech and Tracey 3 517.
Swain, T. and Bate-Smith, E. C., "Flavonoid Compounds", Comparative Biochemistry 3 755, M. Florkin and H. S. Mason, eds., Academic Press, New York, 1962.
"Vegetable Tannins--A Symposium", J. Soc. Leather Trades Chemists 1956 7.
Venkataraman, K. "Flavones and Isoflavones", Fortschr. Chem. Org. Naturstoffe 17 1 (1959).

BIBLIOGRAPHY

1. Hendershott, C. H. and Walker, D. R., Science 130 798 (1959).
2. Mumford, F. E., Smith, D. H. and Castle, J. E., Plant Physiol. 36 752 (1961).
3. Furuya, M., Galston, W., and Stowe, B. B., Nature 193 45 (1962).
4. Moewus, F., Erbebn, Enzymforsch. 12 173 (1951).
5. Kuhn, R. and Löw, I., Chem. Ber. 82 474 (1949).
6. Hartshorne, J. N., Nature 182 1382 (1958).
7. Lyman, R. L., Bickoff, E. M., Booth, A. N., and Livingston, A. L., Arch. Biochem. Biophys. 80 61 (1959).
8. Bredenberg, J. B. and Shoolery, J. N., Tetrahedron Letters 1961 285.
9. Hörhammer, L., Wagner, H. and Grasmaier, H., Naturwiss. 45 388 (1958).
10. Geissman, T. A., in Paech and Tracey, see under "General References".
11. Freudenberg, K., Sci. Proc. Royal Dublin Soc. 27 153 (1956).
12. Ito, S. and Oshima, Y., Agr. Biol. Chem. (Japan) 26 156 (1962).
13. Birch, A. J., Clark-Lewis, J. W. and Robertson, A. V., J. Chem. Soc. 1957 3586.
14. Swain, T., Chem. and Ind. 1954 1144.
15. Robinson, G. M. and Robinson, R., Biochem. J. 27 206 (1933).
16. Bate-Smith, E. C. and Swain, T., Chem. and Ind. 1953 377.
17. Bokadia, M. M., J. Indian Chem. Soc. 38 616 (1961).
18. Freudenberg, K. and Weinges, K., Chem. and Ind. 1959 486.
19. Freudenberg, K., Stocker, J. H. and Porter, J., Chem. Ber. 90 957 (1957).
20. Russel, A., Chem. Revs. 17 155 (1935).
21. Roux, D. G., Chem. and Ind. 1962 278.
22. Weinges, K., Chem. Ber. 94 3032 (1961).
23. Freudenberg, K. and Weinges, K., Angew. Chem. 74 182 (1962).
24. Raudnitz, H., Science 128 782 (1958).
25. Pachéco, H., Bull. soc. chim. biol. 39 971 (1957).
26. Nord, F. F. and de Stevens, G. in Ruhland 10 420.
27. Bate-Smith, E. C., Sci. Proc. Royal Dublin Soc. 27 165 (1956).
28. Warburton, W. K., Quart. Revs. 8 67 (1954).
29. Whalley, W. B., Chem. and Indust. 1958 361.
30. Hörhammer, L., Wagner H. and Dhingra, H. S., Arch. Pharm. 292 83 (1959).
31. Bate-Smith, E. C. and Swain, T., Chem. and Ind. 1960 1132.
32. Börner, H., Contribs. Boyce Thompson Inst. 20 39 (1959).
33. Robinson, R., Bull. soc. Chim. France 1958 125.
34. Polansky, J., Compt. rend. 242 2961 (1956).
35. Steele, C. C., An Introduction to Plant Biochemistry, G. Bell and Sons, London, 1934. p. 218.
36. Sondheimer, F. and Meisels, A., J. Org. Chem. 23 762 (1958).
37. Billek, G. and Kindl, H., Monatsh. 92 493 (1961).
38. Endres, H., Qualitas Plant et Material Vegetables 5 367 (1959). (Chem. Abstr. 53 14234).
39. Roberts, J. C., Chem. Revs. 61 591 (1961).
40. Baker, W., Finch, A. C. M., Ollis, W. D. and Robinson, K. W., Proc. Chem. Soc. 1959 91.
41. Kawano, N., Chem. and Ind. 1959 368.
42. Freudenberg. See under General References.
43. Schmidt. See under General References.
44. Ice, C. H. and Wender, S. H., Anal. Chem. 24 1616 (1952).
45. Sondheimer, E. and Karash, C. B., Nature 178 648 (1956).
46. Bradfield, A. E. and Penney, M., J. Chem. Soc. 1948 2249.
47. Karrer, P. and Strong, F. M., Helv. Chim. Acta 19 25 (1936).
48. Forsyth, W. G. C., Biochem. J. 51 511 (1952).
49. Garber, E. D., Redding, W. F. and Chorney, W., Nature 193 801 (1962).
50. Williams, B. L. and Wender, S. H., J. Am. Chem. Soc. 74 4372 (1952).
51. ibid. 74 5919 (1952).

52. Levin, H. J. and Harris, L. E., J. Am. Pharm. Assoc. 47 820 (1958).
53. Chandler, B. V. and Swain, T., Nature 183 989 (1959).
54. Neu, R., Arch. Pharm. 293 169 (1960).
55. Malkin, T. and Nierenstein, M., J. Am. Chem. Soc. 52 2864 (1930).
56. Pacheco, H., Bull. Soc. Chim. France 1956 (1600).
57. Neu, R. and Neuhoff, E., Naturwiss. 44 10 (1957).
58. Dunlap, W. J. and Wender, S. H., J. Chromatog. 3 505 (1960).
59. Chandler, B. V. and Harper, K. A., Austral. J. Chem. 15 114 (1962).
60. Bate-Smith, E. C. and Westall, R. G., Biochim. Biophys. Acta 4 427 (1950).
61. Harborne, J. B., J. Chromatog. 2 581 (1959).
62. Roux, D. G. and Maihs, A. E., J. Chromatog. 4 65 (1960).
63. Roux, D. G. and Evelyn, S. R., J. Chromatog. 1 537 (1958).
64. Neu, R., Arch. Pharm. 292 431 (1959).
65. Bate-Smith, E. C., Biochem. J. 58 126 (1954).
66. Roux, D. G., Nature 180 973 (1957).
67. Hörhammer, L. and Müller, K. H., Arch. Pharm. 287 310 (1954).
68. Spada, A. and Cameroni, R., Gazz. Chim. Ital. 86 965 (1956).
69. Inglett, G. E., J. Org. Chem. 23 93 (1958).
70. Jurd, L. and Horowitz, R. M., J. Org. Chem. 22 1618 (1957).
71. Jurd, L. and Horowitz, R. M., J. Org. Chem. 26 2561 (1961).
72. Harborne, J. B., Biochem. J. 70 22 (1958).
73. Harborne, J. B., J. Chromatog. 1 473 (1958).
74. Jurd, L., Arch. Biochem. 63 376 (1956).
75. Hörhammer, L. and Hänsel, R., Arch Pharm. 288 315 (1955).
76. Roux, D. G., Nature 179 305 (1957).
77. Horowitz, R. M. and Jurd, L., J. Org. Chem. 26 2446 (1961).
78. See Geissman and Hinreiner under "General References".
79. Bogorad, L., Ann. Rev. Plant Physiol. 9 417 (1958).
80. Grisebach, H. and Ollis, W. D., Experientia 17 4 (1961).
81. Geissman, T. A. and Swain, T., Chem. and Ind. 1957 984.
82. Watkin, J. E., Underhill, E. W. and Neish, A. C., Can. J. Biochem. Physiol. 35 229 (1957).
83. Grisebach, H., Z. Naturforsch 13b 335 (1958).
84. Hutchinson, A., Taper, C. D. and Towers, G. H. N., Can. J. Biochem. Physiol. 37 901 (1959).
85. Zaprometov, M. N., Biokhimiya 27 366 (1962).
86. Reznik, H. and Urban, R., Naturwiss. 44 592 (1957).
87. Schmidt, H. and Boehme, H., Biol. Zentr. 79 423 (1960).
88. Harborne, J. B., Biochem. J. 68 12P (1958).
89. Krugman, S., Forest Sci. 2 273 (1956).
90. Alston, R. E., Bot. Gaz. 120 99 (1958).
91. Hillis, W. E., Nature 175 597 (1955).
92. Seshadri, T. R. Tetrahedron 6 169 (1959).
93. Grisebach, H. and Patschke, L., Chem. Ber. 93 2326 (1960).
94. Grisebach, H., and Patschke, L., Z. Naturforsch. 16b 645 (1961).
95. Grisebach, H. and Doerr, N., Z. Naturforsch. 15b 284 (1960).
96. Harborne, J. B., Biochem. J. 74 262 (1960).
97. Hillis, W. E., Nature 182 1371 (1958).
98. Hathway, D. E., J. Chem. Soc. 1958 520.
99. Hathway, D. E., Biochem. J. 70 34 (1958).
100. Hathway, D. E., and Seakins, J. W. T., Biochem. J. 67 239 (1957).
101. Hathway, D. E., Biochem. J. 71 533 (1959).
102. Herz, A., Z. Naturforsch. 12b 326 (1957).
103. Roux, D. G. and Evelyn, S. R., Biochem. J. 70 344 (1958).

Chapter 10
AMINO ACIDS AND PROTEINS

by Ernest Sondheimer

Amino acids, peptides and proteins are among the most important and well-known constituents of living matter. Consequently much of their chemistry and metabolic significance is adequately described in general textbooks of biochemistry. In our treatment we have chosen to stress some less familiar aspects of them and to emphasis a few unusual compounds which occur in plants.

AMINO ACIDS

Amino acids can be defined as carboxylic acids having at least one amino group. Most naturally occurring ones can be depicted by the general formula R $CH(NH_3^+)CO_2^-$. These are the so-called alpha amino acids since the amino group is adjacent to the carboxylic acid function. If R is a group other than hydrogen, the compound has an asymmetric carbon atom and can, therefore, occur in an optically active form. The isomers having the L-configuration are the ones most widely distributed in nature. The first amino acid isolated was asparagine. This substance was obtained by Vauquelin and Robiquet in 1806 (1) who succeeded in separating it from asparagus juice by taking advantage of differences in the shape, transparency and flavor of the crystals. Since then chemists have continued their attempts to isolate new amino acids; and although more than seventy such compounds have been obtained from higher plants, new ones are being discovered yearly. It is convenient to divide the amino acids into two major groups; one group is found in all living systems either in the free state or condensed as peptides while the members of the second group apparently occur only in a limited number of organisms and do not serve as protein monomers.

The physical properties of the amino acids are to a very large extent determined by the dipolar ionic structure of these compounds. Thus, they are all white solids. They either have high melting points or decompose on heating. As a group they display much greater solubility in water than in organic solvents. Since they are amphoteric they form salts with acids or bases. Under appropriate conditions they will migrate in an electric field, i. e. show electrophoretic properties. Each amino acid has one pH value at which there is no net charge on the molecule and at which, therefore, no migration in an electric field will occur. This pH value is called the isoelectric point. It is between pH 5 and 6 for the "neutral" amino acids - the mono carboxylic, mono amino compounds, near pH 3 for the dicarboxylic mono amino acids, and above 7. 5 for the basic amino acids. The latter group includes diamino mono carboxylic acids and mono amino mono carboxylic acids with other basic substituents.

WIDELY DISTRIBUTED AMINO ACIDS AND PROTEIN CONSTITUENTS

The structure and R_f values of the most widely distributed amino acids are listed in Table 1. These are also the amino acids commonly found as the monomeric units of

TABLE 1. WIDELY DISTRIBUTED AMINO ACIDS

A. Neutral Amino Acids

	Name	Structure	Ninhydrin color	R_f values[1] phenol water (pH 5.0-5.5)	R_f values[1] n-butanol-acetic acid (9:1) - water
1.	glycine	$CH_2(NH_2)CO_2H$	Red violet	.38	.06
2.	L-alanine	$CH_3CH(NH_2)CO_2H$	Violet	.59	.11
3.	L-serine	$HOCH_2CH(NH_2)CO_2H$	Violet	.36	.05
4.	L-cysteine	$HSCH_2CH(NH_2)CO_2H$	-	-	-
5.	L-cystine	$[-SCH_2CH(NH_2)CO_2H]_2$	-	-	-
6.	L-cysteic acid[2]	$HO_3SCH_2CH(NH_2)CO_2H$	Violet	.07	.01
7.	L-threonine	$CH_3CH(OH)CH(NH_2)CO_2H$	Violet	.49	.09
8.	L-valine	$(CH_3)_2CHCH(NH_2)CO_2H$	Violet	.78	.24
9.	L-methionine	$CH_3S(CH_2)_2CH(NH_2)CO_2H$	-	-	-
10.	L-methionine sulfoxide[3]	$CH_3SO(CH_2)_2CH(NH_2)CO_2H$	Violet	.79	.05
11.	L-methionine sulfone[3]	$CH_3SO_2(CH_2)_2CH(NH_2)CO_2H$	Violet	.60	.27
12.	L-leucine	$(CH_3)_2CHCH_2CH(NH_2)CO_2H$	Violet	.84	.34
13.	L-isoleucine	$CH_3CH_2CH(CH_3)CH(NH_2)CO_2H$	Violet	.84	.36

[1] R_f values are those reported by F. C. Steward, R. M. Zacharius and J. K. Pollard, Suomalaisen Tiedeakat Toimituksia series A 60, 321 (1955). The R_f values have been rounded off to two decimal places here and were determined on Whatman number 1 filter paper.
[2] from cystine or cysteine
[3] from methionine

14.	L-proline	CH_2—CH_2 / CH_2 $CHCO_2H$ / N-H (ring)	Yellow	.86	.14
15.	L-phenylalanine	C_6H_5—$CH_2CH(NH_2)CO_2H$	Grey-violet	.84	.28
16.	L-tyrosine	HO—C_6H_4—$CH_2CH(NH_2)CO_2H$	Grey-violet	.67	.16
17.	L-tryptophan	(indol-3-yl)—$CH_2CH(NH_2)CO_2H$ (N-H)	Grey-violet	.80	.22
18.	L-asparagine	$H_2NOCCH_2CH(NH_2)CO_2H$	Orange-brown	.44	.02
19.	L-glutamine	$H_2NOC(CH_2)CH(NH_2)CO_2H$	Violet	.60	.04

Table 1: Continued

		B. Acidic Amino Acids			
20.	L-aspartic acid	$HO_2CCH_2CH(NH_2)CO_2H$	Blue-violet	.18	.03
21.	L-glutamic acid	$HO_2C(CH_2)_2CH(NH_2)CO_2H$	Violet	.31	.05
		C. Basic Amino Acids			
22.	L-arginine[4]	$NH_2C(=NH)NH(CH_2)_3CH(NH_2)CO_2H$	Violet	.56	.03
23.	L-lysine[4]	$NH_2(CH_2)_4CH(NH_2)CO_2H$	Violet	.48	.02
24.	L-histidine	(imidazole ring: HC=C–, N, NH, CH) $-CH_2CH(NH_2)CO_2H$	Grey-violet	.64	.03

[4]Chromatographed as the mono hydrochloride

proteins. Glycine, alanine, valine, leucine and isoleucine are "neutral" amino acids and differ from each other only with respect to the aliphatic side chain. Of these, glycine is the only one without an asymmetric carbon atom and is therefore the only one that cannot occur in an optically active form.

Serine and threonine contain one hydroxyl group adjacent to the amino function. Because of this they are unstable in hot sodium hydroxide solution and react quantitatively with sodium periodate (2). Cysteine, in which a sulfhydryl group replaces the hydroxyl group of serine also gives the above reactions. However, cysteine can be easily distinguished from the oxygen analogue by the red color obtained with nitroprusside reagent. Also cysteine is very easily oxidized aerobically to the disulfide cystine and to cysteic acid. Therefore, the isolation of cystine or cysteic acid is no proof that the compounds existed in that oxidation state in the intact cell. Methionine, another important sulfur-containing amino acid, can also yield spurious oxidation products. In this case, methionine sulfoxide or methionine sulfone are formed. Methionine is known to play an important biological role in transmethylation reactions, and there is ample evidence that the methyl group attached to the sulfur of methionine can be transferred in plants to yield oxygen and nitrogen methylated substances (3). The actual reactant in these methyl group transfers is S-adenosylmethionine ("active" methionine) formed by reaction of methionine with ATP:

L-methionine + ATP $\rightarrow$ S-adenosylmethionine + pyrophosphate + orthophosphate

Proline is a cyclic aliphatic amino acid and differs from the above compounds due to the presence of a secondary amino group. It is quite soluble in 95% ethanol.

Phenylalanine, tyrosine and tryptophan contain aromatic rings and therefore absorb light in the ultraviolet region. In fact, the light absorption of the simple proteins is attributable to the presence of these amino acids. Tyrosine, has abnormally low water solubility, 45 mg. in 100 ml. at 25° C. This property can be taken advantage of in isolation procedures. Tryptophan is readily oxidized in hot acidic solutions and is, therefore, completely destroyed during acid-catalyzed hydrolysis of proteins. It can be recovered from proteins by using either alkaline or enzymatic hydrolysis. Evidence is accumulating that tryptophan is a precursor of indole-3-acetic acid (4), a compound with well known growth hormonal action in plants. (cf. Chap. 14)

The acidic amino acids aspartic acid and glutamic acid as well as their amides asparagine and glutamine are very widely distributed in higher plants and play a key role in metabolic reactions. Glutamine is quite reactive and is readily decomposed in boiling water to ammonium pyrrolidone carboxylate. Glutamic acid can also be cyclized but requires somewhat more vigorous reaction conditions than glutamine. Due to unfavorable steric factors asparagine and aspartic acid do not give these reactions. This is not always recognized. Thus, the product obtained on treatment of asparagine in phosphate buffer of

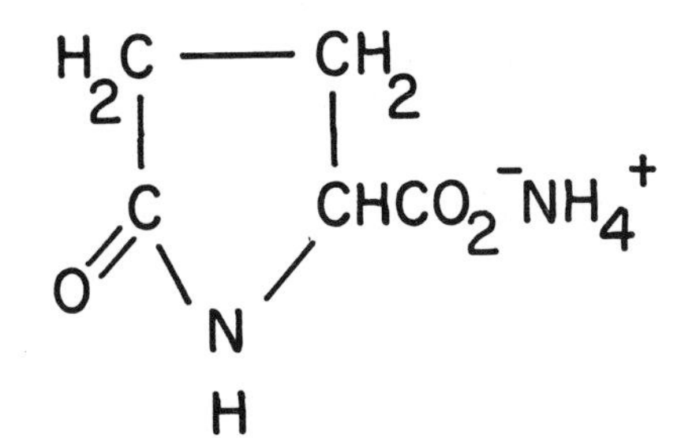

ammonium pyrrolidone carboxylate

pH 6.4 was at first believed to be the cyclic 4-oxoazetidine-2-carboxylic acid (5a) but was later shown to be fumaramic acid (5b). It should also be pointed out that the suggestion

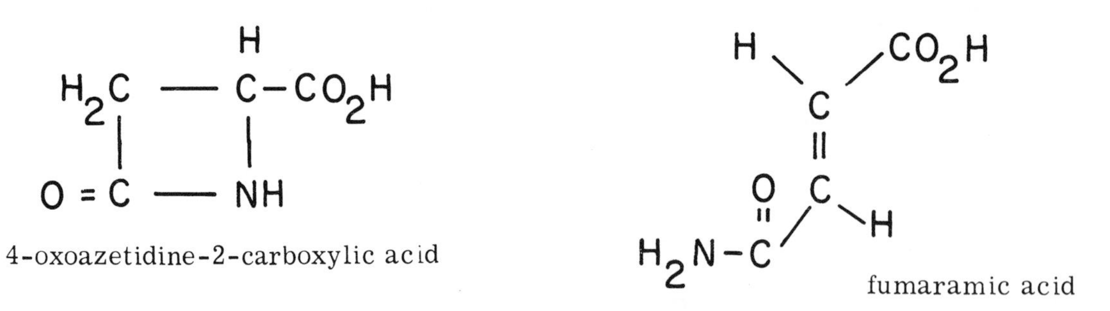

4-oxoazetidine-2-carboxylic acid

fumaramic acid

that asparagine exists in a hydrated cyclic imide form (6) had to be discarded when it was shown that alpha-amino succinimide and asparagine were readily distinguishable in aqueous solution (7). Due to the liability of the primary amide bonds neither glutamine nor asparagine can be recovered from the acid or base catalyzed hydrolyses of proteins.

The metabolic importance of these substances stems from the fact that they provide links between carbohydrate and protein interactions, that they can act as precursors of many other naturally occurring amino acids and that they appear to be involved in nitrogen transport.

The basic amino acids found in proteins and in the free state in higher plants are histidine, lysine and arginine. Of these, arginine is by far the strongest base having an isoelectric point of 10.76. Although arginine is quite stable in acidic medium it is readily hydrolyzed to citrulline, $NH_2C(=O)NH(CH_2)_3CH(NH_2)CO_2H$, or ornithine, $NH_2(CH_2)_3CH(NH_2)CO_2H$, in basic solution. Both of these amino acids occur in higher plants (8), (9). Lysine owes its basic character to the presence of two amino groups in the molecule. Plant proteins are rather poor sources of this amino acid and since lysine is an essential amino acid for man, a diet containing plant proteins as the sole source of nitrogen will lead to a deficiency syndrome. The availability of synthetic lysine as a food additive will go a long way in raising the nutritional standards of those countries in which animal proteins are available only in insufficient amounts.

Histidine is listed with the basic amino acids because it contains an imidazole group. This group is also involved in the formation of colored derivatives when proteins are treated with diazotized amines.

SPECIAL AMINO ACIDS FOUND IN HIGHER PLANTS

Since the introduction of partition chromatography, the isolation techniques available to chemists have gained in sophistication to the point where the number of new amino acids being discovered is increasing at an almost exponential rate. Therefore, no attempt will be made to list all the new plant amino acids, but it is hoped that the compounds selected for discussion will indicate the scope of the chemical variations being encountered. These compounds are not constituent amino acids of proteins and are found as free amino acids in a variety of higher plants. Comprehensive reviews of these non-protein amino acids have been published (10 a and b).

The discovery of amino acids which are widely distributed in higher plants in which the amino group is not in the alpha position is of interest. Their structures are listed in Table 2. Of these, gamma aminobutyric acid is the most ubiquitously distributed compound, and it is a rare event when it is absent from a plant extract.

TABLE 2. NON-ALPHA-AMINO ACIDS

Name	Structure	Ninhydrin color	R_f values: phenol water (pH 5.0-5.3)	R_f values: 1-butanol-acetic acid (9:1) water
gamma-aminobutyric acid	$H_2N(CH_2)_3CO_2H$	violet	.75	.15
beta-alanine	$H_2N(CH_2)_2CO_2H$	blue	.65	.09
alpha-methylene-gamma aminobutyric acid	$H_2N(CH_2)_2C(=CH_2)HCO_2H$			
beta amino isobutyric acid	$H_2NCH_2CH(CH_3)CO_2H$	grey-violet	.76	.20
gamma-amino-alpha-hydroxy-butyric acid	$H_2N(CH_2)_2(OH)CO_2H$			

Another interesting class contains new heterocyclic and alicyclic amino acids. Thus in addition to the long familiar histidine, proline and tryptophan, the compounds listed in Table 3 must now be added. It will be noted that with the finding of azetidine-2-carboxylic acid and pipecolic acid a homologous series of 4, 5 and 6-membered nitrogen-containing rings is now established. A new cyclopropyl derivative, 1-aminocyclopropane-1-carboxylic acid, has been isolated from pears (11), and hypoglycine A from the fruits of *Blighia sapida* (12). This compound, whose structure is shown below, has the ability to decrease the blood glucose level of experimental animals.

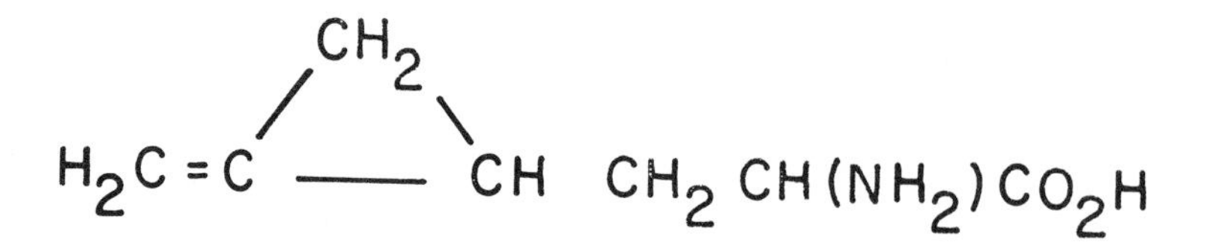

hypoglycine A

The number of naturally occurring dicarboxylic acids and amides has also been extended. Representative compounds are listed in Table 4. There is particular interest in gamma-methyleneglutamine since evidence exists that in the peanut this compound plays a major role in nitrogen transport (13). In most cases, however, the biological function of these compounds, if any, is still obscure.

New sulfur containing amino acids have also been discovered, Table 5. As already mentioned, great caution is required in those cases where the only difference between the previously known compounds and the newer ones is in the oxidation state of the sulfur. There is always the possibility that these substances are artifacts which are formed during isolation. S-methylcysteine sulfoxide which has been isolated from cabbage (14) and from turnip roots (15) appears to be a true plant constituent since S-methylcysteine cannot be oxidized to the sulfoxide at room temperature (15). This is contrary to the behavior of methionine which is oxidized under those conditions. Alliin, which is also a sulfoxide, has been isolated from garlic (16). (cf. Chap. 14)

Possibly, alliin is also closely related biochemically to cyclo alliin, isolated from onion bulbs (17), since the latter is the cyclized form of alliin. Djenkolic acid was first isolated from the urine of natives of Java who had eaten the djenkol bean but was later shown to occur in the bean (18). Inspection of the structural formula (Table 5) shows that this compound can be considered to be a thio acetal between cysteine and formaldehyde.

A number of amino acids have been discovered in higher plants in which the presence of a hydroxyl group is the major distinction from the more common compounds, Table 6. However, this is not meant to imply that the biosynthesis of these compounds proceeds by oxidation of the parent compounds. Several other hydroxy amino acids have been isolated but their structure assignments are not yet definite (10a). Another interesting compound which may be considered in this group is canavanine, which, as the structure below indicates, is a hydroxyguanidine derivative. The similarity of this compound to arginine is

$$H_2N\text{-}\underset{\displaystyle H}{\overset{\displaystyle NH}{\overset{\|}{\underset{|}{C}}}}\text{-}NOCH_2CH_2\underset{\displaystyle NH_2}{\underset{|}{C}}HCO_2H$$

sufficient to permit hydrolysis of canavanine by arginase to urea and canaline, $H_2NOCH_2CH_2CH(NH_2)CO_2H$. The latter compound is frequently found together with canavanine in jack bean meal and other leguminous species (19).

TABLE 3. STRUCTURE OF HETEROCYCLIC AMINO ACIDS

CH_2 — $CH-CO_2H$
CH_2 — NH

azetidine-2-carboxylic acid

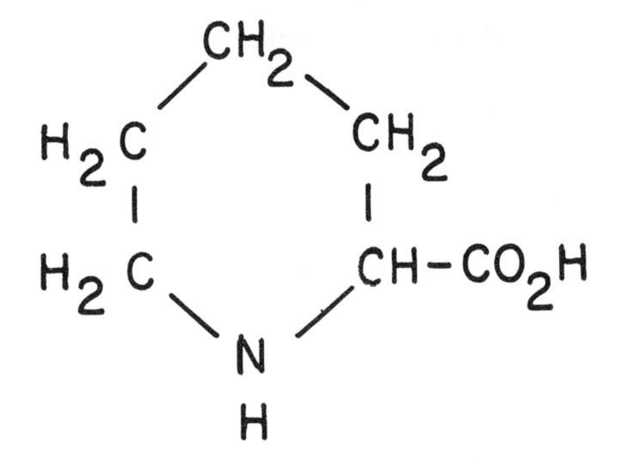

pipecolic acid

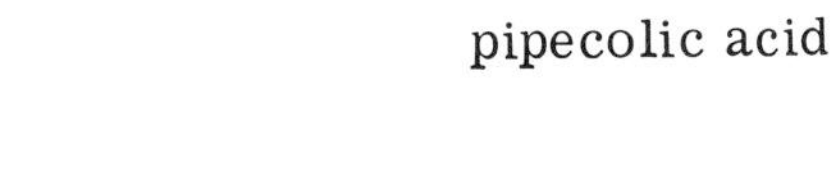

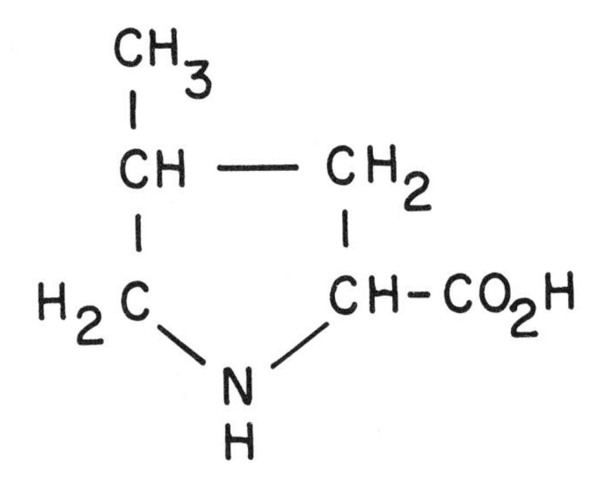

4-methyl proline

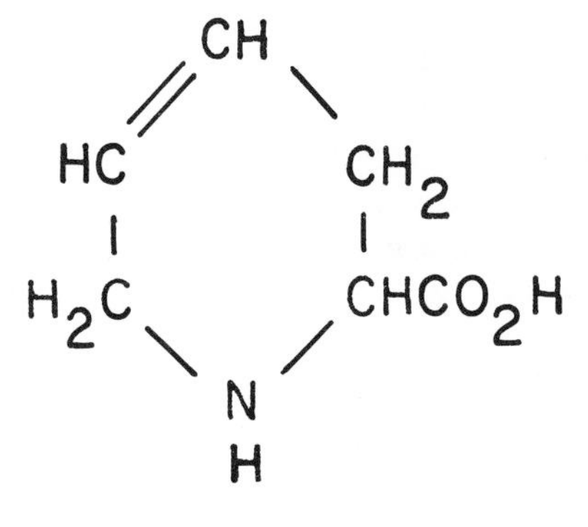

baikiain

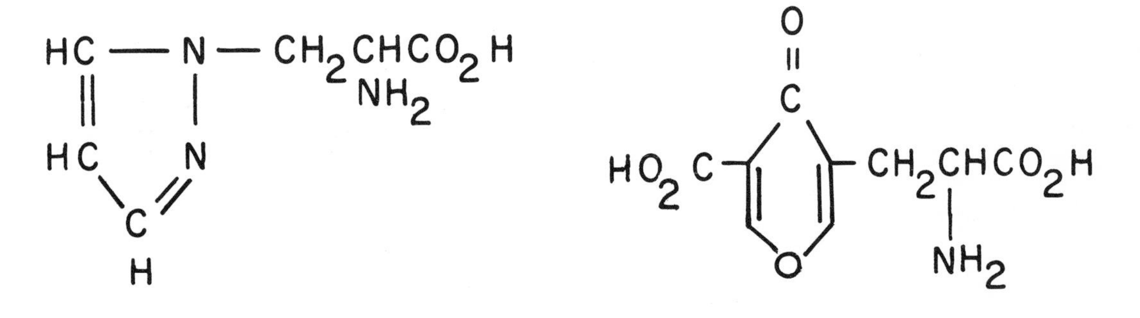

beta pyrazol-1-ylalanine

stizolobic acid

TABLE 4. DICARBOXYLIC AMINO ACIDS

Name	Structure
γ-methylene glutamic acid	$HO_2CC(=CH_2)CH_2CH(NH_2)CO_2H$
γ-methylene glutamine	$H_2NOCC(=CH_2)CH_2CH(NH_2)CO_2H$
γ-methyl glutamic acid	$HO_2CCH(CH_3)CH_2CH(NH_2)CO_2H$
γ-glutamyl ethylamide	$C_2H_5HNOC(CH_2)_2CH(NH_2)CO_2H$
α-amino adipic acid	$HO_2C(CH_2)_3CH(NH_2)CO_2H$
α-amino pimelic acid	$HO_2C(CH_2)_4CH(NH_2)CO_2H$

TABLE 5. SULFUR CONTAINING AMINO ACIDS

Name	Structure
S-methylcysteine	$CH_3SCH_2CH(NH_2)CO_2H$
Methyl methionine sulfonium hydroxide	$[(CH_3)_2S^+(CH_2)_2CH(NH_2)CO_2H]OH^-$
Djenkolic acid	$HO_2CCH(NH_2)CH_2SCH_2SCH_2CH(NH_2)CO_2H$
S-methyl cysteine sulfoxide	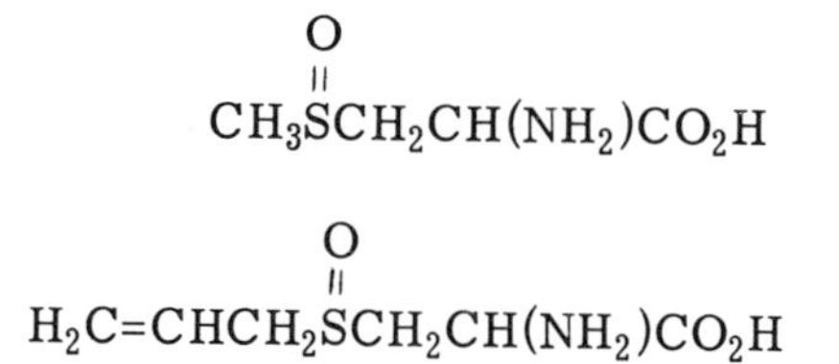
Allin	
S-2-carboxyethyl-L-cysteine	$HO_2CCH_2CH_2SCH_2CH(NH_2)CO_2H$
Cycloalliin	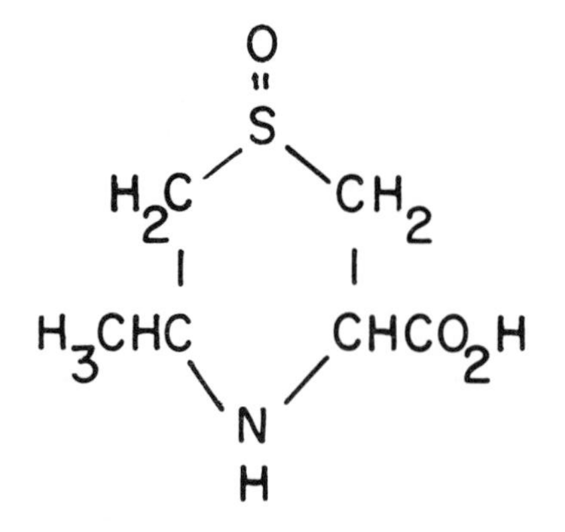

Since the number of plant species examined for various amino acids is still very small, it is difficult to reach definite conclusions on the distribution of the amino acids that are not generally found in proteins. Apparently, gamma-aminobutyric acid, pipecolic acid (20), beta gamma-dihydroxyglutamic acid (21) and alpha-amino-adipic acid (22) are rather widely distributed. Others are of only very limited distribution. For example, theanine has been detected only in tea leaves (23), azetidine-2-carboxylic acid appears to be limited to certain species of the *Liliaceae* family where it was detected in twenty-five per cent of the eighty-nine species examined (24). The results indicate that it will not be possible to predict the distribution of these amino acids from the taxonomic classification of the plants in which they occur.

TABLE 6. HYDROXY AMINO ACIDS

1.	homoserine	$HO(CH_2)_2CH(NH_2)CO_2H$
2.	gamma-hydroxy valine	$HOCH_2CH(CH_3)CH(NH_2)CO_2H$
3.	gamma-hydroxy glutamic acid	$HO_2CCH(OH)CH_2CH(NH_2)CO_2H$
4.	beta-gamma-dihydroxy glutamic acid	$HO_2CCH(OH)CH(OH)CH(NH_2)CO_2H$

5. gamma-methyl-gamma hydroxy-glutamic acid

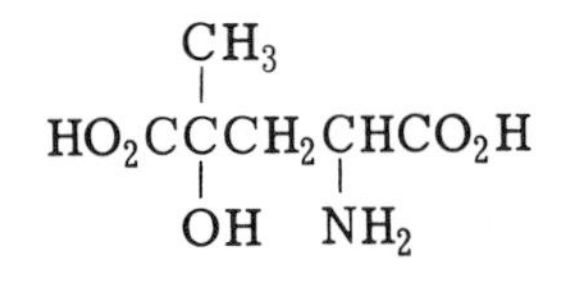

6. 5-hydroxy pipecolic acid

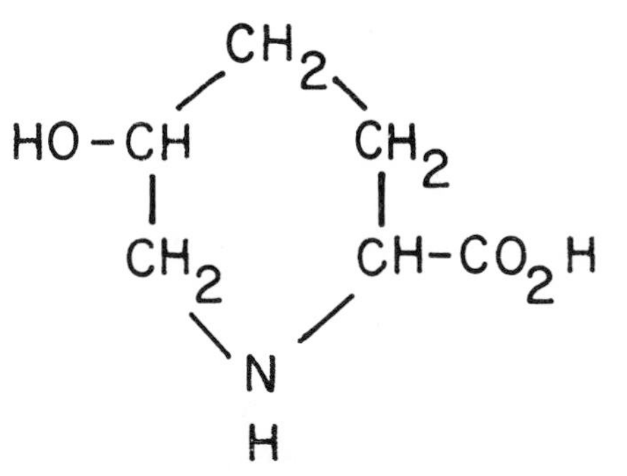

PEPTIDES AND PROTEINS

Peptides and proteins are condensation polymers of amino acids in which the elements of water have been eliminated between an amino and a carboxyl group. If the molecular weight of the compound is below 6000 it is generally classified as a peptide. All available evidence indicates that the amino acids of the proteins have the L-configuration and that amide bonds form only between alpha amino and alpha carboxyl groups of amino acids. Sixteen to twenty different amino acids are usually found on hydrolysis of a given protein. The amino acids in proteins are linked together to form linear polymer chains with cross-links possible between the sulfhydryl groups of cysteine, resulting in disulfide bridges. Greater variations are found with peptides. For example, peptides are known that contain D-amino acids, others have non-amino acid substituents and some are known in which not all the amide links are between the alpha amino and alpha carboxyl groups.

PEPTIDES

Most likely the number of pure peptides that have been isolated from higher plants represents only a small portion of the total. Thus, the presence of a large number of unidentified, acid labile, ninhydrin-positive substances have been detected by paper chromatography in higher plants (23). Many of these may turn out to be new peptides. Also, a chromatographic examination of rye grass extracts showed the presence of a number of peptides (25). The discussion below is limited to peptides which have been isolated in what is believed to be a pure state.

Glutathione, gamma-L-glutamyl-L-cysteinyl-glycine, was first isolated from yeast but has now been shown to be very widely distributed and can be detected by paper chromatography in the extracts from many higher plants (23). A cyclic peptide, named evolidine, has been isolated from the leaves of *Evodia xanthoxyloides*. The complete structure of this cyclic heptapeptide has been reported (26). A dipeptide isolated from beans has been shown to be gamma-L-glutamyl-S-methyl-L-cysteine (27).

Peptides which contain non-amino acid moieties are also known. Pteroyl-L-glutamic acid, also called folic acid is an example of this group and can be detected in the leaves of a large number of green plants. (cf. Chap. 14) Another representative of this group of peptides is the "lathyrus factor", isolated from *Lathyrus odoratus* seeds (28). (cf. Chap. 14) Pantothenic acid, an integral part of the coenzyme A molecule (Chap. 11) is a peptide of pantoic acid and bèta-alanine. As its name indicates, it is universally distributed in nature although at very low concentrations. It is a growth factor for many organisms.

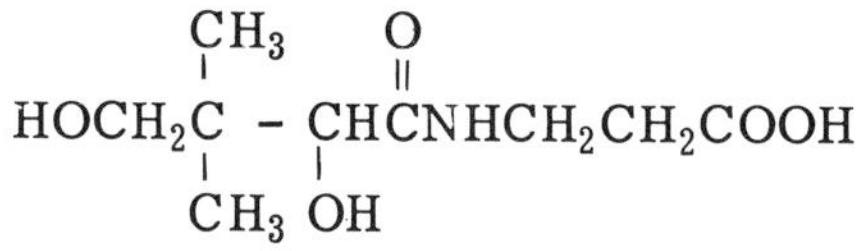

$$HOCH_2\overset{\overset{\displaystyle CH_3}{|}}{\underset{\underset{\displaystyle CH_3}{|}}{C}} - \underset{\underset{\displaystyle OH}{|}}{C}H\overset{\overset{\displaystyle O}{\|}}{C}NHCH_2CH_2COOH$$

pantothenic acid

Mistletoe contains a cardiotoxic, necrotizing substance named viscotoxin which appears to be a peptide. Its structure is still subject to controversy. According to Winterfeld and Rink the toxic material contains a hydrogenated naphthalene ring, a glucuronic acid radical and a tetrapeptide chain (29). However, later work by Samuelson (30) indicates that the material does not contain any sugars but is a peptide composed of eleven different amino acids. Among other peptides with uncertain structures one can list a basic substance with weak antibiotic activity isolated from wheat (31) and the so-called "allergens" present in plant pollens (32).

PROTEINS

All living systems contain a large number of different proteins. These may differ in the amino acid composition, in the sequence of the amino acids, in the non-amino acid constituents, in molecular weight and in those factors that determine the conformation of the protein. In order to elucidate the structure of a given protein it is necessary that the substance be separated from non-proteinaceous material as well as from other proteins. This is sometimes a most formidable task and a number of different criteria have to be used in order to establish the homogeneity of a given sample.

The complexity and diversity of the proteins has prompted a number of different classification schemes. However, these have only been partially successful. Plant proteins have been classified according to their source, thus one speaks of seed or leaf proteins. These are further subdivided into endosperm and embryo proteins for the seed, and chloroplastic proteins for those found in leaf tissue. A better scheme rests on a subdivision into simple proteins which on hydrolysis yield only alpha-amino acids, and conjugated proteins, which on hydrolysis yield amino acids plus other substances. The major subdivisions of the simple proteins are listed below.

Albumins - proteins that are soluble in water and in dilute salt solutions and are coagulable by heat. An example of an albumin is the leucosin from wheat.

Globulins - proteins that are insoluble in water but soluble in dilute salt solutions. Globulins are very prevalent in vegetable seeds.

Glutelins - proteins that are insoluble in all neutral solvents but readily soluble in very dilute acids and bases. Examples are the glutenin from wheat and oryzenin of rice.

Prolamines - proteins that are insoluble in water but soluble in 70-80% ethanol. Typical examples are zein from corn, gliadin from wheat, and hordein from barley. The peculiar solubility of these proteins is probably due to their high proline content. Proline itself has unusually high solubility in ethanol.

The name given to the conjugated proteins is determined by the nature of the non-amino acid moieties of the protein. Thus, nucleoproteins contain nucleic acids, glycoproteins are composed partially of carbohydrate, and chromoproteins are colored due to the presence of porphyrin ring systems, flavins or other pigmented fragments.

One of the characteristics of proteins is their great lability under very mild conditions. This lack of stability manifests itself by changes in the physical properties, the detection of functional groups or the side chains of the constituent amino acids, and the loss of the catalytic properties of the enzymes. These changes in the properties of proteins are usually called denaturation. Another characteristic of proteins is the great precision with which they are synthesized in nature. Thus, a pure protein from a particular species always contains the same number of amino acids in the same sequence. Mention should also be made of the fact that contrary to many other polymers, proteins in aqueous solution are not in equilibrium with the solvent. This means that in solution the proteins retain definite shapes and orientations which are held together by the disulfide bridges, hydrogen bonds and other attractive forces.

The proteins are such complex molecules that the determination of their structures is among the most challenging problems encountered by chemists. Yet, because of the vital role that these compounds play as biological catalysts it is imperative that we fully understand the nature of these compounds. A tremendous effort is therefore being made by chemists to increase our knowledge of the structure, the properties and biosynthesis of the proteins. So voluminous is the literature and so rapid are the advances in this field that only a very incomplete look at the exciting developments taking place can be presented here. A great deal is known about the covalent structure of proteins. All the evidence indicates that the amide bonds in the protein chains are formed only between alpha amino and alpha carboxyl groups. The only other type of covalent linkage that is well established is the disulfide bridge formed by oxidation of the sulfhydryl groups of two cysteine molecules. This can produce crosslinks between two or more peptide chains, or introduce folds into a long single chain. Insulin is an example of the first type (33) and ribonuclease of the second (34). Several methods for the determination of the sequence of amino acids are available. The most important of these are end group determinations, stepwise degradations, random partial hydrolysis and specific cleavage. Methods for the location of the disulfide bridges have also been developed. Application of these techniques has led to the elucidation of the entire amino acid sequence of ribonuclease, a single chain protein composed of 124 amino acid units (34) and of the protein from tobacco mosaic virus, a high molecular weight substance with repeating units composed of 158 amino acids (35).

The contributions to the final structure of a protein made by the covalent linkages are frequently termed the primary structure; and although they are of course extremely important, they do not by themselves fix the conformation of a protein in solution. To describe the structure of a protein completely one must also take other bonding forces into account. These are referred to as the secondary and tertiary structure. Information about these forces comes from such physical chemical measurements as X-ray defraction patterns, optical rotatory dispersion measurements, spectral data and deuterium-hydrogen exchange experiments. Proline, by virtue of its cyclic imino group, also plays a role in the determination of the final structure of proteins.

Hydrogen bonds between the amide links are believed to make major contributions to the secondary structure of proteins. One manifestation of these forces is the presence of helical structures in certain proteins. A spiral arrangement that accommodates peptide chains in a strain-free form and which is believed to play an important role in the conformation of proteins is the so-called alpha helix (36). This configuration is a right handed helix for the L-amino acids, held together by hydrogen bonds between the NH group of one amide and the O=C group of another amide link four units up the chain. There are 3. 6 residues per turn and the pitch is 5. 4 Angstroms. The hydrogen bonds are in the direction of the fiber axis, and the side chains of the constituent amino acids are at the outer periphery of the helix. The amount of helical content of different proteins varies quite extensively and is maintained intact through the disulfide bridges and a favorable tertiary structure. The tertiary structure is due to still weaker interactions; Van der Waals forces, solvent-protein interactions and hydrophobic bonds seem to play a predominant role in these stabilization forces.

Correlation of the results from many different types of structural data obtained for the enzyme ribonuclease has permitted the construction of a tentative three-dimensional model for this protein as it might exist in aqueous solution (37). The construction of a three-dimensional working model of an enzyme, even if in the final analysis it should prove incorrect, demonstrates very effectively the great advances that have been made.

ISOLATION

AMINO ACIDS AND PEPTIDES

Before the advent of ion exchange and partition chromatography most amino acids were isolated from specific protein hydrolysates or from the amino acids present in the tissues of particular plants or animals. Thus asparagine, the first amino acid to be isolated from nature was obtained by concentration of asparagus juice (1). Aspartic acid can be prepared from asparagine by acid hydrolysis. Glutamic acid is obtained from acid hydrolysates of wheat gluten. Isoleucine was isolated from sugar beet molasses. Phenylalanine and arginine were isolated from etiolated lupine seedlings. Arginine can also be isolated as the relatively insoluble mono or diflavianate (38). The other common amino acids can in most cases be conveniently isolated from animal sources.

The isolation of the newer plant amino acids generally requires more sophisticated techniques, since these compounds are present in the cell sap together with a large number of other cell constituents and frequently occur only in small amounts. Almost every case presents unique problems that have to be solved on an individual basis. However, ion exchange processes in one form or another are often extremely useful. These procedures are particularly desirable for the concentration of amino acids, the removal of neutral contaminants and the subdividsion of the amino acids into neutral, acidic, and basic fraction (39). After preliminary concentration and purification steps have been taken, it may be necessary to separate the desired amino acids from a number of closely related compounds. For this purpose chromatographic methods are frequently used. A typical example that illustrates these procedures is the isolation of pipecolic acid from green beans (40).

An aqueous extract of 26 gallons was prepared from 175 pounds of fresh green beans. The extract was concentrated to six liters and a one liter fraction was adsorbed on an eight hundred gram column of cation exchanger in the hydrogen form. Washing of the column with distilled water removed the sugars and other non-ionic material. The column was then treated with seven liters of 2N-hydrochloric acid. This removed eight contaminating amino acids but resulted in the retention of pipecolic acid, gamma-amino butyric acid and the basic amino acids on the column. The latter compounds were eluted with six liters of 0. 5 N and two liters of 1 N ammonium hydroxide. Examination of the eluate by paper chromatography located the fractions that contained the bulk of the pipecolic acid. These were combined, the solvent evaporated and the pipecolic acid crystallized as the hydrochloride. A total of 60 mg. of chromatographically pure, crystalline material was obtained. Later modifications resulted in an improved procedure which permitted the isolation of 13. 4 g L-pipecolic acid from about 150 pounds of green beans (41).

The isolation of gamma aminobutyric acid from potato tubers illustrates a very elegant method of separating a non-alpha amino acid (42). The alpha amino acids form stable chelates with divalent cations, whereas the non-alpha acids do not. This difference can be utilized to effect separation of non-alpha amino acids from the alpha amino acids by using a column consisting of alumina and copper carbonate. With this technique the alpha amino acids are retained on the column under conditions which cause elution of the non-alpha amino acids.

Quantitative amino acid determinations are most conveniently carried out by column procedure utilizing chromatography with ion exchange resins (43). Completely automatic recording analyzers are available commercially. Another inovation is the use of volatile buffers as eluting solvents for ion-exchange columns (44). With these solvents the amino acids are frequently obtained in a very high state of purity after evaporation of the solvents. Mention should also be made of procedures which combine ion exchange resins with filter paper partition chromatography (45). Other methods that can be used for separation or isolation of amino acids are paper electrophoresis (46) and vapor phase chromatography. In the latter procedure the amino acids are first converted to the N-acyl esters and a procedure has been described for the separation of 18 amino acids that requires only 90 minutes for acetylation and esterification and less than 60 minutes for resolution (47).

The isolation of peptides can usually be accomplished by the same techniques as those used for amino acids. Countercurrent distribution (48) and membrane diffusion (49) appear to be particularly valuable for those compounds.

PROTEINS

Tremendous variations exist in the degree of difficulty encountered in the purification of proteins. Some can be obtained in a homogeneous, crystalline state by exceedingly simple procedures. For example, extraction of jack bean meal with aqueous acetone, filtration, and storage of the filtrate near 0° yields a precipitate which after several recrystallizations consists of pure urease. On the other hand, cases are known where the most persistent efforts of highly skilled operators have been fruitless. However, no matter what procedure is finally adopted, it is of paramount importance that conditions be employed which do not lead to denaturation of the protein. Generally it is advisable to work at low temperatures and to avoid extreme pH ranges. It is also helpful to keep the protein concentration as high as possible.

Proteins can frequently be fractionated by control of the ionic strength of the medium through the use of salts. For example, a crystalline globulin fraction has been obtained from squash seeds by extraction of the ground seeds with 10% sodium chloride at 40° (50).

When the filtered and centrifuged extract was diluted with four volumes of water and stored at 2° C., crystalline protein precipitated. Ammonium sulfate precipitations are also employed very frequently. Other techniques that occupy important places in many fractionation schemes are dialysis and the use of organic solvents as precipitants.

In these cases in which those relatively simple techniques do not prove satisfactory, the protein chemist can turn to more sophisticated methods. Ultracentrifugation (51) and electrophoresis (52) have proven their value in many separation problems. Chromatographic methods based on the use of modified cellulose derivatives such as diethylaminoethyl cellulose have been shown to be extremely effective (53). Separations with these columns are to a very large extent due to ion exchange interactions. The protein concentration in the eluate can frequently be estimated by ultraviolet scanning near 280 millimicrons due to the presence of aromatic amino acids in many proteins.

With the simpler organic solids, crystallinity can usually be taken as a safe criterion for homogeneity. Unfortunately, this is not true for proteins since many crystalline preparations can be shown to be heterogeneous according to other tests. The purity of an isolate can be tested by phase solubility studies, electrophoretic separations at different pH values, ultracentrifugation and chromatography. Only after application of each of these tests has indicated lack of heterogeneity can it be concluded that according to these criteria the isolate is homogeneous.

CHARACTERIZATION

At present the best-known method for rapid identification of the amino acids in a mixture is paper chromatography. Usually two dimensional chromatography is needed for good separations of complex mixtures. The required apparatus is inexpensive, the manipulations can be learned rapidly, and in most cases as little as 5-10 micrograms of a given amino acid can be detected routinely. The R_f values for a large number of naturally occurring and synthetic amino acids have been compiled (23, 10b), and some of these are presented in Table 1. The most popular developing solvents seem to be 1-butanol/acetic acid/water mixtures and water-saturated phenol. A 0.1% solution of ninhydrin in butanol or ethanol is almost universally used as the detecting reagent. Spots show up after standing at room temperature for several hours or in a few minutes if the paper sheet is heated to 100° C. after spraying. Thin layer chromatography on silica gel (54) and paper electrophoresis (55) are also effective methods for amino acid analysis. Further characterization of the amino acids, peptides and proteins is based on chemical reaction with the amino group, the specific side chains, the carboxyl groups and the amide bonds. Molecular weight determinations are also used frequently. Many of the older procedures are assuming new significance due to their application to chromatographic techniques.

REACTION WITH THE AMINO GROUP

Several quantitative procedures have been developed which are based on interactions with the amino group. One very useful method for the estimation of total amino nitrogen of proteins, peptides and free amino acids of a plant extract is a micro adaptation of the Kjeldahl method (56). The nitrogen-containing material is digested with concentrated sulfuric acid in the presence of catalysts yielding ammonium salts. The digestion mixture is made alkaline and the resulting ammonia distilled into standard acid and determined quantitatively by titration. To obtain a rough estimate of the total percent protein, etc., the percentage nitrogen is multiplied by the factor 6.25.

The fact that primary amines react with nitrous acid to yield nitrogen forms the basis of the manometric Van Slyke method for the estimation of amino acids (57).

$$HO_2C - \overset{R}{\overset{|}{C}}H - NH_3^+ + HNO_2 \rightarrow HO_2C - \overset{R}{\overset{|}{C}}H - OH + N_2 + H_3O^+$$

There are, however, complications. Imino acids, for example, proline and azetidine carboxylic acid do not contain primary amino groups and, therefore, yield no gaseous nitrogen on reaction with nitrous acid. On the other hand, glutamine yields almost two moles of nitrogen per mole.

Formaldehye reacts with amino acids to give a mixture of compounds. Since in these substances the acidity of the ammonium group is increased,

$$R\overset{NH_3^+}{\overset{|}{C}}HCO_2^- + H\overset{O}{\overset{||}{C}}H \rightarrow R\overset{H_2N^+CH_2OH}{\overset{|}{C}}HCO_2^- + R\overset{HN^+(CH_2OH)_2}{\overset{|}{C}}HCO_2^- + \text{others}$$

the addition of formaldehyde to amino acids permits the quantitative determination of these substances by titration with standardized base to the phenolphthalein endpoint (58).

The reaction of primary and secondary amines with ninhydrin is used very extensively for the detection of amino acids and for their quantitative determination (59). Amides and tertiary amines do not react. With ammonia and most primary and secondary amines intensely colored violet, blue, brown or yellow pigments are obtained.

In the reaction of most alpha amino acids with ninhydrin the violet color formation is accompanied by carbon dioxide formation. Therefore, the combined determination of carbon dioxide and color makes this reaction fairly specific for alpha amino acids. The reaction is believed to involve several steps (59). Ninhydrin (I) reacts with an alpha amino acid to produce the amine II plus carbon dioxide and an aldehyde with one carbon atom less than the original amino acid. At the appropriate pH, compound II condenses

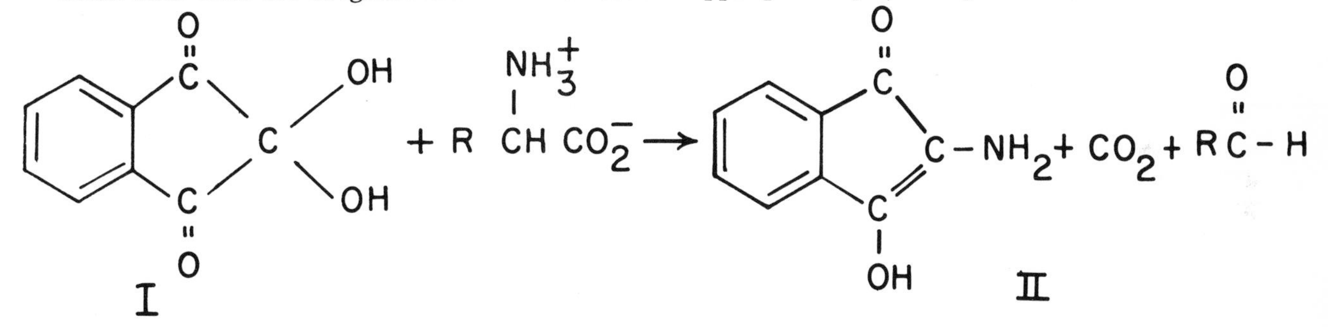

with a molecule of ninhydrin to yield III, a violet pigment. The reaction of a given alpha amino acid with ninhydrin does not necessarily yield compound III in stoichiometric

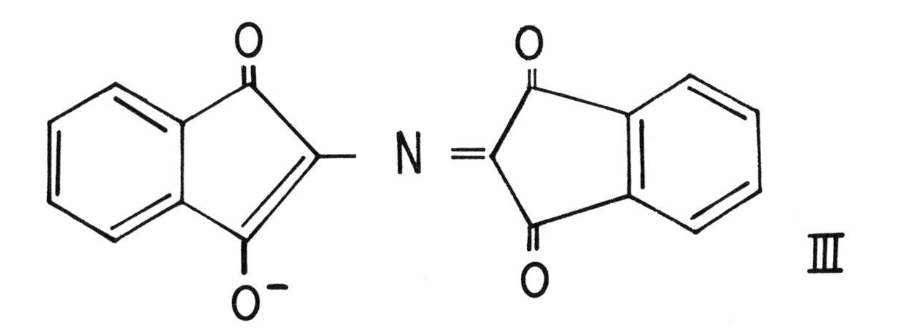

amounts. However, a procedure has been described in which equivalent amounts of color formation is claimed for all common amino acids except tryptophan, 80%, and lysine, 110%, (60). Another advantage of this procedure is its low sensitivity to ammonia.

When alpha imino acids, such as proline, are reacted with ninhydrin, a yellow pigment is usually obtained. In this reaction carbon dioxide is also formed and the pigment is believed to have structure IV.

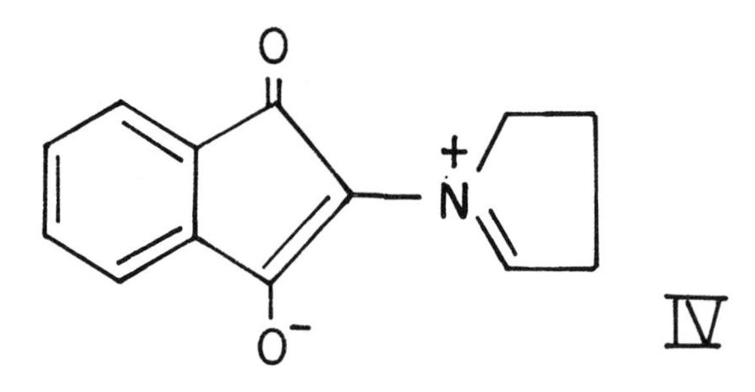

REACTIONS WITH AMINO ACID SIDE CHAINS

Specific tests, which in some cases are quantitative, have been developed for several amino acids. These depend on differences in the structure of the side chains for their selectivity and can be applied to peptides and proteins. Thus, the guanidino group of arginine permits the colorimetric determination of this compound by reaction with sodium hypochlorite and alpha naphthol in alkaline solution (61). Histidine and tyrosine are converted to azo dyes by treatment with diazotized sulfanilic acid (62). Tyrosine also gives a positive Millon test, a red precipitate with mercurous nitrate in nitric acid, a reaction which is specific for phenols containing a free ortho position (63). Cysteine, due to the presence of a sulfhydryl group, gives a transient purple violet color with sodium nitroprusside, $Na_2[Fe(CN)_5(NO)]$ in the presence of base (64). Tryptophan yields various colored products on reaction with various aldehydes in the presence of sulfuric acid (65).

On treatment with a 1% solution of tert-butyl hypochlorite in cyclohexane, aeration in a stream of air and spraying with an aqueous solution of potassium iodide and starch, peptides, acyl amino acids and proteins develop blue spots against a white background (66). This test is applicable to any amino derivative that contains a N-H bond. It should be added that most of the reactions described above have been applied to paper chromatography.

SPECIFIC REACTIONS OF PROTEINS

The specific tests listed in the above section for amino acids and peptides are of course also given by many proteins. Sometimes it is found that these reactive side chains are more accessible after a protein has been denatured. In addition to these reactions there are a few that are more or less diagnostic for proteins. The biuret test is given by proteins and other substances that contain two amide groups either joined directly or through a single atom of nitrogen or carbon (67). The reagent consists of copper sulfate in concentrated sodium hydroxide, and a positive test is indicated by a pink or purple color. The action of many agents in converting soluble proteins to insoluble products is also useful. General precipitants are heavy metal ions (mercuric chloride, silver nitrate, lead acetate), "alkaloidal reagents" (picric acid, phosphotungstic acid, tannic acid), and concentrated salt solutions (ammonium sulfate, sodium chloride and sodium sulfate).

Molecular weight determinations are of extreme importance in work with proteins. Many different methods have been developed. Osmotic pressure measurements can be used but since they give number average molecular weights a small percentage of a low molecular weight impurity produces a rather large error. Light scattering procedures and ultracentrifugation, methods that yield weight average molecular weights, are used very extensively. The molecular weight of edestin, a seed protein, has been obtained by electron microscopy (68). One of the problems encountered in molecular weight determinations of proteins is that under different conditions the apparent molecular weight of a protein may vary greatly. This is due to the ability of proteins to form dissociable aggregates. It is therefore necessary to state the conditions used in the molecular weight determination very precisely and to bear in mind that a given experimental value may not represent the minimum molecular weight.

METABOLIC PATHWAYS

Striking advances have been made in the elucidation of the biosynthetic pathways of amino acids and proteins. However, because of the ready availability of mutants of micro-organisms most of the work has been carried out with these primitive plants. Unfortunately, one has no assurance that these processes are universal and it is therefore extremely risky to attempt to apply the results obtained with micro-organisms to higher plants. The pathways shown in Figures 1-3 represent a composite derived from many different organisms, and in some cases intermediate steps are omitted in the transformations. Reviews of amino acid biosynthesis and breakdown appear rather frequently in the literature.

NITROGEN FIXATION AND NITRATE REDUCTION

Molybdenum appears to be of prime significance in both the symbiotic and non-symbiotic nitrogen fixations (69). A great deal of evidence can be cited to support the belief that atmospheric nitrogen is reduced stepwise to the ammonia level, and that it enters the metabolic pools in the form of glutamine and glutamic acid. The exact nature of the intermediates is not known, and they may remain bound to the enzyme until released as ammonia. The suggestion of Bach (70) that 3, 4-dihydropyridazinone-5-carboxylic acid (V) may be an intermediate has not been verified by other workers. Cell-free preparations with which nitrogen fixation can be carried out are available (71, 72) and should be of great utility in the determination of the intermediates and enzymes involved in the process.

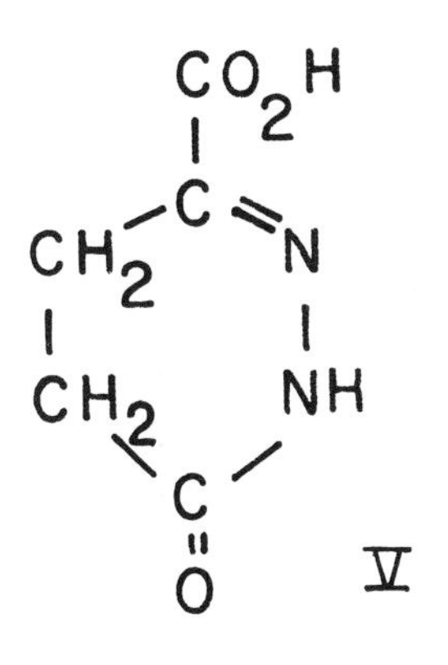

Most species of higher plants possess the ability to reduce nitrate to the ammonia level. The first intermediate in this process is nitrite. The enzyme involved in this process in some organisms is a molybdenum flavoprotein (73) and the electron donor is TPNH. Hyponitrous acid and hydroxylamine or addition products formed with alpha keto acids may be other intermediates in this reduction process.

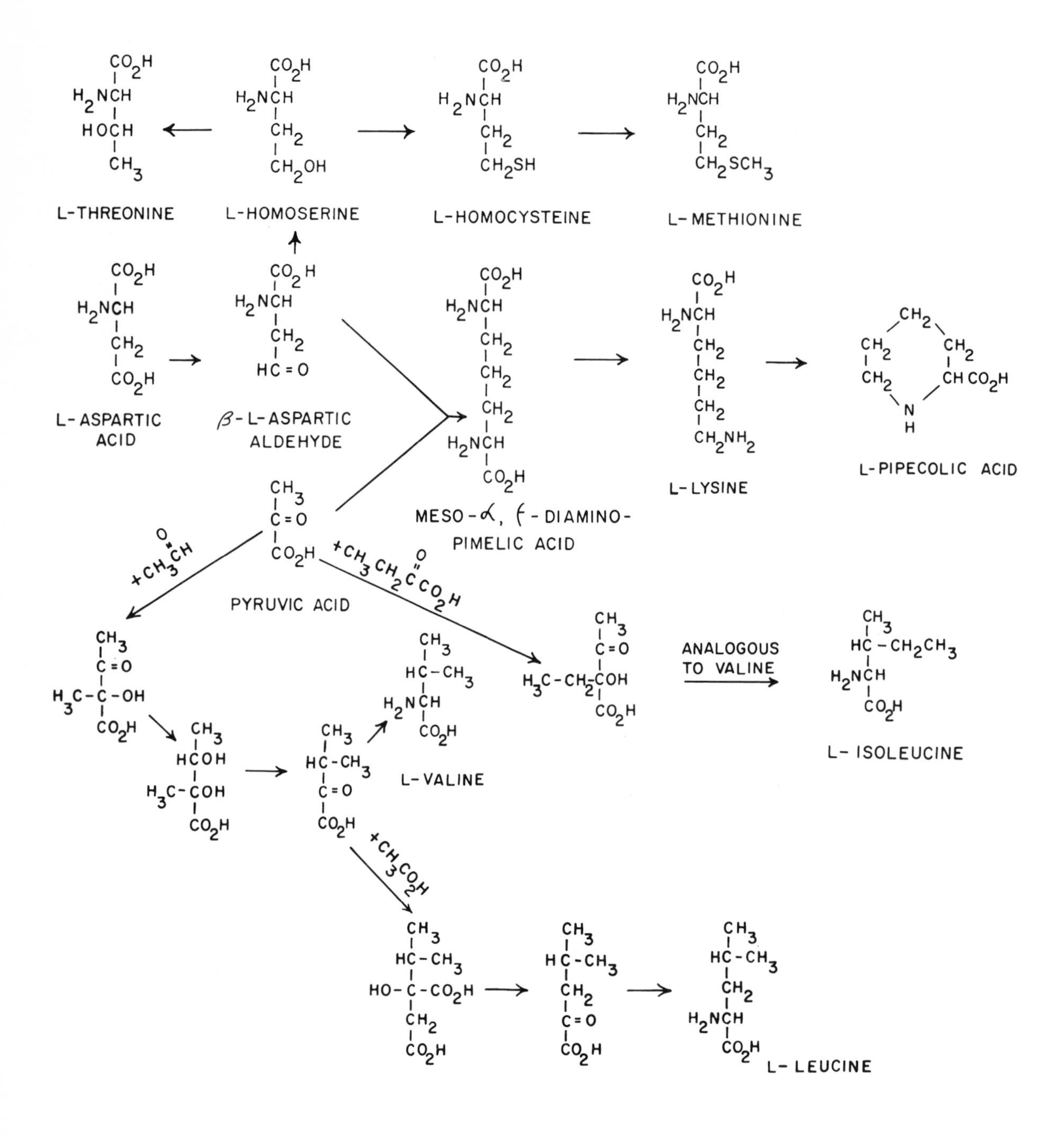

FIGURE 10-1. AMINO ACID PATHWAYS

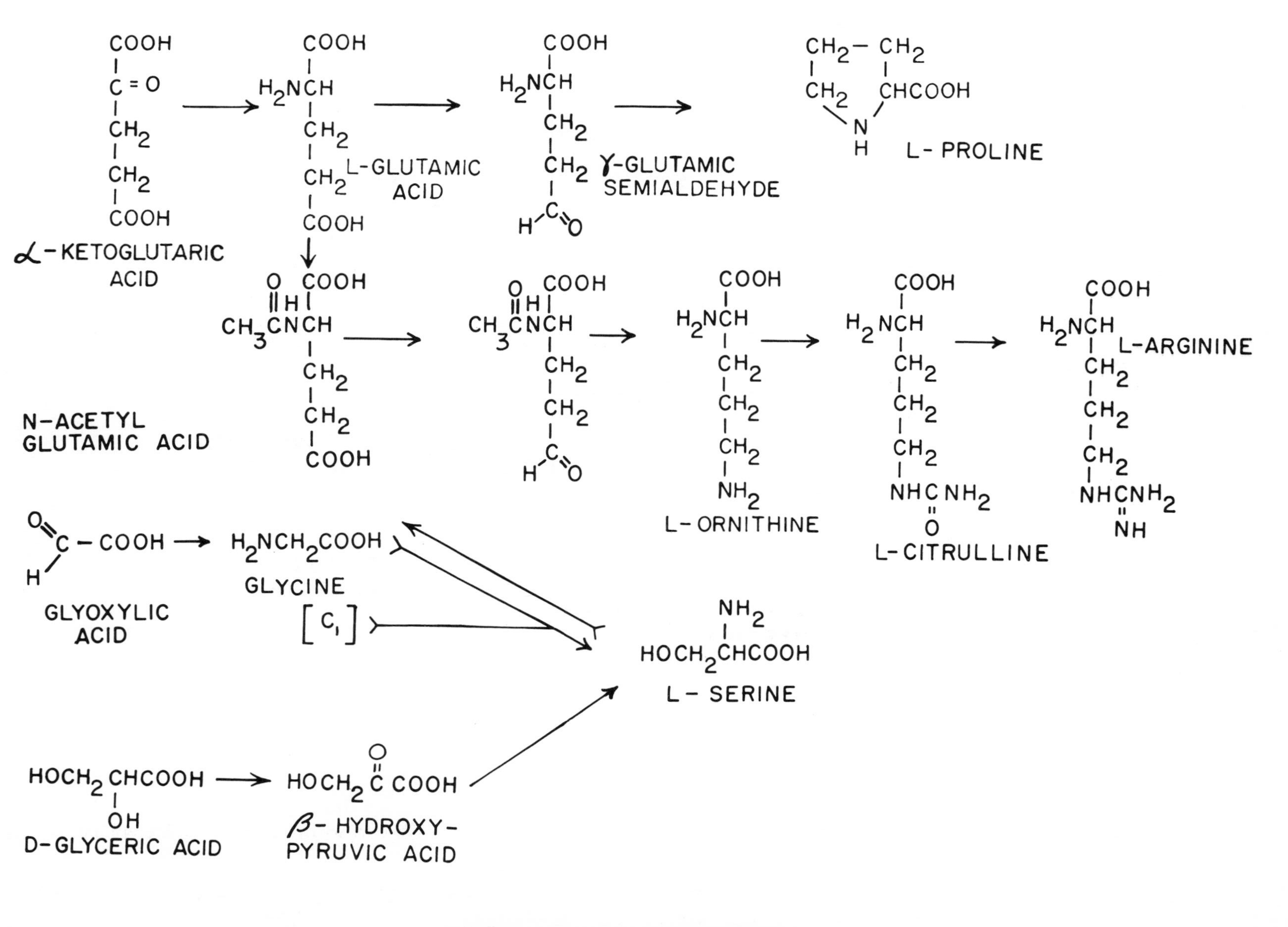

FIGURE 10-2. AMINO ACID PATHWAYS

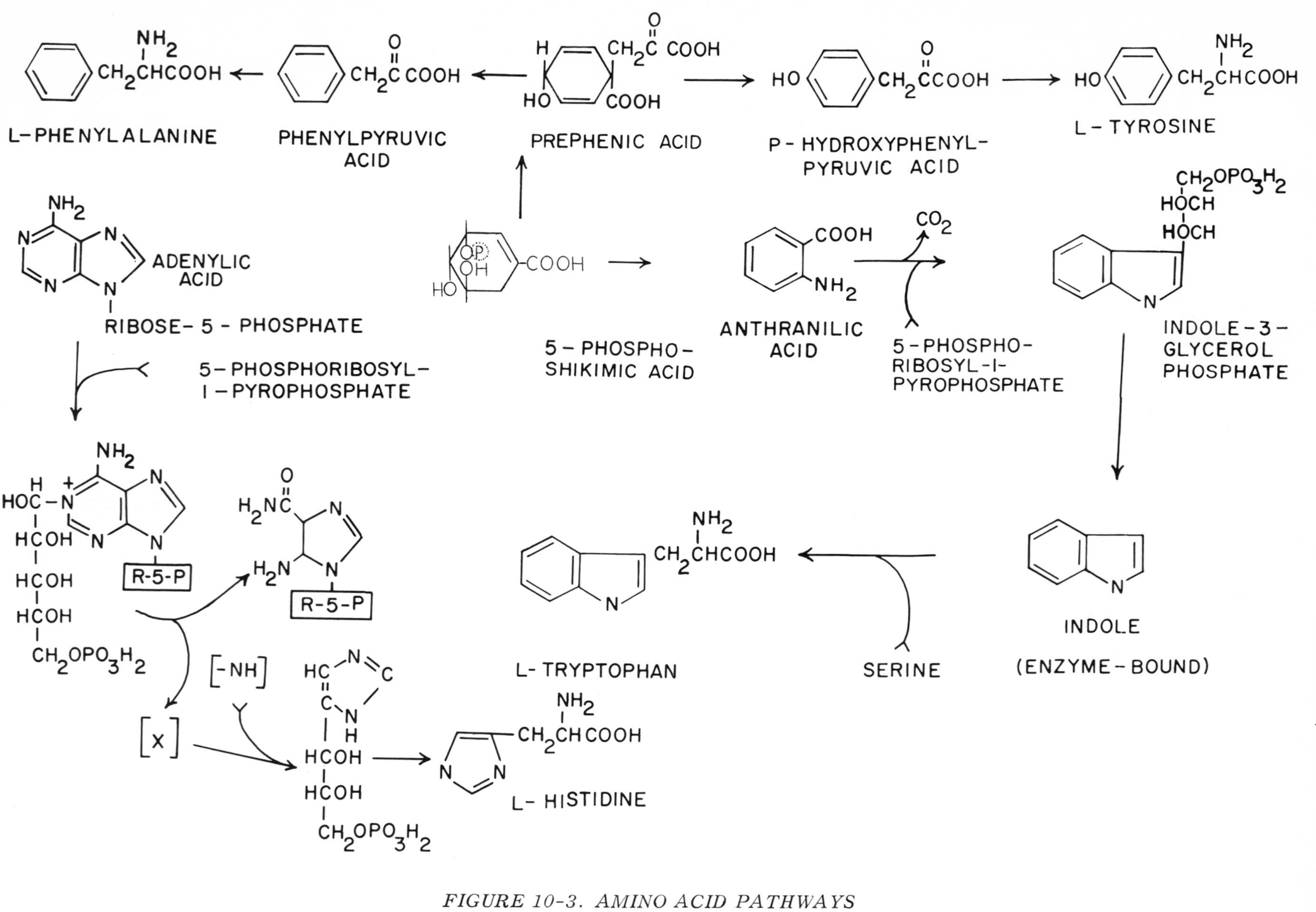

FIGURE 10-3. AMINO ACID PATHWAYS

BIOSYNTHESIS OF AMINO ACIDS

The close interrelationships between carbohydrate and amino acid metabolism has been known for a long time. Thus, pyruvic acid, oxalacetic acid and alpha-ketoglutaric acid, compounds arising during the oxidation of glucose, can be converted by transamination or reductive amination reactions to L-alanine, L-aspartic acid and L-glutamic acid, respectively. Glutamic acid and aspartic acid, are in turn, precursors of a large number of other amino acids. For example the interconversion of glutamic acid and glutamine has been demonstrated in higher plants (74). Evidence exists that in microorganisms (75) and possibly also in higher plants (76) glutamic acid is reduced to the semi-aldehyde an intermediate from which proline can form by ring closure and reduction. In the formation of ornithine glutamic acid is first acetylated, then reduced and transaminated.

Ornithine in turn is a precursor of critrulline and arginine in microorganisms, and possibly also in higher plants (77). Enzymes that can catalyze the decarboxylation of glutamic acid to gamma-aminobutyric acid have been demonstrated to be widely distributed in higher plants (78). Aspartic acid is readily interconvertible with asparagine and can apparently give rise to beta-alanine, homoserine and threonine. Serine and glycine are interconvertable by a reaction involving a tetrahydrofolic acid derivative. This reaction has been shown to occur in higher plants (79).

The biosynthesis of tyrosine and phenylalanine from intermediates of the shikimic acid (VII) pathway has been established for three different families of higher plants, Labiatae, Gramineae and Polygonaceae (80).

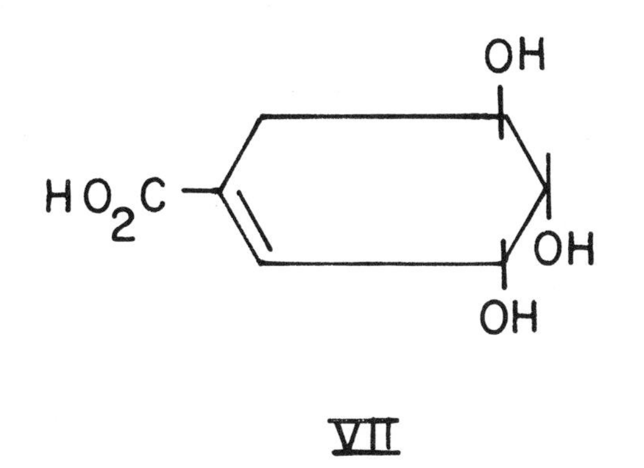

Shikimic acid can be considered a carbohydrate derivative since it is formed from phosphoenol pyruvate and D-erythrose-4-phosphate (Chap. 2). In microorganisms, tryptophan may also be formed from shikimic acid-5-phosphate through anthranilic acid (81).

The biosynthetic pathways of leucine, isoleucine and valine are quite similar. A scheme which appears to account for the results obtained with microorganisms is presented below for the synthesis of valine. Pyruvic acid and acetaldehyde condense to yield alpha-acetolactic acid (VIII); this may be reduced to the glycol IX. On rearrangement by a reaction analogous to a pinacol-type rearrangement, alpha-keto isovaleric acid (X) is formed.

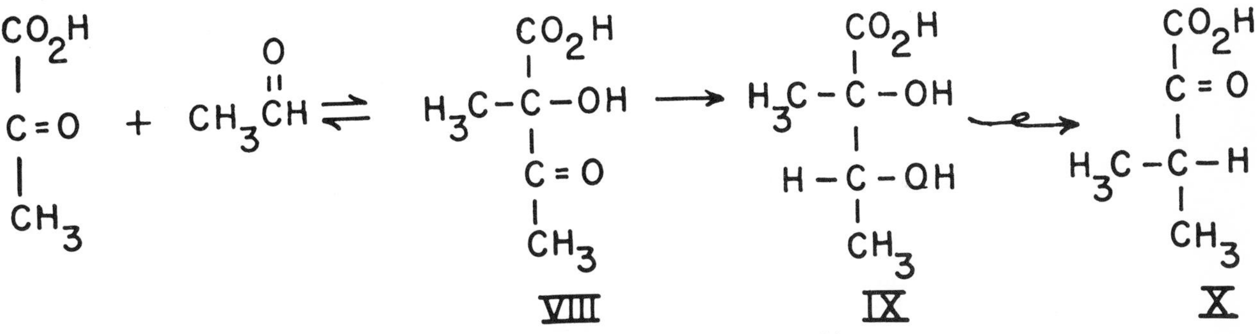

By a transamination reaction X may be converted to valine.

A certain amount of evidence exists that gamma-methyleneglutamic acid and related compounds originate in the peanut through condensation of two molecules of pyruvic acid. The amino acid analogues of the keto acids XI, XII, and XIII occur in some plants.

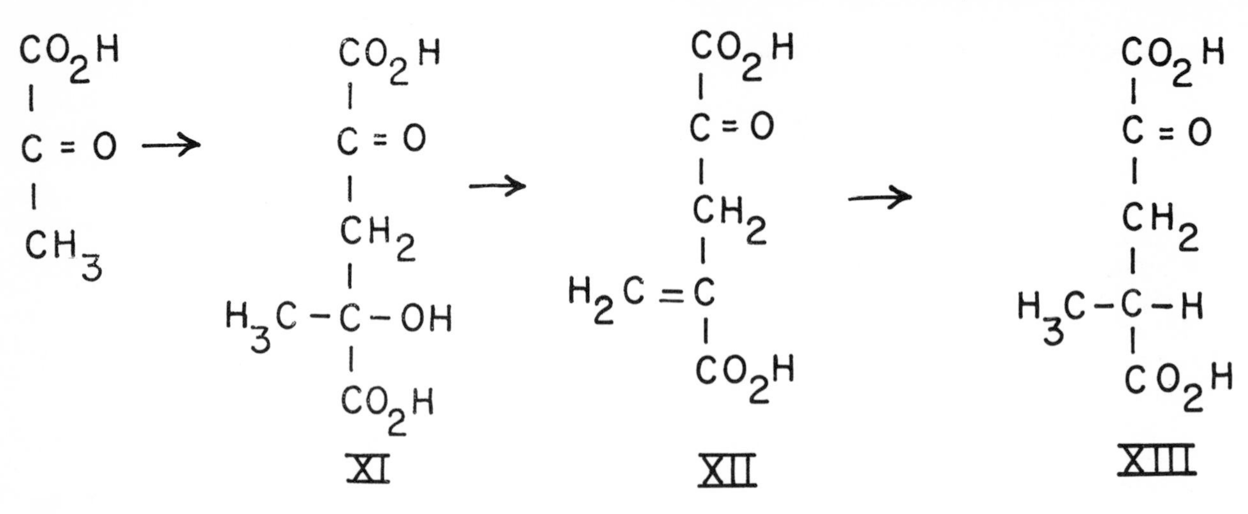

PROTEIN BIOSYNTHESIS

A dramatic development, the demonstration of protein synthesis in stable cell-free systems, by Nirenberg and Matthai (82) promises to lead to the complete elucidation of the reactions involved in the biosynthesis of these compounds and at the same time confirms a great deal of the earlier hypotheses concerning their mode of formation.

The preponderance of the available evidence indicates that proteins are synthesized from free amino acids and not by the condensation of preformed peptides or keto acids. The free amino acids are believed to be activated by a reaction with ATP to yield enzyme-bound amino-acyladenylates (83). In this complex the carboxyl group of the amino acid is linked to the 5' -phosphate of AMP as a mixed anhydride. Each individual amino acid has its own activation enzyme. This type of reaction has been shown to occur in many of the higher plants including spinach, rye, asparagus and tobacco (84). The next major step forward was the finding that amino acids from the AMP-complexes are transferred to soluble ribonucleic acids (sRNA) yielding amino acyl-sRNA complexes (85). No separate enzyme is required for the transfer of the amino acid from the AMP complexes to the sRNA. The reaction sequence is shown below. There seems to be at least one sRNA for each

$$\text{ATP} + \text{amino acid} + \text{enzyme} \rightleftharpoons \text{enzyme} - (\text{AMP} - \text{amino acid}) + \text{PP}$$

$$\text{enzyme} - (\text{AMP} - \text{amino acid}) + \text{sRNA} \rightleftharpoons \text{sRNA} - \text{amino acid} + \text{enzyme}$$

amino acid and these substances all have molecular weights of approximately 30, 000. Partial separations have been achieved by several procedures but counter current distribution appears to be particularly suitable (86). In addition to the sRNA at least two other nucleic acid fractions are involved in protein biosynthesis, messenger RNA (mRNA) and ribosomes. mRNA is believed to carry the information necessary to synthesize a given protein. Because the mRNA is only a small portion of the total RNA present in the cell it is difficult to get precise information concerning its composition and properties. However, evidence does exist that it acts as the template for protein synthesis, that it is rapidly synthesized and metabolically unstable and that it may mimic the N-base composition of DNA. The hypothesis therefore is that mRNA acts as an information carrier from DNA and plays the role of a template in protein synthesis.

The ribosomes are associated with the particulate fractions of the cell and have been obtained from microsomes, nuclei and mitochondria (87). They are isolated by ultracentrifugation and their size depends on the magnesium ion concentration of the medium. The major constituents (40 to 60 percent) of the ribosomes are proteins that resemble histones and RNA. Experimental evidence indicates that although ribosomes are required for protein synthesis they do not determine the nature of the protein produced. Presumably the ribosomes represent a non-specific part of the total machinery necessary for protein production and only after they have interacted with a specific mRNA will a given protein be synthesized.

Another development of major significance was the demonstration by Nirenberg and Matthai (82) that DNAse treated cell-free preparations will synthesize polypeptides in response to synthetic polynucleotides. Thus, the addition of polyuridylic acid led to the formation of polyphenylalanine. By using synthetic polynucleotides composed of more than one N-base and making the assumption that a triplet code is involved it has been possible to devise a nucleotide code for the amino acids that are incorporated into proteins. It is to be anticipated that future experiments will permit the elucidation of the nucleotide sequence requirement for every amino acid.

GENERAL REFERENCE

Alexander, P., and Block, R. J., Laboratory Manual of Analytical Methods of Protein Chemistry, 3 Vols., Pergamon Press, N. Y., 1960-1961.
Fowden, L., "Non-Protein Amino Acids of Plants", Endeavour 21 35 (1962).
Greenberg, D. M., ed., Metabolic Pathways, Vol. II, Academic Press, N. Y., 1961.
Greenstein, J. P. and Winitz, M., Chemistry of the Amino Acids, 3 Vols., John Wiley and Sons, Inc., New York, N. Y., 1961.
Meister, A., Biochemistry of the Amino Acids, Academic Press, New York, N. Y., 1957.
Paech and Tracey 4 (Several Articles).
Ruhland 8 (Several Articles).
Scheraga, H. A., Protein Structure, Academic Press, New York, N. Y., 1961.
Webster, G. C., Nitrogen Metabolism in Plants, Harper and Row, N. Y., 1959.
Advances in Protein Chemistry, Vol. I, 1946 to present, Academic Press, New York, N. Y.

BIBLIOGRAPHY

1. Vauquelin, L. N. and Robiquet, P. J., Ann. Chim. (Paris) 57 88 (1806).
2. Nicolet, B. H., and L. A. Shinn, J. Biol. Chem. 139 687 (1941).
3. Mudd, S. H., Biochim. Biophys. Acta 38 354 (1960).
4. Weissbach, H., King, W., Sjoerdsma, A. and Udenfriend, S., J. Biol. Chem. 234 81 (1956).
5. Talley, E. A., Fitzpatrick, J. T. and Porter, W. L., J. Am. Chem. Soc.
   a. 78 5836 (1956).
   b. 81 174 (1959).
6. Steward, F. C. and Thompson, J. F., Nature, 169 739 (1952).
7. Sondheimer, E. and Holley, R. W., Nature, 173 773 (1954).
8. James, W. O., New Phytologist 48 172 (1949).
9. Wada, M., Biochem. Z. 224 420 (1930).
10a. Fowden, L., Biological Reviews 33 393 (1958);
   b. Fowden, L., Ann Rep. Chem. Soc. 56 359 (1959).
11. Burroughs, L. F., Nature 179, 360 (1957).
12. Hassall, C. H. and Reyle, K., Biochem. J. 60, 334 (1955).
13. Fowden, L., Ann. Bot. Lond. 18 417 (1954).
14. Synge, R. L. M. and Wood, J. C., Biochem. J. 60 xv (1955); 64 252 (1956).
15. Morris, C. J. O. R. and Thompson, J. F., J. Am. Chem. Soc. 78 1605 (1956).
16. Stoll, A. and Seebeck, E., Experientia 3 114 (1947).
17. Virtanen, A. I. and Matikkala, E. J., Acta Chem. Scand. 13 623 (1959).
18. du Vigneaud, V. and Patterson, W. I., J. Biol. Chem. 114 533 (1936).
19. Kitagawa, M. and Monobe, S., J. Biochem. (Japan) 18 333 (1933).
20a. Grobbelaar, N., Zacharius, R. H. and Steward, F. C., J. Am. Chem. Soc. 76 2912 (1954);
   b. Morrison, R. I. Biochem. J. 53 474 (1953).
21. Virtanen, A. I. and Ettala, T., Acta. Chem. Scand. 11 182 (1957).
22. Berg, A. M., Kari, S., Aldthan, M. and Virtanen, A. I., Acta Chem. Scand. 8 358 (1954).
23. Steward, F. C., Zacharius, R. M. and Pollard, J. K., Suomalaisen Tiedea kat Toimituksia series A 60 321 (1955).
24. Fowden, L., and Steward, F. C., Ann. Bot. Lond. 21 53 (1957).
25. Synge, R. L. M., Biochem. J. 49 642 (1951).
26. Law, D. H., Millar, J. T., Springall, N. D., and Birch, A. J., J. Chem. Soc. 1958 198.
27. Morris, C. J., and Thompson, J. F., Arch. Biochem. Biophys. 73 281 (1958).
28. Schilling, E. D., and Strong, F. M., J. Am. Chem. Soc. 77 2843 (1955).
29. Winterfeld, K. and Rink, M., Ann. Chem. 561 186 (1948).

30. Samuelsson, G., Svensk Farm. Tidskr. 62 169 (1958); ibid. 63 415 (1959).
31. Balls, A. K., and Harris, T. H., Cereal Chem. 21 74 (1944).
32. Rockwell, G. E., J. Immunol., 43 259 (1942).
33. Ryle, A. P., Sanger, F., Smith, L. F., and Kitai, R., Biochem. J. 60 541 (1955).
34. Hirs, C. H. W., Moore, S., and Stein, W. H., J. Biol. Chem. 235 648 (1960).
35. Tsugita, A., Gish, D. T., Young, J., Fraenkel-Conrat, H., Knight, C. A., Stanley, W. M., Proc. Natl. Acad. Sci., U. S. 46 1463 (1960).
36. Pauling, L., and Corey, R. B., Progress in the Chemistry of organic natural products, XI 180 (1954).
37. Scheraga, H. A., J. Am. Chem. Soc. 82 3847 (1960).
38. Kossel, A., and Gross, R. E., Z. Physiol. Chem. 135 167 (1924).
39. Kunin, R. Ion Exchange Resins, Second Edition, John Wiley and Sons, New York, 1958; O. Samuelson, Ion Exchangers in Analytical Chemistry, John Wiley and Sons, Inc. New York, 1953.
40. Zacharius, R. M., Thompson, J. F. and Steward, F. C., J. Am. Chem. Soc. 76 2908 (1954).
41. Grobbelaar, N., Zacharius, R. M., and Steward, F. C., J. Am. Chem. Soc. 76 2912 (1954).
42. Thompson, J. F., Pollard, J. K., and Steward, F. C., Plant Physiol. 28 401 (1953).
43. Moore, S. and Stein, W. H., Adv. in Protein Chem. 11 191 (1956). Spackman, D. H., Stein, W. H. and Moore, S. Anal. Chem. 30 1190 (1958).
44. Hirs, C. H. W., Moore, S., and Stein, W. H., J. Biol. Chem. 195 669 (1952).
45. Tuckerman, M. M., Anal. Chem. 30 231 (1958).
46. Wieland, T. and Fischer, E., Naturwissenschaften, 35 29 (1948).
47. Johnson, D. E., and Meister, A., Am. Chem. Soc., 138th meeting, Abstracts 59 C (1960).
48. Konigsberg, W. and Craig, L. C., J. Am. Chem. Soc., 81 3452 (1959).
49. Craig, L. C., Konigsberg, W., Stracher, A. and King, T. P., Symposium on Protein Structure: 104, A. Neuberger, Ed. John Wiley and Sons, Inc. New York, N. Y., 1958.
50. Fuerst, C. R., McCalla, A. G. and Colvin, J. R., Arch. Biochem. 49 207 (1954).
51. Svedberg, T. and Pedersen, K. O., The Ultracentrifuge, The Clarendon Press, Oxford, 1940.
52. Svensson, H., Adv. in Protein Chem. 4 251 (1948).
53. Coates, J. H. and Simmonds, D. H., Cereal Chem. 38 256 (1961).
54. Fahmy, A. R., Niederwieser, A., Pataki, G., and Brenner, M., Helv. Chim. Acta 44 2022 (1961).
55. Rothman, F. and Higa, A., Anal. Biochem. 3 173 (1962).
56. Miller, L. and Houghton, J. A., J. Biol. Chem. 159 373 (1945).
57. Peters, J. P. and Van Slyke, D. D., Quantitative Clinical Chemistry, Vol. II, Williams and Wilkins Co., Baltimore, (1932).
58. Sörensen, Biochem. Z. 7 45 (1907).
59. McCaldin, D. J., Chem. Rev. 60 39 (1960).
60. Moore, S. and Stein W. M., J. Biol. Chem. 176 367 (1948).
61. Sakaguchi, S., J. Biochem. (Japan) 5 25, 133 (1925).
62. Hanke, M., J. Biol. Chem. 66 475 (1926).
63. Folin, O. and Ciocalteu, V., J. Biol. Chem. 73 627 (1927).
64. Brand, E., Harris, M. M., Biloon, S., J. Biol. Chem. 86 315 (1930).
65. Holm, G. E. and Greenbank, G. R., J. Am. Chem. Soc. 45 1788 (1923).
66. Mazur, R. H., Ellis, B. W., and Cammarata, P. S., J. Biol. Chem. 237 1619 (1962).
67. Gies, W. J., J. Biol. Chem. 7, lx (1910).
68. Hall, C. E., J. Biol. Chem. 185 45 (1950).
69. Yocum, C. S., Ann. Rev. Plant Physiol. 11 25 (1960).
70. Bach, M. K., Biochim. Biophys. Acta 26 104 (1957).
71. Carnahan, J. E., Mortenson, L. E., Mower, H. F., and Castle, J. E., Biochim. et Biophys. Acta, 38 188 (1960); Wilson, P. W., and Burris, R. H., Science 131 1321 (1960).
72. Schneider, K. C., Bradbeer, C., Singh, R. N., Wang, L. C., Wilson, P. W., and Burris, R. H., Proc. Natl. Acad. Sci. U. S. 46 726 (1960).
73. Nason, A., Inorganic Nitrogen Metabolism, W. D. McElroy and H. B. Glass, eds., Johns Hopkins Press, 1956, p. 109.
74. Geddes, W. F., and Hunter, A., J. Biol. Chem. 77 197 (1928).
75. Vogel, H. J. and Davis, B. D., J. Am. Chem. Soc. 74 109 (1952).
76. Leete, E., Marion, L. and Spenser, I. D., J. Biol. Chem. 214 71 (1955).
77. Barnes, R. L. and Naylor, A. W., Botan. Gaz. 121 63 (1959).
78. Schales, O., and Schales, S. S., Arch. Biochem. 11 155 (1946).
79. Hauschild, A. H. W., Can. J. Biochem. and Physiol. 37 887 (1959); McConnell, W. B., and Bilinski, E. ibid. 37 549 (1959).
80. Neish, A. C., Ann. Rev. Plant Physiol. 11 55 (1960).
81. Srinivasan, P. R., J. Am. Chem. Soc. 81 1772 (1959).
82. Nirenberg, M. W., and Matthai, J. H., Proc. Natl. Acad. Sci. U. S. 47 1588 (1961).
83. Hoagland, M. B., Biochim. Biophys. Acta 16 288 (1955).
84. Clark, J. M., Jr. Studies on amino acid activation and protein synthesis. Thesis, Calif. Instit. Technology, 1958.
85. Holley, R. W., J. Am. Chem. Soc. 79 658 (1957).
86. Holley, R. W., Apgar, J. and Doctor, B. P., Annals of the N. Y. Acad. Sciences 88 Art. 3, 745 (1960).
87. Ts'o, P. O. P., Ann. Rev. Plant Physiol. 13 45 (1962).

Chapter 11
NUCLEIC ACIDS AND DERIVATIVES

Toward the end of the nineteenth century nucleic acid was established as the universal component of cell nuclei and recognized to be a complex high-molecular weight material which could be hydrolyzed to yield a sugar, several nitrogen bases, and inorganic phosphate. Later developments seemed to show that nucleic acid from animal cells was characterized by having D-2-deoxyribose as its sugar constituent, while plant nucleic acid had D-ribose. However, by the 1930's it became clear that plants and animals each have both types of nucleic acid but that the deoxyribonucleic acid is found only in the nucleus, and ribonucleic acid is predominantly in the cytoplasm. The earlier supposition resulted from the fact that the animal cells used had been ones with a prominent nucleus and little cytoplasm, while the reverse was true of the plant cells. It was early recognized that each type of nucleic acid contains four different nitrogen bases, two purines and two pyrimidines. The purines adenine and guanine and the pyrimidine cytosine are common to both types of nucleic acid whereas deoxyribonucleic acid (DNA) has thymine as its second pyridine base, and ribonucleic acid (RNA) has uracil. There have been reports of the occurrence of other nitrogen bases in nucleic acid from some sources. The structures will be discussed in more detail in a later section.

Partial hydrolysis of nucleic acids yields varied sized fragments known as polynucleotides if they contain several nitrogen bases combined with sugar and phosphate, mononucleotides if they have only one nitrogen base plus sugar and phosphate, or nucleosides when they have merely a nitrogen base bound to sugar by a glycosidic bond. Smaller molecules of these different types also occur as such in nature as well as being derived from breakdown of nucleic acid. Some nucleotides of great physiological importance contain nitrogen bases which are not found in the nucleic acids. They are nevertheless included in this chapter.

Very little of our present knowledge of nucleic acids and related compounds has been derived from observations on the higher plants. Animal tissues and microorganisms have been most frequently used as experimental material, and possibly some generalizations derived from them may not be applicable to higher plants. An attempt will be made to indicate which facts are certainly known for higher plants and which are derived from observations on other types of organisms.

FREE PURINES AND PYRIMIDINES

The parent substances purine and pyrimidine have the structures and ring numbering shown on the following page.

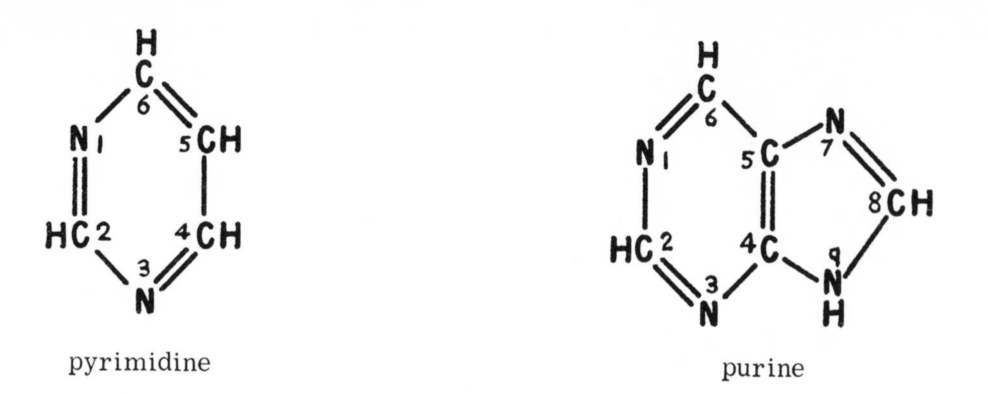

Neither of them occurs free in nature, although a nucleoside of purine (1) occurs in *Clitocybe nebularis*.

The two purines and the pyrimidine found in all nucleic acids are as follows:

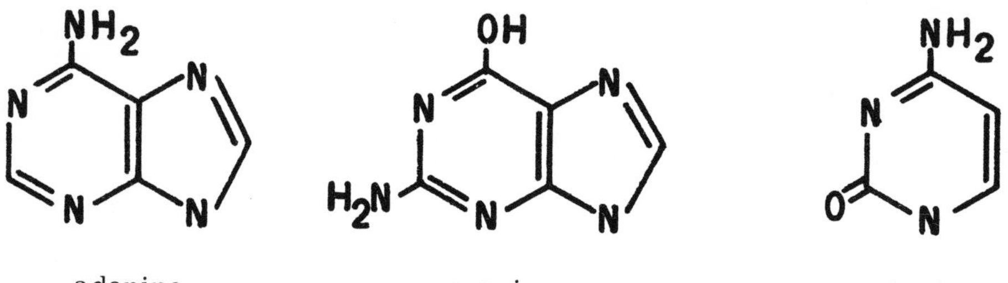

Thymine and uracil found respectively in deoxyribonucleic acid and ribonucleic acid are:

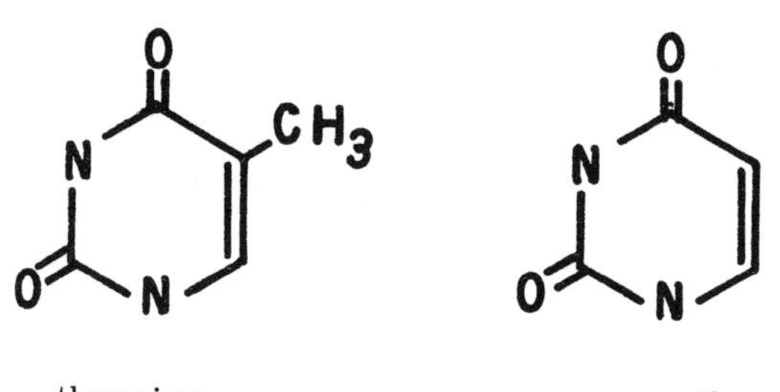

Although structures are shown with fixed double bonds, it should be recognized that in many cases their reactivities can be understood better if they are regarded as resonance hybrids. Tautomerization also may play an important role. Thus uracil may be represented by three different contributing structures:

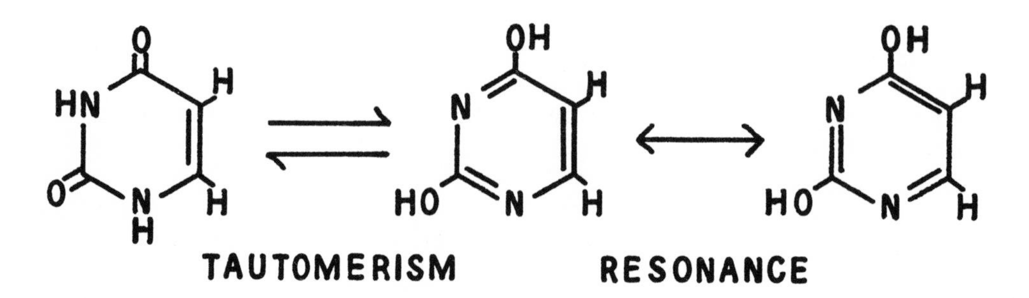

Deoxyribonucleic acid from wheat germ and the leaves of several plants has been reported to contain, in addition to the expected bases, 5-methylcytosine (2, 3).

Some of these free bases have been found in higher plants although they may be artifacts arising from decomposition of nucleic acid. Adenine is probably the most widespread, followed by guanine. Free thymine has been found in *Equisetum palustre* (4). Other purines and pyrimidines which are not components of nucleic acid have been found to occur free in some plants although they are certainly not widespread in the plant kingdom. As nitrogen-containing compounds they are often classed with the alkaloids, but biosynthetically they are presumably closely related to other purines and pyrimidines. Structures of some of these compounds are given in Table 1 with selected natural sources.

Although uric acid is usually regarded as an end product of purine metabolism in animals, it has been found in several different plants. In many animals uric acid is further broken down to allantoin and then allantoic acid. These two compounds are also rather widely distributed in plants. They seem to function as major nitrogen storage compounds in some trees (5). Although not purines, the structural relationship of these two to the purines is obvious, and tracer experiments have shown the conversion of adenine to allantoin, allantoic acid and urea in *Acer saccharinum* leaves (6).

allantoin allantoic acid

The free purines and pyrimidines are colorless, crystalline compounds. Many of them are only very slightly soluble in water but all are readily soluble in either dilute acid (e.g. guanine) or alkali (e.g. uric acid). They are generally rather insoluble in organic solvents. Their characteristic ultra-violet absorption spectra are discussed below under "Characterization." Long heating with acid or alkali (as in hydrolysis procedures) may cause some decomposition, but generally the purines and pyrimidines are sufficiently stable so that losses are small.

Little is known regarding the possible functions of the free purines and pyrimidines in plants. Some may serve as nitrogen storage compounds. Others show pronounced morphological effects when applied to plants artificially and may act in such ways under natural circimustances (7, 8).

NUCLEOSIDES

The nucleosides have a sugar molecule bound by a β-glycosidic bond to position-3 of the pyrimidines or position-9 of the purines. Deoxyribonucleosides occur only as breakdown products of DNA or of nucleotides, but a few ribonucleosides apparently occur as such in plants --- e.g. adenosine and guanosine (vernine). Some of the nitrogen bases found in specific nucleosides are never found as components of any other compound. The vitamin, riboflavin, is usually included with the nucleosides although, strictly speaking, it contains a ribityl moiety related to D-ribitol rather than a ribosyl moiety derived from D-ribose. Structures and occurrence of some of the natural free nucleosides are given in the following pages. A review on the chemistry and natural occurrence of pyrimidine nucleosides has recently appeared (9).

TABLE 1. SOME NATURALLY OCCURRING PURINES

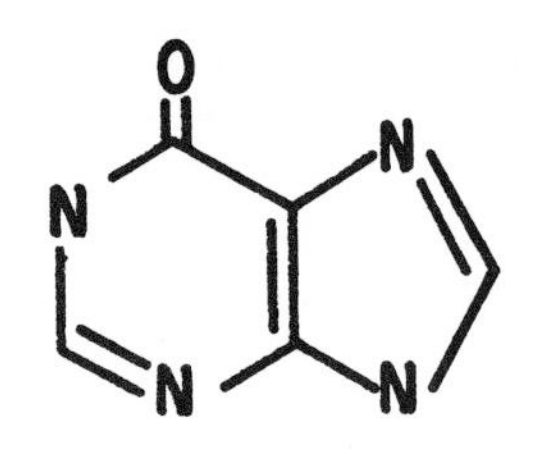

hypoxanthine *(Lupinus luteus)*

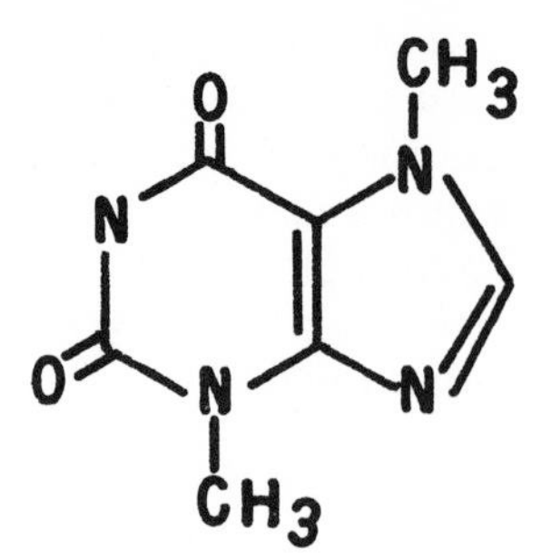

theobromine *(Theobroma cacao)*

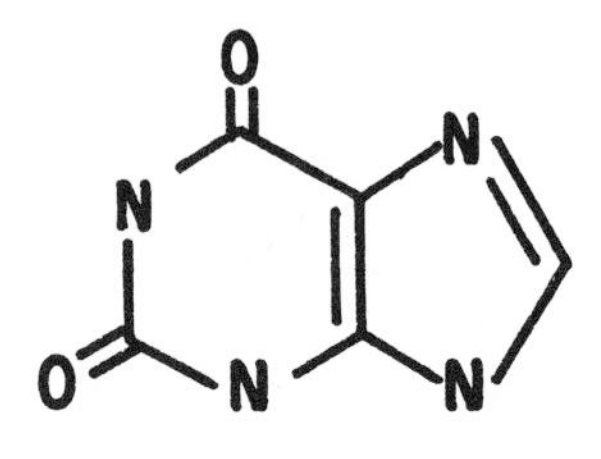

xanthine (*Coffea* spp.)

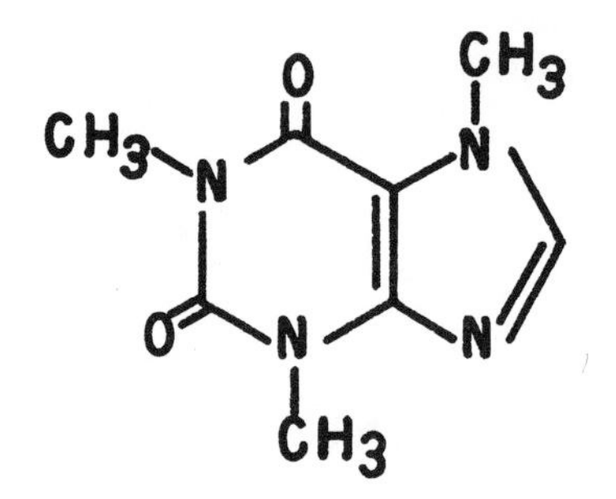

caffeine (*Coffea* spp.)

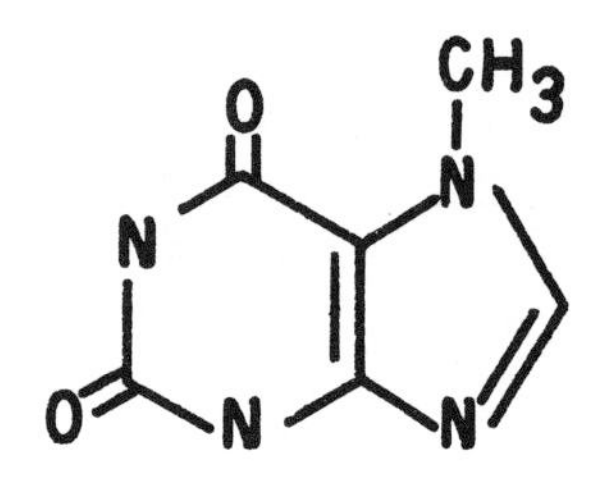

heteroxanthin *(Beta vulgaris)*

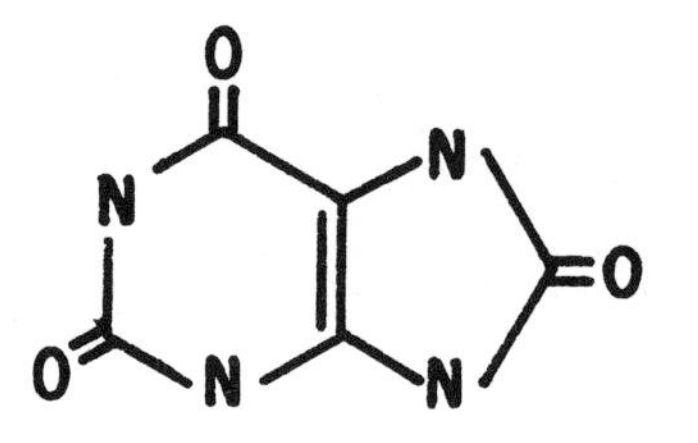

uric acid *(Melilotus officinalis)*

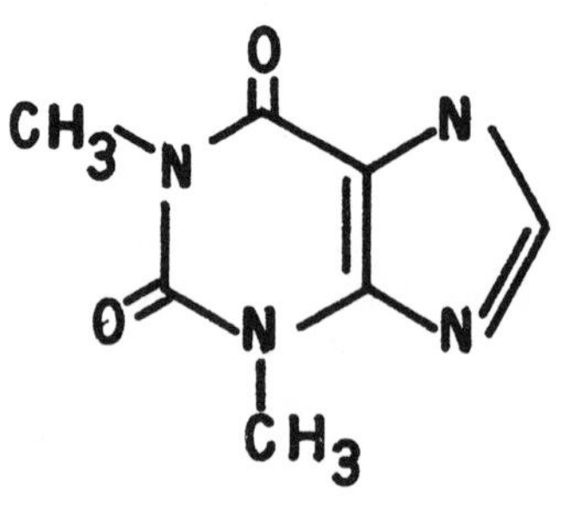

theophylline *(Camellia sinensis)*

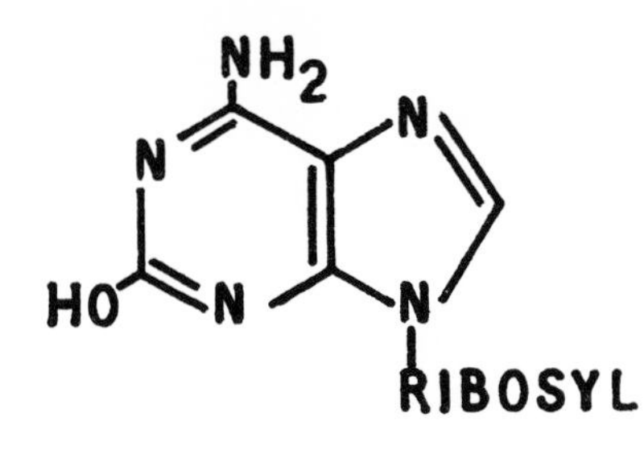

crotonoside, riboside of isoguanine *(Croton tiglium)*

guanosine *(Coffea arabica)*

riboflavin

Two unusual pyrimidine glucosides occur in vetch (*Vicia* spp.), peas, and beets. They are not nucleosides since the glucosyl group is linked through oxygen rather than nitrogen. However, in chemical properties they bear a resemblance to the true nucleosides. Structures are given below:

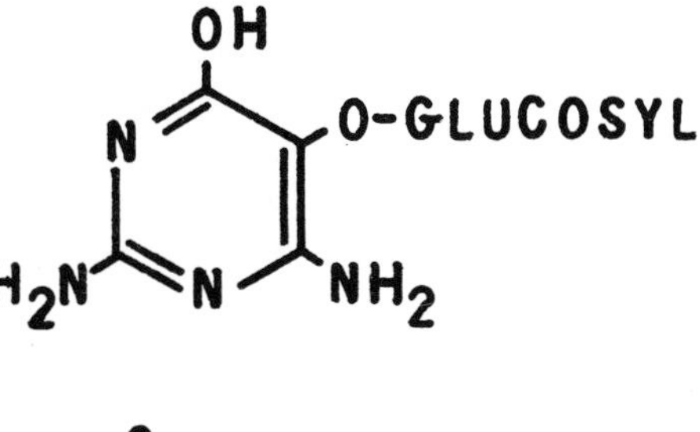

vicin, glucoside of divicin

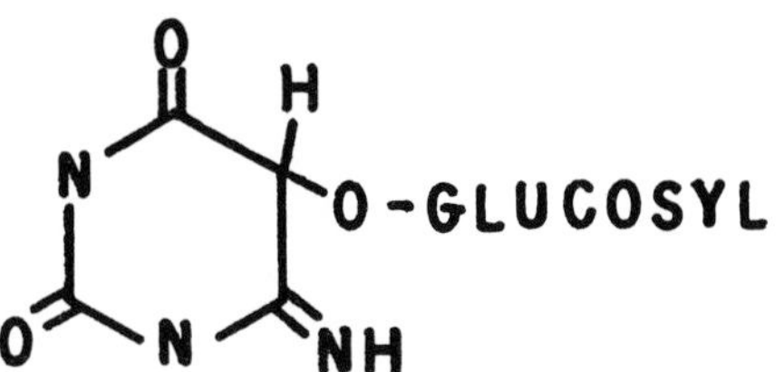

convicin, glucoside of 4-imidodialuric acid

The nucleosides are colorless, crystalline compounds, generally more soluble in water than are the free nitrogen bases. Pyrimidine nucleosides are more soluble in water than purine nucleosides. Purine nucleosides are readily hydrolyzed to base and sugar by boiling with dilute acid, while pyrimidine nucleosides are considerably more resistant to hydrolysis so that autoclaving with strong acid is required, and some decomposition may occur (e.g. deamination of cytosine to form uracil).

NUCLEOTIDES

The nucleotides, aside from their function as components of nucleic acid, constitute one of the most physiologically interesting groups of natural products. Many of the important coenzymes for dehydrogenation and group transfer reactions are nucleotides. The mononucleotides have one or more phosphoric acid groups esterified to the sugar portion of a nucleoside. The dinucleotides may be regarded as having two nucleoside units joined through a pyrophosphate bridge which esterfies their sugar units. Additional phosphate groups may also be present. Nucleotides containing adenine appear to be the most common in nature. Three different monophosphates of adenosine are known, depending on which hydroxyl group of the ribose is esterfied. Muscle adenylic acid is the 5'-phosphate, while 2' and 3' phosphates have been isolated from hydrolyzed nucleic acid of both fungi and higher plants. These last two compounds have not been reported to occur in a free form in higher plants. Mono-, di-, and triphosphates of adenosine, guanosine, cytidine, and uridine have all been found in young *Vicia faba* plants (10).

By far the most important adenine mononucleotide is adenosine-5'-triphosphate (ATP):

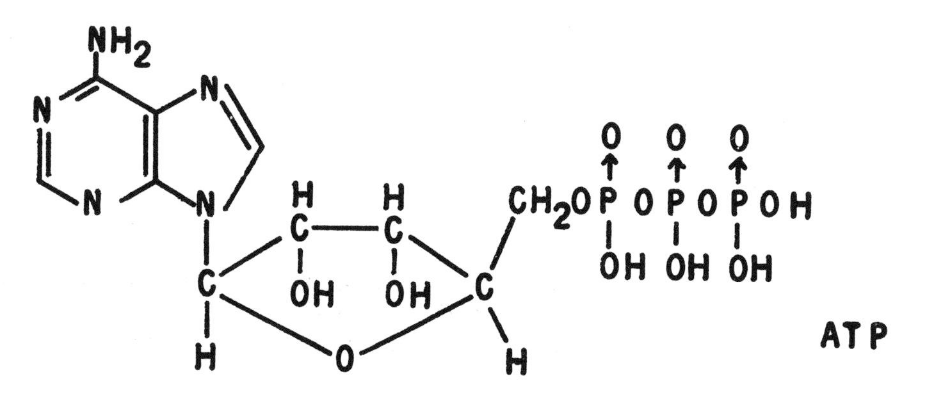

It has been isolated from animals, fungi and higher plants where it serves as a coenzyme for many phosphokinases and may be regarded as an energy storage compound since hydrolysis of the third phosphate group releases energy which can be used to drive endergonic reactions. The role of ATP in activating amino acids for protein synthesis and activating methionine for transmethylation is discussed in Chapter 9. Adenosine-5'-nucleotides are also found as subunits of some other important coenzymes.

Diphosphopyridine nucleotide (DPN) or nicotinamide adenine dinucleotide (NAD), triphosphopyridine nucleotide (TPN) or nicotinamide adenine dinucleotide phosphate (NADP), riboflavin phosphate (flavin mononucleotide, FMN), and flavin-adenine dinucleotide (FAD) serve as hydrogen carriers in oxidation-reduction reactions. Their complete structures are given in Table 2. In the first two coenzymes the pyridine ring is involved in the reversible reduction, and in the flavine coenzymes the isoalloxazine ring functions, as follows:

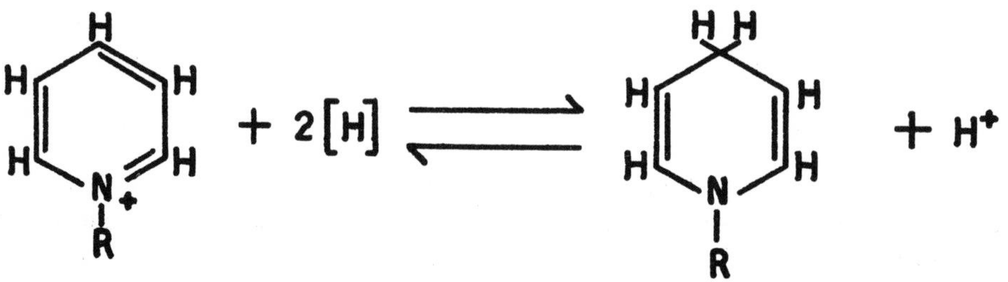

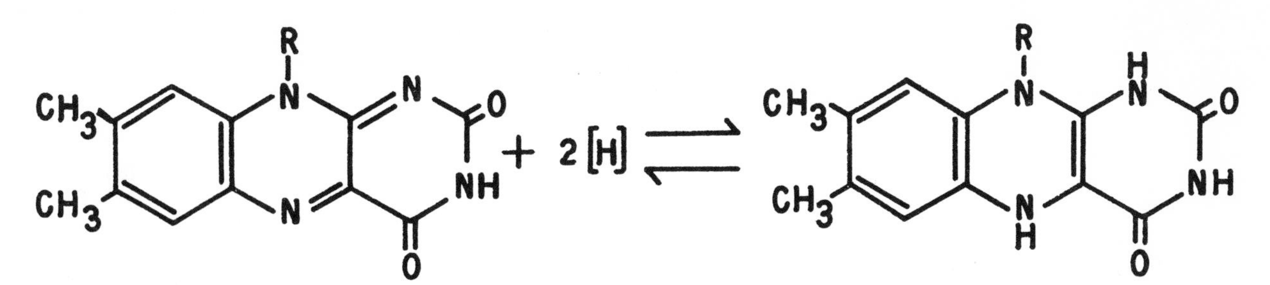

Most plant tissues have a higher concentration of TPN than of DPN---the reverse of the situation in animal tissues. Very little free riboflavin is extractable from tissues. It is largely in the coenzyme form, and this is rather tightly bound to proteins known as flavoproteins.

The functioning of uridine triphosphate (UTP) as a coenzyme for transfer of glycosyl groups is discussed in Chapter 2. The functioning of coenzyme A in transfer of acyl groups is discussed in Chapters 3, 5, 6 and 7. The complete structures of these two nucleotides are given below. Neither one has been isolated in high purity from higher plants, but there is ample evidence for their occurrence, and partially purified preparations have been obtained. The pantothenic acid portion of coenzyme A is discussed separately in Chapter 10.

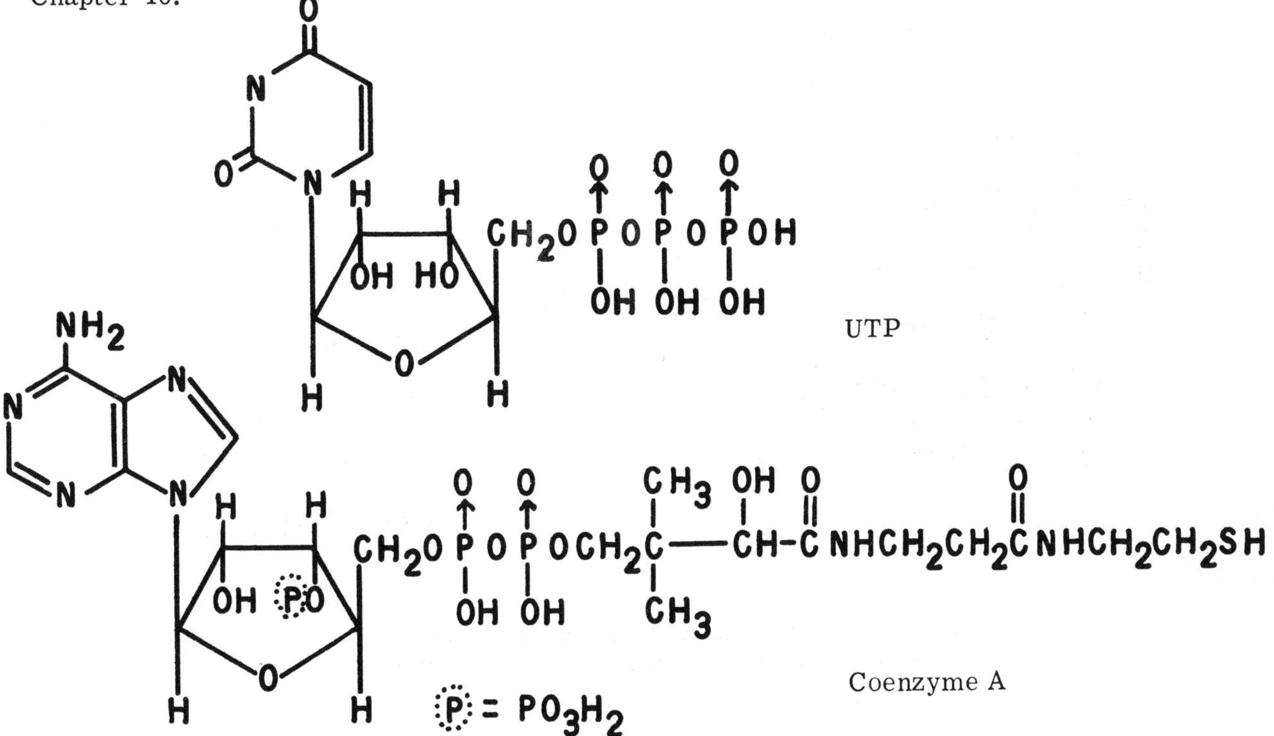

Cytidine-5' diphosphate-choline has been isolated from yeast (11) where it acts as a coenzyme to transfer choline for the synthesis of phosphatides (cf. Chapter 5). It has not, so far, been isolated from higher plants.

The nucleotides resemble the nucleosides in many of their properties but are distinguished by being strong acids. Pyrophosphate bonds found in several of the nucleotides are readily cleaved by boiling with dilute acid. Thus two moles of orthophosphate are released from ATP. The monophosphates are much more resistant to acid hydrolysis.

TABLE 2. NUCLEOTIDE STRUCTURES

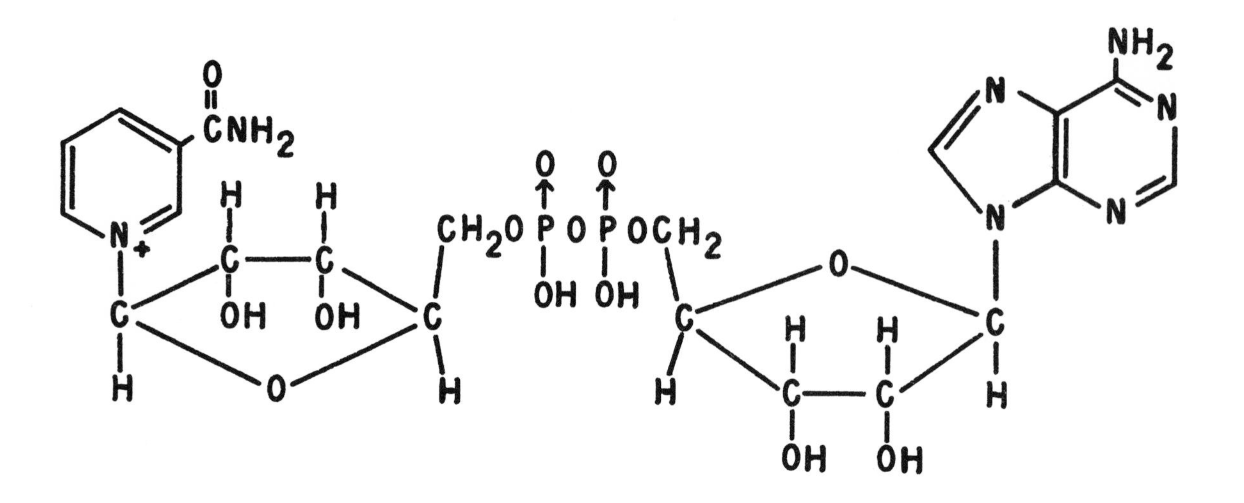

diphosphopyridine nucleotide, nicotinamide adenine dinucleotide

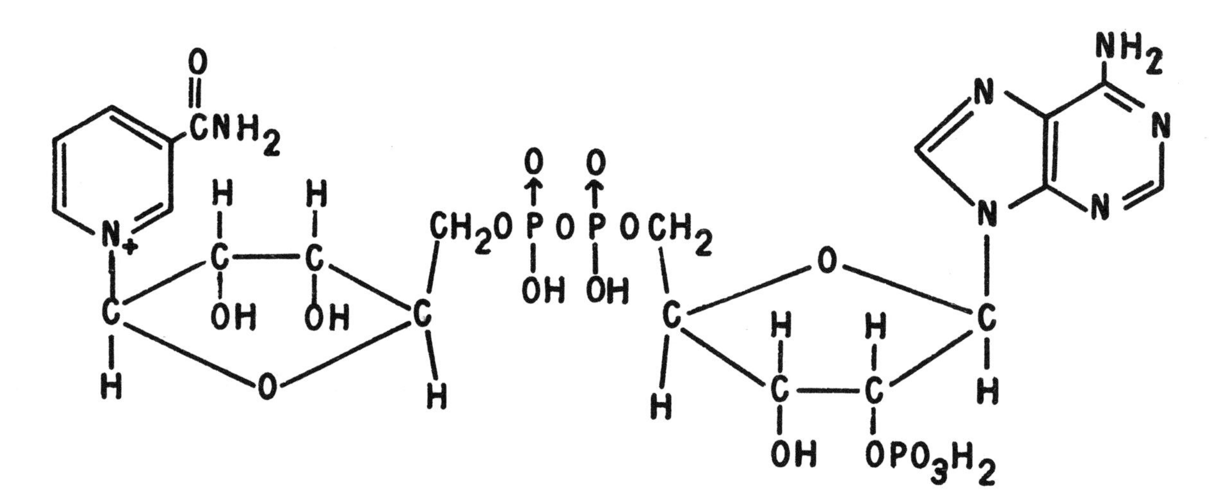

triphosphopyridine nucleotide,
nicotinamide adenine dinucleotide phosphate

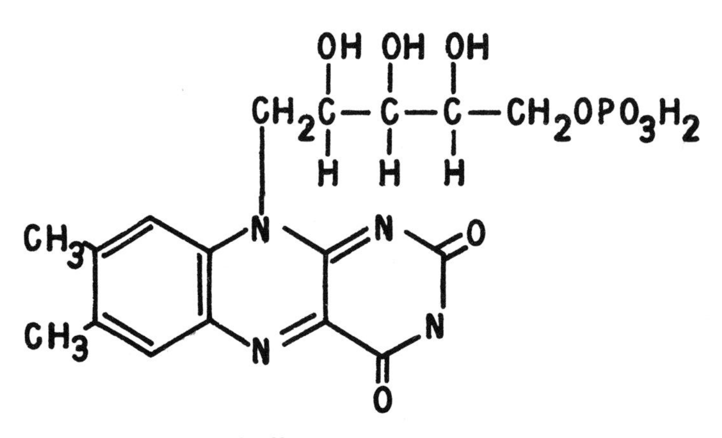

riboflavin phosphate

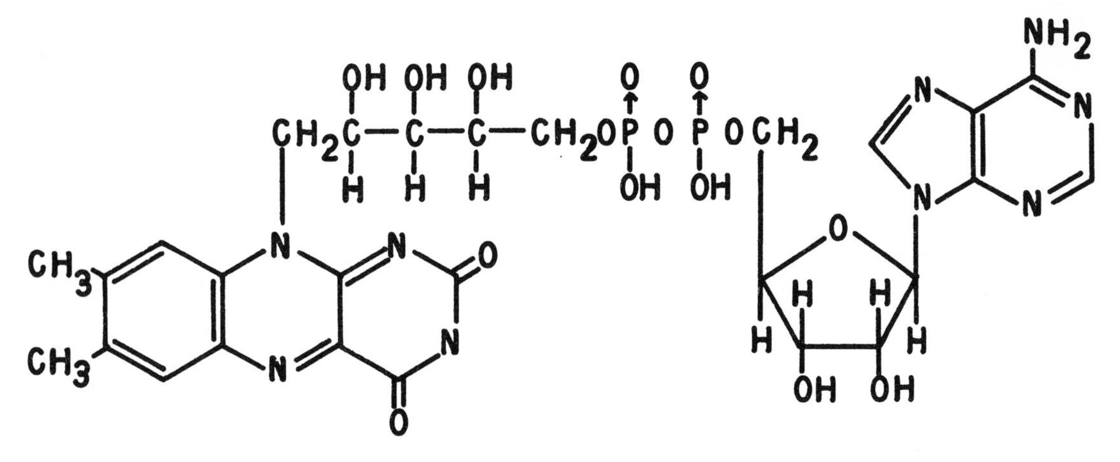

flavine adenine dinucleotide

A review of naturally occurring nucleotides has been prepared by Henderson and Le Page (12).

NUCLEIC ACIDS AND POLYNUCLEOTIDES

Both deoxyribonucleic acid and ribonucleic acid are high molecular weight polymers, each containing four different nitrogen bases, phosphate, and respectively deoxyribose or ribose. The generalized structure of both of them may be represented as follows:

```
                 |
base   -   sugar   -   phosphate
                            |
              base   -   sugar   -   phosphate
                                         |
                          base   -   sugar   -   phosphate
                                                     |
```

Phosphate is present as a diester between C-3' of one nucleotide and C-5' of the next. The detailed structure for a segment containing adenine and cytosine would be:

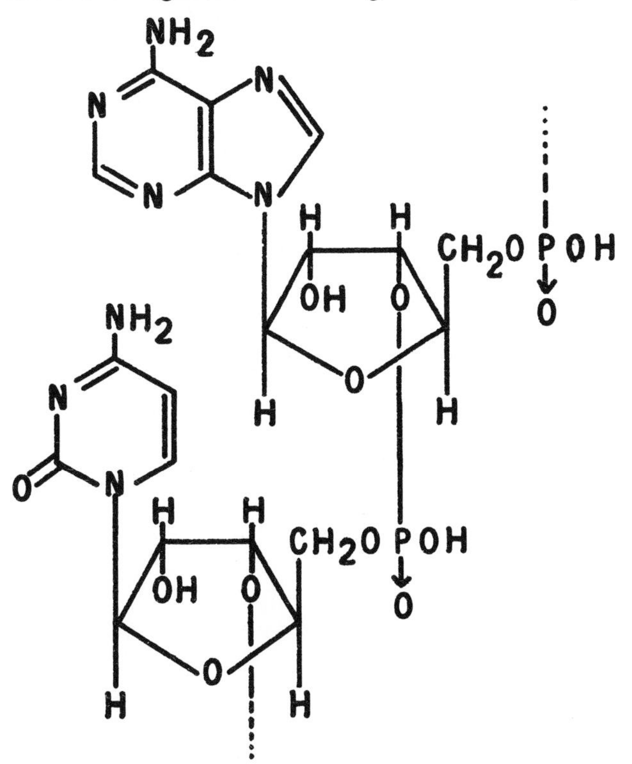

Deoxyribonucleic acid (DNA) contains the bases adenine, guanine, cytosine and thymine. Some plant DNA has been found to contain, in addition, 5-methylcytosine. Contrary to earlier ideas of structure there is no indication of a regular sequence of bases. However to call the sequence random would be equally erroneous since the heredity of an organism apparently depends on the specific sequence of bases present in its DNA. Further discussion of this genetic coding is beyond the scope of the present work. DNA prepared from various sources has been found to have molecular weights ranging from somewhat less than a million to several million. There is no reason to believe that all the DNA even in a single nucleus is homogeneous, and a wide range of molecular weights may be present. The accepted macromolecular structure of DNA based on the original proposal of Watson and Crick (13) represents it as a two stranded helix with each strand consisting of a chain of polynucleotides and the strands bound together by hydrogen bonds. Adenine of one chain is always paired with thymine of the other, and guanine with cytosine. The hydrogen bonding of the latter pair may be represented as:

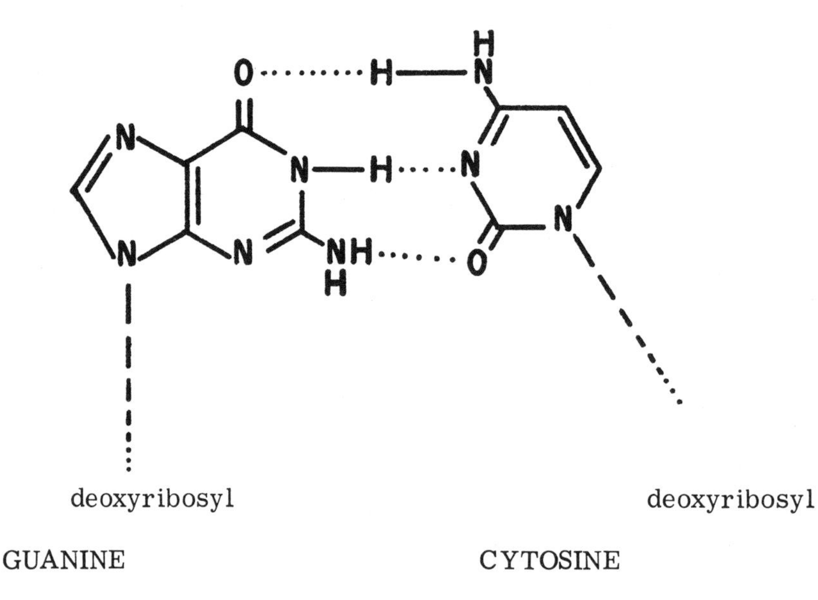

The geometry of the helix allows for the presence of a third strand and it is possible that in the cell protein occupies this position. Both DNA and RNA can be readily isolated as a combination with protein, but the biological significance of these nucleoproteins is not clear. Non-specific binding between the acidic nucleic acids and basic proteins readily occurs so that the protein present in a nucleoprotein preparation may not be the same protein originally combined with the nucleic acid in the cell. As would be predicted for a long-chain, polar polymer, DNA forms very viscous solutions in water.

Ribonucleic acid in addition to having ribose rather than deoxyribose and uracil rather than thymine differs in some other properties from DNA. It generally is found to have a somewhat lower molecular weight, ranging around one hundred thousand. There has also been some suggestion that branched chain structures may be present but no certain evidence of this. There is also no evidence bearing on the macromolecular geometry of RNA. Ribonucleic acid is apparently synthesized in the nucleus and then transferred to the cytoplasm where it becomes part of the endoplasmic reticulum or microsome fraction of the cell. Its primary function seems to be concerned with the assembly of amino acids into specific proteins, and a brief discussion of this function will be found in Chapter 10. There is also some evidence that nucleic acids may function as flowering hormones (14).

ISOLATION

Both ribonucleic acid and deoxyribonucleic acid have been prepared from higher plants. However, the latter is present in very low concentration in most plant tissues, and successful isolations generally require as starting material a tissue in which nuclei make up a large proportion of the cells. Wheat germ has been used for this purpose. Many plant tissues contain reasonable amounts of RNA (e.g. 0.01% per weight of leaves), and it may be prepared fairly readily.

Thorough homogenization of the tissue is the first essential for extraction of either type of nucleic acid. Older methods of preparing nucleic acid depended on extraction with alkali but yielded a product which had suffered some degradation. Current methods use extraction with neutral salt solutions and undoubtedly yield a less degraded product, but in the absence of any absolute standard it cannot be claimed that the isolated nucleic acid is obtained in its unchanged, native state. Isolation of nucleoprotein is even more open to question. Products can readily be prepared which contain nucleic acid more or less bound to protein, but in the absence of any standards they may be regarded as anything from the intact nucleoprotein as it exists in the cell to nucleic acid contaminated with extraneous protein.

The four types of non-dialyzable, water-soluble substances likely to be encountered in tissue extracts are polysaccharides, proteins, ribonucleic acids, and deoxyribonucleic acid. The rationale for separating the nucleic acids is generally based on denaturing and coagulating proteins by high speed homogenization in the presence of chloroform-octyl alcohol (8:1). Nucleic acids may then be freed of polysaccharides by making the solution weakly acidic to precipitate the nucleic acid or basic to dissolve the nucleic acid and leave polysaccharides as an insoluble residue. Dialysis removes any small molecules.

DNA is separated from RNA by the choice of original extraction medium. DNA is more tightly bound to cell structure than is RNA. The latter is solubilized by homogenization with dilute (e.g. 0.1 M NaCl). After removal of this supernatant solution, DNA may be extracted with 1-3 M NaCl and re-precipitated by diluting to 0.1 M NaCl. The chief drawback to this extraction procedure is the presence of enzymes which may degrade the nucleic acids. Enzymes may be inactivated by first dropping the tissue into boiling ethanol, which does not dissolve nucleic acid. Tissues containing much lipid or fat-soluble pigment should also be defatted before extraction. The references (15-18) may be consulted for additional details of procedure. It must always be kept in mind that techniques developed for animal tissues may have to be modified for use with plants.

Isolation of nucleotides from plants has been greatly aided by ion exchange chromatography. Initial extraction of the tissue is usually carried out with 10% trichloracetic or perchloric acid so that proteins and nucleic acids are left with the residue. Further steps often depend on precipitating phosphates as barium salts. Careful control of pH is important at this stage since barium salts of nucleotides tend to be more soluble than the barium salt of phytic acid, a common constituent of seedlings. Thus at pH 4 barium phytate is insoluble and the barium salt of ATP remains in solution (19). Further separation and purification of the various nucleotides is most conveniently performed by chromatography over anion exchange resin such as Dowex 1. Chromatography on charcoal columns may also be useful and is commonly used for purification of DPN (NAD) and TPN (NADP) (20).

Nucleosides and free nitrogen bases are also extracted with dilute acid from plant tissues. It is hard to make any generalizations concerning methods of purifying them. A few techniques can be mentioned, but there are rather wide differences in solubility and reactivity so that the general references should be consulted for details. The free bases and their nucleosides are often precipitated as complex mercury salts and then regenerated by removing mercury with hydrogen sulfide. Ion exchange chromatography may be carried out using either anion or cation exchangers since at very high pH values most of the bases act as weak anions. The methylated xanthines which occur in such commercially important plants as coffee and cocoa may be extracted with such organic solvents as ethanol, chloroform or trichloroethylene and chromatographed on silicic acid columns (21). Tannins, which tend to complex with them, may be removed by adsorption on magnesium oxide. Since some of these compounds may be classified as alkaloids, methods discussed in Chapter 12 may be consulted.

CHARACTERIZATION

The discussion of characterization for most plant constituents has been directed toward deciding whether or not they are present in a given tissue. No such question arises for the nucleic acids. It is a foregone conclusion that they are present, and the analytical problem may involve quantitative measurement or the determination of their composition in terms of the constituent nitrogen bases. Several methods have been developed for analysis of the nucleic acids, and probably no one of them is completely satisfactory for plant tissues. In addition to the general references, reviews on the chemical determination (15, 22, 23) and microbiological assay (24) of nucleic acid have appeared. Kern (25) has discussed the problems peculiar to determining the nucleic acids of green leaves. All methods depend on at least a preliminary purification as described under "Isolation." The next step requires separation of the two types of nucleic acid or else a way of determining pentose and deoxypentose in the presence of each other. A proper discussion of these quantitative procedures cannot be given here. They may be found in the general references and (18).

For determination of the bases present in a nucleic acid sample acid hydrolysis followed by paper chromatography is quite satisfactory. If it is desired to separate larger quantities of the bases for additional characterization ion exchange chromatography may be applied to the hydrolysate. RNA is hydrolyzed with normal hydrochloric acid for one hour at 100° C. This yields free purines (adenine and guanine), but the pyrimidine-sugar bond is more resistant so that cytidylic and uridylic acids are formed rather than the free bases. DNA is hydrolyzed with 72% perchloric acid at 100° for 2 hours and yields free bases for both purines and pyrimidines.

For characterization of the mixture of hydrolysis products from nucleic acid by paper chromatography a spot of acidic hydrolysis mixture is applied directly to paper and run in a solvent composed af 170 ml. *iso*-propyl alcohol, 41 ml. concentrated hydrochloric acid, and water to make 250 ml. (26). After drying the paper, spots may be detected by the fact that they absorb ultra-violet light and therefore appear as dark spots against background fluorescence when a U. V. lamp (250-265 mμ) is held behind the paper. Guanine fluoresces in ultra-violet if the paper is strongly acidic. Other nitrogen bases do not. Photographic methods have been developed to provide a permanent record (27). Spray reagents have also been developed with varying specificities. The method of Wade and Morgan (28) detects phosphate esters (i. e. nucleotides). It is described in Chapter 2. Wood's method (29) detects most purines and cytosine but not uracil, thymine or cytidylic acid. A method specific for adenine derivatives has been described by Gerlack and Döring (30). Paper chromatography and ion exchange chromatography of oligonucleotides are reviewed by Cramer (31).

Thin layer chromatography on cellulose powder with a plaster of Paris binder is claimed (32) to offer many advantages over paper chromatography for separation of nucleotides, nucleosides, purines, and pyrimidines. The method is much faster than chromatography on paper, and better resolution is attained.

Identification of free bases, nucleosides or nucleotides in plant extracts is basically the same problem as identifying them in nucleic acid hydrolysates. Some preliminary purification is probably necessary before applying unknowns to paper. Precipitation or ion exchange methods as described under "Isolation" can be used for this purpose. The reader is referred to papers of Rowan (33, 34) and Cherry and Hageman (35) for methods suitable for detection of free nucleotides in plant extracts.

Detailed characterization of many nucleic acid derivatives has rested heavily on the action of specific enzymes on purified materials. Thus an enzyme has been prepared from germinating barley (*Hordeum* spp.) or rye grass (*Lolium* spp.) which specifically hydrolyzes nucleotide 3'-phosphates (36). Application of this and other enzymes to structure determinations may be found in the general references.

Absorption spectra are also useful for identification of purified compounds. All purine and pyrimidine derivatives show strong absorption at about 260 mμ, but shifts in absorption occur with changes in pH. These shifts are characteristic for specific purines and pyrimidines since they depend on the ionizable groups present. In many cases enough material can be extracted from a paper chromatogram to permit its identification by measuring spectra at different pH values. Further discussion and presentation of spectra may be found in the general references as well as references (37, 38). DPN (NAD), TPN (NADP) and riboflavine derivatives have spectral properties useful in characterizing them. The first two have identical spectra with a peak at about 260 mμ; but more important is the appearance of a peak at 340 mμ upon reduction with sodium dithionite or with appropriate enzymes and substrates. Riboflavine derivatives show a strong yellow-green fluorescence when illuminated with light of about 445 mμ.

Qualitative and quantitative analysis for the nucleotides which function as cofactors in enzyme systems may be carried out by setting up the enzyme system without the required cofactor, adding unknown material, and measuring enzyme activity.

METABOLIC PATHWAYS

The biosynthetic pathways leading to formation of nucleic acid derivatives have been well clarified in bacteria and avian liver. In contrast, very few studies have been made concerning metabolic pathways of these compounds in higher plants. The sequences shown in Figure 1, therefore, may be considered as probable but not confirmed for higher plants. Reviews of this area are regularly presented in The Annual Review of Biochemistry (e.g., 39).

In addition to compounds directly related to the nucleic acids, compounds of similar structure have been considered in this chapter since they are probably synthesized along somewhat similar pathways. Riboflavin, for instance, at least in the microorganism *Eremothecium ashbyii,* seems to be synthesized from various purines (40). Guanine is the best precursor. Tracer studies of Krupka and Towers (41) have shown glycine to be a good precursor of allantoin in wheat as would be expected if the indicated scheme of purine synthesis were followed. The methyl groups of thymine and the methylated xanthines has received some attention and probably fit into the usual scheme of biological methylations involving formate and methionine. The synthesis of caffeine in *Coffea arabica* has been indicated by tracer experiments to follow the normal purine pathways with methyl groups coming from methionine (42).

The most important generalization which has emerged from studies of the sequence is that transformations of the nitrogen bases are always carried out not on the free bases but on nucleotide derivatives. In chicken embryos it is likely that ribonucleotides are

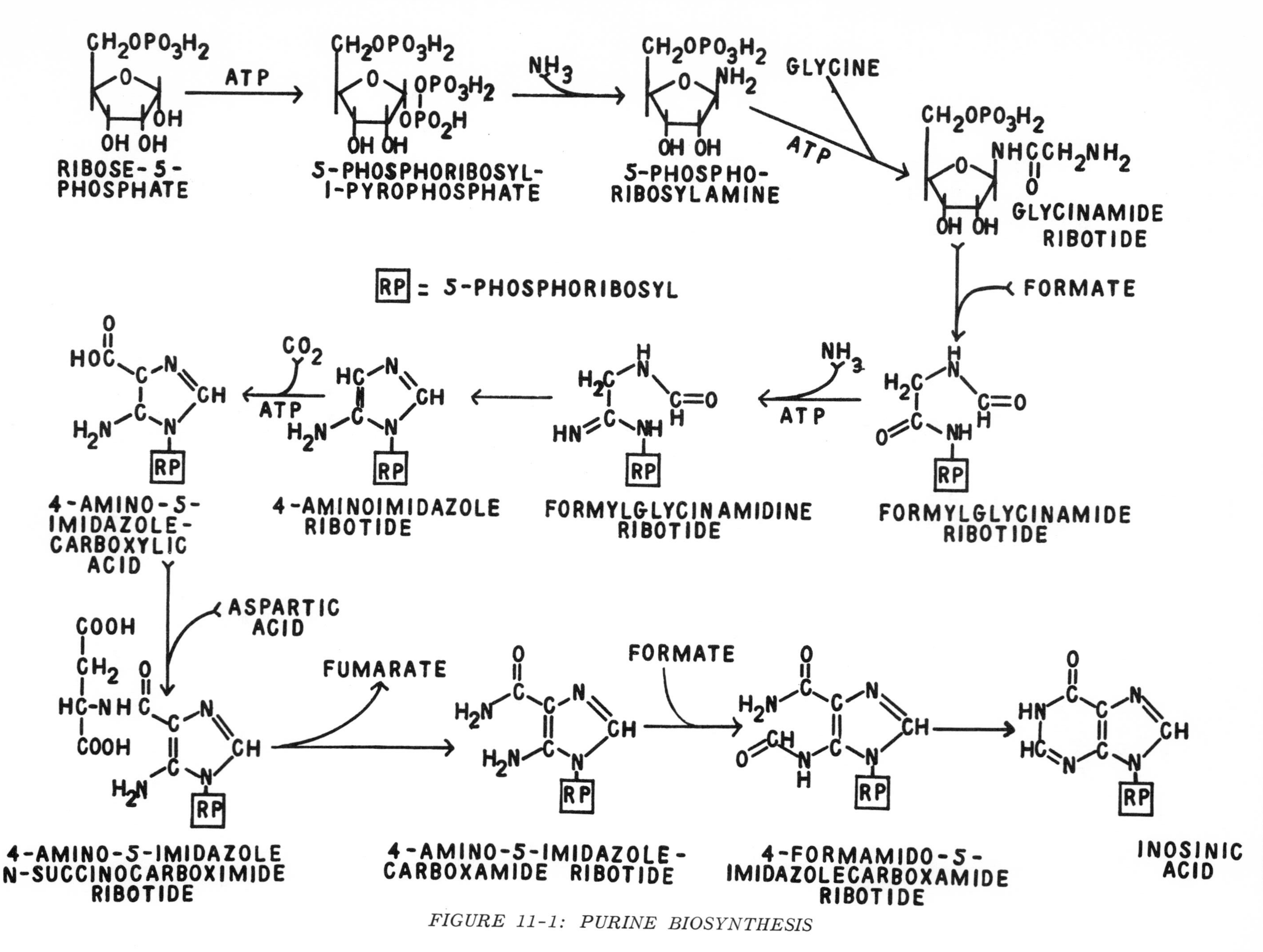

FIGURE 11-1: PURINE BIOSYNTHESIS

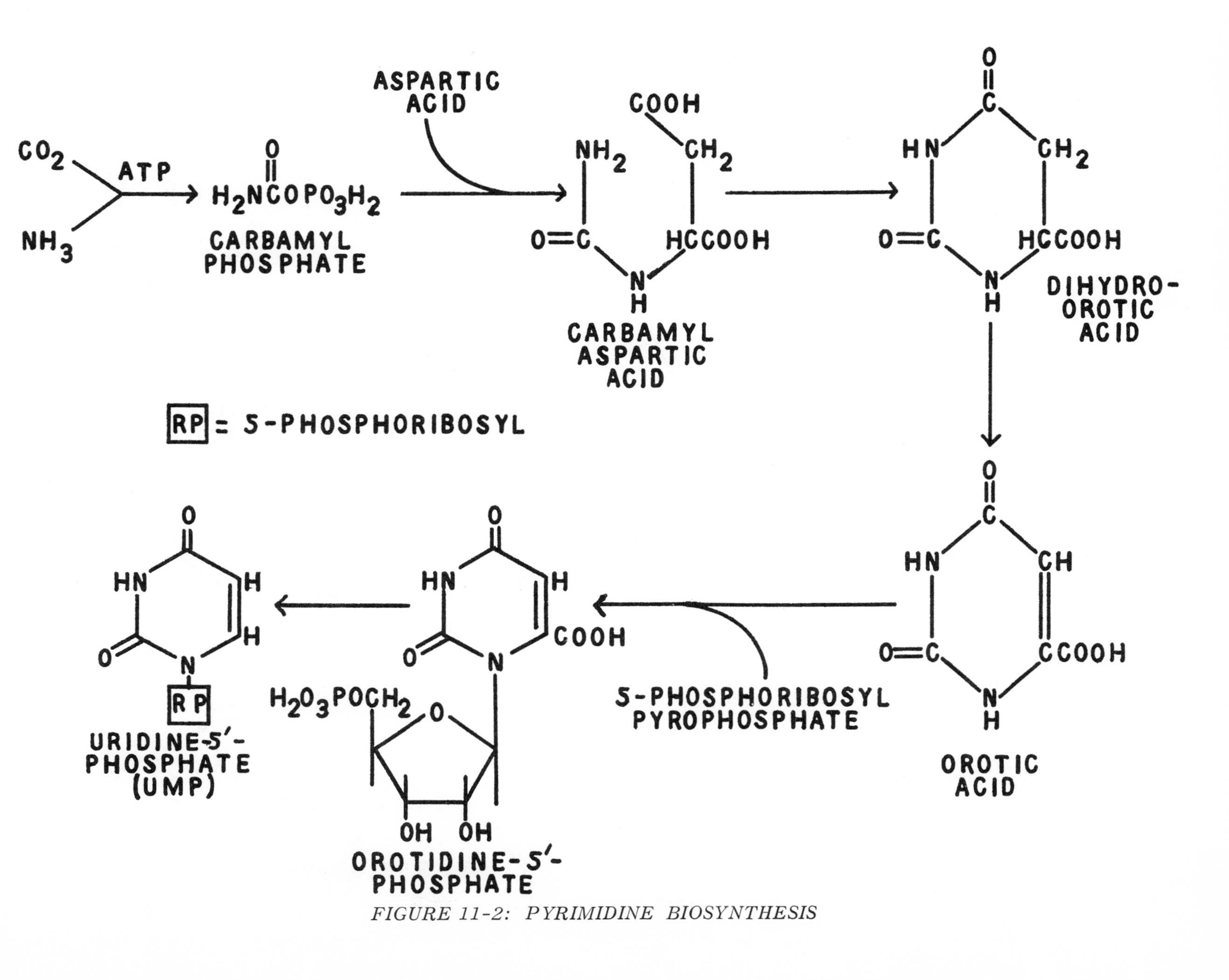

FIGURE 11-2: PYRIMIDINE BIOSYNTHESIS

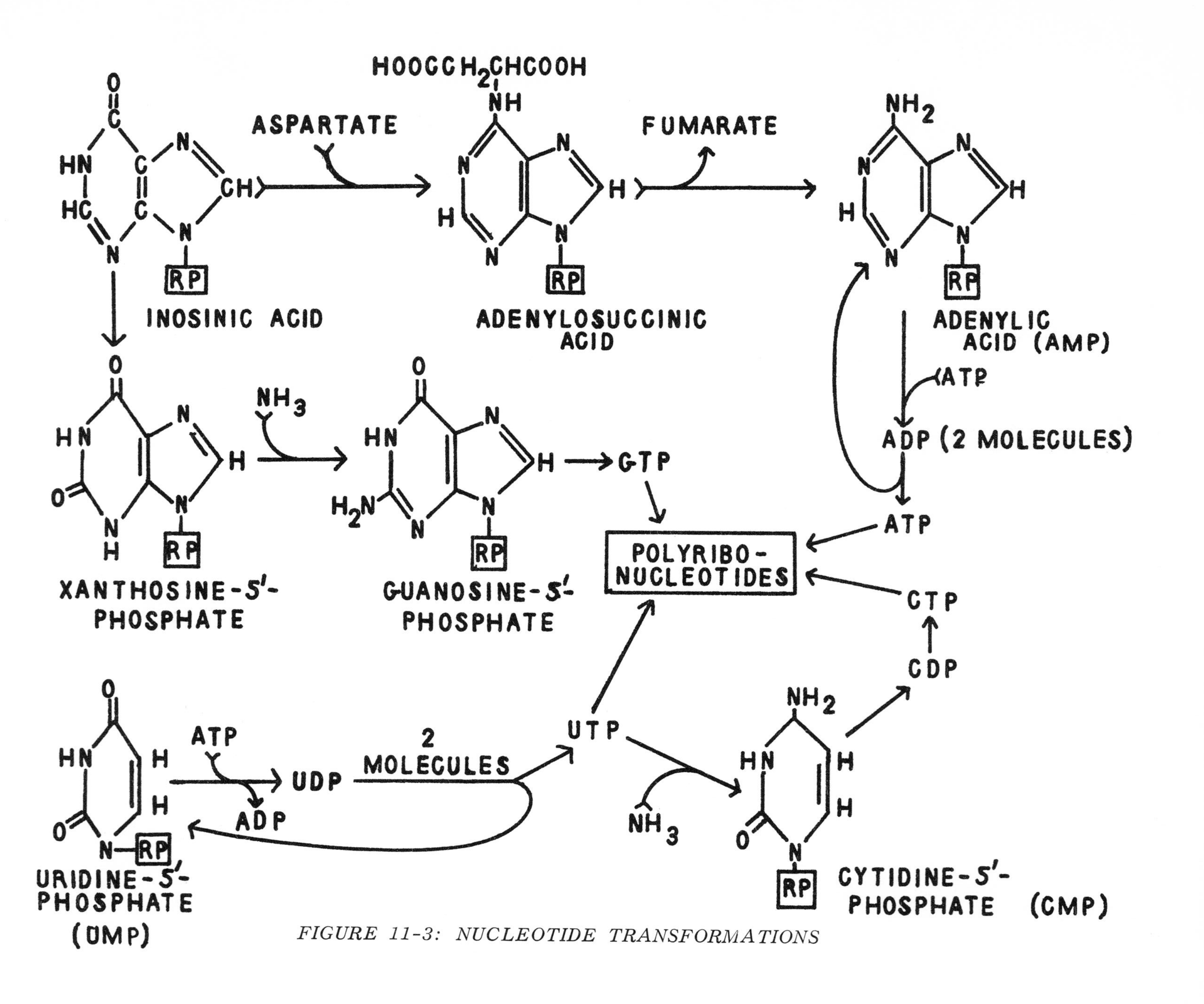

FIGURE 11-3: NUCLEOTIDE TRANSFORMATIONS

first synthesized and then converted to deoxyribonucleotides before incorporation into DNA (43). Little additional evidence is available on this point, and none specifically for the higher plants. An alternative formation of deoxyribose by aldol condensation has been suggested and is incorporated into the metabolic maps of Chapter 2. Where CO_2, NH_3, and formate are shown in the diagram as reactants, it is probable that they actually participate as derivatives. These may be, respectively, carboxylated biotin, glutamine, and N^{10}-formyltetrahydrofolic acid.

The nucleic acids are formed by condensation of nucleotides. DNA is synthesized from nucleotide triphosphates by an enzyme obtained from *Escherichia coli.* The other product is inorganic pyrophosphate, and a small amount of DNA "primer" must be present to initiate the reaction. The formation of RNA by an enzyme present in both fungi and higher plants apparently follows a course similar to that of DNA synthesis except that nucleoside -5' diphosphates are used rather than triphosphates. This enzyme is named polynucleotide phosphorylase and catalyzes the reversible reaction:

nucleoside-5' diphosphate ⇌ ribonucleic acid + orthophosphate

GENERAL REFERENCES

Böttger, I. "Stoffwechsel der Purine und Pyrimidine" in Ruhland 8 763.
Böttger, I. "Stoffwechsel der Nucleinsäuren" in Ruhland 8 814.
Chargaff, E. and Davidson, J. N. eds., The Nucleic Acids 3 vols., Academic Press, N. Y. 1955, 1960.
Davidson, J. N., The Biochemistry of the Nucleic Acids 4th ed. John Wiley and Sons, N. Y., 1960.
Jordan, D. O., The Chemistry of Nucleic Acids, Butterworth's, London, 1960.
Markham, R. "Nucleic Acids, Their Components, and Related Compounds" in Paech and Tracey 4 246.

BIBLIOGRAPHY

1. Löfgren, N. and Lüning, B., Acta Chem. Scand. 7 15 (1953).
2. Thomas, A. J. and Sherratt, H. S. A., Biochem. J. 62 1 (1956).
3. Brawerman, G. and Chargaff, E., J. Am. Chem. Soc. 73 4052 (1951).
4. Karrer, P. and Eugster, C. H., Helv. Chim. Acta. 32 957 (1949).
5. Bollard, E. G., Nature 178 1189 (1956).
6. Barnes, R. L., Nature 184 Suppl. 25, 1944 (1959).
7. Gorton, B. S., Skinner, C. G. and Eakin, R. E., Arch. Biochem. Biophys. 66 493 (1957).
8. Kessler, B., Bak. R., and Cohen, A., Plant Physiol. 34 605 (1959).
9. Fox, J. J. and Wempen, I., Adv. Carbohyd. Chem. 14 283 (1959).
10. Abdel-Wahab, M. F. and El-Kinawi, S. A., Acta Chem. Scand. 13 1653 (1959).
11. Kennedy, E. and Weiss, S. B., J. Biol. Chem. 222 193 (1956).
12. Henderson, J. F. and LePage, G. A., Chem. Revs. 58 645 (1958).
13. Watson, J. D. and Crick, F. H. C., Nature 171 737 (1953).
14. Gulich, L., Planta 54 374 (1960).
15. Smillie, R. M. and Krotkov, G., Can. J. Botany 38 31 (1960).
16. Kupila, S., Bryan, A. M. and Stern, H., Plant Physiol. 36 212 (1961).
17. Ergle, D. R. and Katterman, F. R. H., Plant Physiol. 36 811 (1961).
18. Hutchinson, W. C. and Munro, N. N., Analyst 86 768 (1961); ibid. 87 303 (1962).
19. Albaum, H. G. and Ogur, M., Arch. Biochem. Biophys. 15 158 (1947).
20. Stambaugh, R. L. and Wilson, D. W., J. Chromatog. 3 221 (1960).
21. Shingler, A. J. and Carlton, J. K., Anal. Chem. 31 1679 (1959).
22. Webb, J. M. and Levy, H. B., Methods of Biochemical Analysis 6 1 (1958).
23. De Deken-Grenson, M. and De Deken, R. H., Biochem. et Biophys. Acta 31 195 (1959).
24. Miller, H. K., Methods of Biochemical Analysis 6 31 (1958).
25. Kern, H., Planta 53 595 (1959).

26. Venner, H., Z. Physiol. Chem. 322 122 (1960).
27. Markham, R. and Smith, J. D., Biochem. J. 49 401 (1951).
28. Wade, H. E. and Morgan, D. M., Nature 171 529 (1953).
29. Wood, T., Nature 176 175 (1955).
30. Gerlach, E. and Döring, H. J., Naturwiss. 42 344 (1955).
31. Cramer, F., Z. Anal. Chem. 181 545 (1961).
32. Randerath, K., Biochem. Biophys. Res. Comms. 6 452 (1962).
33. Rowan, K. S., J. Exptl. Botany 8 256 (1957).
34. Rowan, K. S. Biochim. et Biophys. Acta 34 270 (1959).
35. Cherry, J. H. and Hageman, R. H., Plant Physiol. 35 343 (1960).
36. Shuster, L. and Kaplan, N. O., J. Biol. Chem. 201 535 (1953).
37. Volkin, E. and Cohn, W. E., Methods of Biochemical Analysis 1 287 (1954).
38. Volkin, E. and Cohn, W. E. in Methods in Enzymology 2 ed. by S. P. Colowock and N. O. Kaplan, Academic Press, N. Y. 1955.
39. Hartmann, S. C. and Buchanan, J. M., Ann. Rev. Biochem. 28 365 (1959).
40. Brown, E. G., Goodwin, T. W., and Jones, O. T. G., Biochem. J. 68 40 (1958).
41. Krupka, R. M. and Towers, G. H. N., Can. J. Botany 37 539 (1959).
42. Anderson, L. E. and Gibbs, M., J. Biol. Chem. 237 1941 (1962).
43. Reichard, P., Biochim. et Biophys. Acta. 27 434 (1958).

Chapter 12
ALKALOIDS

The alkaloids do not represent a chemically homogeneous group, so that any generalizations about them are subject to many exceptions. They all contain nitrogen, frequently in a heterocyclic ring, and many but not all, are basic as their name indicates. Simple, aliphatic amines are not included here although the distinction is not sharp -- ephedrine and mescaline are often placed with the alkaloids although their nitrogens are aliphatic:

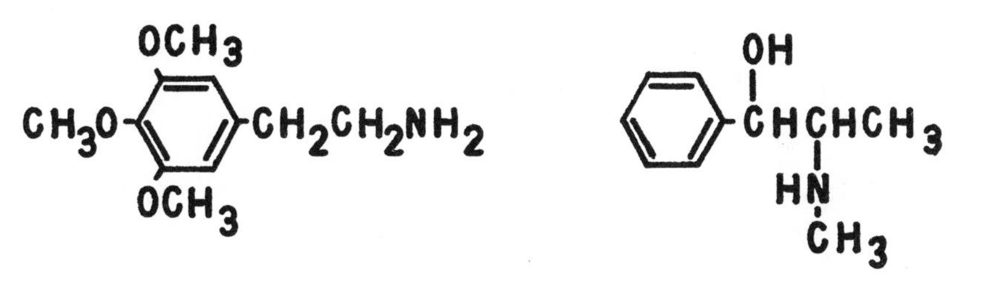

mescaline ephedrine

Classification of alkaloids is done on the basis of the ring system present, e.g.

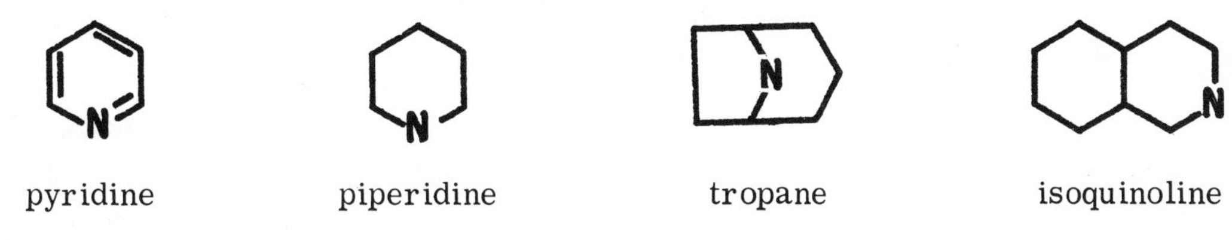

pyridine piperidine tropane isoquinoline

The purines and pyrimidines are conveniently considered separately because of their biochemical relation to the nucleic acids. The purines, caffeine and theobromine, are frequently placed with the alkaloids, though; and the distinction appears to be a physiological rather than a chemical one. Some alkaloid structures with their ring-numbering systems are given in Figure 12-1.

The alkaloids as a group are distinguished from most other plant components by their basic (cationic) nature. Therefore, they normally exist in plants as the salts of various organic acids and are frequently handled in the laboratory as salts of hydrochloric or sulfuric acid. These salts, and frequently the free alkaloids, are colorless crystalline compounds. A few alkaloids are liquids, and colored ones are even more rare (berberine and serpentine are yellow). Alkaloids are frequently optically active; and normally only one of the optical isomers is found naturally, although in a few cases racemic mixtures are known.

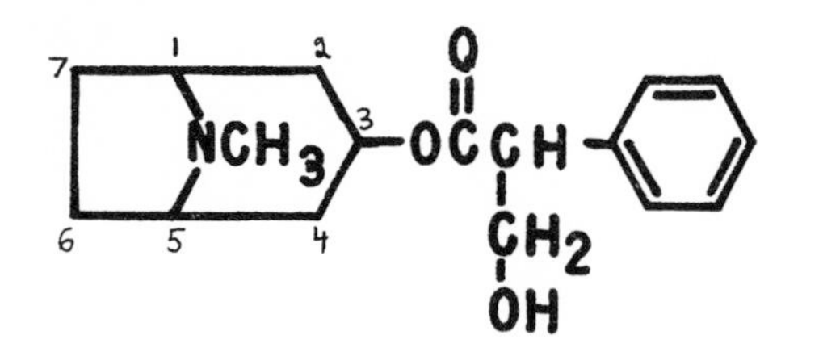

atropine (DL-hyoscyamine)

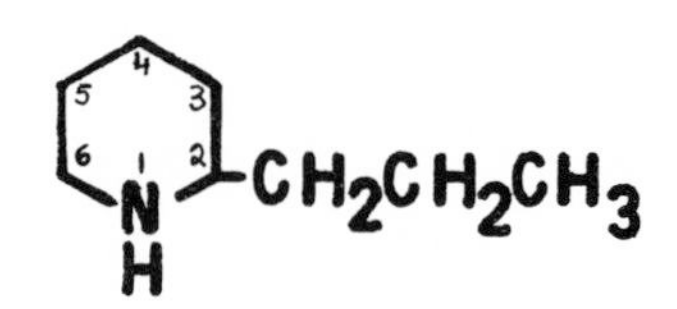

coniine

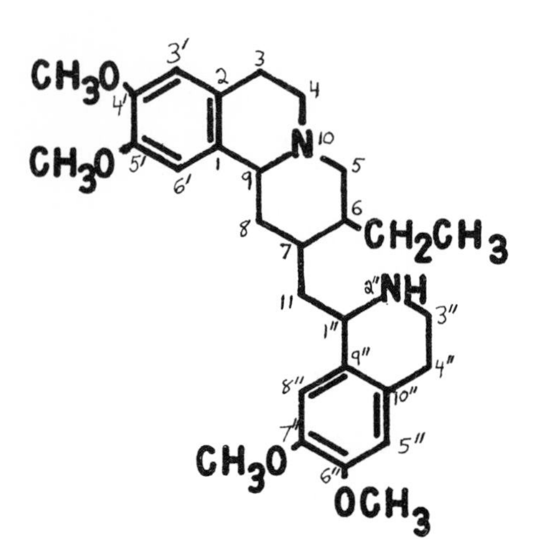

emetine

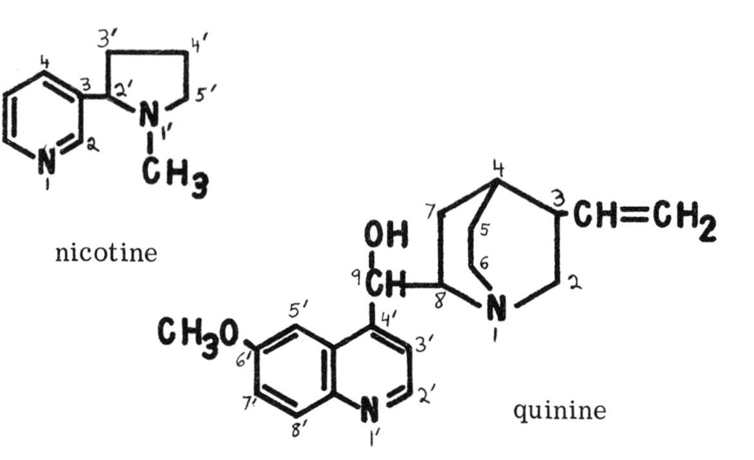

nicotine

quinine

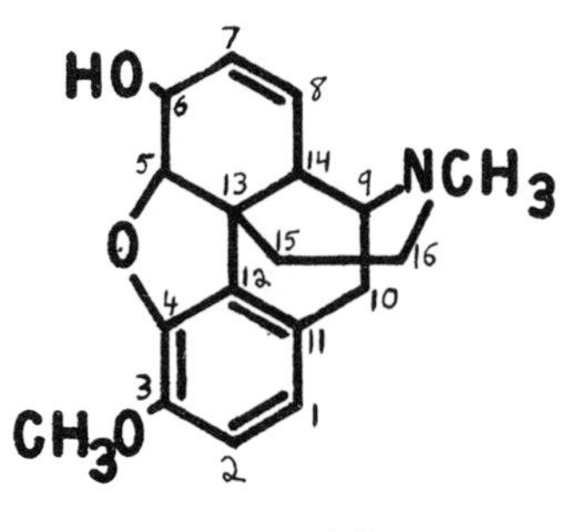

morphine

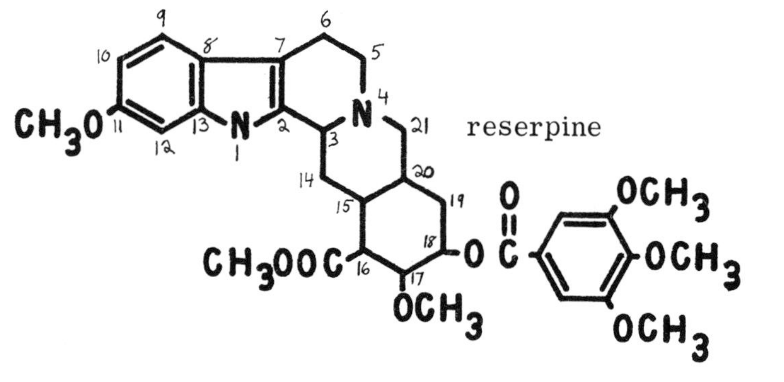

reserpine

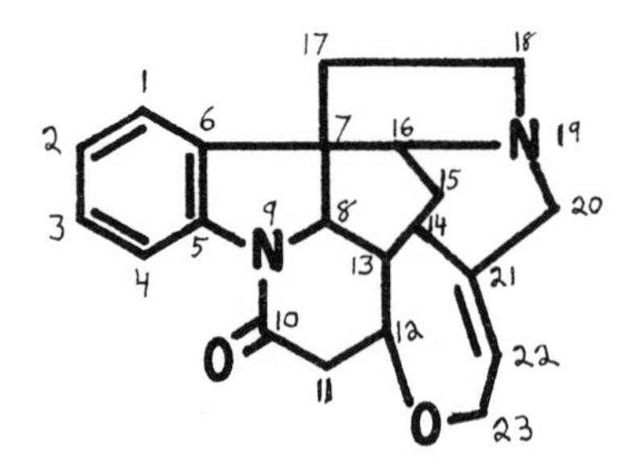

strychnine

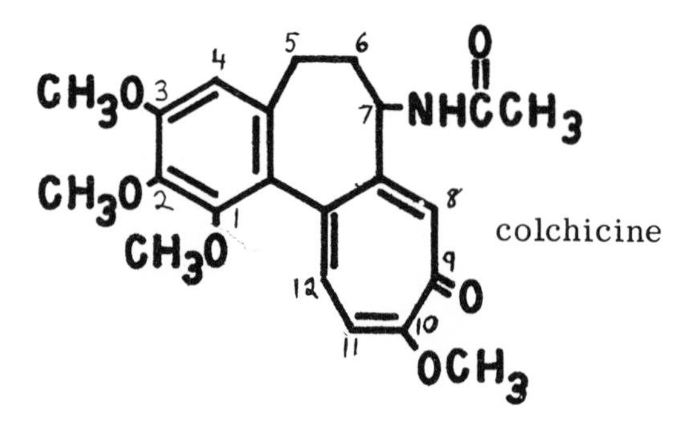

colchicine

FIGURE 12-1: STRUCTURES AND NUMBERING FOR SOME WELL-KNOWN ALKALOIDS

The alkaloids have been known for many years and have been of interest mostly because of their physiological effects on man and their use in pharmacy. Some of the pharmacological effects of alkaloids are tabulated below:

PHYSIOLOGICAL ACTION	ALKALOID	PLANT SOURCE
emetic	emetine	ipecacuanha
local anesthetic	cocaine	coca
antihemorrhagic	hydrastine	hydrastis
antispasmodic	hyoscyamine, atropine	belladonna
narcotic	morphine	opium poppy
vermifuge	pelletierine	pomegranate
aphrodisiac	yohimbine	*Pausinystalia yohimba*
tranquilizer	reserpine	*Rauwolfia serpentina*
cardiac depressant	quinine	*Cinchona* spp.
diaphoretic	pilocarpine	*Pilocarpus pennatifolius*
muscle paralysant	tubocurarine	*Chondodendron* spp.
nervous stimulant	strychnine	*Strychnos nux-vomica*

This listing provides only a sketchy illustration of some alkaloid effects. Many alkaloids have more than one type of action, depending for instance on the dose level.

The function of alkaloids in plants is almost completely obscure although many suggestions have been made. Some of these follow:

1. One of the earliest suggestions was that alkaloids function as nitrogen waste products like urea and uric acid in animals.
2. Some alkaloids may serve as nitrogen storage reservoirs although many seem to accumulate and are not farther metabolized even in severe nitrogen starvation.
3. In some cases alkaloids may protect the plant against attack by parasites or herbivores. Although evidence favoring this function has been brought forward in some instances, it is probably an overworked and anthropocentric concept. Many alkaloids poisonous to man have no effect on other (and more significant) enemies of the plants.
4. Alkaloids may serve as growth regulators since structures of some of them resemble structures of known growth regulators. More specifically, certain plant hormones may act by virtue of their chelating ability, and some alkaloids may also possess chelating ability. Maisuryan (1) has shown that lupine alkaloids may act as germination inhibitors and Jacquiot (2) has shown that alkaloids may remove the inhibitory effect of tannins on growth of plant tissue cultures.
5. It was originally suggested by Liebig that the alkaloids being mostly basic might serve in the plant to replace mineral bases in maintaining ionic balance. In

line with this suggestion is the observation of Dawson (3) that feeding nicotine to tobacco root cultures increased their uptake of nitrate. Laroze and Alves da Silva (4) favor the view that alkaloids function by exchanging with soil cations, and they have found alkaloids to be excreted by the roots of several alkaloid plants.

Further discussion of the function of alkaloids may be found in the reviews of James (5) Mothes (6, 7) and Bezanger-Beauquesne (8).

Alkaloids are widely distributed throughout the plant kingdom. Although some groups of plants are rich in alkaloids and other groups have none, there does not appear to be any facile generalization to be made about alkaloid distribution. There is some tendency for higher plants to have more than lower plants, but alkaloids are well known in the club mosses and horsetails, not to mention certain fungi (ergot). Alkaloids are not known in the Bryophytes, but probably no thorough search has been made for them there. It has been suggested (9) that the formation of volatile terpenes somehow competes with the formation of alkaloids so that plants having one lack the other. A special illustration of this principle is shown by the work of Tallent and Horning (10) who found that species of pine which have alkaloids also have straight-chain, aliphatic hydrocarbons rather than terpenes in their turpentines.

ISOLATION

The single, most important chemical property of the alkaloids is their basicity. Purification and characterization methods generally rely on this property, and special approaches must be developed for those few alkaloids (e. g. rutaecarpine, colchicine, ricinine) which are not basic.

Alkaloids are normally obtained by extracting the plant material with an acidic, aqueous solvent which dissolves the alkaloids as their salts, or the plant material may be made alkaline with sodium carbonate, etc. and the free bases extracted into organic solvents such as chloroform, ether, etc. Some volatile alkaloids such as nicotine may be purified by steam distillation from an alkaline solution. An acidic aqueous solution containing alkaloids may be made basic and the alkaloids extracted with an organic solvent so that neutral and acidic water-soluble compounds are left behind. Another useful way of removing alkaloids from acidic solution is by adsorption on Lloyd's reagent (11). They can then be eluted with dilute base. Many alkaloids can be separated by precipitating them as reineckates. A mixture of reineckates can then be resolved into its components by ion exchange chromatography (12). For detailed applications of these methods consult the articles by Cromwell (13) and Manske (14). Sangster (15) has also presented a general discussion on methods for isolating and characterizing alkaloids.

Additional purification of alkaloids can sometimes be carried out by extraction with selective solvents. The most general and convenient method of separation now available for separation of mixtures is column chromatography either using ion exchange resins or adsorbents such as aluminum oxide. Paper chromatography (see below) is useful for preliminary determination of the number of components to be separated and something of their nature. A procedure for isolation and identification of alkaloids from milligram quantities of plant material uses a combination of column chromatography on alumina and paper chromatography (16).

CHARACTERIZATION

Qualitative evidence for the presence of alkaloids in a solution and a rough characterization may be obtained by application of the various "alkaloidal reagents".

Mayer's reagent (potassium mercuric iodide) is most commonly used for detection of alkaloids since it gives a precipitate with nearly all of them. As it also precipitates other plant components, a preliminary purification is advisable before applying the test. Other reagents such as 5% silicotungstic acid, 5% tannic acid, Dragendorff's reagent (potassium tetraiodobismuthate) and saturated picric acid are also frequently used. For rapid testing plant juice can be squeezed onto paper impregnated with Dragendorff's reagent (17). Some alkaloids contain specific functional groups which may be determined by special reagents. For example, morphine is phenolic so that phenol reagents can be used to distinguish it. Systematic application of such reagents can be used for classification of alkaloids, and procedures have been given by Fulton (18) for dividing the alkaloids into large groups on the basis of orderly use of reagents.

If a more complete characterization of alkaloids is desired, the techniques of paper chromatography and spectrophotometry can be used to provide the most information with the least effort. Macek *et al.* (19) have proposed a classification scheme based on paper chromatographic behavior. By using several different solvents and reagents, an alkaloid may be placed into one of 6 major categories. The application of special reagents and comparison with knowns can then be used for a more nearly complete identification. Another paper chromatographic classification based on polarity is described by Waldi (20).

Resplandy (21) has claimed that the use of electrolytes for the chromatography of alkaloids is especially useful for providing insights into chemical structure. The literature on paper chromatography of alkaloids has been periodically reviewed by Bräuniger (22-28). The most useful solvents seem to have been formamide-chloroform mixtures and butanol-acetic acid mixtures. The most useful detection reagents have been iodine vapor on still moist paper and Dragendorff's reagent (potassium tetraiodobismuthate). Improvements in the Dragendorff's reagent have been suggested (29, 30). A modification of the Mayer reaction for use on chromatograms has been described by Pan and Wagman (31). Resplandy (32) has devised a method for indicating the structures of alkaloids on a micro scale by pyrolyzing either isolated alkaloid or intact plant tissue with calcium oxide and identifying the volatile products by paper chromatography.

Paper electrophoresis is also useful for separating many alkaloids. It is often faster and more reproducible than paper chromatography (33). Thin layer chromatography is also a rapid technique which can be applied to alkaloid separations. Waldi *et al.* (34) have devised a routine procedure for alkaloid identification using silica gel G as the adsorbent with 8 different solvent systems. In spite of the low volatility of many alkaloids it has also been possible to use gas chromatography for separating them (35).

If a pure alkaloid can be obtained, determination of its absorption spectrum can provide a valuable means of identification. Elution of a spot from a paper chromatogram may provide enough material for this purpose. Ultraviolet absorption spectra for a great many alkaloids have been presented by Elvidge (36) and by Oestreicher *et al.* (37). Infra red spectra are given by Levi *et al.* (38) and by Marion *et al.* (39).

METABOLIC PATHWAYS

The schemes of alkaloid biosynthesis shown in the accompanying diagrams are largely based on the proposals made by Sir Robert Robinson in 1917 (40). These ideas have since been elaborated both by him and others (cf. 41, 42). They constitute a comprehensive and reasonable picture of alkaloid biosynthesis but are based primarily on analogy with reactions of organic chemistry and by considerations of structural similarity rather than direct, biochemical evidence. In the diagrams only carbon skeletons are shown with no indication of detailed structures. Names in parentheses are specific alkaloids having the accompanying carbon skeleton. Other names refer to classes of alkaloids. The assumptions of Robinson's scheme of biosynthesis may be summarized as follows:

1. The basic skeletons of alkaloids are derived from common amino acids and other small biological molecules.
2. A few simple types of reactions suffice to form complex structures from these starting materials. For example the aldol condensation:

$$\gt C=O + HC\text{-}X \rightarrow \text{-}\overset{OH}{C}\text{-}C\text{-}$$

the carbinolamine condensation:

$$\gt N\text{-}C\text{-}OH + H\text{-}C\text{-}X \rightarrow \gt N\text{-}C\text{-}C + H_2O$$

as well as simple dehydrations, oxidations, and decarboxylations. (X represents an "activating" group such as carbonyl.)

For example the formation of the tropane alkaloid skeleton was pictured as follows:

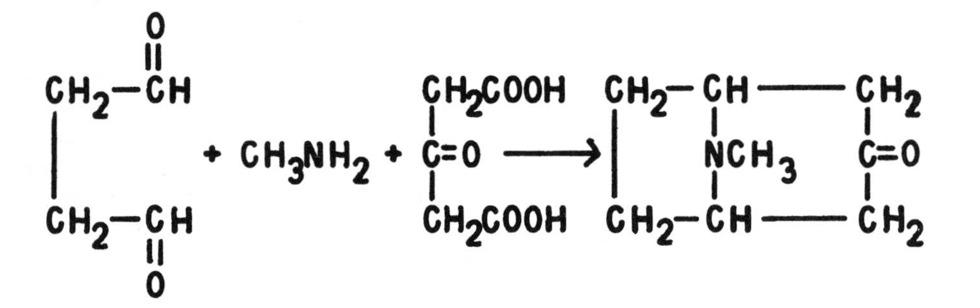

No specific order of the steps is implied, so that intermediates of many different structures might appear, e.g.:

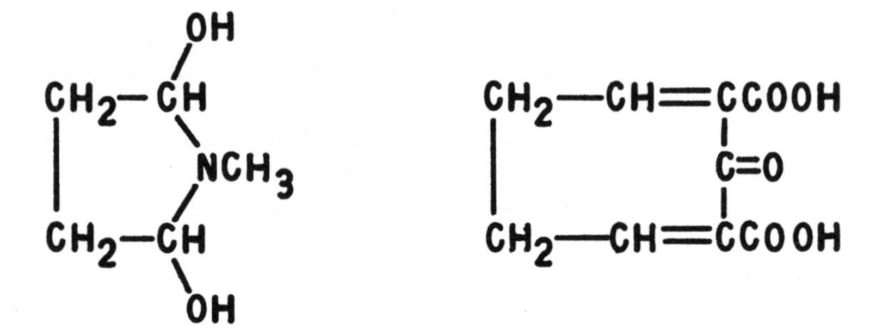

Succindialdehyde could arise in plants either by a reduction of succinic acid or by an oxidative decarboxylation of ornithine. Another pathway starting from ornithine might also be possible and would use one of the amino groups of ornithine in the final tropane skeleton:

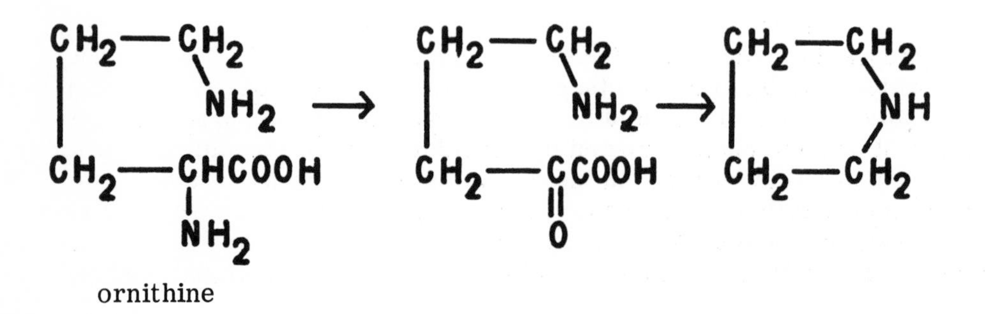

Similarly, the participation of methylamine as such is not essential. The actual reactant could be glycine followed by a decarboxylation. Thus the Robinson proposals are not tied to specific compounds. Rather, the pyrrolidine ring may be thought of as derived from any one of a group of related compounds (i. e. ornithine, glutamic acid, succinic acid) which have structural similarities and which are now known to be biochemically interrelated as well. The first specific derivative of say, ornithine which is irrevocably committed to forming an alkaloid rather than some other compound remains unknown. In fact, it would seem that the crucial problem in alkaloid biosynthesis is the identification of the point in the pathways of metabolism where an intermediate is formed whose subsequent transformations are directed solely toward an alkaloid with no links to other classes of compounds.

The types of compounds suggested by Robinson do occur in plants, and the required reactions take place so readily that large structures similar to alkaloid skeletons may be formed *in vitro* by mere mixing of the supposed precursors. On the other hand, Wenkert (43, 44) believes that alkaloid formation may be more closely related to carbohydrate and acetate metabolism than to amino acid metabolism.

Experiments have been carried out where supposed alkaloid precursors were labelled with isotopic tracers and fed to plants. Isolated alkaloids were then found to have the label just where it would be predicted by the theory. On the whole, then, the pathways indicated serve, at least, as helpful guides. What biochemical evidence is available suggests that in the main they give a picture close to the truth. However, specific aspects of alkaloid biosynthesis can be discussed in more detail and biochemical evidence for or against steps presented. There are reviews on alkaloid biosynthesis by Battersby (45) Marion (46), Mothes (47) and Franck (48). Mothes has also reviewed methods for investigating alkaloid biosynthesis (49, 50).

The clearest generalization concerning alkaloid precursors concerns the methyl groups found in many alkaloids, both as N-methyl and O-methyl groups. Tracer experiments have, almost without exception, shown that, as might be expected, these are derived from the methyl group of methionine (51, 52, 53). Enzyme systems from various plants have been shown to catalyze the transfer of methyl groups from S-adenosylmethionine to form gramine, hordenine and trigonelline (54, 55). Byerrum *et al.* (56) have found, however, that glycine-2-C^{14} was at least as good a donor for the methyl group of nicotine. Formate does not appear to be an efficient precursor in this system although it apparently works well as a methyl donor for ephedrine formation (57). Choline and betaine have also been found to act as methyl donors in some cases (46).

The participation of C_3, C_4 and C_5 compounds at various points in the scheme is evident, and these participants are most likely interrelated--for example, as acetone, acetoacetic acid and acetonedicarboxylic acid. These three compounds, although readily derived from plant components by well-known enzymatic reactions, are found, if at all, in very small amounts. Kaczkowski *et al.* (58) have shown by tracer experiments that the "C_3 unit" of hyoscyamine is derived from two molecules of acetate with loss of one carboxyl group. Tuppy and Faltaous (59) have described an enzyme system which can utilize acetoacetic or acetonedicarboxylic acid for synthesis of hygrine and other alkaloids.

Quite good tracer evidence exists for the formation of the pyrrolidine ring from ornithine (keeping in mind that the ornithine itself probably does not immediately cyclize). This generalization apparently holds whether we are dealing with an isolated ring as in nicotine or a more complex structure as in hyoscyamine (60). The degradation data of Leete and Siegfried (61) showed equal activity in the α-carbons of the pyrrolidine ring of nicotine when ornithine-2-C^{14} was fed. This indicates the existence of a symmetrical intermediate such as putrescine or succindialdehyde. However only one bridgehead carbon in hyoscyamine received tracer from ornithine-2-C^{14} (60). Mann and Smithies (62) have shown that amine oxidase preparations from plants can catalyze the formation of heterocyclic rings from diamino compounds like putrescine. Leete (63) using 1, 4-labelled putrescine fed to tobacco found that it was an efficient precursor of the pyrrolidine ring in nicotine. It seems possible to say that the group of C_4 and C_5 compounds related to ornithine and succinic acid is also closely related to the pyrrolidine alkaloids. The precise precursors have not been identified and may vary from alkaloid to alkaloid and plant to plant. In addition, the pyrrole rings of indole compounds and of porphyrins have quite different origins.

The precursors of six-membered heterocyclic rings are less certain. It seems likely that pyridine and piperidine rings may arise from quite separate pathways. Leete (64) fed lysine-2-C^{14} to *Nicotiana tabacum* (whose alkaloid is nicotine) and to *N-glauca* (whose alkaloid is anabasine). Isolated nicotine contained no radioactivity. The anabasine had activity in the 2-carbon of the piperidine ring, but not in the pyridine ring. Formation of the piperidine ring from lysine apparently does not involve a symmetrical intermediate since the 6-carbon contained no label.

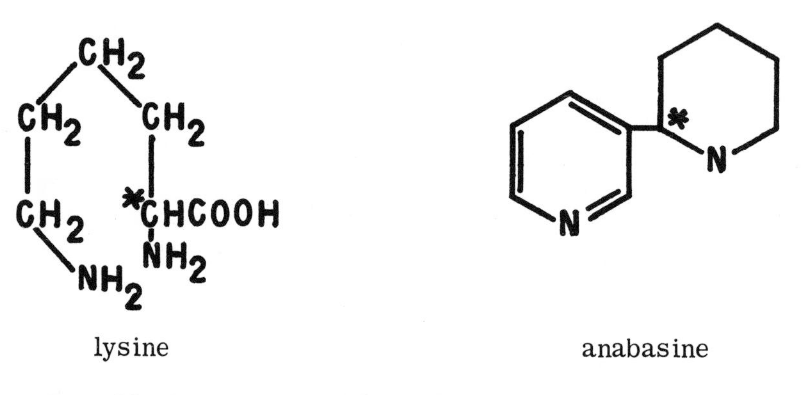

lysine anabasine

The conversion of lysine to a piperidine ring may take place in two possible ways. Lysine may be directly oxidized to the corresponding α-keto acid which spontaneously undergoes ring closure to Δ^1-piperideinecarboxylic acid (65). Alternatively, lysine may be first decarboxylated and the resulting cadaverine (1, 5-diaminopentane) oxidized and cyclized to Δ^1-piperideine. The conversion of labelled lysine or cadaverine to such piperidine alkaloids as coniine, anabasine, lupinine, hydroxylupanine, and sparteine has been amply demonstrated (66, 67, 68). The key role of the enzyme diamine oxidase in catalyzing such transformations is also clear. Mothes *et al.* (69) have shown that a crude preparation of this enzyme from peas can catalyze conversion of labelled cadaverine into both the pyridine and piperidine rings of anabasine--in contrast to the situation in *Nicotiana* (64).

Except for the last example, it appears that the aromatic-type pyridine ring found in many alkaloids and in the vitamin nicotinic acid is not derived via the lysine-cadaverine pathway. Nicotinic acid and/or nicotinamide have been shown to be good precursors of the pyridine ring in such alkaloids as nicotine (70), and ricinine (71). However, the pyridine ring is, of course, already present in nicotinic acid; and how it is originally formed remains unknown. There is some indication that C-2, C-3 and the carboxyl group may be derived from a C_4 compound such as succinate whereas C-4, C-5, and C-6 may come from a C_3 precursor such as glycerol (72, 73). There is convincing evidence that in higher plants nicotinic acid is not made by the pathway:

tryptophan→kynurenine→3-hydroxyanthranilic acid→nicotinic acid

even though this pathway has been well-established in fungi (74, 75).

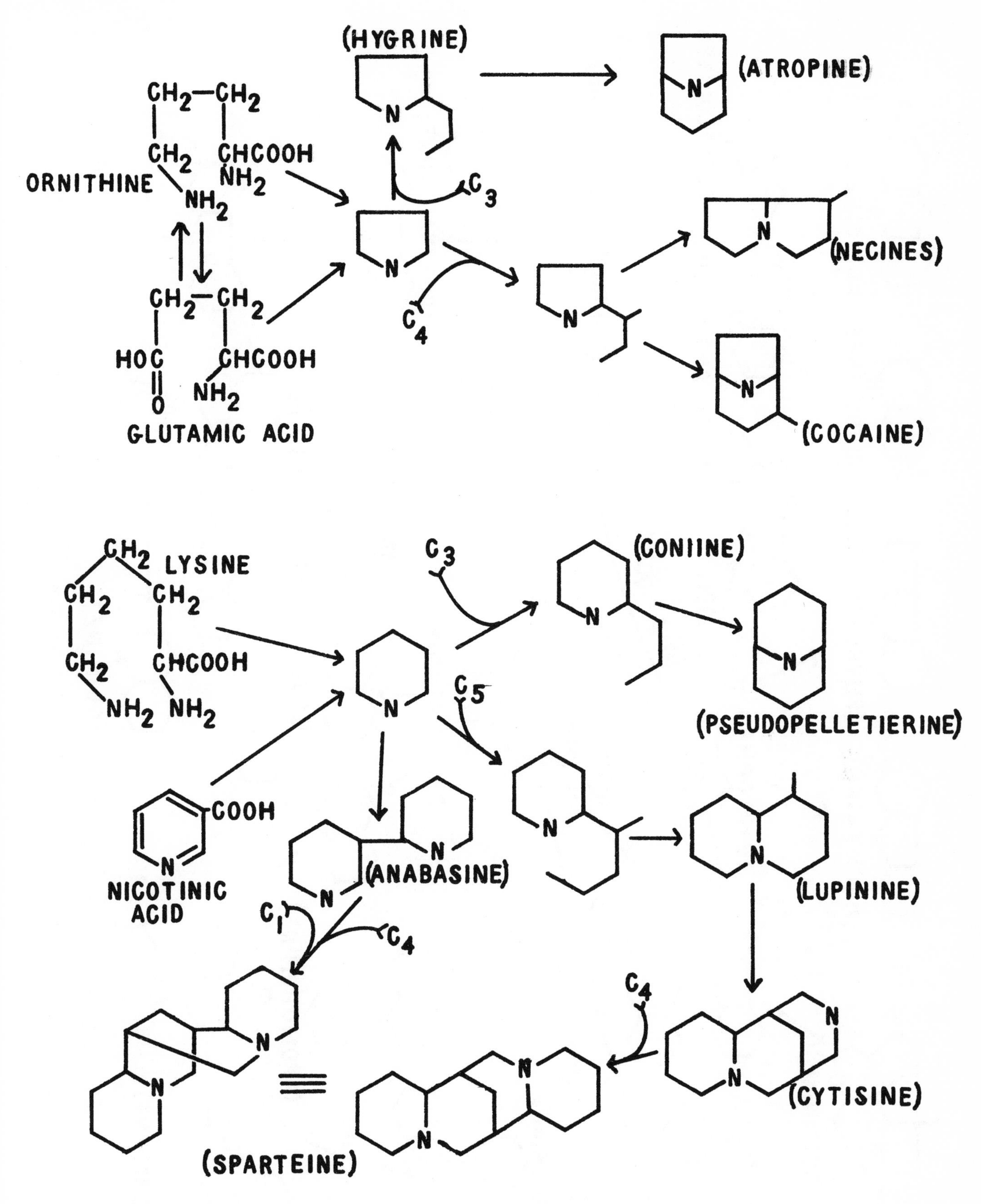

FIGURE 12-2: PATHWAYS OF ALKALOID BIOSYNTHESIS

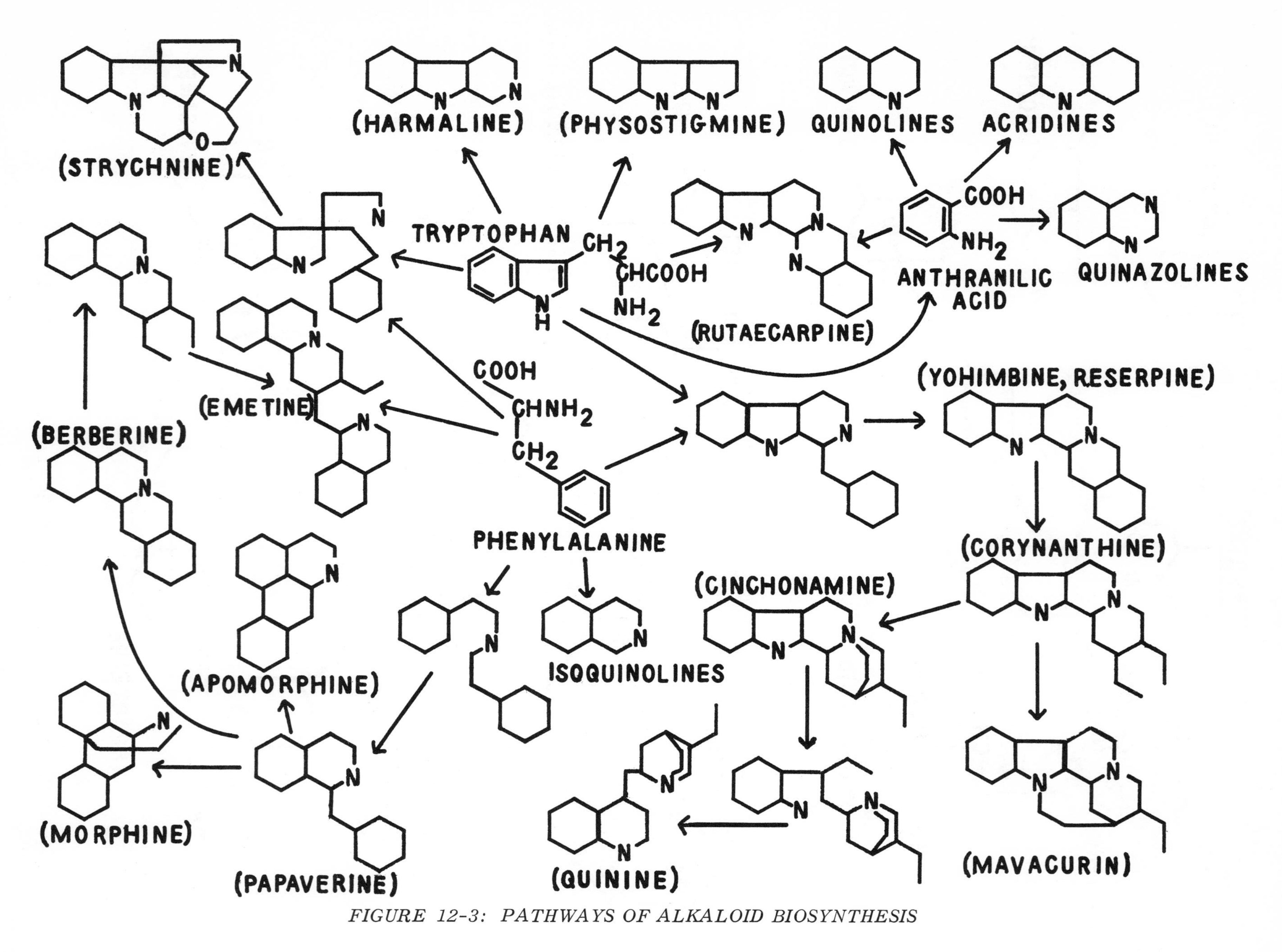

FIGURE 12-3: PATHWAYS OF ALKALOID BIOSYNTHESIS

The quinoline alkaloids are usually presumed to arise from anthranilic acid (75) although there seems to be no tracer evidence in support of this view. Some quinoline alkaloids have structures resembling the flavonoids with the substitution of nitrogen for oxygen in the heterocyclic ring. Such a substitution can occur non-enzymatically (77) and suggests that certain alkaloids could be biogenetically related to the flavonoids or other oxygen heterocycles.

In the formation of several alkaloids such as quinine, emetine, and strychnine a type of reaction apparently occurs which was not foreseen in the original proposals of Robinson, namely the breaking of a six-membered ring. The generality of this pathway has been discussed by Woodward (42), and in cases where an ethyl or vinyl group appears, one can assume that it originally was part of a six-membered ring. Seven-membered rings (as in strychnine) also seem to arise from the breaking or an expansion of six-membered rings, and six-membered rings may rarely (e.g. quinine) arise from expansion of five-membered rings:

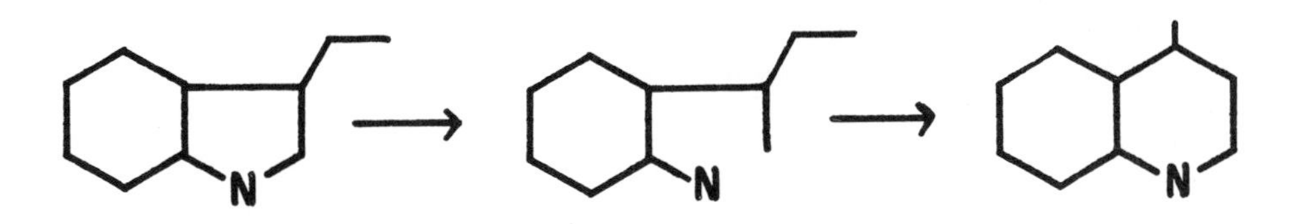

Some other, quite different, suggestions have been made regarding synthetic pathways for certain alkaloids. Thomas (78) has suggested a possible relationship between cyclopentanoid monoterpenes and certain indole alkaloids. Conroy (79) has proposed that the *Lycopodium* alkaloids could reasonably arise from polyacetate condensations (cf. Chapter 6).

Space does not permit consideration of the many experiments which have been carried out to elucidate pathways of biosynthesis for some other alkaloids, but a few references to recent literature are tabulated below:

ALKALOIDS STUDIED	REFERENCE
Amaryllidaceae alkaloids	80
morphine alkaloids	81, 82
hydrastine	83
colchicine	84, 85
berberine	86
Rauwolfia alkaloids	87
Strychnos alkaloids	88, 89

GENERAL REFERENCES

Battersby, A. R., ed. "Symposium on New Developments in Alkaloid Chemistry", Tetrahedron 14 1 (1961).
Bentley, K. W. The Alkaloids, Interscience Publishers, N. Y., 1957.
Cromwell, B. T. "The Alkaloids" in Paech and Tracey 4 367.

Henry, T. A., The Plant Alkaloids, Blakiston, Phila., 1939.
Manske, R. H. F. and Holmes, H. L. The Alkaloids 7 vols., Academic Press, N. Y., 1951-1960.
Mothes, K., editor "Biochemie und Physiologie der Alkaloide," Abhandlungen deut. Akad. Wiss., Berlin, No. 7, 1956. (cf. Chem. Abstr. 52 15655 (1958).)
Mothes, K. and Romeike, A. "Die Alkaloide" in Ruhland 8 989.

BIBLIOGRAPHY

1. Maisuryan, N. A., Doklady Akad. Nauk Armyan S. S. R. 22 91 (1956). (Chem. Abstr. 50 10863.)
2. Jacquiot, C., Compt. rend. 225 434 (1947).
3. Dawson, R. F., Plant Physiol. 21 115 (1946).
4. Laroze, A. and Alves da Silva, J., Anais. fac. farm. Porto. 12 85 (1952). (Chem. Abstr. 48 233.)
5. James, W. O., The Alkaloids, Manske, R. H. G., and Holmes, H. L. 1 15, Academic Press, N. Y. (1951).
6. Mothes, K., Ann. Rev. Plant Physiol. 6 393 (1955).
7. Mothes, K., The Alkaloids, Manske, R. H. G. and Holmes, H. L., eds. 6 1 Academic Press, N. Y., (1960).
8. Bezanger-Beauquesne, L., Bull. soc. botan. France 105 266 (1958).
9. Treibs, W., Sitzber, deut. Akad. Wiss. Berlin, Kl. Math. u. allgem. Naturw. 1953.
10. Tallent, W. H. and Horning, E. C., J. Am. Chem. Soc. 78 4467 (1956).
11. Lloyd, J. U., J. Am. Pharm. Assoc. 5 381 (1916).
12. Kum-Tatt, L., Nature 188 65 (1960).
13. Cromwell, B. T. in Paech and Tracey 4 367.
14. Manske, R. H. F., The Alkaloids 1 1 (1951).
15. Sangster, A. W., J. Chem. Educ. 37 454 (1960), ibid. 37 518 (1960).
16. Clarke, E. G. C. and Hawkins, A. E., Forensic Sci. Soc. J., 1 120 (1961).
17. Kraft, D., Pharmazie 8 170 (1953).
18. Fulton, C. C., Am. J. Pharm. 111 184 (1939).
19. Macek, K., Hacaperkova, J., and Kakac, B., Pharmazie 11 533 (1956).
20. Waldi, D., Arch. Pharm. 292 206 (1959).
21. Resplandy, A. Compt. rend. 239 496 (1954).
22. Bräuniger, H., Pharmazie 9 643 (1954).
23. ibid. 9 719 (1954).
24. ibid. 9 834 (1954).
25. ibid. 11 28 (1956).
26. ibid. 11 115 (1956).
27. Bräuniger, H. and Honerjager, L., Pharmazie 12 203 (1957).
28. Bräuniger, H., Pharmazie 12 271 (1957).
29. Robles, M. A., Pharm. Weekblad 94 178 (1959). (Chem. Abstr. 53 12588 (1959).)
30. Vágújfalvi, D., Planta Medica 8 34 (1960). (Chem. Abstr. 54 15836 (1960).)
31. Pan, S. C. and Wagman, G. H., J. Chromatog. 2 428 (1959).
32. Resplandy, A., Compt. rend. 246 461 (1958).
33. Buff, C., Orantes, J., and Kirk, P. L., Microchem. J. 3 13 (1959).
34. Waldi, D., Schnackerz, K., and Munter, F., J. Chromatog. 6 61 (1961).
35. Lloyd, H. A., Fales, H. M., Highet, P. F., VandenHeuvel, W. J. A., and Wildman, W. C., J. Am. Chem. Soc. 82 3791 (1960).
36. Elvidge, W. F., Quart. J. Pharm. Pharmacol. 13 219 (1940).
37. Oestreicher, P. M., Farmilo, C. G., Levi, L., Bull. Narcotics U. N. Dept. Social Affairs 6 No. 3/4, 42 (1954).
38. Levi, L., Kubley, C. E., Hinge, R. A., Bull. Narcotics U. N. Dept. Social Affairs 6 No. 3/4 48 (1954).
39. Marion, L., Ramsay, D. A., and Jones, R. N., J. Am. Chem. Soc. 73 305 (1951).
40. Robinson, R., J. Chem. Soc. 111 876 (1917).
41. Robinson, R., The Structural Relations of Natural Products, Oxford University Press, 1955.
42. Woodward, R. B., Ang. Chem. 68 13 (1956).
43. Wenkert, E., Experientia 15 165 (1959).
44. Wenkert, E., J. Am. Chem. Soc. 84 98 (1962).
45. Battersby, A. R., Quart. Revs. 15 259 (1961).
46. Marion, L., Bull. soc. chim. France 1958 109.
47. Mothes, K., Symposia Soc. Exptl. Biol. 13 258 (1959).
48. Franck, B., Naturwiss. 47 169 (1960).
49. Mothes, K., Pharmazie 14 121 (1959).
50. ibid. 14 177 (1959).
51. Leete, E. and Németh, P. E., J. Am. Chem. Soc. 83 2192 (1961).

52. Battersby, A. R. and Harper, B. J. T., Chem. and Ind. 1958 365.
53. Leete, E. and Marion, L., Can. J. Chem. 646 (1954).
54. Mudd, S. H., Biochim. Biophys. Acta 37 164 (1960).
55. Joshi, J. G. and Handler, P., J. Biol. Chem. 235 2981 (1960).
56. Byerrum, R. U., Hamill, R. L. and Ball, C. D., J. Biol. Chem. 210 645 (1954).
57. Imaseki, I., Pharm. Bull. (Tokyo) 5 594 (1957) (C. A. 52 8285).
58. Kaczkowski, J., Schütte, H. R. and Mothes, K., Biochim. Biophys. Acta 46 588 (1961).
59. Tuppy, H. and Faltaous, M. S., Monatsh. Chem. 91 167 (1960).
60. Leete, E., J. Am. Chem. Soc. 84 55 (1962).
61. Leete, E. and Siegfried, K. J., J. Am. Chem. Soc. 79 4529 (1957).
62. Mann, P. J. G. and Smithies, W. R., Biochem. J. 61 89 (1955).
63. Leete, E., J. Am. Chem. Soc. 80 2162 (1958).
64. Leete, E., J. Am. Chem. Soc. 78 3520 (1956).
65. Hasse, K., Homan, P., Schührer, K. and Wieland, A., Ann. 653 114 (1962).
66. Leete, E., J. Am. Chem. Soc. 80 4393 (1958).
67. Schütte, H. R., Nowacki, E., and Schäfer, C., Arch. Pharm. 295 20 (1962).
68. Schiedt, V. and Hoss, H. G., Z. Naturforsch. 13b 691 (1958).
69. Mothes, K., Schütte, H. R., Simon, H. and Weygand, F., Z. Naturforsch. 14b 49 (1959).
70. Dawson, R. F., Christman, D. R., D'Adamo, A. F., Solt, M. L., and Wolf, A. P., Chem. and Ind. 1958 100.
71. Waller, G. R. and Henderson, L. M., J. Biol. Chem. 236 1186 (1961).
72. Waller, G. R. and Henderson, L. M. Biochem. Biophys. Res. Comms. 5 5 (1961).
73. Griffith, T., Hellman, K. P. and Byerrum, R. U., Biochemistry 1 336 (1962).
74. Leete, E., Marion, L. and Spenser, I. D., Can. J. Chem. 33 405 (1955).
75. Henderson, L. M., Someroski, J. F., Rao, D. R., Pei-Hsing Lin Wu, Griffith, T. and Byerrum, R. U., J. Biol. Chem. 234 93 (1959).
76. Price, J. R., Fortschr. Chem. Org. Naturstoffe 13 302 (1956).
77. Kubota, T. and Tomita, Y., Tetrahedron Letters 1961 453.
78. Thomas, R., Tetrahedron Letters 1961 544.
79. Conroy, H., Tetrahedron Letters 1960, 34.
80. Wildman, W. C., Fales, H. M. and Battersby, A. R., J. Am. Chem. Soc. 84 681 (1962).
81. Kleinschmidt, G. and Mothes, K., Z. Naturforsch. 14b 52 (1959).
82. Stermitz, F. R. and Rapoport, H., J. Am. Chem. Soc. 83 4045 (1961).
83. Spenser, I. D. and Gear, J. R., J. Am. Chem. Soc. 84 1059 (1962).
84. Leete, E. and Nemeth, P. E., J. Am. Chem. Soc. 82 6055 (1960).
85. Scott, A. I., Nature 186 556 (1960).
86. Spenser, I. D. and Gear, J. R., Proc. Chem. Soc. 1962 228.
87. Leete, E., Ghosal, S. and Edwards, P. N., J. Am. Chem. Soc. 84 1068 (1962).
88. Hendrickson, J. B. and Silva, R. A., J. Am. Chem. Soc. 84 643 (1962).
89. Casinovi, C. G., Marini-Bettolo, G. B., and Bisset, N. G., Nature 193 1178 (1962).

Chapter 13
PORPHYRINS

The porphyrin ring system is widely distributed in nature, occurring throughout the plant and animal kingdoms. Porphyrins serve as part of the oxygen transport and storage systems of vertebrates, in the respiratory chains of most cells, and as prosthetic groups of certain enzymes in plants and animals. A different modification of the porphyrin nucleus serves as a basis for the chlorophyll and related pigments of green plants.

The parent nucleus of the natural porphyrins is the simplest cyclic tetrapyrrole, porphin (here shown with the ring-numbering used for all porphyrins):

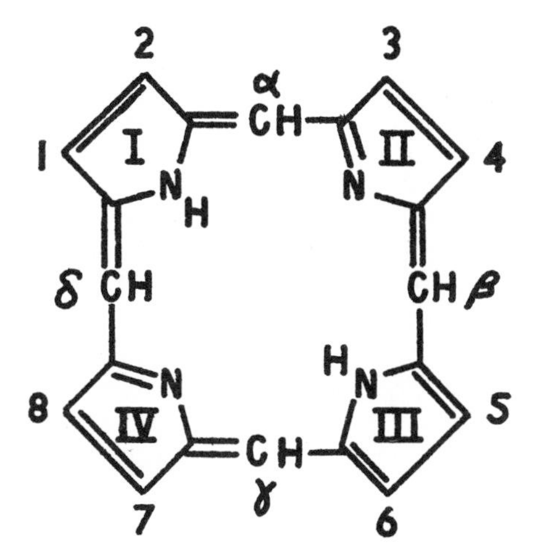

Although fixed double bond positions are shown, it is more likely that the entire molecule is a resonance hybrid of several possible double bond arrangements. The two central hydrogen atoms may also be shared among the four nitrogens. These considerations also apply to the more complex porphyrins, although certain combinations of substituent groups may stabilize one resonance form more than another.

All of the natural porphyrins carry alkyl substituents in the available positions of the pyrrole rings. The variety and arrangement of substituents is quite limited so that important generalizations may be drawn concerning them. The reasons for these regularities in porphyrin structure become apparent on considering the pathways of biosynthesis. The groups which occur may be divided into two categories:

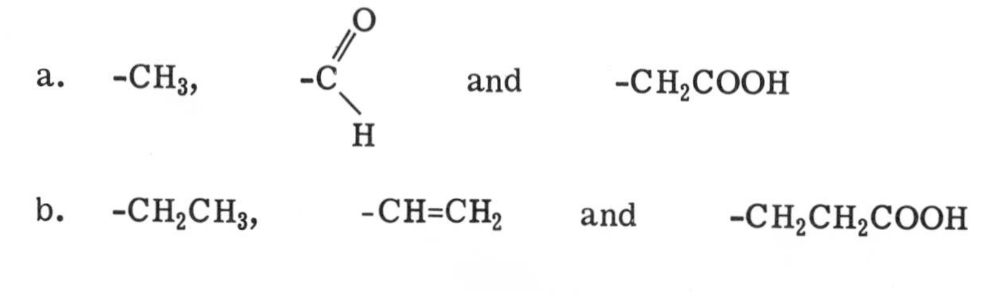

A given pyrrole ring always has one type a and one type b substituent, never two of the same type. Four basic types of porphyrins would then appear to be possible:

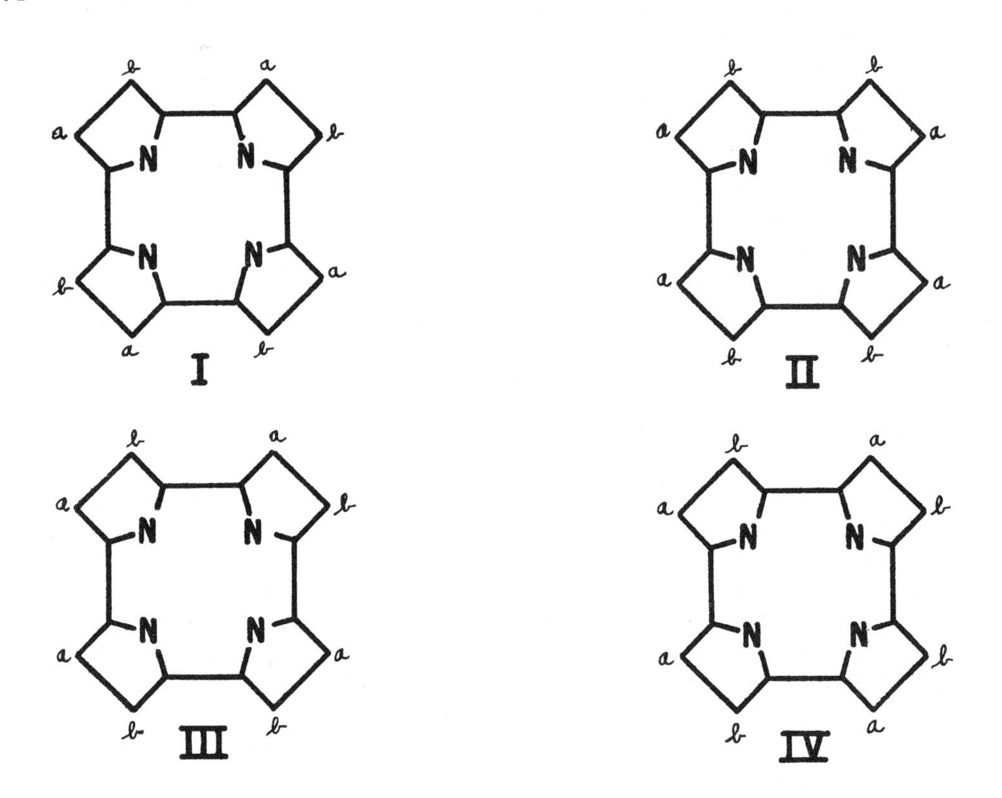

Fortunately type III porphyrins are by far the most common. Type I occurs rarely and the other two types never in nature. A Roman numeral following the name of a porphyrin refers it to one of these types (e.g. "coprophorphyrin III").

Chlorophyll derivatives have an additional 5-membered ring derived from a propionic acid side-chain on position 6. It is numbered as shown:

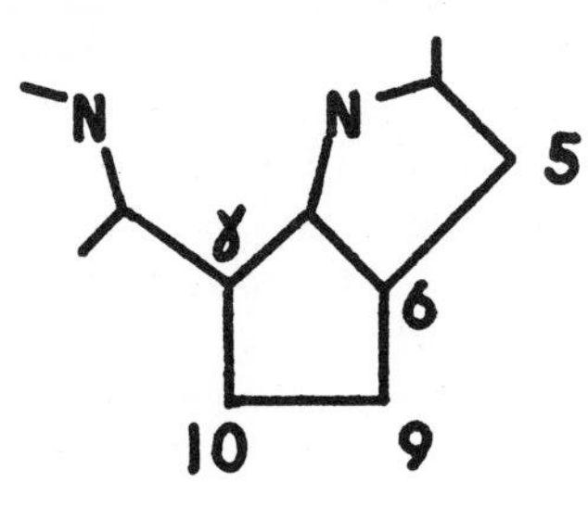

The functional forms of natural porphyrins all seem to have a metal bound as a chelate complex in the center of the molecule replacing the two hydrogens otherwise present. Naturally-occurring porphyrins which do not contain a metal are precursors or degradation products of the functional compounds. Significant amounts of them are found only under abnormal circumstances.

In plants we are most concerned with iron-containing hematin pigments and magnesium-containing chlorophyll pigments. These are biogenetically closely related, but experimentally they are approached in quite different ways. The hematin pigments are tightly bound to protein, difficult to purify and present in plants in very small concentrations. Chlorophyll, conversely, is easily extractable in large quantities and more conveniently purified. Probably in its functional form it is bound loosely to protein, and chlorophyll-protein complexes have been isolated from leaves by special techniques (1, 2). Non-polar solvents such as benzene are unable to split chlorophyll from its complex, but only slightly polar ones such as acetone readily extract the pigment. Since hematin compounds can be isolated only in special cases, they must be studied and identified by indirect techniques in crude homogenates or *in situ*. The study of chlorophyll derivatives, on the contrary, usually begins with their purification. The quantitative difference in these two pigment types becomes apparent when one considers that on a dry weight basis a green leaf may have about 1% chlorophyll pigments whereas total hematin in the richest tissues is practically never more than 0.01% and usually about 0.001%.

Vitamin B_{12} has a porphyrin-like structure, but its synthesis by higher plants is questionable. It has been reported to occur in turnip greens but may actually be synthesized by associated microorganisms (3).

HEME AND RELATED COMPOUNDS

The hematin (or iron porphyrin) pigments have been well-known in animal tissues for many years (e.g. hemoglobin), but they are equally wide-spread and important in plants. Hemoglobin itself occurs in the root nodules of legumes but is produced only in the presence of the bacterial partner. The enzymes catalase and peroxidase occur throughout the plant kingdom and have iron porphyrin prosthetic groups. However, the predominant hematin compounds are the cytochrome respiratory pigments which in all aerobic tissues transport electrons along the chain (or slight variants of it):

$$\text{cytochrome b} \rightarrow \text{cytochrome } c_1 \rightarrow \text{cytochrome c} \rightarrow \text{cytochrome a} \rightarrow \text{cytochrome } a_3 \text{ (cytochrome oxidase)} \rightarrow O_2$$

Other cytochromes are known in plants (e.g. b_3, b_7, f) but their functions are not as clear. Small letters are used to refer to individual cytochrome molecules, whereas capital letters refer to a group of cytochromes with a particular type of structure (4). The reviews of Hartree (5), Smith and Chance (6), James and Leech (7) and King (8) discuss the distribution and participation of these pigments in metabolism.

The most common porphyrin structure among the hematin pigments is protoporphyrin IX. (Here the Roman numeral refers to the particular side-chain arrangement among all the isomers having the same groups as substituents.) Its structure is shown in Figure 13-3, p. 271. As the ferrous chelate complex this is the pigment known specifically as "heme." Peroxidase, catalase, hemoglobin, oxyhemoglobin, methemoglobin, and the B-cytochromes all contain the same porphyrin as a ferrous or ferric complex. Four of iron's six coordinate valences are utilized in this complex; the other two are directed as summarized in Table 1. Cytochromes c and f apparently differ in structure from the B type in having their vinyl side-chains condensed with sulfhydryl groups of the protein as well as bound through iron to the protein:

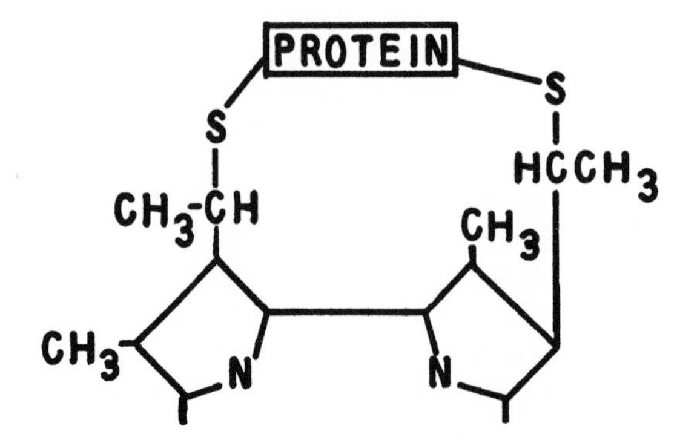

The structure of the porphyrin associated with A cytochromes is as yet unknown. It apparently has a formyl side chain and a large alkyl side chain.

Other porphyrins related structurally to this group are occasionally found and probably represent precursors. Hence their structures are given in the section on biosynthesis.

TABLE 1. NOMENCLATURE OF SOME IRON PROTOPORPHYRIN DERIVATIVES

Compound	Iron Oxidation Number	Coordination Positions 5	and 6
heme	2	water	water
hematin	3	water	OH^-
hemin	3	water	Cl^-
hemochromogen	2	nitrogen base	nitrogen base
peroxidase	3	water	protein
catalase	3	water	protein
hemoglobin	2	water	protein
oxyhemoglobin	2	oxygen	protein
methemoglobin	3	water or OH^-	protein
B cytochromes	2 or 3	protein	protein

CHLOROPHYLL AND RELATED COMPOUNDS

Chlorophylls a and b are the only green pigments of all plants higher than the algae. The ratio of chlorophyll a to b is usually about 3:1, and there is no ready interconversion between them. The structure is given for chlorophyll a. Chlorophyll b has a formyl group instead of methyl at position 3:

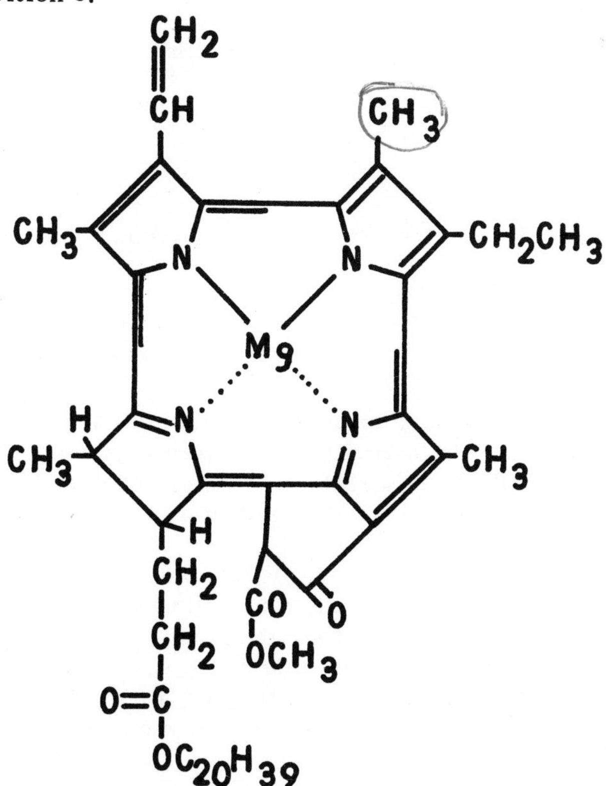

Note particularly that ring IV has been partially reduced in comparison with the hematin porphyrins. The C_{20} alcohol esterified to one of the carboxyl groups is phytol, a diterpene. The various chlorophyll derivatives which occur naturally or as artifacts in working with chlorophyll involve removal of the magnesium and hydrolysis of one or both ester groups. A summary of such derivatives is given in Table 2.

Following this nomenclature, chlorophyll may be described as the phyllin of pheophytin, phytyl chlorophyllide, etc. The letters a and b may be suffixed to any of the above to denote whether a methyl or formyl group is present at position 3. An additional compound in this group is protochlorophyll, which occurs in seedlings grown in the dark and in seed coats of the *Cucurbitaceae*. Its structure is the same as that of chlorophyll a except that ring IV is in the unreduced form. Magnesium-free protopheophytin may also occur in some seed coats.

TABLE 2. NOMENCLATURE OF CHLOROPHYLL DERIVATIVES

NAME	STRUCTURE
chlorin	a dihydroporphyrin
rhodin	a dihydroporphyrin with carbonyl adjacent to a pyrrole ring
phorbin	dihydroporphyrin with additional carbocyclic ring
phorbide	an ester of phorbin
pheophorbide	methyl ester of phorbin
phytin	phytyl ester of phorbin
pheophytin	methyl and phytyl ester of phorbin
phyllin	a magnesium derivative of any of the above
chlorophyllin	magnesium derivative of phytin
chlorophyllide	magnesium derivative of pheophorbide

ISOLATION

The metal-free porphyrins may be extracted at a pH of 2-5 using ether or ether-acetic acid mixtures. The highly carboxylated uroporphyrins, however, are insoluble in ether and can be adsorbed on talc or calcium phosphate gel after ether extraction to remove any other porphyrins (cf. Sveinsson *et al.*, 9).

There are no generally applicable procedures for the preparation of hematin compounds from plants. Since all of them are firmly bound to protein, the procedures used are those of protein chemistry rather than porphyrin chemistry. A method suitable for preparing a given cytochrome from one organism may be entirely unsuited for preparing the same cytochrome from another organism, or for preparing a different cytochrome from the same organism. A few specific papers in this field may be cited as guides and are listed on the following page:

COMPONENT	SOURCE	AUTHOR AND REFERENCE
Cytochrome c	wheat germ	Goddard (10), Hagihara *et al.* (11)
Cytochrome f	parsley	Davenport and Hill (12)
Peroxidase	horse radish	Kenten and Mann (13)
Catalase	spinach	Galston, Bonnichsen and Arnon (14)
Hemoglobin	soybean nodules	Sternberg and Virtanen (15)

This situation is somewhat better with regard to the chlorophyll pigments. Here the problem is not so much one of obtaining a goodly quantity of pigment as in being assured that the pigment obtained is not an artifact, since degradation easily occurs during the purification procedure. Acetone is most commonly used to extract the pigments from either fresh or dried leaves (80% acetone is used for dried leaves). Ethanol is effective, but the enzyme chlorophyllase present in fresh leaves catalyzes the reaction:

$$\text{ethanol} + \text{chlorophyll} \rightarrow \text{phytol} + \text{ethyl chlorophyllide}$$

so that unless chlorophyllase is inactivated or extraction is carried out for a very short time, the chlorophyll will be contaminated. Another pitfall in the initial extraction is the ready removal of magnesium from chlorophyll in acidic solutions. Many plant extracts contain enough organic acids to bring about this degradation to pheophytin. It can be avoided by grinding with acetone in the presence of a weak base such as 1% magnesium carbonate or dimethylaniline. Other precautions may sometimes be taken such as grinding in the cold and/or in the dark.

Some separation of the pigments in the acetone extract may be achieved by solvent partition methods, but column chromatography is generally the method of choice. Water and petroleum ether are added to the acetone extract and the petroleum ether layer which now contains the pigments is washed with water to remove acetone and dried with anhydrous sodium sulfate before chromatography. The most valuable adsorbent is powdered sucrose. Stronger adsorbents, such as magnesium oxide, which are useful for carotenes, may cause subtle, isomeric changes in the delicate chlorophyll pigments. Anderson and Calvin (16) have found that the purest chlorophyll can be obtained by chromatographing first on powdered polyethylene and then on sucrose. More detailed purification procedures and tests for impurities are given in the review of Smith and Benitez (17) and the book by Strain (18).

CHARACTERIZATION

The observation of absorption spectra is probably the one most important technique for characterization of both hematin and chlorophyll derivatives, although it does not permit distinction between closely related compounds. All porphyrins have four absorption bands in the visible region between 500-700 mμ. The heights of these peaks relative to each other vary with the particular structure. Stronger than any of these bands is the so-called Soret band in the near ultra violet at about 400-450 mμ. Application of a low dispersion, direct vision spectroscope to intact plant tissues has yielded many important results and is still the most useful method for studying plant cytochromes. Details of the procedures are well described by Hartree (19). Because of the low concentration of hematin compounds in most plant tissues, rather thick sections must be used to observe light absorption; a powerful light source is required; and the tissues may be infiltrated with glycerol or pyridine to increase transparency. Since the bands of reduced cytochromes are most distinct and informative, oxygen must be excluded or a reducing agent such as sodium dithionite (hydrosulfite) added. Under these conditions a spectrum like that of Figure 13-1 may be observed in, for example, an onion bulb:

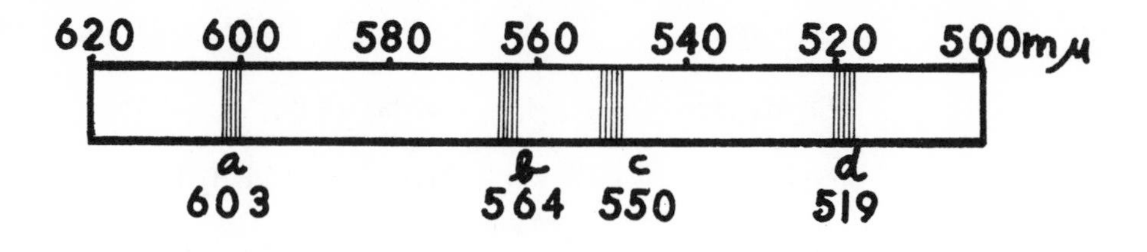

FIGURE 13-1

The bands labelled a, b, and c represent the so-called α-bands of cytochromes a, b, and c. Band d represents the combined β-bands of cytochromes b and c. If bands are not observable in the intact tissue because other pigments interfere (e.g. chlorophyll in leaves) or because the hematin compounds are too dilute, modified approaches may be possible (20). Interfering pigments can be removed by solvent extraction and/or a particulate preparation from the homogenized tissue used for observation as in the procedure of Bhagvat and Hill (21). Faint bands may be intensified by observation at the temperature of liquid air. This intensification, which may be as much as 20-fold, depends on the microcrystalline structure of the frozen medium rather than any change in the pigments themselves. A sensitive method for determining total hematin involves treatment of the material with pyridine (20%) and sodium dithionite (1%) in alkaline solution (0. 1N NaOH). This results in denaturation of associated proteins and formation of hemochromogens from any iron porphyrins which may be present. In these derivatives the 5 and 6 coordination positions of ferrous porphyrin are occupied by pyridine, and a strong absorption band at 556 mμ results for protoporphyrin hemochromogen, at 551 mμ for the hemochromogen from cytochrome c, and 585 mμ for the hemochromogen of the A cytochromes. Hemochromogen formation may be made the basis for quantitative estimation of total hematin in plant tissues (22).

The absorption spectra of chlorophyll derivatives may be observed in intact tissues using the direct vision spectroscope, but more frequently purified preparations are studied spectrophotometrically. The exact positions of absorption maxima may vary slightly with the solvent used. Figure 2 gives the spectra for chlorophylls a and b. The sharp band at about 660 mμ is characteristic of dihydroporphyrins. It is also seen in pheophytin, but the addition of chelated magnesium makes it even more intense. The absorption spectroscopy of chlorophyll and other porphyrins has been reviewed by Rabinowitch (23) and Aronoff (24). The application of spectrophotometry to quantitative measurement of chlorophyll is described by Smith and Benitez (17) and Bruinsma (25).

Fluorescence spectra of porphyrins have also been extensively studied and are important in characterization. However, among natural products only the metal-free porphyrins and chlorophylls fluoresce. The iron porphyrins do not. Fluorescence spectrum curves for a variety of compounds are presented by French *et al.* (26).

The second most important property in characterizing porphyrins has been their solubility behavior especially with regard to dilute hydrochloric acid. This solubility is naturally related to the proportion of polar and non-polar groups in the molecule. Phytol-containing compounds are much less soluble than compounds with free carboxyl groups, so that partition between ether and various concentrations of HCl has been useful in separating porphyrins from mixtures. Quantitatively a "hydrochloric acid number" can be assigned to each porphyrin and defined as the percentage concentration of HCl which will extract 2/3 of the compound from an equal volume of its ether solution (usually at a concentration of 0. 02%). Some representative HCl-numbers are given in the accompanying table on p. 270.

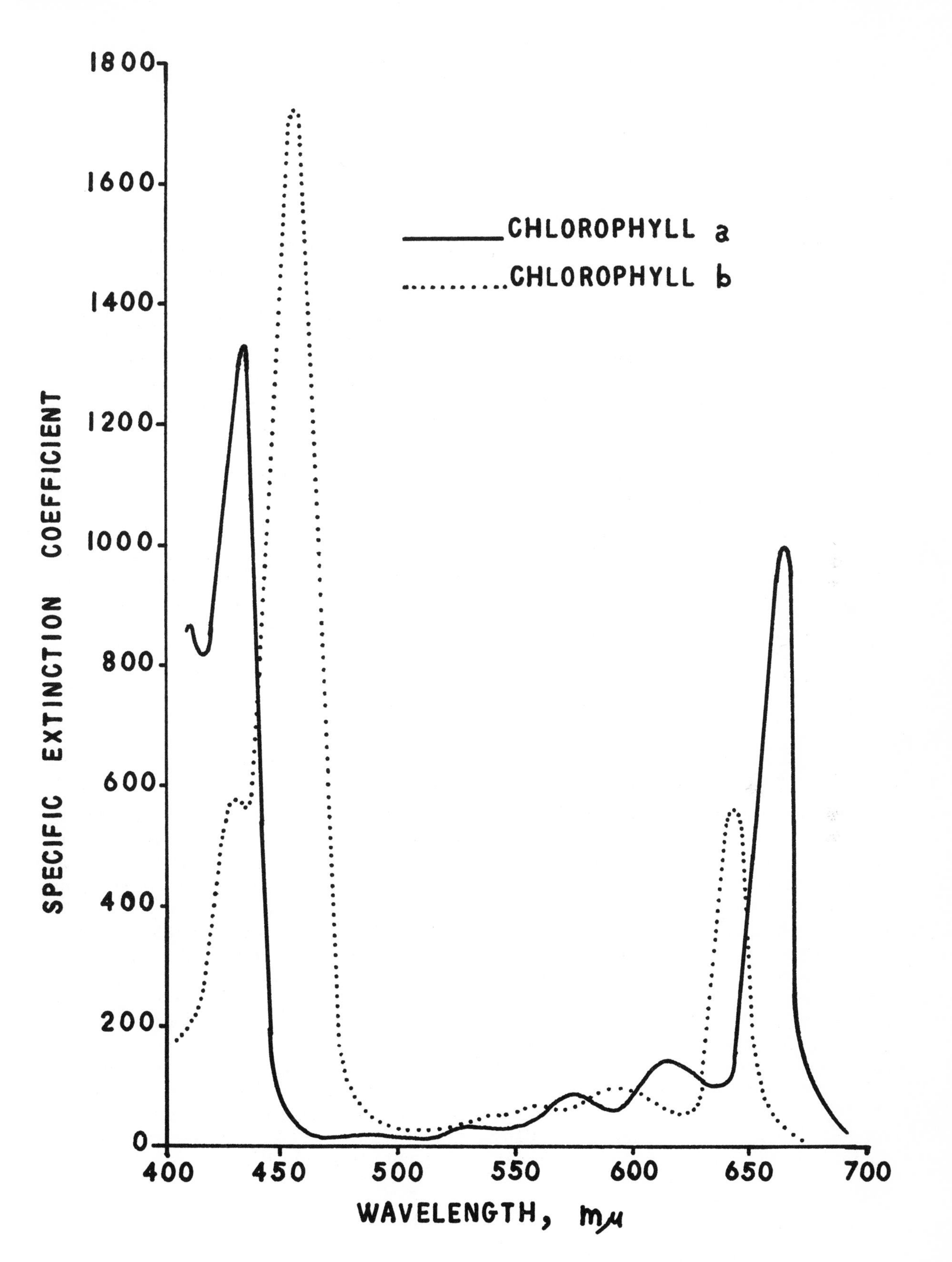

FIGURE 13-2: ABSORPTION SPECTRA OF CHLOROPHYLLS

COMPOUND	HCl NUMBER
Coproporphyrin III	0.09
Protoporphyrin IX	2.0
Pheophytin a	29.0

A larger compilation of values is given by Granick and Gilder (27).

Paper chromatographic procedures have not been applied to the porphyrins as extensively as to some other classes of compounds. Separation of metal-free porphyrins has been achieved by Nicholas (28) and Kehl and Stich (29) with a lutidine-water system, but closely related isomers cannot be separated in this way. By converting porphyrins to their methyl esters and using solvent mixtures of chloroform, kerosene, propanol and dioxane, Chu, Green and Chu (30) were able to separate closely allied compounds (cf. also 31). Paper chromatography of the pigments related to chlorophyll has been developed by several workers (32-36). Non-polar solvents such as petroleum ether, toluene, chlorobenzene, with sometimes a trace of an alcohol added, have been most effective. Spots on the chromatograms are easily detected, even at minute concentrations, because of their intense fluorescence in ultraviolet light. No attempt seems to have been made to apply paper chromatography to the iron porphyrins.

Preliminary structure determinations on the porphyrins should be facilitated by the procedure of Nicolaus *et al.* (37, 38, 39) whereby small quantities of porphyrin can be oxidized with alkaline permanganate and the split products identified on paper chromatograms. These products are pyrrole acids and can be detected by spraying with diazotized sulfanilic acid. The acids obtained indicate what side chains are present but not, of course, the order of the pyrrole rings around the porphyrin nucleus.

METABOLIC PATHWAYS

The accompanying chart shows the probable course of biosynthesis for both the hematin and chlorophyll pigments in higher plants.

Biosynthesis of porphyrins (including chlorophyll) has been reviewed by Gibson *et al.*(40). Several of the enzymes catalyzing reactions of porphyrin synthesis have been demonstrated in wheat leaves (41); but, in general, the porphyrin biosynthetic pathway has been studied very little in the higher plants. The first stages from succinate plus glycine to protoporphyrin have been primarily investigated in vertebrate tissues. The later stages in chlorophyll formation have been developed by studies on algae (42, 43). The conversion of protochlorophyll to chlorophyll has been well-substantiated in higher plants although there may be differences in detail from plant to plant. In some, phytol may be already esterified to the protochlorophyll so that a single reductive step forms chlorophyll. In others protochlorophyll may have a free carboxyl group which is esterified with phytol after ring IV has been reduced (44-48). There is also some question about whether a single protochlorophyll is present which forms chlorophyll a, followed by conversion of a into b or whether there may be separate protochlorophylls a and b (49, 50). Bogorad (51, 52) has shown that spinach leaf preparations can catalyze the formation of uroporphyrin from porphobilinogen; and Goodwin *et al.* (53) have identified a compound like uroporphyrin as a normal constituent of certain *Vicia* cells.

The overall reaction:

$$\delta\text{ - aminolevulinic acid} \rightarrow \text{chlorophylls}$$

has been studied by Duranton *et al.* (54) who fed δ - aminolevulinic acid-4-C^{14} to tobacco plants. In the dark radioactivity appeared in protochlorophyll, in the light in chlorophylls a and b with three times higher activity in the a form. Similar results have also been

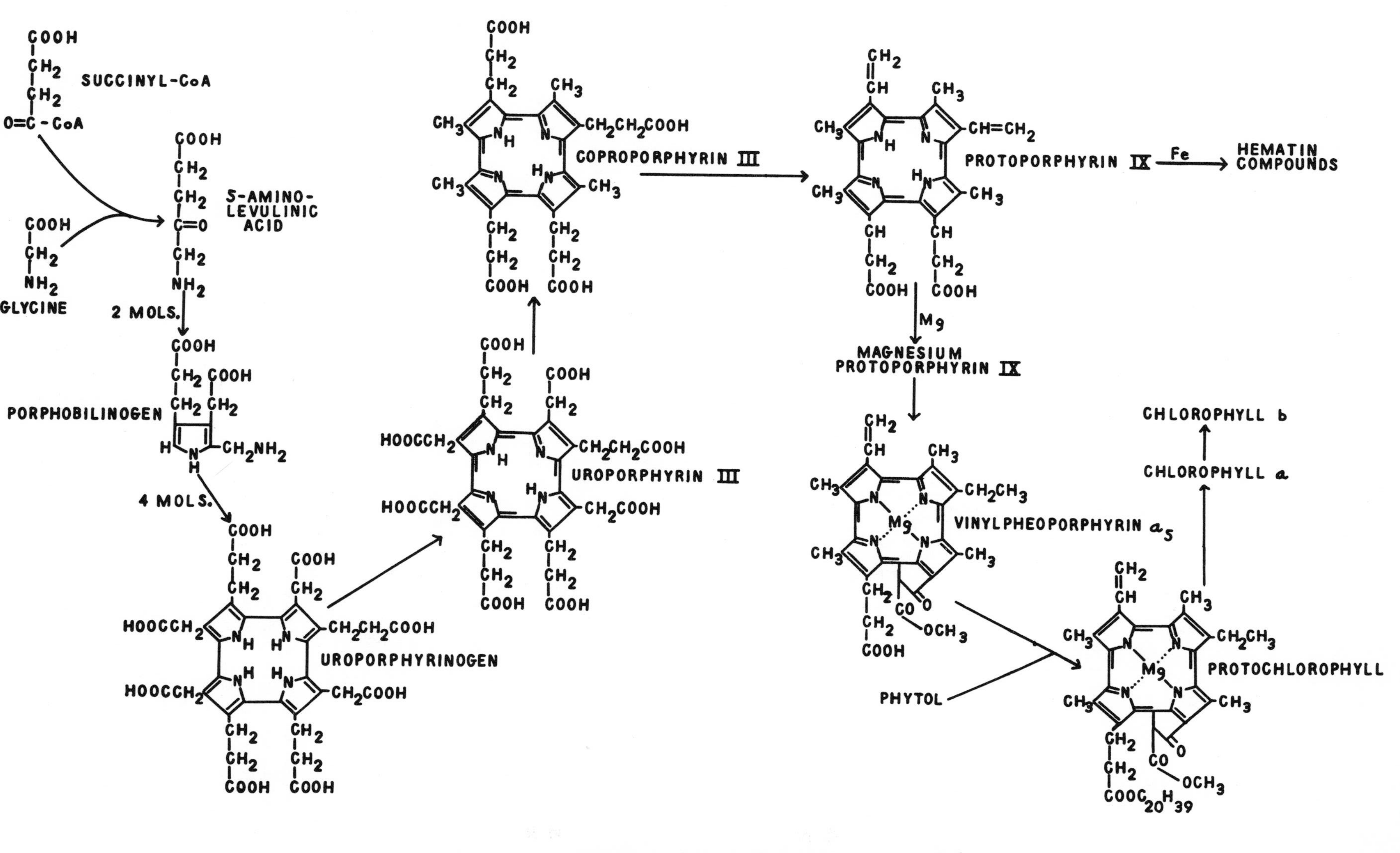

FIGURE 13-3: PATHWAYS OF PORPHYRIN BIOSYNTHESIS

obtained with barley (55). The mechanism by which the unsymmetrical type III prophyrins are formed from porphobilinogen is still in doubt. For a discussion of possible ways whereby one of the pyrrole rings might be "turned around" see (56-58).

GENERAL REFERENCE

Granick, S. and Gilder, H., "Distribution, Structure and Properties of the Tetrapyrroles," Adv. Enzymol. 7 305 (1947).
Hartree, E. F., "Haematin Compounds" in Paech and Tracey 4 197.
Lemberg, R.: "Porphyrins in Nature." Fortschr. Chem. Org. Naturstoffe 11 299 (1954).
Lemberg, R. and Legge, J. W.: Hematin Compounds and Bile Pigments, Interscience, N. Y., 1949.
Rabinowitch, E. I., Photosynthesis, Vol. 2 Pt. 1, Interscience, N. Y., 1951.
Smith, J. H. C. and Benitez, A. "Chlorophylls" in Paech and Tracey 4 142.
Many articles in Ruhland 5.

BIBLIOGRAPHY

1. Takashima, S., Nature 169 182 (1952).
2. Ardao, C. and Vennesland, B., Plant Physiol. 35 368 (1960).
3. Gray, L. F. and Daniel, L. J., J. Nutrition 67 623 (1959).
4. Thompson, R. H. S., Science 137 405 (1962).
5. Hartree, E. F., Adv. Enzymol. 18 1 (1957).
6. Smith, L. and Chance, B., Ann. Rev. Plant Physiol. 9 449 (1958).
7. James, W. O. and Leech, R. M., Endeavour 19 108 (1960).
8. King, H. K., Sci. Prog. 48 695 (1960).
9. Sveinsson, S. L., Rimington, C., and Barnes, H. D., Scand. J. Clin. Lab. Invest. 1 2 (1949).
10. Goddard, D. R., Am. J. Bot. 31 270 (1944).
11. Hagihara, B., Tagawa, K., Morikawa, I., Shin, M. and Okunuki, K., J. Biochem. (Japan) 46 321 (1959).
12. Davenport, H. E. and Hill, R., Proc. Royal Soc. (B) 139 327 (1952).
13. Kenten, R. H. and Mann, P. J G. Biochem. J. 57 347 (1954).
14. Galston, A. W., Bonnichsen, R. K. and Arnon, D. I.; Acta. Chem. Scand. 5 781 (1951).
15. Sternberg, H. and Virtanen, A. I., Acta. Chem. Scand. 6 1342 (1952).
16. Anderson, A. F. H. and Calvin, M., Nature 194 285 (1962).
17. Smith, H. G. C. and Benitez, A., in Paech and Tracey, 4 142.
18. Strain, H. H., Chloroplast Pigments and Chromatographic Analysis, Phi Lambda Upsilon, Penn. State Univ., University Park, Penna., 1958.
19. Hartree, E. F., in Paech and Tracey. 4 197.
20. Lundegårdh, H., Physiol. Plantarum 15 390 (1962).
21. Bhagvat, K. and Hill, R., New Phytol. 50 112 (1951).
22. Elliott, K. A. C. and Keilin, D., Proc. Royal Soc. (B) 114 210 (1934).
23. Rabinowitch, E., Rev. Mod. Phys. 16 226 (1944).
24. Aronoff, S., Chem. Rev. 47 175 (1950).
25. Bruinsma, J., Biochim. Biophys. Acta 52 576 (1961).
26. French, C. S., Smith, J. H. C., Virgin, H. I., Airth, R. L., Plant Physiol. 31 369 (1956).
27. See General References to this chapter.
28. Nicholas, R. E. H., Biochem. J. 48 309 (1951).
29. Kehl, R. and Stich, W., Z. Physiol. Chem. 290 151 (1952).
30. Chu, T. C., Green, A. A. and Chu, E. J., J. Biol. Chem. 190 643 (1951).
31. Falk, J. E. and Benson, A., Biochem. J. 55 101 (1953).
32. Bauer, L., Naturwiss. 39 88 (1952).
33. Lind, E. F., Lane, H. C., and Gleason, L. S., Plant Physiol. 28 325 (1953).
34. Douin, R., Rev. Gen. Bot. 60 777 (1953).
35. Šesták, Z., J. Chromatog. 1 293 (1958).
36. Holden, M., Biochim. Biophys. Acta 56 378 (1962).
37. Nicolaus, R. A., Mangoni, L. and Caglioti, L., Ann. Chim. (Rome) 46 793 (1956).
38. Nicolaus, R. A., Mangoni, L. and Nicoletti, R., ibid. 47 178 (1957).
39. Mangoni, L. and Nicolaus, R. A., Ann. Chim. (Rome) 49 531 (1959). (Chem. Abstr. 53 22007 (1959).
40. Gibson, K. D., Matthew, M., Neuberger, A. and Tait, G. H., Nature 192 204 (1961).

41. Nandi, D. L. and Waygood, E. R., Plant Physiol. 36 Suppl. xlvi (1961).
42. Granick, S., J. Biol. Chem. 172 717 (1948).
43. Granick, S., J. Biol. Chem. 175 333 (1948).
44. Koski, V. M., French, C. S., and Smith, J. H. C., Arch. Biochem. Biophys. 31 1 (1951).
45. Wolff, J. B. and Price, L., Arch. Biochem. Biophys. 72 293 (1957).
46. Godnev, T. N., Shlyk, A. A. and Lyakhnovich, Y. P., Fiziol. Rastenii 4 393 (1957). (Chem. Abstr. 52 4755).
47. Fischer, F. G. and Rüdiger, W., Ann. 627 35 (1959).
48. Butler, W. L., Biochem. Biophys. Research Communications 2 419 (1960).
49. Seybold, A., Planta 26 712 (1936/37).
50. Egle, K., Naturwiss. 40 569 (1953).
51. Bogorad, L., J. Biol. Chem. 233 501 (1958).
52. Bogorad, L., Biol. Chem. 233 510 (1958).
53. Goodwin, R. H., Koski, V. M. and Owens, O. V. H., Am. J. Bot. 38 629 (1951).
54. Duranton, J., Galmiche, J. M. and Roux, E., Compt. rend. 246 992 (1958).
55. Wolwertz, M. R., Arch. intern. physiol. et biochim. 68 849 (1960).
56. Wittenberg, J. B., Nature 184 876 (1959).
57. Mathewson, J H. and Corwin, A. H., J. Am. Chem. Soc. 83 135 (1961).
58. Kay, I. T., Proc. Nat. Acad. Sci. U. S. 48 901 (1962).

Chapter 14
MISCELLANEOUS NITROGEN AND SULFUR COMPOUNDS

The compounds treated in this chapter have a wide diversity of chemical and functional characteristics. Their biogenetic interrelationships are also for the most part obscure. However, in the absence of metabolic evidence, it seems likely that many of the simpler nitrogen and sulfur compounds found in plants are derived by common types of reaction schemes from the amino acids. By extension, plausible pathways can be suggested leading from the amino acids to more complex compounds of this group. The plausibility of such pathways has justified the organization of this chapter; but as direct evidence becomes available, considerable revision may be necessary. Because of the diversity of compounds covered, each section of this chapter is independent of the others as regards characterization, isolation and metabolic pathways.

AMINES

It is not generally realized how widespread simple amines are in higher plants although they are well-known as metabolic products of microorganisms. A survey of 220 species of flowering plants and mosses by Kamienski (1) revealed amines in a large number of them. Most widespread was isopentyl amine:

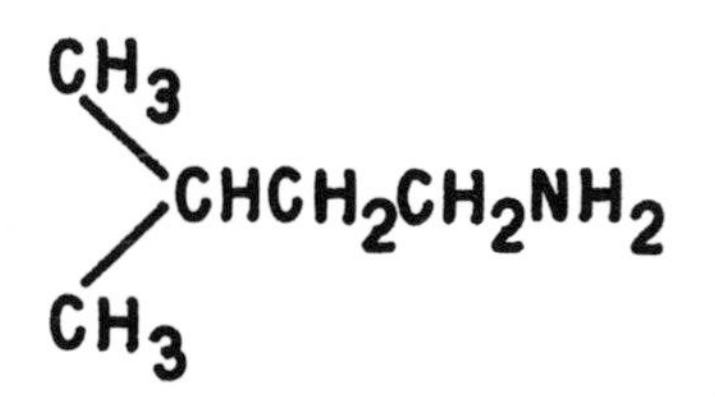

This occurred in 75 of the species examined. Twenty-five species had methylamine and 19 trimethylamine. Strangely, only one had dimethylamine. The chemistry of simple amines is well described in general textbooks of organic chemistry and will not be discussed in any detail here. The standard reference on natural amines is the book of Guggenheim cited under "General References". There is no sharp dividing line between amines and alkaloids. This ambiguity becomes particularly evident with the more complex amines such as histamine which might well be called an alkaloid except that it was first found in animals and does not occur at a high concentration in plants. Several distinctions have been made to separate simple amines from alkaloids, but none is completely satisfactory--e.g.:

1. Alkaloids must have nitrogen in a heterocyclic ring.
2. Alkaloids are more soluble in organic solvents like chloroform, while simple amines are more soluble in water.

The distinction made here, based on biogenesis, is that a simple amine has its complete carbon skeleton (except for N-methyl groups) derived from a single precursor, normally an amino acid. In the formation of alkaloids carbon--carbon and carbon-nitrogen condensations occur both inter-and intra-molecularly. Thus, by decarboxylation methylamine is derived from glycine, ethanolamine from serine, putrescine from ornithine, etc. The methylamines may also be derived by an oxidative splitting of choline. The N-methyl groups found in secondary and tertiary amines, or quaternary ammonium compounds like choline, are derived from methionine and/or formate.

Of great pharmacological interest are the so-called pressor amines which show a powerful effect on the blood pressure of animals. Many of these compounds are decarboxylation products of aromatic amino acids and histidine. They are found widely distributed in plants although usually in small amounts (2). In some cases, though, the presence of pressor amines may account for the toxicity or pharmacodynamic effects of certain plants. For example, tyramine is found in the poisonous berries of mistletoe *(Viscum album);* histamine, serotonin, and acetylcholine in the hairs of stinging nettles (*Urtica* spp.); and ephedrine in the ancient Chinese drug plant ma-huang (*Ephedra* spp.).

Some amine structures are given in Table 1 which shows the amino acid from which each is derived. The common names of corresponding N-methyl and quaternary ammonium compounds (betaines) are given in the third column only if these are known as higher plant constituents. Indole amines derived from tryptophan are discussed in a later section.

No generalization can be expected to describe the function of all amines in plants, and for most of them even suggestions are lacking. Methylated compounds may serve as reservoirs for methylation reactions. Choline has been the most widely investigated of these compounds. It is a part of many phospholipids (q. v.); its phosphoryl derivative may function as an important phosphate carrier in plant sap (3):

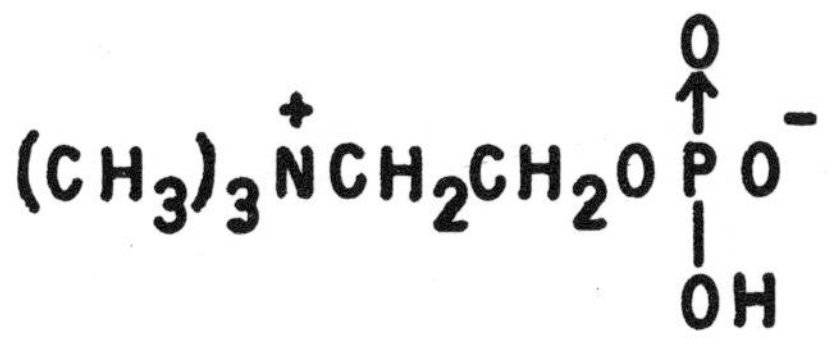

$$(CH_3)_3\overset{+}{N}CH_2CH_2O\overset{\overset{O}{\uparrow}}{\underset{\underset{OH}{|}}{P}}O^-$$

After oxidation to glycinebetaine, choline can sometimes serve as a methyl donor (e.g. in nicotine synthesis). Choline sulfate may function as a sulfur transporting agent and reservoir (4).

Isolation of the simple amines from plants takes advantages of their basic nature. Thus, they may be separated on cation exchange resins. The more volatile ones may be separated from plant materials by steam distillation from an alkaline mixture (after preliminary removal of volatile neutral and acidic compounds). One danger to be recognized is that many plants contain amine oxidases which must be promptly inactivated if amines are to be preserved when cellular structure is broken down. Non-volatile amines can be isolated by first removing proteins from the plant extract with heat, trichloracetic acid, etc. and then precipitating the amines with various reagents. A reagent useful for precipitating amines from protein-free solutions is phosphotungstic acid in 5% H_2SO_4. Ammonium and potassium ions should be removed since they are also precipitated by this reagent. Several techniques are available for fractionating the phosphotungstate precipitate and recovering free amines from it. Dragendorff's reagent ($KBiI_4$) and Reinecke's salt ($NH_4Cr(NH_3)_2 \cdot SCN_4 \cdot H_2O$) have been extensively used to precipitate the quaternary ammonium bases (5, 6).

Several simple tests are available for characterization of amines, in particular for determining whether an unknown compound is a primary, secondary, or tertiary amine or a quaternary ammonium base. Some of these tests may be effectively applied to paper

TABLE 1. SOME NATURALLY OCCURRING AMINES

AMINO ACID	AMINE	N-METHYL DERIVATIVES
glycine	CH_3NH_2 methylamine	$(CH_3)_4N^+$ tetramine
serine	$HOCH_2CH_2NH_2$ ethanolamine (colamine)	$(CH_3)_3N^+CH_2CH_2OH$ choline
ornithine	$H_2N(CH_2)_4NH_2$ putrescine	-------
lysine	$H_2N(CH_2)_5NH_2$ cadaverine	-------
valine	$(CH_3)_2CH\ CH_2NH_2$ isobutylamine	-------
phenylalanine	$C_6H_5-CH_2CH_2NH_2$ β-phenylethylamine	$C_6H_5-CH(OH)CH(NHCH_3)CH_3$ ephedrine
tyrosine	$HO-C_6H_4-CH_2CH_2NH_2$ tyramine	$HO-C_6H_4-CH_2CH_2N(CH_3)_2$ hordenine $HO-C_6H_4-CH_2CH_2\overset{+}{N}(CH_3)_3$ candicine
histidine	(imidazolyl)$-CH_2CH_2NH_2$ histamine	-------
leucine	$(CH_3)_2CHCH_2CH_2NH_2$ isopentylamine	-------

Table 1. Continued

AMINO ACID	AMINE	N-METHYL DERIVATIVES
pipecolic acid	(ring structure with NH) piperidine	-------
arginine	$H_2N\text{-}(CH_2)_4\ NHCNH_2$ (C=NH) agmatine	-------

chromatograms so that separation and at least a partial identification can be made at once. Kamienski (7) has developed a general method for determining volatile amines in plants. Paper chromatography is carried out with a butanol-acetic acid-water solvent. Primary amines are detected with ninhydrin, secondary amines with nitroprusside, and tertiary amines with phosphomolybdic acid. Secondary and tertiary amines may also be detected with iodine vapor. Tertiary amines and quaternary ammonium compounds can be detected with potassium tetraiodobismuthate (Dragendorff's reagent). A preliminary separation of the amines by distillation, precipitation, etc. is necessary before paper chromatography since the detection reagents are not specific--- i. e. ninhydrin reacts with amino acids, nitroprusside with sulfhydryl compounds, and alkaloids with Dragendorff's reagent. Other special reagents may be applied for detection of certain amines, such as diazotized sulfanilic acid (Pauli's reagent) for tyramine, histamine, etc. Blau (8) has identified amines in biological materials by concentrating them on ion exchange resin and then chromatographing on paper. Many other specific reactions will be found in the general references.

ISOBUTYLAMIDES

Brief mention needs to be given to a group of isobutylamine derivatives which are combined by an amide linkage with various unsaturated fatty acids. Analogous compounds involving other aliphatic amines are not known to be naturally occurring, and the isobutylamides are of particular interest because of their insecticidal properties. Several plants which have been used as insecticides since ancient times owe their effectiveness to the presence of isobutylamides. Pellitory *(Anacyclus pyrethrum)* is probably the best known of these plants. Its roots yield the insecticide pellitorine which has been shown to be a mixture of several different isobutylamides. The most abundant is an amide of 2, 4-decadienoic acid:

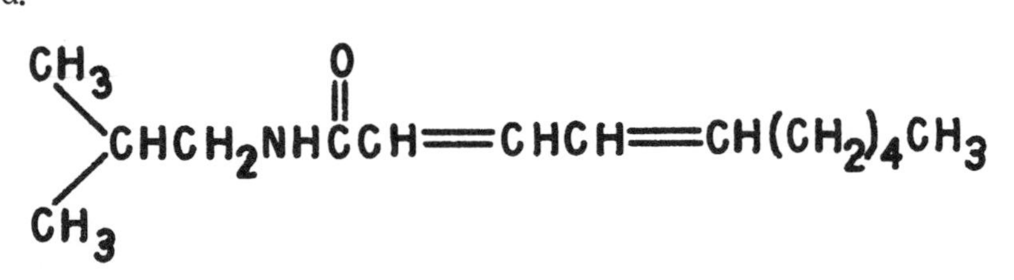

Other isobutylamides of unsaturated acids (some acetylenic) from C_{10} to C_{18} are found in the same plant and also in a few others. In most cases mixtures seem to be present and it is difficult to separate them, so that it is not always possible to decide which component is the active ingredient of a natural isobutylamide insecticide. Characterization of the isobutylamides depends on acidic hydrolysis and identification of the fatty acid and isobutylamine. A discussion of these compounds may be found in a review of naturally occurring insecticides by Feinstein and Jacobson (9).

THIOLS AND SULFIDES

The simple alkyl thiols (mercaptans) and sulfides have much in common with the amines discussed in the previous section. They are both volatile, with an offensive odor; and biogenetically they are probably both derived from amino acids. The basic structures of the sulfur compounds to be discussed in this section are as follows:

RSH	thiols (mercaptans)
RSR'	sulfides
RSSR'	disulfides
RS_xR'	polysulfides
$R\overset{O}{\overset{\uparrow}{S}}R'$	sulfoxides
$(CH_3)_2\overset{+}{S}R$	methylsulfonium compounds

Examples of all of these types occur in higher plants, and many more probably remain to be discovered. Some of the best known ones appear to be artifacts which are formed during the isolation process. The sulfur amino acids are treated in Chapter 10. The simple mercaptans are readily soluble in aqueous alkali and form insoluble mercaptides with many heavy metal cations. The name mercaptan was originally given to them because of the readiness with which they form mercury salts. Mercaptans are readily oxidized in the air to disulfides, so that it may be advisable to maintain a nitrogen atmosphere while working with them. Methyl mercaptan (methanethiol) is found in radish *(Raphanus* spp.) roots; n-propyl mercaptan in onions *(Allium cepa)*. 2, 2'-dithioisobutyric acid and the corresponding disulfide are found in asparagus:

$$(HSCH_2)_2CHCOOH$$

An unusual thiol of the following structure has been reported in cabbage *(Brassica oleracea)* (10):

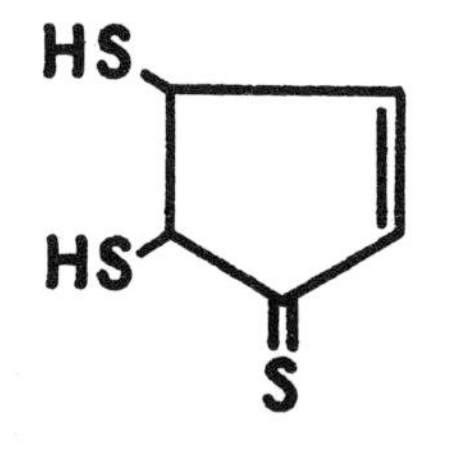

Other thiol compounds are known to have important metabolic functions (e.g. coenzyme A, thioctic acid), but no metabolic role has been assigned to the simple mercaptans unless they serve an ecological function in repelling some herbivores or parasites.

The dialkyl sulfides are less volatile than the mercaptans and have a less unpleasant odor. With mercuric salts they form coordination complexes rather than true salts. Some essential oils have been reported to contain dimethyl sulfide, and divinyl sulfide is the major constituent of ramsons oil *(Allium ursinum)*. Pineapple juice *(Ananas comosus)* has the methyl ester of 2-methylthiopropionoic acid. Garlic oil which was formerly believed to contain diallyl sulfide is now known to have only di- and polysulfides. Dimethyl sulfide probably occurs more frequently than other sulfides because it is a decomposition product of the thetins (q. v.). Cyclic sulfides have been found in plants of the family *Compositae*. Obviously related terthienyl, and bithienyl compounds are found in the marigold *(Tagetes erecta)* (11). Another thiophene derivative has recently been reported in the roots of *Chrysthanthenum vulgare* (12).

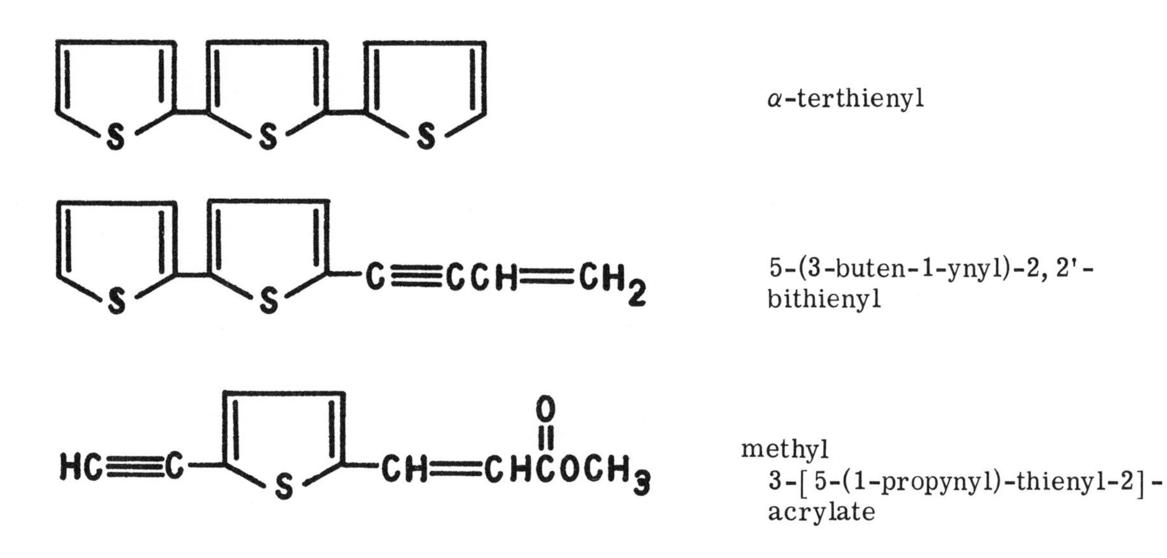

It seems clear that such compounds are derived from the acetylenic compounds which are widespread in the *Compositae* (cf. Chap. 6).

Disulfides and polysulfides are less volatile than the sulfides but have a more offensive odor. They react slowly with mercuric chloride. The S-S bond is split and mercaptide-like derivatives are formed. Polysulfides tend to lose sulfur and form disulfides when they are distilled. There is no conclusive evidence for the occurrence of di- and polysulfides *as such* in plants. Although they are found in essential oils of garlic, asafetida and onion, they probably arise through secondary transformations brought about by plant enzymes and the heat of distillation. Alliin, the native constituent of garlic, is broken down enzymatically to allicin when the plant is crushed:

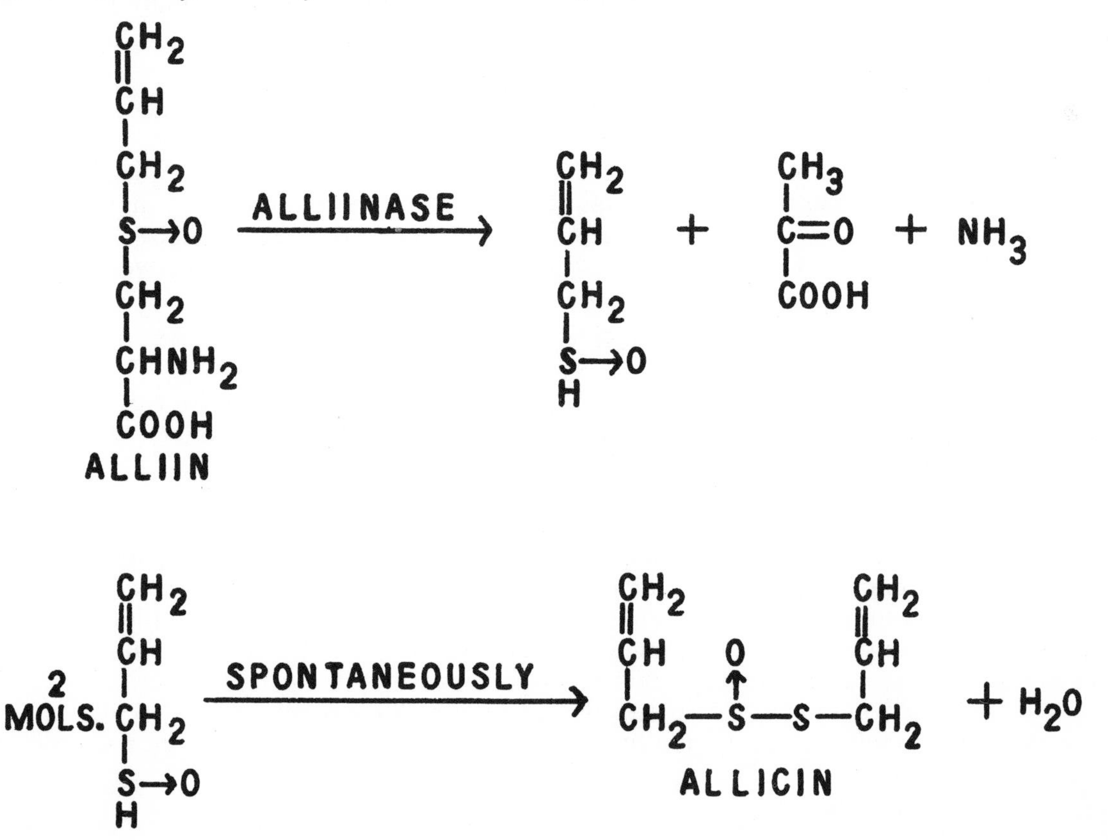

Upon distillation the sulfoxide, allicin, forms diallyl-disulfide, diallyltrisulfide and allyl propyl disulfide which are constituents of commercial garlic oil. Some such series of reactions probably accounts for the presence of disulfides in other similar oils. Even carbon disulfide has been reported in cabbage (13).

Alliin was the first natural sulfoxide to be discovered, but a few others have since been found. Some sulfoxide amino acids are included in Chapter 10. Other natural sulfoxides are also isothiocyanates and will be mentioned with this group of compounds. Further oxidation of a sulfoxide yields a sulfone (RSO_2R'). Only a few natural sulfones are known, and they are regarded as secondary products derived from sulfoxides. A sulfonic acid, sulfoacetic acid, has been found in *Erythrina* spp. (14), and another sulfonic acid is present as the sulfolipid of chloroplasts (15).

The sulfoxides are of interest because of their antibiotic action. Allicin is bacteriocidal and also inhibits several enzymes *in vitro* (16). In onion S-methyl-and S-n-propylcysteine-sulfoxides occur. When the onion is crushed, these are enzymatically converted to thiosulfinates which have an even stronger anti-microbial action (17):

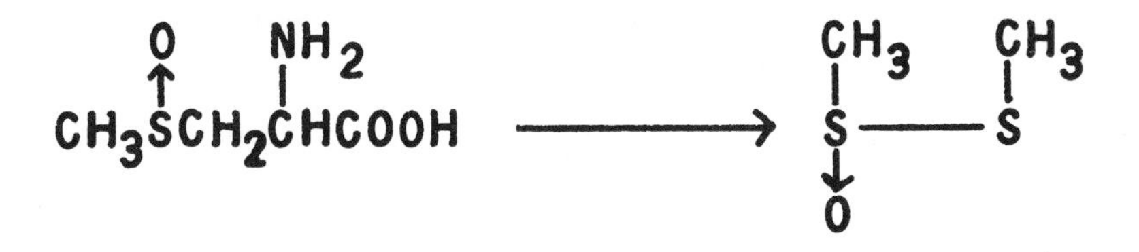

This reaction is clearly analogous to the formation of allicin shown previously. Sulfur compounds of food plants have recently been reviewed by Virtanen (18).

The thetins are metabolically the most interesting of the compounds discussed in this section since they are able to act as donors of methyl groups for several important methylation reactions (19). They are sulfonium salts analogous to the quaternary nitrogen bases. Like the quaternary nitrogen compounds they may be precipitated as Reineckates, picrates, etc. Dimethyl-β-propiothetin:

$$(CH_3)_2\overset{+}{S}CH_2CH_2COOH$$

was the first sulfonium compound to be found in plants. It is rather common in algae, but has not been reported in higher plants. Similar sulfonium compounds may, however, be found in *Equisetum* spp. and some ferns (20). On treatment with cold alkali or with an enzyme present in some marine algae dimethyl-β-propiothetin decomposes as follows:

$$(CH_3)_2\overset{+}{S}CH_2CH_2COOH \rightarrow (CH_3)_2S + CH_2 = CHCOOH + H^+$$

Where dimethyl sulfide is found as a natural product, it probably results from a similar reaction. Methylmethioninesulfonium salts have been detected in a variety of plants. They release dimethyl sulfide on treatment with boiling alkali.

The simple thiols and sulfides are generally isolated by taking advantage of the insoluble salts or complexes which they form with certain metal ions, primarily mercuric. Insoluble mercaptides are formed by reacting thiols with mercuric chloride or cyanide. Sulfides form insoluble corrdination complexes with mercuric chloride but not with mercuric cyanide. This difference in reactivity may be used to separate mercaptans from sulfides. The original compounds are regenerated by treating the insoluble precipitates with acid. As noted before, disulfides are split by mercuric salts; so that they may not be isolated in their original form by this method. However, it must be recalled that simple disulfides are probably artifacts rather than true natural products; and their precursors (i. e. amino acid sulfoxides) may be isolated by the methods used for other amino acids. The sulfonium compounds are distinguished from other sulfur compounds by their positive charge, and may therefore be separated on cation exchange resins or precipitated by complex anions such as Reineckates, chloroplatinates, phosphotungstates, etc. The original compound is then regenerated by treatment of the precipitate with acid. No procedures can be discussed in general terms for isolating the more unusual sulfur compounds since each one represents a special case.

Characterization of the simple sulfur compounds has relied heavily on the reactions with mercuric salts which have been described above. Basic amines may also be precipitated as mercury complexes. However, by distilling from an acidic mixture and passing volatile compounds into a solution of mercuric salt amines will be left behind and cause no interference. Under these conditions the appearance of a precipitate may be taken as evidence for simple sulfur compounds. It should also be noted that in many cases odor alone may be sufficient evidence for distinguishing between amines and volatile sulfur compounds.

For distinguishing among the different classes of sulfur compounds specific modifications of the mercury reaction have been developed. Other special reagents are also available. The best known of these is alkaline sodium nitroprusside solution which gives a purple color with sulfhydryl compounds. If disulfides are present, preliminary treatment with potassium cyanide splits the S-S bond so that nitroprusside is able to react. Amines also react with nitroprusside in the presence of carbonyl compounds such as acetone or acetaldehyde. The presence of methyl sulfonium compounds is indicated by the evolution of dimethyl sulfide on treating with alkali. Some sulfonium compounds require boiling with sodium hydroxide solution; others release dimethyl sulfide in the cold.

Because of their volatility the low molecular weight sulfur compounds are unsuited to paper chromatography. Gas chromatography has been useful in characterizing them (13). The non-volatile sulfur compounds may be separated and identified by paper chromatography. Valuable methods for this purpose have been described by Toennies and Kolb (21). A platinum chloride-potassium iodide reagent was found most generally valuable for detecting sulfur compounds on chromatograms although it does not react well with sulfoxides. Nitroprusside was used for sulfhydryl compounds and nitroprusside followed by sodium cyanide for disulfides.

A few suggestions have been made regarding the biosynthetic pathways of simple sulfur compounds, but not enough is known to attempt construction of a metabolic map. It may be assumed that sulfur amino acids are precursors, but the nature and number of enzymatic steps leading from them can only be guessed at. A general review of sulfur metabolism can be found in the book of Young and Maw listed under "General References." However, this gives very slight treatment to higher plants.

MUSTARD OIL GLYCOSIDES

The mustard oils have been known for many years and are economically important as the flavor constituents of such condiments as mustard, horseradish, and water cress. For the most part they are colorless liquids with a sharp, irritating odor and the ability to raise blisters on the skin. Before 1900 it was understood that the mustard oils are actually secondary products arising from breakdown of glucosides when cellular structure is disrupted. In addition to the general references, reviews of these compounds may be found in articles by Kjaer (22) and Zinner (23). It seems probable that a single general structure can be written for all glucosides of this group. Upon hydrolysis, however, the aglycones undergo rearrangement. In some cases the rearrangements are so extensive that the final product bears no apparent resemblance to the aglycone as it exists in the glucoside.

The general structure of all the parent glucosides is:

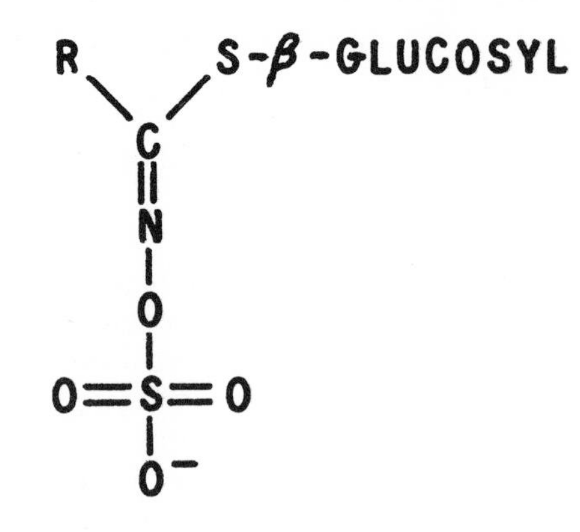

R may be a simple alkyl group or may be rather complex. As shown, the glucosides are anions which normally are found as potassium salts but may also occur as salts of organic nitrogen bases. The salts are colorless, water-soluble compounds which can be crystallized with difficulty. The glucosides are split by the action of an enzyme or enzyme complex known as myrosinase (24) which is present in all plants containing these glucosides. Simple hydrolysis would be expected to yield a hydroxamic acid, glucose, and inorganic sulfate. In fact, the hydromamic acid usually undergoes an immediate Lossen rearrangement to form an *iso*-thiocyanate:

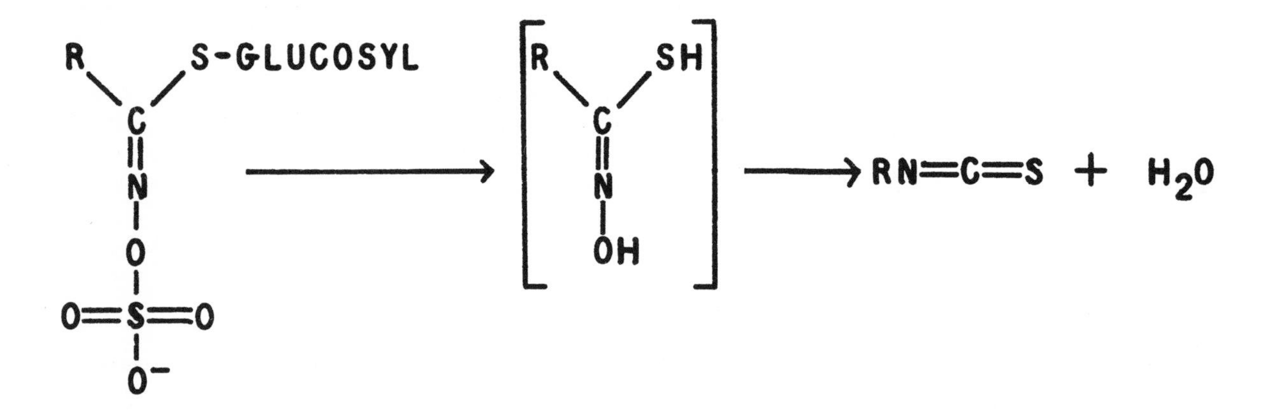

There are other alternate enzymatic processes which frequently occur to some extent. In some plants the R group migrates to sulfur rather than to nitrogen so that thiocyanates rather than *iso*-thiocyanates are formed (25). In *Lepidium sativum* both types of reaction go on simultaneously. In still other plants nitriles are formed by an entirely obscure reaction:

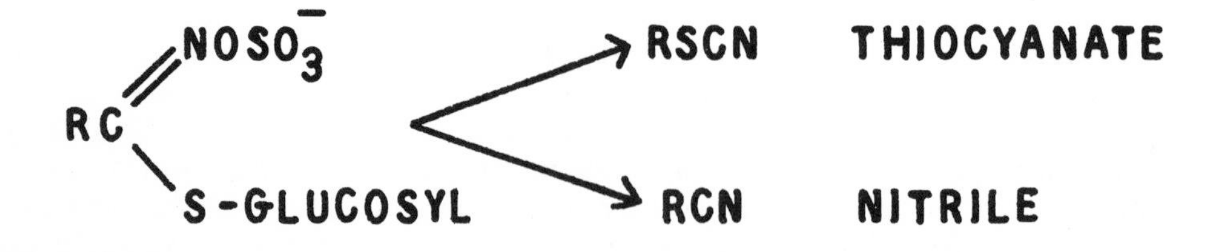

If an *iso*-thiocyanate is produced, it may undergo further non-enzymatic reaction with sufficiently active hydroxyl groups which may be present. This is a well-known reaction of all *iso*-thiocyanates and results in an N-substituted thiourethane:

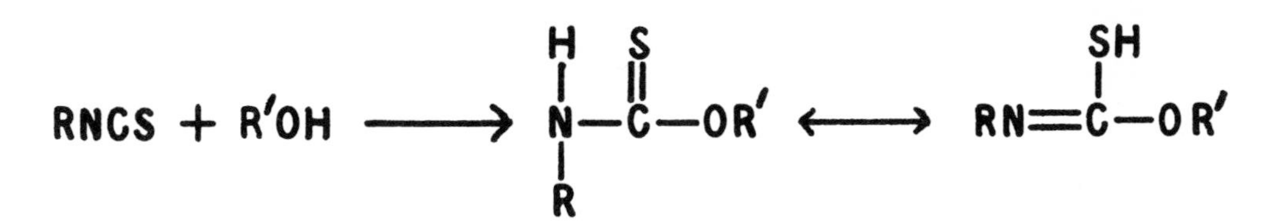

Usually R'OH is actually part of the RNCS molecule so that the reaction is intramolecular, and a heterocyclic ring is produced, or polymers may form. These complex reactions need much more clarification at the single-step, enzymatic level. They have been indicated here in order to show that four different types of compound may all arise as secondary products from a single glucoside precursor. Specific examples will be given below.

The mustard oil glucosides are widespread among the *Cruciferae* but are occasionally found in other plant families as well. About thirty different ones are presently known, and most plants which have them have more than one. There is good reason to believe that they function to protect plants against parasites. It is, of course, the aglycones formed enzymatically upon cellular disintegration which are the active compounds in this respect. Virtanen (26) describes the mustard oils as the most active antibiotics found in higher plants. Goitrin (see below for structure) which occurs in *Brassica* spp. is also of economic interest since it acts as a goitrogenic or antithyroid compound toward animals (27).

In Table 2 some mustard oil glucosides are listed together with their enzymatic hydrolysis products and selected species in which they occur. It will be noted that in different species the same glucoside (e.g. sinigrin) may form different hydrolysis products. It should also be mentioned that although the hydrolysis products are usually called "mustard oils" and thought of as being volatile and odoriferous, some are non-volatile solids. The complex glycoside glucobrassicin is mentioned below under "Indole Derivatives".

Only a few of the original glucosides have been isolated and purified. Most work has been done with the hydrolysis products, which are more easily obtained. In order to obtain the unchanged glucosides from plants it is necessary to inactivate the myrosinase by heating to 100° C. Glucosides may be extracted with boiling water, ethanol, methanol etc. If lipids are also present, as in some seeds, they should first be removed with fat solvents. Crude glucoside solutions are concentrated, chromatographed on alumina or anion exchange resin and crystallized from alcohol-water. Addition of silver nitrate to the glycosides cleaves off the glucose with precipitation of a silver salt:

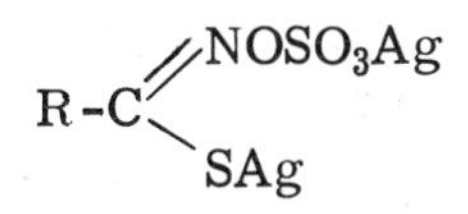

This can be converted to the corresponding *iso*thiocyanate by shaking with aqueous sodium thiosulfate. Volatile mustard oils are prepared by macerating plant parts in water for several hours to permit enzymatic hydrolysis to occur, then steam distilling or extracting with ether to obtain the volatile oil. Further purification can be achieved by fractional distillation or column chromatography. Non-volatile hydrolysis products such as goitrin have been purified by extraction with water and ether (28).

Several simple spot reactions have been developed for characterization of the mustard oils and their glucosides. For the volatile ones their sharp odor and biting taste are distinctive enough to indicate their presence. Paper chromatography has been of great assistance in the characterization of these compounds. The glucosides themselves

TABLE 2. MUSTARD OILS AND THEIR GLYCOSIDES

Glucoside	Hydrolysis Product	Plant Source
not known	HSCN, thiocyanic acid (or its salts)	onion, *Allium cepa*
$CH_2{=}CHCH_2C({=}NOSO_3)\text{S-GLUCOSE}$ sinigrin	$CH_2{=}CHCH_2NCS$ allyl *iso*-thiocyanate	Black mustard, *Brassica nigra*
sinigrin	$CH_2{=}CHCH_2SCN$ allyl thiocyanate	Penny cress, *Thlaspi arvense*
glucoraphenin	$CH_3S(\rightarrow O)CH{=}CHCH_2CH_2NCS$ sulforaphene	Radish, *Raphanus sativus*

Table 2. Continued

Glucoside	Hydrolysis Product	Plant Source
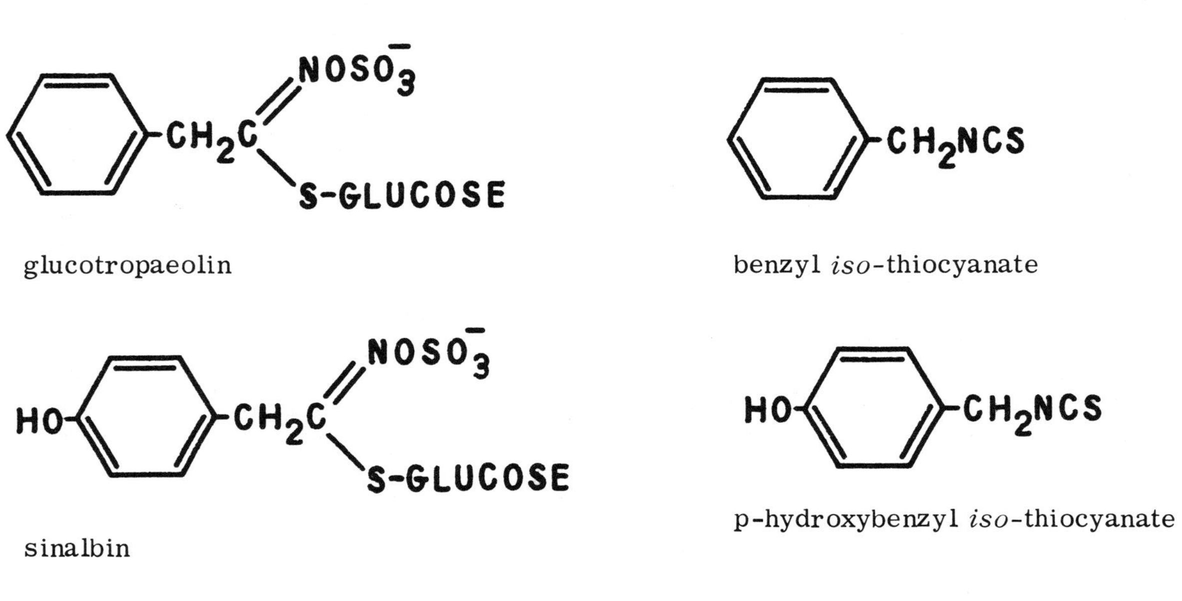 glucotropaeolin	benzyl *iso*-thiocyanate	Nasturtium, *Tropaeolum majus*
sinalbin	p-hydroxybenzyl *iso*-thiocyanate	White mustard, *Sinapis alba*
progoitrin, glucoapiferin	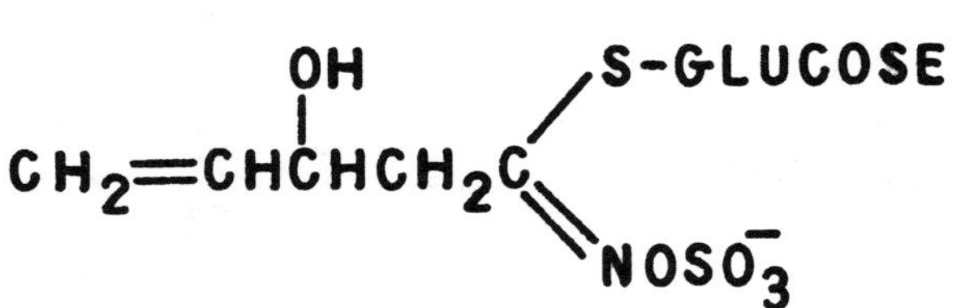 goitrin, (-)-5-vinyl-2-oxazolidinethione	*Brassica* spp.

have been extensively chromatographed by Schultz and coworkers (29, 30) using a butanol-acetic acid-water solvent. The glucosides are recognized by spraying with 0.02 M silver nitrate, drying at 100° C. and spraying with 0.02 M potassium dichromate. Glucosides appear as yellow spots against a red background of silver chromate. Paper chromatography of the mustard oils is usually carried out using the corresponding thiourea derivatives prepared by allowing the *iso*-thiocyanate to react with concentrated ammonia in ethanol:

$$RNCS + NH_3 \rightarrow R\text{-}NH\overset{\overset{\displaystyle S}{\|}}{C}NH_2$$

These substituted thioureas also make nicely crystalline derivatives for other characterization procedures. The thioureas are chromatographed in solvents such as water-saturated chloroform or butanol-ethanol-water. One of the most used sprays is Grote's reagent--a mixture of sodium nitroprusside, hydroxylamine and bromine which gives blue spots with thiourea derivatives. This method was developed by Kjaer and Rubinstein (31) and has been used by Kjaer and coworkers in a large number of studies on the mustard oils. Similar surveys have been carried out by Delaveau (32) using ammoniacal silver nitrate to detect free *iso*-thiocyanates. Gas phase chromatography is also useful for volatile members of this group. Spectroscopic evidence is valuable in some cases. The mustard oils show an absorption peak at about 250 mμ. On reaction with ammonia to form a thiourea this changes to about 243 mμ. Compounds such as goitrin (oxazolidinethiones) also show the 243 mμ peak.

Practically nothing can be said regarding biosynthetic pathways of the mustard oil glycosides. It is evident that the alkyl groups of many of them are similar to the carbon chains of many amino acids less their carboxyl groups. This correspondence suggests a biochemical relationship, but no experiments have been carried out to elucidate it.

NITRILES

The nitriles or organic cyanides are widely distributed throughout the plant kingdom, although certain types appear to be taxonomically restricted. The largest single group of natural nitriles is made up of the cyanogenic glycosides whose general structure is as follows:

$$R-\underset{\underset{\displaystyle R'}{|}}{\overset{\overset{\displaystyle O\text{-}\beta\text{-GLYCOSYL}}{|}}{C}}-CN$$

In some cases R' is hydrogen rather than an alkyl group. These compounds possess the general characteristics of other glycosides as colorless compounds soluble in water and to some extent in alcohol but insoluble in fat solvents. They are very common in seeds of the *Rosaceae* but occur throughout the plant kingdom, including some ferns and fungi. Only a few different aglycones are known, but there are over a dozen different glycosides since the same aglycone may be found with several different sugar components. Like the mustard oil glucosides the cyanogenic glycosides on enzymatic hydrolysis do not normally yield the aglycone as such, but a second reaction occurs to form hydrogen cyanide:

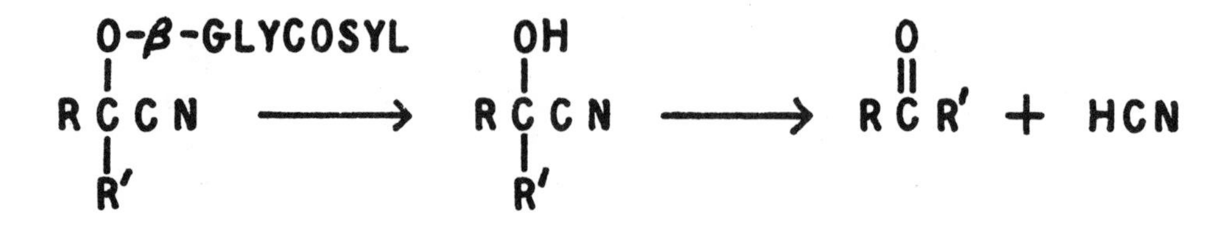

These two reactions are catalyzed by two separate enzymes, β-glycosidase and oxynitrilase. The cyanide poisoning of livestock from eating such leaves as wild cherry is a practical problem of some importance, but hydrocyanic acid as such does not exist in plants. It is evolved according to the reaction outlined above when the plants are injured. Table 3 lists the structures of some cyanogenic glycosides along with the carbonyl compounds which are formed from them by the two-stage hydrolysis process.

In addition to the cyanogenic glycosides of the structure shown above, it has been noted in the previous section of this chapter that nitriles sometimes arise from hydrolysis of typical mustard oil glucosides. Thus, small amounts of nitriles may be present in some impure mustard oils. For example, enzymatic hydrolysis of glucotropaeolin may produce benzyl cyanide as well as benzyl *iso*thiocyanate:

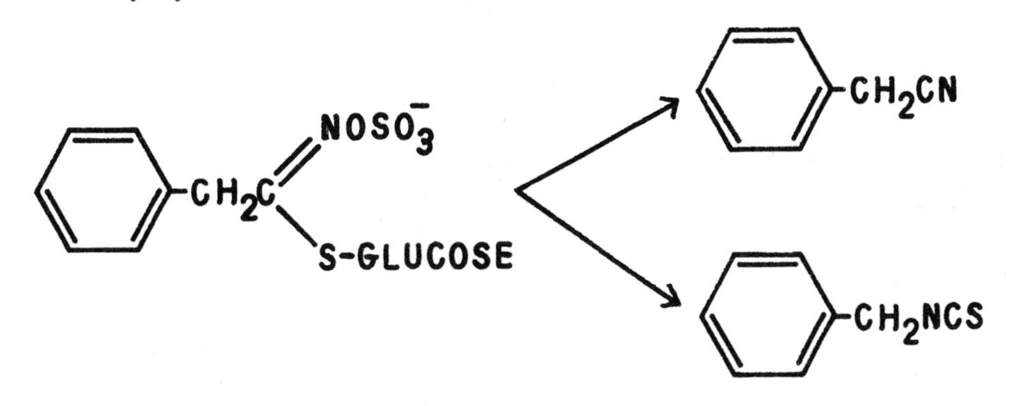

When a nitrile is formed by such a reaction, the sulfur atom appears as elemental sulfur--the only example of the occurrence of this free element in higher plants. Presumably as the result of analogous reactions allyl cyanide occurs along with allyl *iso*-thiocyanate in black mustard oil and the nitrile corresponding to sulforaphene in radish oil. These nitriles are stable, volatile compounds and do not release hydrogen cyanide. To some extent they may be artifacts formed from unhydrolyzed glucoside during steam distillation, but there is also evidence that at least in some cases they are true natural products. Careful study of this obscure reaction is needed.

A few other miscellaneous nitriles have been found in higher plants. Consumption of seeds of the sweet pea *(Lathyrus odoratus)* by animals causes a disease known as odoratism which is characterized by changes in bone and connective tissue structure. The causative agent is γ-glutamyl-β-aminopropionitrile (33):

$$HOOC\underset{}{\overset{NH_2}{\overset{|}{C}}}HCH_2CH_2\overset{O}{\overset{\|}{C}}NCH_2CH_2CN$$

Another chronic human disease known as lathyrism has been rather common in parts of India and Spain. Although it is caused by eating seeds of *Lathyrus sativus* or contaminating seeds of *Vicia* spp., the causative agent is not γ-glutamyl-β-aminopropionitrile; and the chief symptom is paralysis caused by irreversible nerve damage. The poisonous constituent in this case is probably β-cyano-L-alanine, which might reasonably be related biosynthetically to β-aminopropionitrile (34).

Isolation of the cyanogenic glycosides follows the general lines described for other glycosides based on their solubility in water and lower alcohols and lack of solubility in most fat solvents. They also show some solubility in ethyl acetate, and this property may

TABLE 3. SOME CYANOGENIC GLYCOSIDES, THEIR HYDROLYSIS PRODUCTS AND OCCURRENCE

Glycoside	Carbonyl Compound	Selected Plant Source
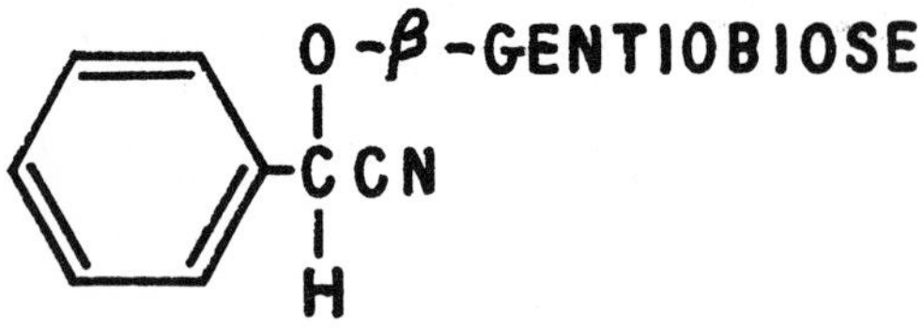 O-β-GENTIOBIOSE CCN H amygdalin	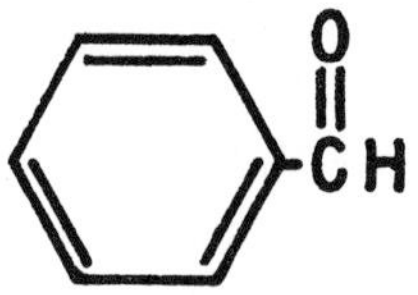 O CH benzaldehyde	*Amygdalus nana*
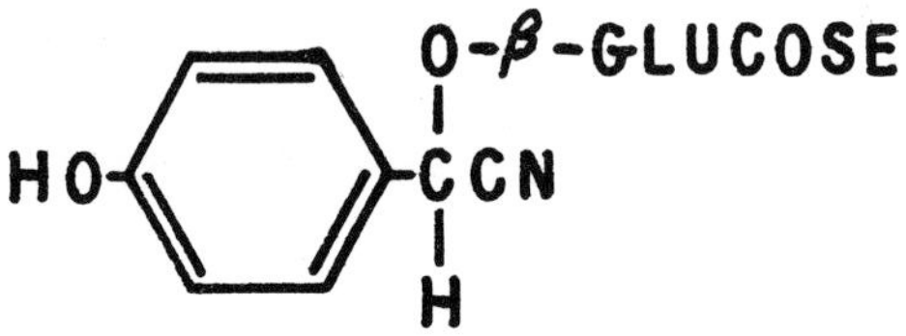 O-β-GLUCOSE HO- CCN H dhurrin	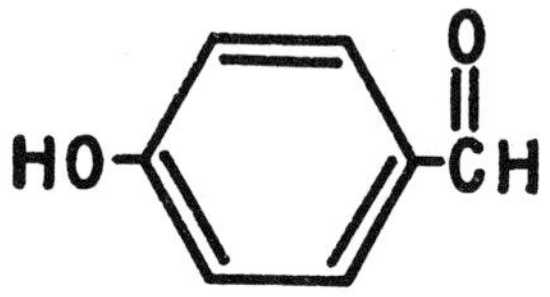 O HO- CH p-hydroxybenzaldhyde	*Sorghum vulgare*
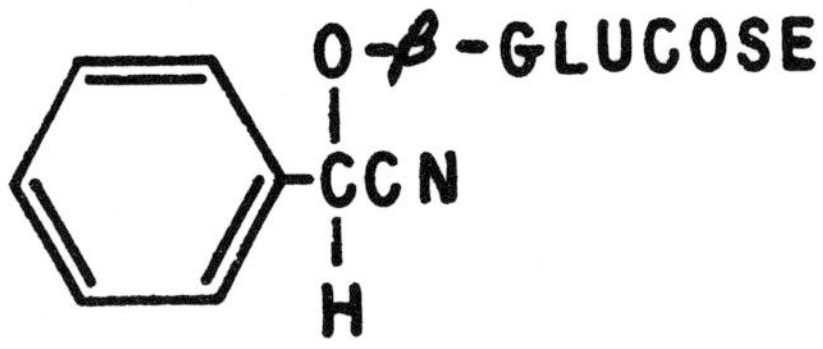 O-β-GLUCOSE CCN H prunasin	benzaldehyde	*Prunus* spp.
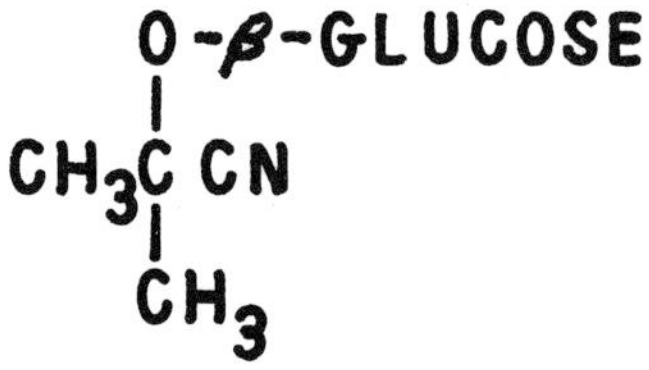 O-β-GLUCOSE CH_3C CN CH_3 linamarin	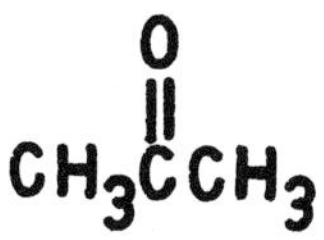 O CH_3CCH_3 acetone	*Linum* spp.
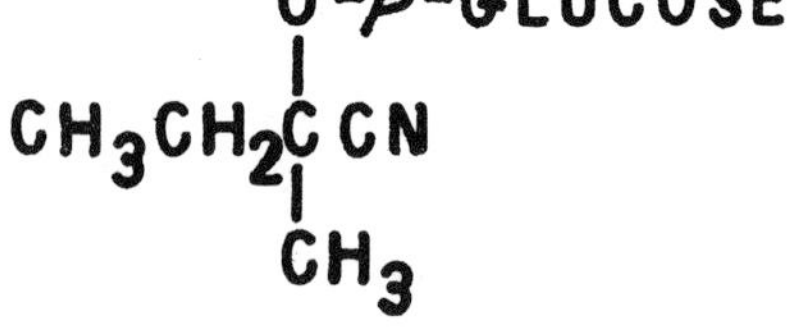 O-β-GLUCOSE CH_3CH_2C CN CH_3 lotaustralin	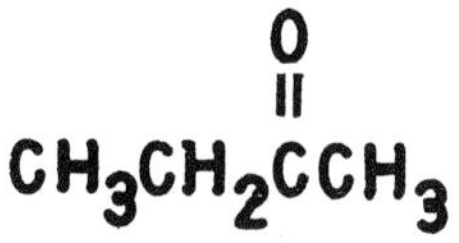 O $CH_3CH_2CCH_3$ methylethyl ketone	*Lotus* spp.

be used to separate them from other carbohydrates. For isolation of unhydrolyzed glycosides it is necessary to inactivate the hydrolytic enzymes with boiling water or alcohol and to neutralize plant acids with calcium carbonate. There is little interest in isolating the hydrolysis products except where they are needed to establish the structure of the original glycoside. The sugars may be obtained by methods outlined in Chapter 2 and the carbonyl compounds by distillation. The nitriles which occur along with mustard oils may be separated by adding ammonia sufficient to form a nonvolatile thiourea derivative with the *iso*-thiocyanate and then distilling off the volatile, unreacted nitrile. During the distillation if water is present, some of the nitrile may be hydrolyzed to the corresponding acid.

There is no general method for rapid characterization of all compounds having a nitrile group. The presence of cyanogenic glycosides in plants is indicated by the evolution of HCN when the tissues are broken. This gas is easily detected by putting the crushed plant part in a sealed tube with a piece of filter paper which has been dipped in alkaline picric acid solution. The yellow dye turns red when HCN comes in contact with it. Similar color reactions will be found in the general references. A few plants contain cyanogenic glycosides but not the enzymes to hydrolyze them. In these cases HCN is evolved only if the required enzymes are added. Other nitriles which do not evolve hydrogen cyanide are customarily identified by hydrolyzing them to the corresponding acids and identifying these acids by methods described in Chapters 3 and 4.

Little is known about the biosynthesis of the nitrile group in plants. Tracer experiments of Conn and Bove (35) have shown that the complete carbon skeleton of the aglycone of dhurrin is derived from tyrosine. Presumably the nitrogen comes from the amino group of tyrosine also. Similarly, Butler and Butler (36) have shown that the carbon skeletons of linamarin and lotaustralin come respectively from valine and isoleucine. This evidence dispels older ideas that the glycosides might be built up by a reversal of the hydrolysis reaction. Since tyrosine probably can also form p-hydroxybenzyl cyanide by way of a mustard oil glucoside, there may exist pathways for the formation of two different types of nitriles from the same precursor in different plants. Ahmad and Spenser (37) have shown that the oximes of α-keto acids are readily converted non-enzymatically to the corresponding nitriles:

$$RCH_2\overset{\overset{NOH}{\|}}{C}COOH \rightarrow RCH_2CN + H_2O + CO_2$$

They suggest that such a reaction may account for the biosynthesis of certain nitriles. Mentzer and Favre-Bonvin (38) have used this reaction as a basis for a proposed mechanism for prunasin biosynthesis and have shown that results of tracer experiments are in accord with it. It is suggestive that no plant apparently has both mustard oil glucoside and cyanogenic glycoside. Possibly they represent alternative approaches to the same function.

INDOLE DERIVATIVES

Plants contain a large number of compounds based on the indole ring system:

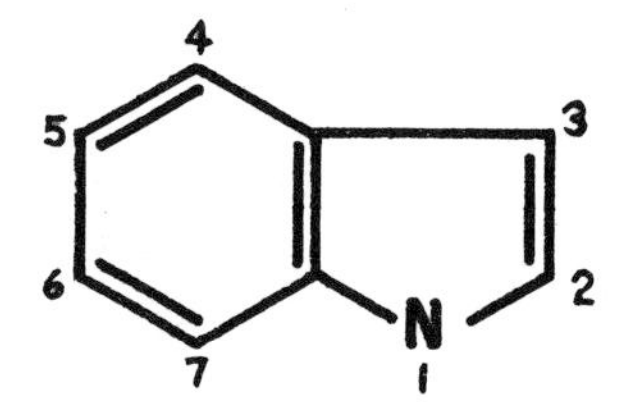

These include the amino acid tryptophan and many alkaloids. Besides these there are several other indole compounds which do not fit well into any large category but are too important to be ignored. Indole itself is partly responsible for the odor of jasmine flowers. A review of indole derivatives found in plants has been presented by Stowe (39).

Of most interest in plant physiology are the compounds closely related to indole-3-acetic acid, the most important natural auxin. Other natural indole derivatives whose structures are given below have auxin activity similar to that of indole-3-acetic acid, but it is generally believed that they are active only after being enzymatically converted to indole-3-acetic acid.

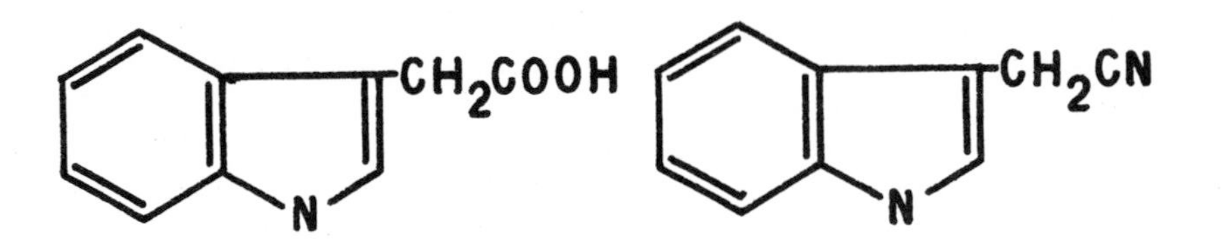

indole-3-acetic acid   indole-3-acetonitrile

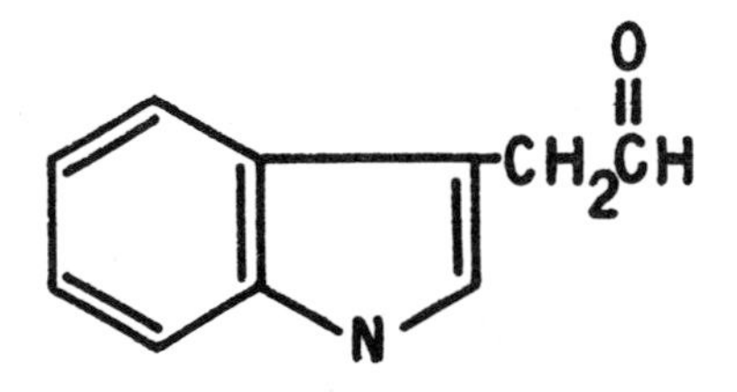

indole-3-acetaldehyde

More complex derivatives such as indole-3-acetylaspartic acid (40) and 1-(indole-3-acetyl)-β-D-glucose (41) have also been found. All of these compounds are rather unstable and occur in plants at very low concentrations, so that isolation of them represents a formidable problem. The general references should be consulted for information about such methods. The indole-containing auxins have been separated and identified by paper chromatography and electrophoresis according to methods developed by several different workers (42, 43, 44). Stowe and Thimann (45) studied 35 different indole compounds and found the best all-round solvent for paper chromatography to be *iso*-propyl alcohol/28% NH_4OH/H_2O (8:1:1). Various spray reagents have been used to detect these compounds on chromatograms. Best-known is the Salkowski reagent (0.001 M ferric chloride in 5% perchloric acid) which gives a red color. Compounds with auxin activity can of course be located by eluting sections of the chromatogram and testing the eluates for activity.

The pathways of indole-3-acetic acid biosynthesis and breakdown are not well-clarified. Tryptophan is generally believed to be an obligatory precursor, and evidence summarized by Gordon (46) suggests that indole-pyruvic acid and indoleacetaldehyde are intermediates. Other compounds such as the nitrile are probably side issues rather than normal intermediates. Breakdown of indoleacetic acid is oxidative, catalyzed by indoleacetic acid oxidase or a peroxidase. Auxin destruction has been reviewed by Ray (47).

Whereas the indole auxins are of great interest in plant physiology, other indole compounds found in plants show striking physiological effects on animals. These are tryptamine and derivatives of it such as 5-hydroxytryptamine (serotonin).

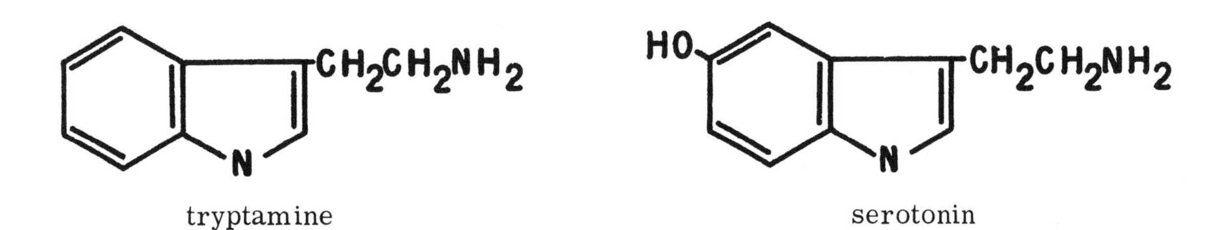

tryptamine serotonin

Both of these compounds are widely distributed in plants, although usually in small amounts (48-51). Tryptamine acts as a pressor amine (q. v.) whereas serotonin produces effects on the central nervous system. Methylated derivatives of serotonin are responsible for the psychic effects produced by certain hallucinogenic mushrooms. These amines may be purified and partially identified by the same types of methods described previously for other amines. On paper chromatograms they may be detected by Ehrlich's reagent (a nearly saturated solution of dimethylaminobenzaldehyde in 12 N hydrochloric acid) which gives blue colors with indole derivatives. There is little question regarding the biosynthesis of these amines from tryptophan. The 5-hydroxy group of serotonin is probably introduced into the tryptophan molecule before it is decarboxylated.

In certain plants, especially *Brassica* spp. ascorbic acid occurs in a bound form known as ascorbigen which is equal to ascorbic acid in nutritional value but does not react in the usual chemical tests for ascorbic acid. Ascorbigen is an indole derivative of ascorbic acid whose structure is not fully established but probably something like (52, 53):

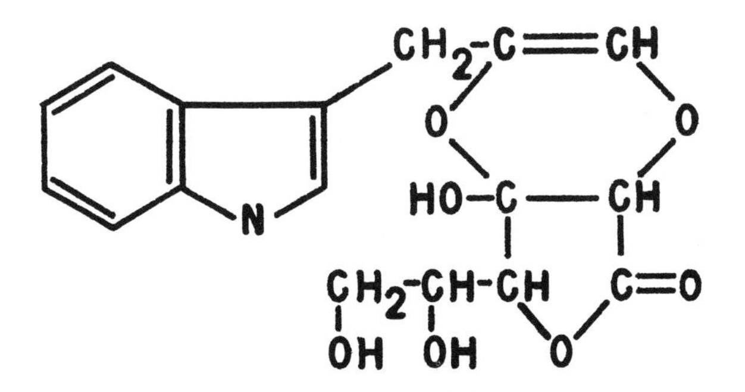

It seems probable that the precursor of the indole moiety of ascorbigen is the mustard oil glucoside, glucobrassicin which is hydrolyzed by the action of myrosinase to form glucose, $SO_4^{=}$, SCN^-, and 3(β-indolyl)-2-hydroxypropanal. The last compound immediately reacts with ascorbic acid to form ascorbigen (54).

The dye indigo is no longer of any commercial importance but is interesting as an unusual natural indole compound. Indigo itself, however, does not occur in plants. Leaves of certain species of the genus *Indigofera* contain a glucoside indican which is first hydrolyzed to the aglycone indoxyl by crushing the plant in water so that β-glucosidases can act. When air is passed through alkaline solutions of indoxyl, it is oxidized to the blue dye indigotin. These reactions are as follows:

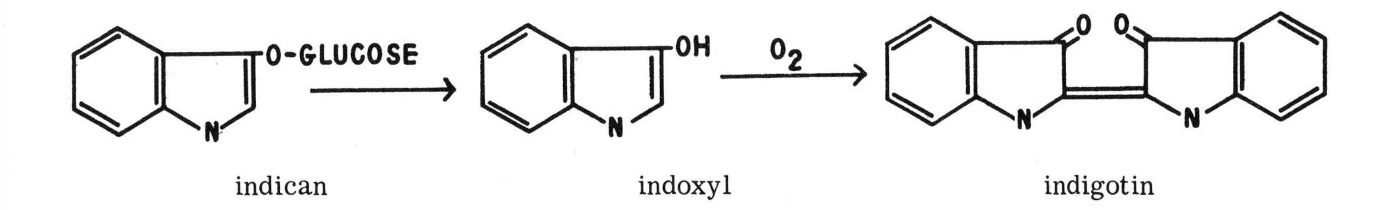

indican indoxyl indigotin

Natural indigo contains some other dyes as well as indigotin. The European woad plant *(Isatis tinctoria)* also contains indican and was at one time an important source of blue dye.

Another pigment (or class of pigments) based on the indole nucleus is melanin. This pigment is responsible for dark hair and skin color in animals. However, its existence in plants is dubious. The probable structure of melanin is indicated below. It is a polymer based on indole-5, 6-quinone.

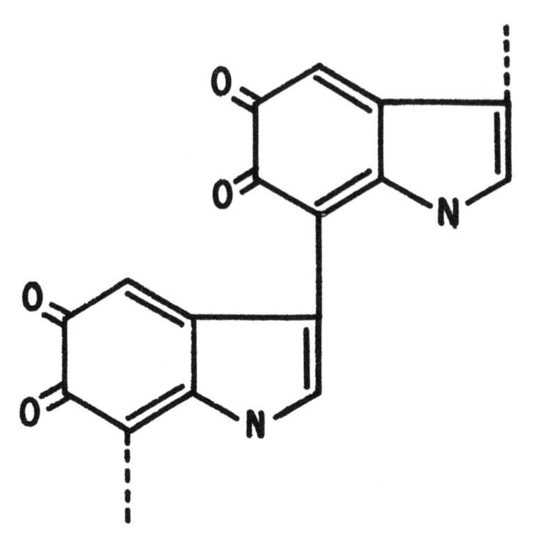

Such compounds may be formed by the action of oxidizing enzymes on tyrosine or dihydroxyphenylalanine. The term melanin should be restricted to compounds of this type and not used for *any* dark pigment. Careful investigation of dark pigments of higher plants will be needed to decide whether true melanins are present. Many dark plant pigments are known to be free of nitrogen and formed by oxidation of such phenolic compounds as chlorogenic acid (see Chap. 4). However, leaves of some composites contain a dark red pigment named intybin which seems to be an indolequinone derivative (55). The red pigments of beets *(Beta vulgaris)* and several other plants (especially in the Chenopodiaceae) were thought for many years to be related to the anthocyanins although they contain nitrogen. It has now been established that they are in fact indole derivatives. The name "betacyanins" has been proposed for them and "betaxanthins" for the related yellow pigments (56). Betanin, the most thoroughly studied of these compounds, is a glucoside which yields the aglycone betanidin on hydrolysis. A tentative structure of betanidin is as follows (57):

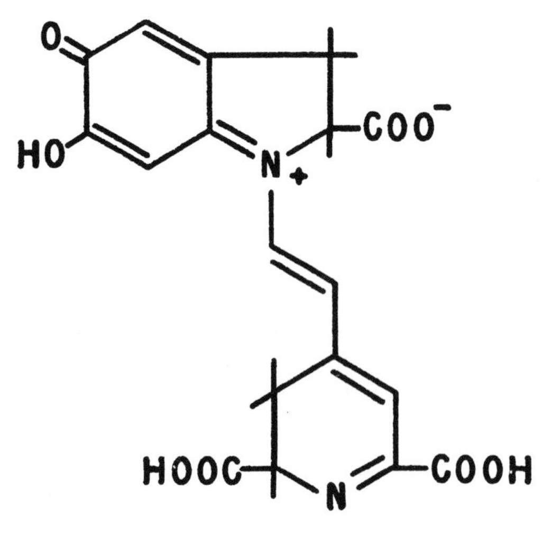

betanidin

SOME VITAMINS

Several important vitamins are nitrogen and/or sulfur compounds which do not fit conveniently under any larger structural category. Some of these will be mentioned briefly here; but since each one is a special case and we are concerned with discussing general categories of compounds, the general references should be consulted for methods of isolation and characterization. Also, for paper chromatography of the vitamins see (58), for biosynthesis (59).

Thiamine or vitamin B_1 probably occurs to some extent in all plants, if not in all cells. Thiamine pyrophosphate (cocarboxylase) is the form in which this vitamin serves as a coenzyme in the decarboxylation of pyruvic acid to acetate, acetyl-coenzyme-A, or other products and in the transketolase reaction. The exact mechanisms of these reactions are still under active investigation. Pathways of thiamine biosynthesis are likewise obscure although it is probable that the pyrimidine and thiazole portions are synthesized separately and then combined. Many aspects of thiamine chemistry and physiology are presented in a symposium publication (60).

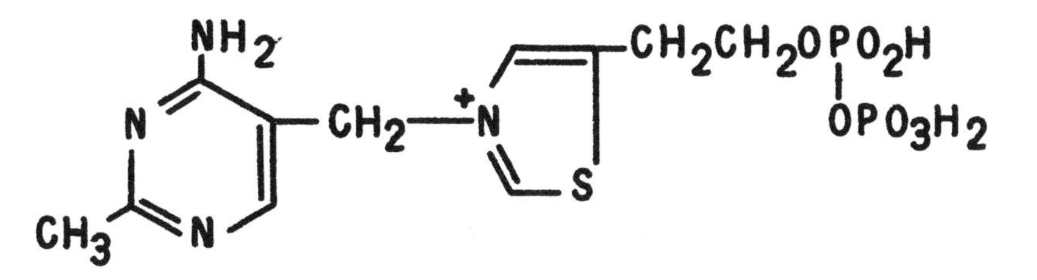

thiamine pyrophosphate

Lipoic acid or 6, 8-thioctic acid has a rather simple structure. It exists in a reduced dithiol form which is readily oxidized to a disulfide.

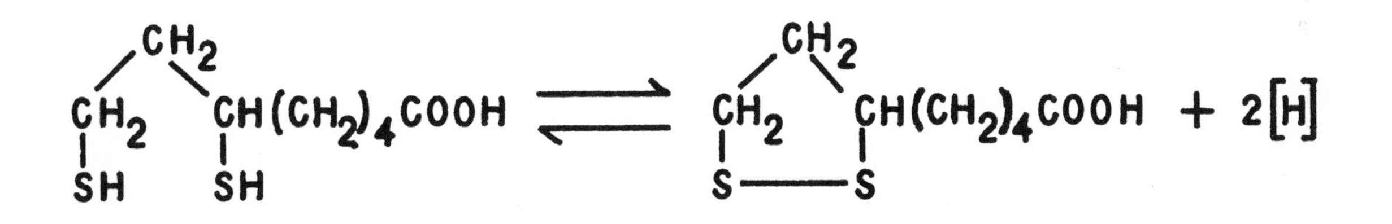

This vitamin functions along with thiamine pyrophosphate as a coenzyme in decarboxylation and acyl group transfer. It may also play a role in photosynthesis where it has been suggested that light energy is used to reduce the disulfide form to the dithiol which can then transfer hydrogen to pyridine nucleotides.

Biotin serves as a coenzyme in several carbon dioxide fixation reactions such as the formation of oxalacetate from phosphoenolpyruvate and the formation of β-methylglutaconyl-CoA from senecioyl-CoA (61). The actual coenzyme form a biotin may be biocytin, ϵ-N biotinyl-L-lysine. In many cases biotin appears to be bound so tightly to its enzyme protein that it might more aptly be described as a prosthetic group rather than a diffusible coenzyme.

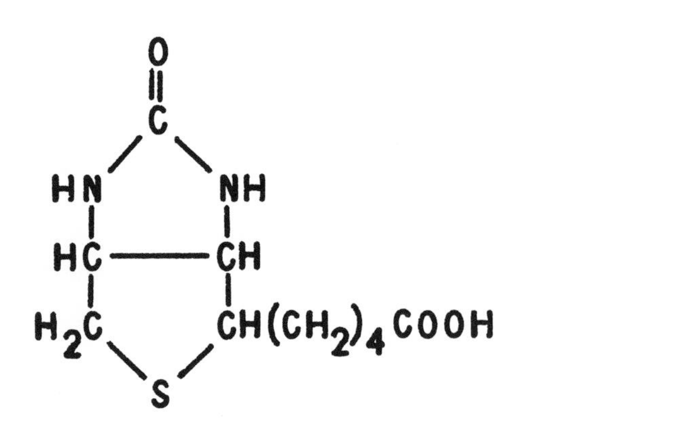

biotin

Folic acid is only one of a series of related compounds which are found widely distributed in nature. It can be regarded as made up of a pteridine nucleus, a molecule of p-aminobenzoic acid, and a molecule of glutamic acid. The exact coenzyme form of folic acid may vary from reaction to reaction, but in all cases the coenzymes are tetrahydro derivatives to which one-carbon units may be attached at position 5 or 10. N^5, N^{10}-anhydroformyltetrahydrofolic acid is active in one step of purine biosynthesis, N^{10}-formyltetrahydrofolic acid at another step. N^5-formyltetrahydrofolic acid (folinic acid, leucovorin, citrovorum factor) has been given much prominence since it was the first formylated folic acid to be discovered, but it must be converted to one of the other derivatives before serving as a coenzyme.

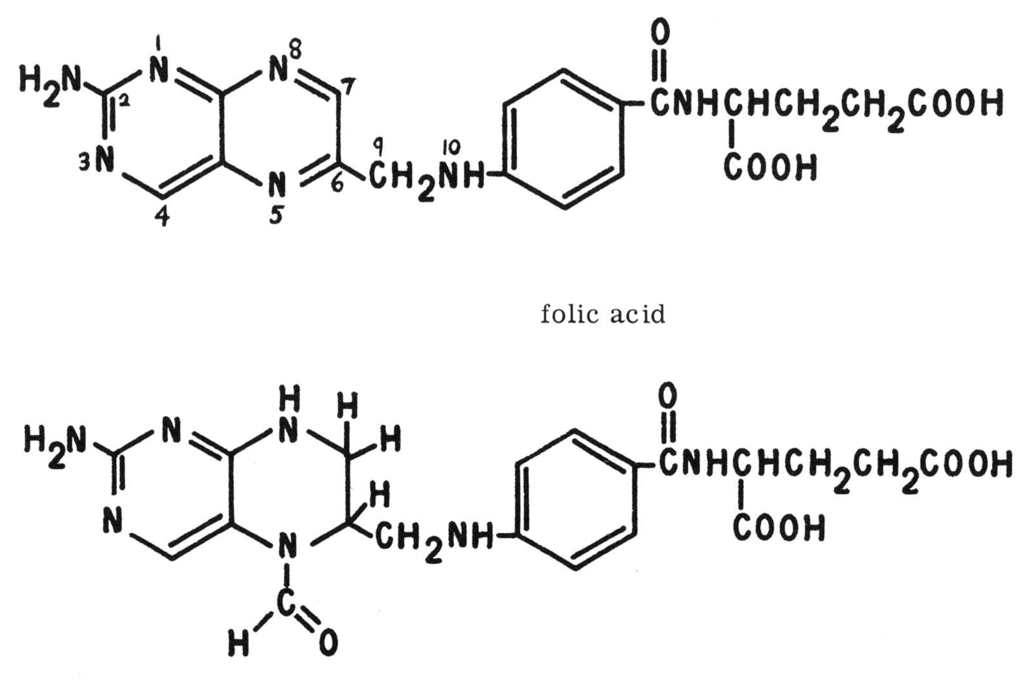

folic acid

folinic acid

Sometimes a polypeptide of glutamic acid is present rather than a single amino acid molecule. Other forms of the vitamin are tightly bound to cellular structure. The active form of folic acid functions as a coenzyme in one carbon metabolism involving formate, such as in the interconversion of glycine and serine and in the synthesis of methyl groups. Transformations of folic acid and one-carbon units have been investigated in germinating pea extracts (62).

NITRO COMPOUNDS

Only three nitro compounds have been isolated from higher plants, but their very rarity contributes to their interest. Naturally occurring nitro compounds are reviewed by Pailer (63). β-nitropropionic acid (hiptagenic acid) occurs in a variety of unrelated plants such as the violet (*Viola odorata*), creeping indigo (*Indigofera endecaphylla*), and the fungus *Aspergillus flavus*. The toxic compounds karakin and hiptagin from *Corynocarpus laevigata* and *Hiptage madablata* respectively are glucose triesters of this acid. It is of some economic importance since it is toxic to animals who may eat plants containing it.

Aristolochic acid found in *Aristolochia clematitis* is a nitrophenanthrene. The bark oil of *Aniba canellila* contains 80% 1-nitro-2-phenylethane (64).

NO_2
|
CH_2CH_2COOH

β-nitropropionic acid

$C_6H_5-CH_2CH_2NO_2$

1-nitro-2-phenylethane

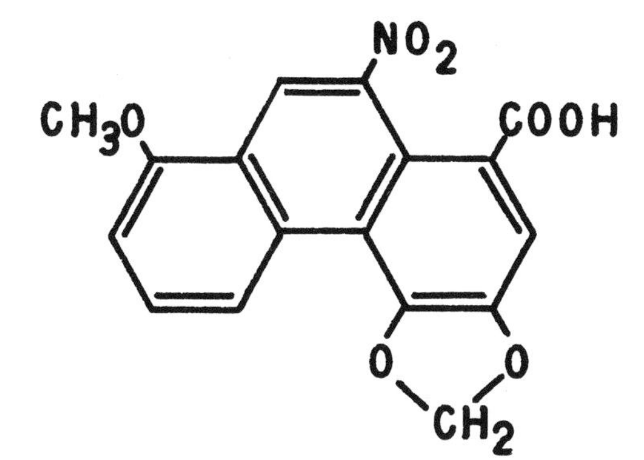

aristolochic acid

Nothing is known regarding the physiological function or biosynthesis of these compounds in higher plants. It has been shown (65) that in fungi β-nitropropionic acid is synthesized from aspartic acid. The alkaloids of *Aristolochia* are based on the aporphine nucleus, which has almost the identical carbon-nitrogen structure as aristolochic acid:

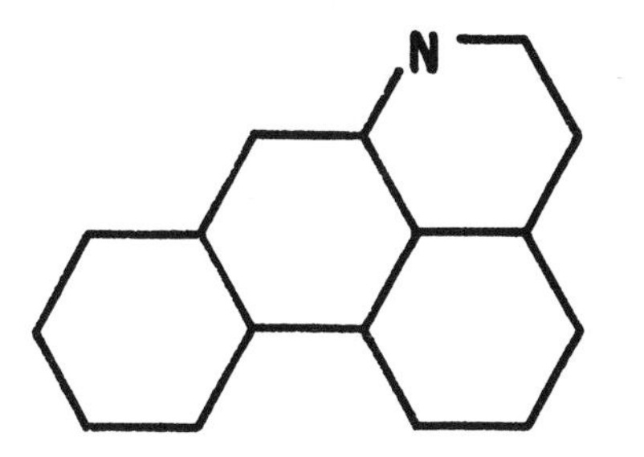

aporphine nucleus

Aporphine alkaloids are presumed to be formed from two molecules of tyrosine, and aristolochic acid might be formed by an oxidation of such an alkaloid (66). Peroxidase catalyzes the oxidation of amines to nitroso compounds (67) which might be oxidized further to nitro derivatives.

Since these compounds are so specialized, the original papers should be consulted for details of isolation and identification.

HYDROXYLAMINE DERIVATIVES

Hydroxylamine itself has not been isolated from higher plants although it is a postulated intermediate in nitrate reduction (Chapter 10) and possibly in formation of the mustard oil glycosides (q. v.). A small group of compounds so far restricted to such grasses as maize *(Zea mays)*, rye (*Lolium* spp.), and wheat (*Triticum* spp.) can be regarded as complex hydroxamates which occur as glucosides (18). Upon hydrolysis the aglycones tend to rearrange forming oxazoles (68, 69):

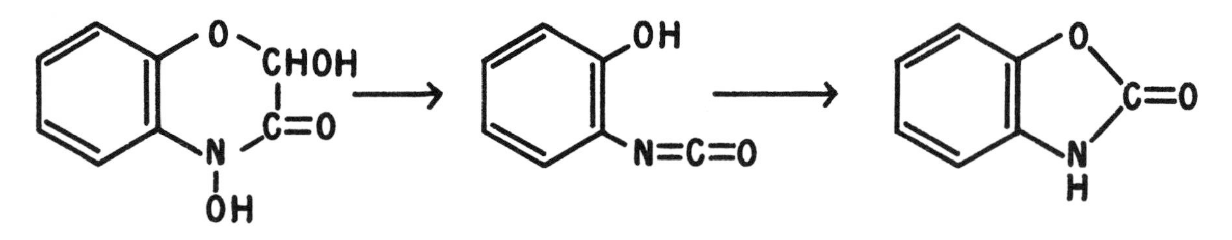

UREA AND RELATED COMPOUNDS

In the older literature urea was often reported to be present in higher plants, but the analytical methods used were not beyond reproach and many workers questioned such reports. More recently it has been found that the ornithine cycle functions in plants (Chapter 10), and the occurrence of free urea in some plant tissues has been well-established. Urea may also arise from purine breakdown via allantoin and allantoic acid (Chapter 11). Other compounds which can be regarded as related to urea have also been isolated from plants. Some structures are given below with their occurrence. The whole area of urea, ureide and guanidine metabolism in plants has been reviewed (70).

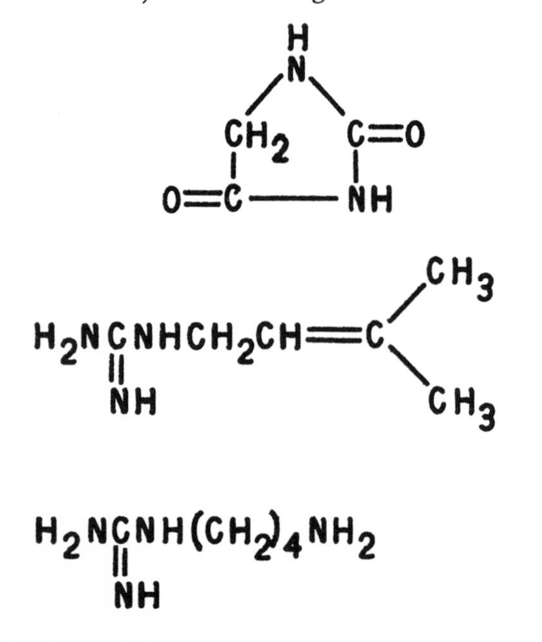

hydantoin
(Beta vulgaris)

galegine
(Galego officinalis)

agmatine
(Ricinus communis)

GENERAL REFERENCE

Bersin, T., "Die Phytochemie des Schwefels," Adv. Enzymol. 10 223 (1950).
Challenger, F., Aspects of the Organic Chemistry of Sulphur, Academic Press, N. Y., 1959.
Dillemann, G., "Composés Cyanogénétiques" in Ruhland 8 1050.
Guggenheim, M., Die Biogenem Amine, S. Karger, Basel 1951.
Guggenheim, M., "Die Biogenen Amine in Der Pflanzenwelt" in Ruhland 8 889.
Kjaer, A., "Secondary Organic Sulfur Compounds of Plants" in Ruhland 9 64.
Seifert, P., "Blausaure-Verbindungen" in Paech and Tracey 4 676.
Stoll, A. and Jucker, E., "Senföle, Lauchöle und andere schwelfelhaltige Pflanzenstoffe" in Paech and Tracey 4 689.
Thomas, M., "Melanin" in Ruhland 8 1076.
Thomas, M., "Melanins" in Paech and Tracey 4 662.
Werle, E., "Amine und Betaine" in Paech and Tracey 4 517.
Young, L. and Maw, G. A., The Metabolism of Sulphur Compounds, John Wiley, N. Y. 1958.

BIBLIOGRAPHY

1. von Kamienski, E. S., Planta 50 315 (1957).
2. Udenfriend, S., Lovenberg, W. and Sjoerdsma, A., Arch. Biochem. Biophys. 85 487 (1959).
3. Maizel, J. V. and Benson, A. A., Plant Physiol. 31 Supp. XXIV (1956).
4. Nissen, P. and Benson, A. A., Science 134 1759 (1961).
5. Christanson, D. D., Wall, J. S., Dimler, R. J., and Senti, F. R., Anal. Chem. 32 874 (1960).
6. Kum-Tatt, L., Anal. Chim. Acta 24 397 (1961).
7. von Kamienski, E. S., Planta 50 291 (1957).
8. Blau, K., Biochem. J. 80 193 (1961).
9. Feinstein, L. and Jacobson, M., Fortschr. Chem. Org. Naturstoffe 10 423 (1953).
10. Jirousek, L. and Stárka, L., Naturwiss. 45 386 (1958).
11. Uhlenbroek, J H. and Bijloo, J D., Rec. trav. chim. 78 382 (1959).
12. Guddal, E. and Sörensen, N. A., Acta Chem. Scand. 13 1185 (1959).
13. Bailey, S. D., Bazinet, M L., Driscoll, J. L. and McCarthy, A. I., J. Food Sci. 26 163 (1961).
14. Folkers, K., Koniuszy, F., and Shavel, J., J. Am. Chem. Soc. 66 1083 (1944).
15. Miyano, M. and Benson, A. A., J. Am. Chem. Soc. 84 59 (1962).
16. Wills, E. D., Biochem. J. 63 514 (1956).
17. Virtanen, A. I. and Matikkala, E. J., Acta Chem. Scand. 13 1898 (1959).
18. Virtanen, A. I., Angew, Chem. 74 374 (1962).
19. Maw, G. A., Biochem. J. 63 116 (1956).
20. Challenger, F., Bywood, R., Thomas, P. and Hayward, B. J., Arch. Biochem. Biophys. 69 514 (1957).
21. Toennies, G. and Kolb, J. J., Anal. Chem. 23 823 (1951).
22. Kjaer, A., Fortschr. Chem. Org. Naturstoffe 18 122 (1960).
23. Zinner, G., Deutsch.-Apothek. Z. 98 335 (1958).
24. Gaines, R. D. and Goering, K. J., Arch. Biochem. Biophys. 96 13 (1962).
25. Gmelin, R. and Virtanen, A. I., Acta Chem. Scand. 13 1474 (1959).
26. Virtanen, A. I., Angew. Chem. 70 544 (1958).
27. Altamura, M. R., Long, L. and Hasselstrom, T., J. Biol. Chem. 234 1847 (1959).
28. Astwood, E. B., Greer, M. A. and Ettlinger, M. G., J. Biol. Chem. 181 121 (1949).
29. Schultz, O.-E. and Gmelin, R., Z. Naturforsch 7b 500 (1952).
30. Schultz., O.-E. and Wagner, W., Z. Naturforsch. 11b 73 (1956).
31. Kjaer, A. and Rubinstein, K., Acta Chem. Scand. 7 528 (1953).
32. Delaveau, P., Bull. soc. botan. France 104 148 (1957).
33. Strong, F. M., Nutrition Revs. 14 65 (1956).
34. Ressler, C., J. Biol. Chem. 237 733 (1962).
35. Conn., E. E. and Bove, C., Proc. IX Int. Bot. Cong. 78 (1959).
36. Butler, G. W. and Butler, B. G., Nature 187 780 (1960).
37. Ahmad, A. and Spenser, I. D., Can. J. Chem. 39 1340 (1961).
38. Mentzer, C. and Favre-Bonvin, J., Compt. rend. 253 1072 (1961).
39. Stowe, B. B., Fortschr. Chem. Org. Naturstoffe 17 248 (1959).

40. Klämbt, H. D., Naturwiss. 47 398 (1960).
41. Zenk, M. H., Nature 191 493 (1961).
42. Klämbt, H. D., Ber. deut. botan. Ges. 72 185 (1959).
43. Mueller, F., Planta 57 463 (1961).
44. Bentley, J. A., Methods Biochem. Anal. 7 75 (1962).
45. Stowe, B. B., and Thimann, K. V., Arch. Biochem. 51 499 (1954).
46. Gordon, S. A., The Chemistry and Mode of Action of Plant Growth Substances ed. by R. L. Wain and F. Wightman, pp. 65-75, Butterworths, London 1956.
47. Ray, P. M., Ann. Rev. Plant Physiol. 9 81 (1958).
48. West, G. B., J. Pharm. Pharmacol. 11 319 (1959).
49. Waalkes, T. P., Sjoerdsma, A., Creveling, C. R., Weissbach, H. and Udenfriend, S., Science 127 648 (1958).
50. Bulard, C. and Leopold, A. C., Compt. rend. 247 1382 (1958).
51. Kirberger, E. and Braun, L., Biochim. Biophys. Acta 49 39 (1961).
52. Procházka, Z., Šanda, V., and Šorm, F., Coll. Czech. Chem. Comms. 22 654 (1957).
53. Guha, B. C., J. Indian Chem. Soc. 38 492 (1961).
54. Gmelin, R. and Virtanen, A. I., Suomen Kemistilehti 34B 15 (1961) (Chem. Abstr. 55 1774 (1961).
55. Winter, E., Planta 52 187 (1958).
56. Wyler, H. and Dreiding, A. S., Experientia 17 23 (1961).
57. Mabry, T. J., Wyler, H., Sassu, G., Mercier, M., Parikh, I., and Dreiding, A. S., Helv. Chim. Acta 45 640 (1962).
58. Gadsden, E. L., Edwards, C. H., and Edwards, G. A., Anal. Chem. 32 1415 (1960).
59. Brown, G. M., Physiol. Revs. 40 331 (1960).
60. Wuest, H. M., ed., Ann. N. Y. Acad. Sci. 98 385 (1962).
61. Lynen, F., J. Cell. Comp. Physiol. 54 Suppl. 33 (1959).
62. Shejbal, J., Slavík, K. and Souček, J., Coll. Czech. Chem. Comms. 27 1470 (1962).
63. Pailer, M., Fortschr. Chem. Org. Naturstoffe 18 55 (1960).
64. Gottlieb, O. R. and Taveira, M., Perfumery Essent. Oil Record 51 69 (1960).
65. Birch, A. J., McLoughlin, B. J., Smith, H., and Winter, J., Chem. and Ind. 1960 840.
66. Hegnauer, R., Pharmazie 15 634 (1960).
67. Böttcher, G. and Kiese, M., Naturwiss. 47 157 (1960).
68. Bredenberg, J. B., Honkanen, E. and Virtanen, A. I., Acta Chem. Scand. 16 135 (1962).
69. Karimoto, R. S., Axelrod, B., Wolinsky, J. and Schall, E. D., Tetrahedron Letters 1962 83.
70. Reinbothe, H. and Mothes, K., Ann. Rev. Plant Physiol. 13 129 (1962).

INDEX

Names of persons are indexed only where they are associated with specific reactions or procedures. Plants should be looked up under both English and Latin names; the Latin names are indexed to genus but not species. Iso- compounds are all indexed under this prefix. The most important page numbers are underlined.